Applied Probability and Statistics (*Continued*)

BENNETT and FRANKLIN · Statistical Analysis in Chemistry and the Chemical Industry

BROWNLEE · Statistical Theory and Methodology in Science and Engineering, *Second Edition*

BUSH and MOSTELLER · Stochastic Models for Learning

CHERNOFF and MOSES · Elementary Decision Theory

CHEW · Experimental Designs in Industry

CLARK · An Introduction to Statistics

CLELLAND, deCANI, BROWN, BURSK, and MURRAY · Basic Statistics with Business Applications

COCHRAN · Sampling Techniques, *Second Edition*

COCHRAN and COX · Experimental Designs, *Second Edition*

CORNELL · The Essentials of Educational Statistics

COX · Planning of Experiments

COX and MILLER · The Theory of Stochastic Processes

DEMING · Sample Design in Business Research

DEMING · Some Theory of Sampling

DODGE and ROMIG · Sampling Inspection Tables, *Second Edition*

DRAPER and SMITH · Applied Regression Analysis

FRYER · Elements of Statistics

GOLDBERGER · Econometric Theory

GOULDEN · Methods of Statistical Analysis, *Second Edition*

GUTTMAN and WILKS · Introductory Engineering Statistics

HALD · Statistical Tables and Formulas

HALD · Statistical Theory with Engineering Applications

HANSEN, HURWITZ, and MADOW · Sample Survey Methods and Theory, Volume I

HAUSER and LEONARD · Government Statistics for Business Use, *Second Edition*

HOEL · Elementary Statistics, *Second Edition*

JOHNSON and LEONE · Statistics and Experimental Design: In Engineering and the Physical Sciences, Volumes I and II

KEMPTHORNE · An Introduction to Genetic Statistics

MEYER · Symposium on Monte Carlo Methods

PRABHU · Queues and Inventories: A Study of Their Basic Stochastic Processes

RICE · Control Charts in Factory Management

SARHAN and GREENBERG · Contributions to Order Statistics

TIPPETT · Technological Applications of Statistics

WILLIAMS · Regression Analysis

WOLD and JURÉEN · Demand Anal⌐⌐⌐

YOUDEN · Statistical Methods for C

Tracts on Probability and Statistics

BILLINGSLEY · Ergodic Theory an⌐

CRAMÉR and LEADBETTER · S⌐

Processes

HERMAN WOLD

DEMAND ANALYSIS

DEMAND ANALYSIS

A study in econometrics

BY

HERMAN WOLD

Professor of Statistics, University of Uppsala

in association with

LARS JURÉEN

Director of the Research Bureau
State Agricultural Marketing Board of Sweden

JOHN WILEY & SONS, INC., NEW YORK

ALMQVIST & WIKSELL, STOCKHOLM

To ANNA-LISA

my ideal and beloved idealist

You cannot choose your battlefield,
The gods do that for you,
But you can plant a standard
Where a standard never flew.

Nathalia Crane, at the age of nine.

PREFACE

Economic research muddles along under two heavy handicaps. One is that in economics, as in other social sciences, research has to work without the guidance and support of controlled experiment, the supreme tool of the natural sciences. Secondly, the empirical data are notoriously unreliable in many sections of the economic field, and they may also be scarce or completely lacking. Even for factors of central importance the information is deficient, as witnessed by the statistics on incomes, or on commercial stocks. Thus handicapped, it is no wonder that quantitative economic research displays little of the rigour and precision attained in many natural sciences. An example of the contrast is shown in the two graphs overleaf. Fig. 1 refers to the classical experiments by which Millikan in 1917 estimated the electronic charge as 4.78×10^{-10} electrostatic units. Fig. 2 illustrates the demand function for corn as estimated by H. Schultz from U.S. data 1875–1895, his result being that the price elasticity is 0.77 or 0.99, depending upon which regression line is used for the estimation. Millikan's estimate differs only by about 1/2% from the value later established by improved methods (Bäcklin), whereas the dual estimates given by Schultz differ between themselves by about 25%.

It is bad enough that sound research in economics is rendered difficult by the two handicaps, but perhaps even more serious are their by-effects on the research attitude. In the natural sciences, on the whole, hasty conclusions and other human weaknesses are checked by the careful replication of experiments, and by a high precision of measurement. In economics, these checks on the scientific conscience are weaker, and as a consequence the average quality of the research is lower, the pieces of good work being outnumbered by studies where the contact with reality is a loose one. To judge from the graveyard of forecast failures, the state of affairs is indeed bad.[1] In this respect, econometrics seems to be even worse off than the 'non-quantitative' schools of economics, but this impression may be deceptive, for if a quantitative forecast is wrong it is liable to attract attention and can hardly be glossed over, whereas a qualitative mistake, in itself vaguer, is more likely to be buried in silence.

---

[1] Superior numbers refer to Appendix notes at the end of the volume.

The situation might seem paradoxical if we think of the big arsenal of efficient methods that modern statistics has placed at the research worker's disposal. Not that attempts are lacking to exploit such methods for the purpose of econometric research. The modern methods, however, have been devised primarily for the treatment of experimental data, and in particular this holds true of the epoch-making contributions by R.A. Fisher, such as the analysis of variance and the maximum likelihood method. Highly specified as regards the underlying assumptions, these refined methods are handicapped when applied to economic statistics or other non-experimental data. Here the important thing is to coordinate the statistical methods with a thorough knowledge of the field under analysis, making use of all sorts of experience and prior information. As a consequence, quite simple methods are at a premium, these being more flexible and adaptable to any auxiliary information. This forms a strong argument in favour of a good many traditional methods which have sometimes been declared obsolete, like the least-squares regression or the short-cut of consumer units in the analysis of family budget data. In the author's opinion, these methods are essentially sound. One of the principal incentives in the writing of the present volume and its preparatory studies has been to reveal and take advantage of the wealth of experience and common sense that is embodied in the familiar procedures of the traditional methods.

The analysis of economic demand is a field where statistical data are relatively plentiful and reliable. The pioneer attempts to explore the accumulating material date from before World War I, and the studies soon multiplied. The first systematic studies were due to H. L. Moore. In the 'thirties came Allen-Bowley's and Schultz's monographs on consumer demand, the first comprehensive works in the field. These together picture in broad outline the demand pattern for the countries concerned, and many special aspects of demand were studied in detail. In the work of Allen and Bowley, which is based on family budget data, consumer demand is studied as a function of income. Schultz had for his main purpose the study of demand as a function of prices, a more difficult task since the data here have the form of time-series, known as market statistics.

The present monograph has its origin in a study of consumer demand in Sweden, carried out in 1938–40 on behalf of a government committee. The rich material available invited a thorough investigation. The main line of approach was to combine the analysis of family budget data and market statistics so as to obtain a unified picture of the demand structure in Sweden in 1920–38. Thanks to the accuracy of the data it was possible to subject the methods and the results to efficient checks and cross-checks. A full report of the study was published in Swedish in 1940.

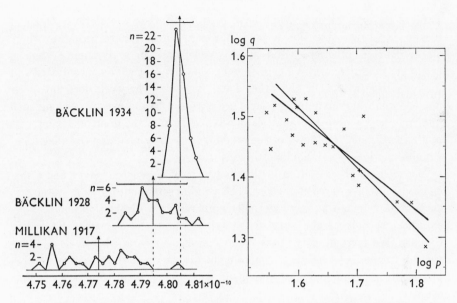

Fig. 1. Millikan's and Bäcklin's estimates
of the electronic charge.[2]

Fig. 2. Schultz's estimates of the price
elasticity for corn.[3]

For the empirical part of this monograph the authorship is shared with
Mr. Lars Juréen. Our collaboration started in 1938, in work on the 1940
report. Serving since 1940 in the State Agricultural Marketing Board of Sweden,
Mr. Juréen has since 1947 been in charge of its Research Bureau. The investigations for which Mr. Juréen has been responsible in this government agency
include (a) a careful revision of production, consumption, and price data for
the main items of Swedish agriculture, (b) the calculation of demand elasticities
on the basis of these and other data, and (c) a forecast of the Swedish consumption in 1949, based on consumption data for 1930–39 and on price and income
elasticities calculated for the inter-war period. The results under (c) give
evidence of a remarkable stability in the demand structure. In spite of the
substantial changes in consumption that were caused by the rationing and
general shortage during World War II, consumer demand did in fact after
the crisis resume the old structure known from the between-war period.

The stability thus displayed by the consumption pattern is of great importance for demand analysis, from the viewpoint of theory and method as well
as of application. Generally speaking, we are led to consider consumer demand
as a relatively stable feature in the pulsating dynamics of the economic development. Gradual shifts in the demand functions are there, of course, but they
can be allowed for without entering upon anticipations, short-term reactions,
or other intricacies of a dynamic approach. This being so, the theoretical

parts of the present monograph have been confined to the static methods of demand analysis. Attention is paid, however, to the general situation where stable demand functions enter as static elements in a dynamic system of economic relationships. We gain thereby the advantage of a concentrated and uniform treatment. On the other hand, however, the work does not cover applications where dynamic features are essential to the picture. Among such applications we note the analysis of savings habits, the demand for imports and exports, and the study of the production sector, including the analysis of supply functions, stock holdings, investments, etc.

The monograph is written in the dual form of a research report and a specialized textbook on econometrics. The volume sets out to give a systematic account of demand analysis methods, employing for illustrative material the empirical studies of the authors into the structure of consumer demand in Sweden. We have already stressed the limitation to static methods of analysis. A further restriction is made in the discussion of the empirical results, practically no comparisons being made with the demand structure in other countries.

In demand analysis, empirical and theoretical inference are interwoven, economic theory being used for guiding and supporting the statistical methods and checking the empirical findings. At the same time, the statistical methods are founded on the theory of probability. To give a self-contained account of methods and results in the present volume, it is therefore necessary to enter upon economic theory as well as statistical methods and probability theory. The subjects of main relevance are on the one hand the theory of consumer demand, on the other the theory of regression analysis and certain topics in the theory of random processes. This forms a rather wide range of theory, so much the more as fairly advanced arguments are involved at some stages. It has accordingly been quite a problem to keep this volume within reasonable limits of space.

The arrangement is as follows. Part I gives a broad summary of the material, written with restricted use of technical terms, and stressing the general lines of development in demand analysis and related fields. Part I will thus serve the double purpose of making a self-contained whole for rapid reading, and of facilitating the reading of the subsequent parts. A reader with little or no interest in theoretical questions or technical details may therefore read only Part I, consulting the tables of Part V for further numerical results, or any other section in which he may be interested. In Part I, the second chapter is devoted to least-squares regression, the principal method of demand analysis, which is examined from the double viewpoint of its rationale and its general scope in econometrics. One of the issues is the dualism exemplified in Fig. 2. It turns out that only one of the two regression lines can be used for the purpose of demand analysis, viz. the regression of demand upon price (thus in Fig. 2 the regression of log q upon log p, giving the estimate 0.77 for the price elasticity). The central theme in Ch. 2 is the statistical treatment of causal relationships in the case of non-experimental data. The exposition here enters a controversial field. Stressing the importance of the causal interpretation, which in every application of regression analysis has to be based on non-statistical considerations ad hoc, the exposition makes an effort to avoid the formalism which is such an alarming feature in much of the modern econometrics.

Parts II-V are more concentrated. Part II is devoted to economic theory. The main theme is Pareto's theory of preference fields, and special attention is paid to the interrelations between demand elasticities. Part III gives a brief survey of the theory of stationary processes. The material is selected so as to give a background for the treatment of market statistics, these having the form of time-series data. Part IV deals with least-squares regression analysis, the purpose being on the one hand to give a theoretical treatment that covers the statements of general scope in Ch. 2, on the other hand to settle a number of special questions that arise in demand analysis.

Part V reports the empirical findings. A first draft of the manuscript of this part was made by Mr. L. Juréen on the joint basis of the 1940 report and his own later research referred to above. Mr. Juréen has further read and commented upon the entire volume in manuscript. Further I wish to acknowledge with deep gratitude the years of collaboration that preceded the preparation of this monograph, Mr. Juréen having at all times been ready to place his practical experience and wide knowledge of demand analysis at my disposal.

Being an extended and rewritten version of my 1940 report, the monograph includes material from a number of preparatory studies, and some fresh material has also been added. Since 1942 these studies have been carried out in close contact with my statistical seminar at Uppsala University. The group includes Mr. R. Bentzel, Mr. G. Eklund, Mr. I. Galvenius, Dr. E. von Hofsten, Dr. S. Malmquist, Mr. K. Medin, and Dr. P. Whittle, all of whom have carried out independent research in demand analysis and related fields. The seminar has formed a most stimulating discussion milieu, and I am further indebted to its members for assistance in preparing the exercises and in other work on the monograph. Similarly I have profited greatly from conducting research seminars abroad, in Madrid February–March 1949 and November–December 1951, and in Calcutta November 1949–February 1950. For these exhilarating intermezzos my sincere thanks are extended to Dr. S. Ríos, Director of the Statistics Department in the Consejo Superiór de Investigaciones Científicas, Madrid, and Dr. P. C. Mahalanobis, Director of the Indian Statistical Institute, Calcutta. Another favourable juncture was an invitation to spend the Lent term 1951 at the London School of Economics and Political Science under its 'Scheme of Northern Studies.' My exposition of the method of regression analysis then having reached its first draft, this visit gave me a valuable opportunity to take up the controversial questions for discussion in economic and statistical seminars at the Universities of London, Oxford, Cambridge and Manchester.

A number of friends have kindly undertaken to read and criticize the volume in manuscript. Mr. J. Durbin, London School of Economics, Dr. O. Reiersöl, Oslo University, and Dr P. Whittle, Uppsala University, have rendered me most valuable assistance by reading the entire manuscript, and by following up their thorough revision by discussions at Uppsala. Part II and in particular Ch. 8·3 was read by Professor R. G. D. Allen, London School of Economics; Ch. 3·2 by Professor E. Lundberg, Stockholm University; Ch. 3·5 by Professor K. Marc-Wogau, Uppsala University; Ch. 8·3 by Dr. E. von Hofsten, Stockholm; and Ch. 9·4 by Dr. U. Grenander, Stockholm University. To all of these I am greatly indebted for comments and suggestions leading to corrections and improvements. My thanks are further due to Miss V. Rajaoja, Mr. F. Billström and Mr. I. Galvenius for assistance in reading the proofs. The monograph and its preparatory studies have involved much computation and typing. I wish to express my sincere thanks to Miss E. Lundwall for her patient and efficient assistance in all phases of this work, not to speak of the rush periods in the office routine, and to Miss H. Laadi and Miss V. Rajaoja for having performed much of the qualified computation and for having helped me to organize the work of a varying number of computing assistants.

With deep gratitude I wish to acknowledge grants from the Swedish Academy of Sciences, the Swedish Research Council of Social Sciences, and the Rockefeller Foundation in support of the monograph and several preparatory studies.

Uppsala, May 1952.

H. W.

Table of Contents

PART I

A broad survey of topics and findings

Chapter 1.

THE ENDS AND MEANS OF DEMAND ANALYSIS

1. Some issues of applied demand analysis. – Let us consider some questions of economic policy that governments have had to deal with in recent years.

World War II is over, but is it safe to abandon food rationing? Granted that price control is maintained, will demand, when free, keep itself within the limits of supply? Will it be necessary to check the increase in demand by raising the prices of the basic foods? Is it possible to forecast the effect of a change in prices? Can the effect be forecasted on the basis of the demand habits observed before the war, or is the afterwar pattern very different? And will the habits change if price control is abolished?

How is demand influenced by the gradual increase of the general income level? Is the demand for food nearly satiated, from the point of view of average calorie intake? Granted that the average real income will continue to increase at about the same rate as before, will this trend be accompanied by a substitution of cheap cereals by more expensive but generally more health-protective foods? What trend can be foreseen in the demand for the protein-rich animal foods, and in the vitamin-rich vegetables and fruits? Will the forecast indicate changes large enough to produce repercussions on the country's agricultural production planning?

The above questions are just a sample from the wide field of application of demand analysis. To answer such questions we have basically to consider problems of a simpler type: If income rises by 10 %, but other factors remain constant, will the consumption of cereals rise by 5 %, by 15 %, or perhaps decline? And if the price of eggs is raised by 5 %, will the egg consumption drop by 5 %, by 10 %, or perhaps remain the same? We have, in other words, to study demand as a function of income, prices, and other relevant factors. We encounter here the notion of a *demand function*. It is unnecessary to stress what a fundamental part this concept plays in economic theory. The notion of a

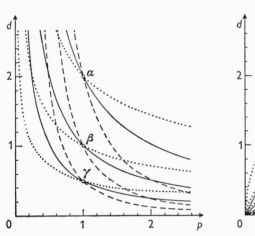 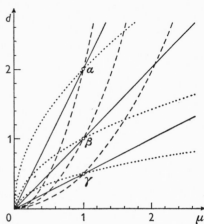

Fig. 1·1·1 a–b.

a. The demand function $d = c_1 \cdot p^{-e}$, with $c_1 = \frac{1}{2}$; 1; 2 and $e = \frac{1}{2}$; 1; 2.

b. The demand function $d = c_2 \cdot \mu^E$, with $c_2 = \frac{1}{2}$; 1; 2 and $E = \frac{1}{2}$; 1; 2.

demand function is, however, theoretical. The empirical demand analysis has for its aim to put real flesh on the theoretical bones of demand functions.

As a field of scientific research, this much is clear, demand analysis has the attractive feature of being of fundamental importance to theory as well as applications.

Demand functions as derived from empirical data should always be regarded as tentative, as more or less successful attempts to cover the complex realities behind the statistical observations by the simple pattern of a specified mathematical function. It is a remarkable fact, however, that very simple functions will often be useful for the purpose, at least as a first approximation. Experience has shown that it is quite often satisfactory to work on the hypothesis that the demand functions are of the simple form

(1) $$d = c_1 \cdot p^{-e} \qquad d = c_2 \cdot \mu^E \qquad (c_1,\ c_2,\ e,\ E \text{ are constants}).$$

The first relation refers to demand as a function of price p, the second to demand as a function of income μ. The parameters e and E are known as the *price* and *income elasticities* of demand, respectively, the interpretation being that if price (income) rises by 1 %, then demand will fall (rise) by e % (by E %), and conversely if price or income falls. Fig. 1 illustrates the functions (1) for different values of the constants. Fig. 2 shows the same curves in logarithmic scale. We see that the curves here reduce to straight lines, as is correct since (1) gives

(2) $$\log d = \log c_1 - e \log p; \qquad \log d = \log c_2 + E \log \mu.$$

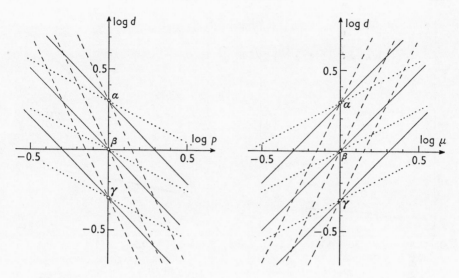

Fig. 1·1·2 a–b. The demand functions of Fig. 1 drawn in logarithmic scales.

According to these relations, the elasticities e and E can be read off directly from Fig. 2 as the slopes of the logarithmic demand curves.

Following up approach (1), we are led to represent demand as a function of the type

$$(3) \qquad d = c \cdot \mu^E \cdot p^{-e} \cdot x^a \cdot y^b \cdot \ldots \cdot u^g$$

where μ is income, p is the price of the commodity considered, and $x, y, \ldots, u$ are other factors that influence the demand of the commodity. Again the relationship becomes linear if we transform to logarithms,

$$(4) \qquad \log d = \log c + E \log \mu - e \log p + a \log x + \cdots + g \log u.$$

By making use of demand functions of type (1) or (3) we gain the advantage that the empirical analysis can be summed up in terms of constant elasticities, here denoted $E, e, a, b, \ldots, g$.

Although the functions (1) and (3) are useful as a first approximation, they are of limited scope, and in particular they cannot be expected to be valid over wide ranges of income and price [Ch. 5·4]. As regards demand as a function of income, reference should here be made to a successful attempt by L. Törnqvist to construct demand functions that may be realistic over a wide range of incomes [Ch. 5·5]. Törnqvist's functions are illustrated in Fig. 3. They are of three types, given by

$$(5) \qquad d = \alpha \cdot \frac{\mu}{\mu + \beta} \qquad\qquad d = \alpha \cdot \frac{\mu - \gamma}{\mu + \beta} \qquad\qquad d = \alpha \cdot \mu \cdot \frac{\mu - \gamma}{\mu + \beta}.$$

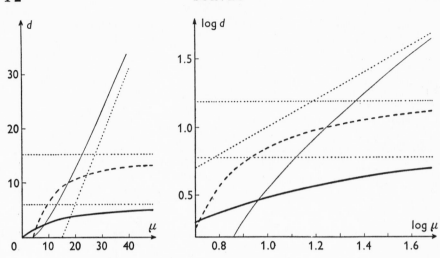

Fig. 1·1·3. Demand functions of Törnqvist's type.

Necessities: ————————   Formula (5a) with $\alpha = 6,\ \beta = 10.$
Relative luxuries: - - - - - - - - - -   "   (5b)   " $\alpha = 15,\ \beta = 3,\ \gamma = 4.$
Luxuries: ————————   "   (5c)   " $\alpha = 1.2,\ \beta = 11,\ \gamma = 4.$

a. Ordinary scales.   b. Logarithmic scales.

The three functions are intended for different types of commodity, viz. necessities, relative luxuries, and luxuries.

Empirical demand analysis derives its results from two main sources of statistical observations, viz. (a) family budget data, and (b) market statistics. The two types of data will now be briefly described, and their use as material for demand analysis will be explained, to provide an introductory discussion.

2. Family budget data. – Sampling surveys for the collection of family budget data were carried out by government agencies in Sweden in 1913, 1923 and 1933. Each survey covered more than 1000 households, chosen so as to represent different family types, income levels, social classes, and so on. During a period of 12 months or more, every household compiled an account of its expenditures, with the budget items specified in great detail [cf Table 16·5·2]. Reports of the surveys were published, likewise in great detail.

Fig. 1a shows a set of family budget data arranged for the purpose of demand analysis. The graph refers to 50 households from the 1913 survey. Each household being represented by a cross, the horizontal scale gives the income of the household, the vertical scale its expenditure on a specified budget item, here a group of foodstuffs. The 50 households are workers' and employees' families in the city of Gothenburg. All families are about the same size, viz. between 2.2 and 2.6 consumer units (the scale of evaluation is: men 1.0, women 0.8, children from 0.1 and upwards according to their age; cf Ch. 14·5).

Suppose for a moment that we had a free hand to arrange an experiment in order to find out how expenditure habits are influenced by income level. In the language of scientific experiment, we should then subject the family income to controlled variation, and for each item of the budget observe the resulting differences in the expenditure. Following experimental routine, the first step would be to select a group of households, making the selection without regard to the family income, but trying to make the group homogeneous as regards regional environment, social class, family size, and other factors that influence the demand. The next step would be to regulate the family income, by allotting the households to different income levels. In order to neutralize the effect of other factors than income, the allotment should follow a random scheme, that is, without favouring or disfavouring any type of household. After allowing the households some time to adapt themselves to the income levels thus fixed, the final step would be to record the expenditures of every household during a period of say 12 months, with the various budget items specified in the accounts. Now, let us imagine that the experimental data thus obtained for food expenditure were as shown in Fig. 1a. We see that the experiment would then have demonstrated that an increase in income is on the whole accompanied by an increase in food expenditure. To express this result of the experiment in quantitative terms we could use the device that in Fig. 1a is illustrated by small circles. The families have here been classified according to income, in this case in three groups [as indicated by the broken verticals]. The average expenditure and the average income are calculated for every income class. The circles show the average expenditure as plotted against average income; we see that *the higher the income, the higher is the average food expenditure.*

The line *L* in Fig. 1a is the *linear regression of expenditure on income.* This is another device for bringing out the tendency established by the small circles. The regression line has the advantage of giving the result in more condensed form, viz. as a functional relationship between expenditure x and income μ, in symbols

(1) $$x = a + b \cdot \mu$$ where in this case $a = 65.1$; $b = 0.143$.

Provided the scatter shows a linear trend, the line and the circles will coincide, and in practice give equivalent results. Further we note, quite generally, that the regression forms a graduation of the trend indicated by the circles. The regression method, which is a fundamental tool in demand analysis, will be examined in detail in Chs. 1·5 and 2·1–9.

Family budget data are dealt with in demand analysis *as if* they had come from an experiment such as just described. The traditional analysis thus being based on a hypothetical analogy, the question is whether or not the hypothesis is realistic enough for its purpose. Let us first consider two objections that are

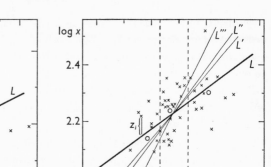

Fig. 1·2·1. Food expenditure, x, plotted against family income, μ, for 50 families in Gothenburg, 1913–14.

a. Ordinary scales.   b. Logarithmic scales.

sometimes raised against the traditional method. One is that what we want to know is how one and the same family would behave at different income levels, whereas the actual budget data refer to *different* families with different incomes· The other is that the effect of income changes cannot be properly distinguished even if we confine ourselves to a homogeneous group of families, for owing to individual tastes and other factors that cannot be taken into account when selecting the group the demand habits will still vary greatly between the families. These objections, however, do not go to the heart of the matter, for in several fields where experimental inference is in everyday use the situation is rather similar. In biological assay, for example, when estimating the 50% lethal dose of a certain drug, different dilutions of the drug are injected simultaneously into different batches of animals [cf Fig. 2·2·1]. Furthermore, the individual variation within the batches is not under direct experimental control, though often quite considerable, but this source of bias may be neutralized by following a random scheme when allotting the animals to different treatments, in the same manner as indicated in the fictitious experiment with family budgets.

From the viewpoint of statistical analysis, what is then the relevant difference, if any, between the fictitious experiment and the actual, non-experimental data? The answer is, I think, that the relationship under analysis is interpreted in the same way in terms of cause and effect, but the logical basis of the causal interpretation differs. Referring once more to the biological experiment, this brings out the causal relationship between dosage and mortality. We see that the relation is *unilateral* in the sense that mortality is causally dependent upon dosage, not the other way around. Or, in the customary terminology of experiments, dosage is the controlled variable, also called the *cause* variable, mortality is the *effect* variable. The essential point is that these notions lie in the very nature of an ordinary experiment, and that it is obvious from the design of the experiment which is the cause variable and which is the effect variable.

Returning to the family budget data, we can now see what is required in order to interpret an income-expenditure relationship as a unilateral causal relation. Since experiments are not possible, the causal interpretation is not obvious from the mechanism of an experiment but has instead to be justified by considerations ad hoc. Generally speaking, the causal interpretation has to be inferred from subject-matter considerations based on empirical evidence and economic theory.

Following up the argument, it stands to reason that for workers, clerks and employees in general the family income determines the demand habits in much the same manner as described in our fictitious experiment. But in contrast to an experiment, the unilateral dependence should be regarded as approximate, and in point of principle it may even be unrealistic for part or the whole of the data under analysis. Specifically, it may be argued that many an entrepreneur or merchant has a demand pattern that is more stable than the varying profit of his business, and so the unilateral dependence between income and expenditure is blurred by a tendency to bilateral interdependence.

In the biological experiment considered the unilateral dependence may be expressed as a functional relationship, with the effect variable as a function of the cause variable. We note that the term *function* is here used in the sense of a relationship that is not necessarily exact, but in general is more or less blurred by random disturbances [again, see Fig. 2·2·1]. The situation is the same in the case of family budget data. The budget data give us an empirical picture of the unilateral dependence, and if the data are subjected to regression analysis, the relationship is brought out directly in functional form. Thus for example the regression (1) is a linear function derived from the statistical data of Fig. 1a. If we work instead on the logarithmic data of Fig. 1b, we obtain the regression shown by the heavy line L, in symbols

$$(2) \qquad\qquad \log x = a + b \log \mu \qquad \text{with } a = 0.189; \quad b = 0.71.$$

The final step of the family budget analysis is to interpret the regressions (1)–(2) in terms of demand functions. This is very easy. Writing p for the price of the commodity or commodity group considered, and d for the quantity purchased, we have $x = pd$. In family budget data we may for each commodity group regard price p as constant over the short period covered by the data, and further the price is approximately the same for all consumers. Hence $d = x/p$, where p may be treated as a constant, and so on insertion in (1) or (2) we obtain demand d as a function of income μ. Specifically, (2) gives us a relation

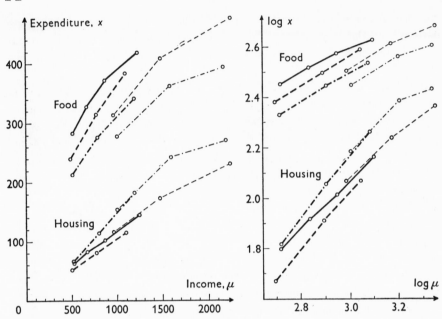

Fig. 1·2·2. Food expenditure and housing expenditure against family income. Budget data.

1913: ———————— 1923: { ————————— } 1933: { —·——·——·——·— }
{ —————————— } { —·—·—·—·—·—·— }

Workers' and employees' families: Heavy lines. Middle-class families: Thin lines.

a. Ordinary scales. b. Logarithmic scales.

of type (1·1·2b), with $E = b = 0.71$. In other words, the analysis has resulted in a demand function estimate of the form (1·1·1b), and the estimate obtained for the income elasticity E allows a simple graphic interpretation: it is nothing else than the slope of the line L in Fig. 1b.

Let us now consider another set of data of the same type. Fig. 2 is based on the data for all households of the 1913, 1923 and 1933 surveys, and refers to the expenditures for food and for housing. The small circles have been obtained in the same manner as in Fig. 1, with separate treatment of (a) workers' and employees' families, (b) middle class families. This is a classical type of graph in the literature of family budget data. The curves based upon the circles are known as *Engel curves*.[1] As we have explained in detail, the Engel curves may be interpreted as demand functions if we assume that the families under investigation have the same demand habits. We note that when forming the regressions (1)–(2) the relations obtained will be practically the same whether the calculations are based on the individual data (crosses) or on the data grouped according to income (circles). Hence we may in Figs. 1—2 use the circles for obtaining approximations to the demand functions in the form of explicit functions, as in (1) or (2). Since the data are grouped, the calculations involved will be very simple [Ch. 14·1]. The resulting demand functions may be regarded as graduations of the Engel curves.

The method outlined applies to any type of family, and so it is possible to carry out the demand analysis separately for different types of households represented in the data. Now if this has been done, the results obtained for the various family types may be pooled together in order to bring out how their aggregate demand will change when there are aggregate changes in their incomes. For example, Fig. 2 gives us demand elasticities for food, and the results obtained for the two social classes will have to be combined or pooled if we are interested in the aggregate demand elasticity of food with respect to a general increase in incomes. In principle such pooling will simply consist in forming a weighted average of the demand elasticities of the two groups. For the formulae required, reference is made to Chs. 5·6 and 6·4. We note that each of the two social classes is itself an aggregate of subgroups that differ in family size, regional environment, etc. This inhomogeneity will be taken into account in our ultimate analysis of the data, by splitting the households into subgroups according to family size. The treatment of family budget data for the purpose of demand analysis may thus be described as a double process: splitting up the data so as to obtain subgroups that are reasonably homogeneous with respect to the demand habits, and then pooling the results so as to obtain aggregate results that are valid for larger groups (and more reliable owing to the damping of individual differences).

3. Market statistics. − By market statistics we understand time-series data on quantities bought and sold, prices, incomes, etc.[1] Fig. 1 shows a set of market statistics studied in the empirical part of this volume.

Fig. 1a refers to the cooperative stores in Stockholm during the interwar period 1925–1937. The horizontal scale is time, the two vertical scales are the sale of butter, d, and the butter price, p. The quantity variable, d, is given in kilograms per member of Stockholm's cooperative societies. The price variable, p, is real price, calculated as the yearly average of the stores' butter price in Sw. crowns per kilogram, divided by a yearly price index. Fig. 1b shows the same data in the form of a scatter diagram, with price on the horizontal scale and demand on the vertical scale.

The treatment of market statistics is analogous to that of family budget data except that demand is now regarded primarily as a function of price instead of income. Thus the data of Fig. 1b are regarded as obtained from an experiment where butter price is the controlled variable, and butter quantity is the effect variable. Again the basis of this approach is hypothetical, and whether sufficiently realistic or not its possible justification has to be sought in nonstatistical considerations.

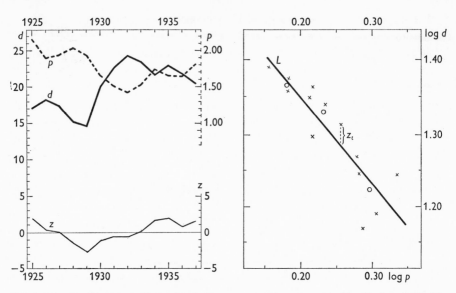

Fig. 1·3·1 a–b. Market statistics for butter; cooperative stores in Stockholm, 1925–37.
a. Data plotted as time-series.   b. Data plotted as a scatter diagram.
Ordinary scales.   Logarithmic scales.

The question is, accordingly, whether for a given market it is legitimate to regard butter demand as causally dependent on butter price. The literature on demand analysis is not very explicit on this point, perhaps because the dependence of demand on price has been regarded as so obvious as not to require any comment, but nonetheless the question has certain aspects that require careful consideration. To begin with, we must convince ourselves that the dependence of demand on price is unilateral in the experimental sense [Ch. 1·2]. Now for the market referred to in Fig. 1 this is rather clear. In fact, when a consumer enters a store he is confronted with a fixed butter price, bargaining being practically absent. When buying the quantity he desires, his transaction is accordingly similar to the reaction in a stimulus-response experiment of the type known from experimental psychology. Further, the buying response is not hampered by rationing, and the stocks of the shop are sufficient to meet his demand.

The conclusion that we are actually concerned with a case of unilateral dependence is seen to be quite general, applying to any ordinary retail market. If we turn to a wholesale market, on the other hand, the situation will be somewhat different. Here the grocer may be in a position to bargain with the producer about the price, by offering to buy more if the producer reduces the price. In a wholesale market, in other words, the unilateral dependence of demand on price is liable to be blurred by a tendency to bilateral interdependence.[2]

Taking the hypothesis of a unilateral dependence as a basis, we may proceed just as in the case of family budget data. The hypothesis again takes the form of a demand function, in this case representing demand as a function of price. An estimate of the demand function can be obtained from the statistical data by the same methods as before. Thus the three small circles in Fig. 1b give a rough indication of demand as a function of price. The line L is the linear regression of log demand on log price, in symbols

(1) $$\log d = a + b \log p \qquad \text{with } a = 1.58; \quad b = -1.17.$$

The interpretation of the regression (1) as a demand function is now immediate, for (1) gives the demanded quantity d directly as a function of price p. We see that relation (1) is of type (1·1·2a), with $e = -b = 1.17$. Hence the demand function arrived at is of type (1·1·1a), and as with family budget data the elasticity estimate $e = 1.17$ may be interpreted graphically as the slope of the line L in Fig. 1b. Since elasticity e appears in (1·1·1a) with a negative sign, the slope must in this case be taken against the negative axis of log p.

Thus far we have only considered price changes, whereas market demand must of course be regarded as dependent also on other factors, primarily on income and on prices of substitutes. In general such factors must be taken into account if the statistical analysis of demand as a function of price is to give correct results. The traditional device is here the method of multiple regression. We shall return to this device in Ch. 1·5. In passing we note only that there is a clear analogy with the pooling method used in the analysis of family budget data [cf Ch. 1·2, final section]. In fact, both methods serve to single out the effect of just one factor, viz. income and price respectively, by neutralizing the simultaneous effect of other factors that influence the demand.

We are now coming to a point in demand analysis about which there has been much controversy and confusion. In order to bring out the issue, let us turn to Table 15·1·1. Referring to butter and margarine, the data are of the same type as in Fig. 1b, except that the quantities and prices are yearly data for the whole of Sweden. By the same argument as in Fig. 1b we are led to regard the total demand for butter and margarine as being causally dependent on the price. But in this case there is a complication, for according to the Cournot-Walras theory of economic equilibrium there is a tendency for the market totals of demand (= quantities bought by the consumers) to equal the market totals of supply (= quantities produced for the market by the entrepreneurs), and so the question arises whether the quantity variable should be interpreted as a sort of hybrid between demand and supply. If so, the market totals would not display a clear-cut, unbiased relationship between demand and price. This is again a question in demand analysis that cannot be dealt with on a purely statistical basis, but calls for further subject-matter consideration. To prepare the subsequent discussion we note the following points.

(i) Demand is not the same thing as supply, and the two notions must be kept apart whether the analysis refers to national totals or some particular submarket. In fact, consumption and production are in general not in perfect equilibrium if we consider data for a limited period, say a year. The stocks of the producers and the merchants serve as a first buffer to even out the discrepancies between demand and supply. For another thing, the balance between national totals of consumption and production is upset by imports and exports. A third fact to be taken into account is that, if there is an excess of supply over demand, part of the surplus will as a rule be transformed to other products; e.g., a large part of the milk supply goes to cheese production.

(ii) A primary requisite in demand analysis is that the statistical data for the quantities should refer to demand, not to supply. As regards the empirical studies reported in Part V, these are throughout based on consumption statistics. Unfortunately, such data are relatively scarce, and difficult to bring forth. Thus national totals usually refer to production, so that corrections have to be made for imports and exports, changes in the stocks, etc. The difficulties are no less for submarkets. For one thing, such data require knowledge of the number of customers in the market; for the cooperative societies' stores this is approximately proportional to the membership of the societies. There is further the question of business secrecy, and the difficulties in specifying the yearly sale of different commodities within a store.

4. Economic models as a hypothetical basis for demand analysis. — As stressed under (i)–(ii) in the previous section, we must not confuse the notions of demand and supply, but the comment gave no clue to the question whether the tendency towards demand-supply equilibrium has any repercussions in the statistical analysis of demand as a function of price. Now, in the recent decades of economic and econometric analysis, a general approach or principle has emerged that may be applied in this type of situation. The principle is that the statistical analysis should be based on a hypothetical, *a priori model* for the relationships that are studied. Gradually improved and developed so as to make combined use of inference methods of economics, probability theory and statistics, this approach seems now to be universally accepted, and much work has been done in studying various types of model both in theory and in applications to empirical data. We shall in this section consider a very simple model, too simple to be realistic, but chosen so as to display the general scope of the approach.

Let us consider the following model[1]

(1) $d_t = D(p_t)$ $s_t = S(p_{t-1})$ $p_t = p_{t-1} + \gamma \cdot (d_{t-1} - s_{t-1}).$

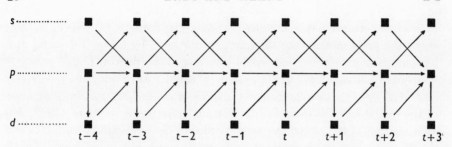

Fig. 1·4·1. Arrow scheme for the economic model (1).

Referring to a specified commodity market, the model gives three hypothetical relations between demand d, supply s, and price p. The index t refers to time, and runs over consecutive periods, say $t = 1, 2, 3, \ldots$.

Equation (1a) explains demand during time period t as a function of the price p_t during the same period. Hence (1a) is in line with what we have said about demand functions in Ch. 1·1–3, and in particular with our comment on Fig. 1·3·1. The demand function $d_t = D(p_t)$ thus gives us the answer to the question: if price p_t is known, what is the demand d_t? At the same time (1a) expresses a causal hypothesis, viz. that the demand function shows how the consumers react to changes in price. We note that, if price is not constant during the whole of a period t, we should in (1) interpret p_t as an average price during the period.

Equation (1b) explains supply during period t as a function of the price p_{t-1} during the preceding period. The assumption of retarded reaction in the supply makes allowance for two facts, viz. (a) the production of any commodity requires time, the finished product emerging a shorter or longer time after the input of raw materials, (b) the production is directed by entrepreneurs according to plans that they change from time to time. The time unit of the model is chosen so as to correspond to the intervals of production planning. Equation (1b) is usually given with specific reference to agricultural production, the assumption being that for the product considered, say wheat, the production volume for next year, say t, is planned in this year, $t-1$, and that the main causal factor is the prevailing wheat price, p_{t-1}.

Equation (1c) explains price during period t as an adjustment in the price during the preceding period. Making $\gamma > 0$ we see that the adjustment will be in agreement with classical equilibrium theory; i.e., price will rise or fall according as demand exceeds or falls short of supply [see Fig. 3·2·1a for illustration]. In other words, equation (1c) serves to explain the causal mechanism behind the price movements. Let us further consider the inverse of the demand function (1a), in symbols

(2) $$p_t = D^{-1}(d_t).$$

It is of importance not to confuse (1c) with (2). Formula (2) tells us nothing about the price mechanism; the question answered by (2) is: if demand d_t is known, what is the price that would give rise to this demand?

Given initial values p_0, s_0, the system (1) enables us to calculate, recursively for $t = 1, 2, 3, \ldots$, the development of the three variables d_t, s_t, p_t. For illustration of the model and the recursive calculation, reference is made to Fig. 1. For each relation of the model the arrows indicate the explanatory variables and the lags involved. This instructive type of graph has been devised by J. Tinbergen (1940), and is known as the *arrow scheme*.

For the statistical treatment of system (1), two properties of the relations involved are of essential relevance. The first point is that system (1) is recursive in a *twofold* sense: (a) if the development of the three variables is known up to time $t-1$, the system gives us the variables at time t, (b) the variables at time t are obtained one by one, in this case first s_t or p_t, and then d_t. The second point is that each equation of (1) may be interpreted as a hypothesis of *unilateral causal dependence* in the sense of Ch. 1·2–3, with the cause variable or variables to the right, and the effect variable to the left. Thus (1a) refers to the consumers, describing how they react to changes in the prices. Similarly, (1b) describes how the producers react to price changes. As regard (1c), this may be taken to refer to the retailers. The main economic function of this group is to bring demand into contact with supply; furthermore, in a market of free competition the retailers act as price regulators, raising or lowering price according as demand exceeds or falls short of supply. Each of the equations (1 a–c) gives of course only a first rough approximation towards describing the reactions of the group in question. A more realistic model would have to include further causal factors; in (1c) for instance, the size of the retailers' stocks.[2]

The two properties just mentioned define a general category of theoretical models. This category, which is of fundamental importance, will be referred to as *recursive systems.* Let us repeat their characteristic properties:

(i) *they are recursive in the twofold sense indicated*, and

(ii) *each equation of the system expresses a unilateral causal dependence*.

We are now in a position to answer the question raised in Ch. 1·3, i.e., whether the tendency towards equilibrium between demand and supply gives rise to any incorrectness or bias in the statistical analysis of demand as a function of price. The answer is in the negative. We have in fact the general theorem that the bias in question is not present in recursive systems. In particular, the bias is absent in system (1 a–c). The situation will be examined in some detail in Ch. 2·7. Further we shall return to the recursive systems in Ch. 3·2, for a discussion of their scope and limitation as a device for dynamic analysis. We state in advance that the recursive systems are of

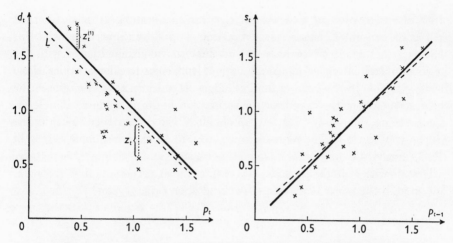

Fig. 1·4·2. Illustration of model (3) by artificial time-series data.

a. Demand d_t against price p_t.   b. Supply s_t against lagged price p_{t-1}.

a very general scope. Further we note that in economic literature until around 1945 all of the systems used in dynamic analysis were of the recursive type.

To give an illustration of the theorem just referred to, let us consider the following model,

$$(3) \qquad d_t = 2 - p_t + z_t^{(1)}; \qquad s_t = p_{t-1} + z_t^{(2)}; \qquad p_t = p_{t-1} + \gamma(d_{t-1} - s_{t-1}) + z_t^{(3)},$$

with $\gamma = 1/4$. The variables $z^{(i)}$ are introduced as *disturbances*, serving to sum up the effect of causal factors that have not explicitly been taken into account in the model. Disturbances should as a rule be introduced in hypothetical models; we may take it that they are present in (1) without having been written down explicitly. Thus we see that model (3) is of type (1), with demand and supply functions specified to be linear, and with equilibrium for $d = s = p = 1$. Now, the demand function in model (3) is $d_t = 2 - p_t$ [the heavy line in Fig. 2 a]. Hence for given price p the demand as calculated from the demand function is $2 - p$. For period t, with price p_t, the model accordingly gives us two values for the demand, viz. the observed value d_t and the value $2 - p_t$ given by the demand function. The difference is the disturbance $z_t^{(1)} = d_t - (2 - p_t)$. Graphically, the disturbance $z_t^{(1)}$ is the vertical distance from the point (d_t, p_t) to the demand function line [one of the disturbances is indicated in Fig. 2 a].

If we suppose that all disturbances $z_t^{(i)}$ are known, and start from initial values s_0, p_0, model (3) will as in (1) determine the development of the three variables. Fig. 2 refers to an artificial experiment where time-series for d_t, s_t, p_t were constructed for $t = 1$, $2, \ldots, 25$. The construction is based on three sequences $z_t^{(i)}$ drawn from tables of random normal deviates [cf Ex. III, 34]. Fig. 2 a gives the 25 values of d_t, plotted against p_t. Fig. 2 a further shows the least-squares regression of d_t on p_t [broken line, L]. In accordance with the general theorem referred to, we see that the regression brings out, approximately, the true demand function $d_t = 2 - p_t$. Similarly, Fig. 2 b shows s_t as plotted against p_{t-1}, and we see that the regression of s_t on p_{t-1} [broken line] approximates the true supply function $s_t = p_{t-1}$ [heavy line].

5. The regression approach. – In the previous sections we have been led to regard consumer demand as a function of price, income, and other influencing factors. In statistical demand analysis we are confronted with the problem of estimating the demand functions from empirical observations, these being available in the form of family budget data and market statistics. The main statistical method used for the estimation of demand functions is least-squares regression analysis. A few simple illustrations have been shown in the graphs of Ch. 1·2–4. The regression method will be examined more closely in Ch. 2, but by way of general introduction we shall now recall its basic features

To start with a simple example, we consider the artificial data of Fig. 1·4·2 a. Let us form the linear regression of demand d_t on price p_t, say

$$(1) \qquad d_t = a + b p_t \quad \text{or} \quad d_t = a + b p_t + z_t$$

where in the second formula the regression residual z_t has been written down explicitly.[1] The coefficients a and b are determined according to the principle of least squares. This principle requires that the sum of squares of the residuals z_t should be a minimum, in symbols

$$(2) \qquad S = \Sigma z_t^2 = \Sigma (a + b p_t - d_t)^2 \text{ a minimum,}$$

where the summation runs over all observations, say n in number. We see that (2) is equivalent to the condition that the residuals should have minimum variance.

To make S a minimum, a and b should satisfy the two conditions $\partial S/\partial a = 0$, $\partial S/\partial b = 0$. This gives

$$(3) \qquad \begin{cases} a \cdot n + b \Sigma p_t = \Sigma d_t \\ a \Sigma p_t + b \Sigma p_t^2 = \Sigma d_t p_t. \end{cases}$$

System (3) is known as the *normal equations* of the regression. For the data of Fig. 1·4·2a the normal equations give $a = 1.86$, $b = -0.93$. Inserting in (1a) we obtain the regression sought for. As pointed out in Ch. 1·4 the regression thus obtained [the broken line in Fig. 1·4·2a] approximates the true demand function (1·4·3a), that is, the estimates a, b come close to the true parameters of the demand function, $a = 2$, $b = -1$. Further we note that the residuals z_t in (1) approximate the demand function disturbances $z_t^{(1)}$ of model (1·4·3). In the scatter diagram, the residual z_t is the vertical distance from the point (d_t, p_t) to the regression line [see Fig. 1·4·2a].

Turning now to demand analysis as based on empirical data, there is here the difference that we have no model, neither (1·4·3) nor any other, that is known a priori to be true. Such models will instead serve as tentative hypotheses, and the regression analysis results in estimates of the hypothetical demand functions. Thus for market statistics and family budget data, respectively, the simplest possible hypotheses are that the demand functions are linear in the price p and income μ, or in symbols

(4) $$d_t = \alpha + \beta\, p_t + \zeta_t \qquad d_\nu = \alpha + \beta\, \mu_\nu + \zeta_\nu$$

where the ζ_t and ζ_ν are hypothetical disturbances. For each of these hypotheses the normal equations (3) may be formed on the basis of empirical data. By solving for the coefficients a, b we obtain estimates for the coefficients α, β of the hypothetical demand function. Having calculated a, b the corresponding regression of type (1) further gives us the residuals, say z_t and z_ν respectively. The residuals are interpreted as estimates of the disturbances in the hypothetical model. In (4 a), where d_t and p_t are given as market statistics and thus have the form of time-series data, the residuals z_t will also take the form of a time-series.

As regards the numerical calculations involved in the least-squares regression, we see that it makes no difference whether models (4) are applied to artificial data, as in Fig. 1·4·2a, or to empirical data, as in Fig. 1·2·1a. In each of these graphs, the line L is the regression calculated in accordance with (2)–(3). The residuals z_t are constructed in the same manner in the two graphs.

The demand functions (4) being the simplest possible hypotheses, it often happens that their fit to the empirical data is too crude, or that they are otherwise unsatisfactory for the particular application. Let us briefly recall the main methods that may be used for a more refined analysis.

(i) The relationship under analysis may not appear to be linear as in (1). In such a case we may graduate the data by *curvilinear regression*. We note two methods for doing this.

a. By subjecting the variables to a suitable functional transformation we may succeed in casting the relationship into linear form. Suppose for example that the demand functions are of type (1·1·1). The logarithmic transformation

(5) $$D = \log d \qquad P = \log p \qquad M = \log \mu$$

will then make the demand functions linear. Introducing disturbance variables, the transformed demand functions are

(6) $$D = a - e \cdot P + z \qquad D = a + E \cdot M + z.$$

To estimate the constants a and the elasticities e and E we may now apply least-squares regression, just as shown in (1)–(3), working instead on the logarithmic data (5). In Figs. 1·2·1b and 1·3·1b (the lines L) we have already seen applications of this method. In Fig. 1·3·1b the empirical data have the form of time-series. Accordingly, the residuals z_t may here be represented as a time-series, as shown in the lower part of Fig. 1·3·1a.

b. The demand variable d may be directly graduated by some suitable nonlinear function. For family budget data, Törnqvist's system of demand functions is very attractive for the purpose. In symbols, this approach may be written

$$d = f(\mu) \quad \text{or} \quad d = f(\mu) + z$$

where $f(\mu)$ is one of the functions (1·1·5), and z a disturbance. The estimation of the parameters of the function f will in general be more complicated than in the case of a linear function [see Exs. IV, 20–22; for applications to empirical data, see also Ch. 16·6].

(ii) The regression approach can be extended by assuming that demand is influenced by several variables, not merely by one variable as in (4). Again we may distinguish two methods for carrying out this extension in practice.

a. If all variables are given in terms of quantitative measurements, demand may be represented as an explicit function of the variables. The traditional hypothesis is that demand is a function of type (1·1·3). Then if the variables are transformed to logarithms, as in (5), the demand hypothesis becomes

(7) $$D = a + E \cdot M - e \cdot P + a \cdot X + b \cdot Y + \cdots + g \cdot U + z$$

where z is a disturbance with the same interpretation as before. In this way the approach has been carried over into an ordinary case of *multiple regression*. That is, to determine the parameters $a, E, e, a, \ldots, g$ we make the residual square sum $S = \Sigma z^2$ a minimum. If the parameters are h in number, this gives us a system of h normal equations for determining them. When applying approach (7) in practice, we are confronted with the question of which variables $x, y, \ldots$ should be included in the regression analysis. This question will be discussed in Ch. 2·3.

b. The approach (7) does not cover the case when one or more of the influencing variables $x, y, \ldots$ are not quantitative. Let us for example consider the case of family budget data. Here the demand pattern varies with social class, family type, geographical district, etc. To make allowance for such factors we may classify the data according to a number of factors, and for each subclass carry through a demand analysis in accordance with the regression approaches (4) or (7). As briefly indicated at the end of Ch. 1·2 the results obtained for the subclasses may then be pooled so as to establish aggregate results for the entire population to which the budget data refer.

The variants a–b considered under (i) are closely related, and experience shows that they give much the same result when applied in practice. Between the two variants under (ii) there is likewise a close connexion [cf Ch. 14·6].

6. Some empirical results. – In the previous sections we have given an outline of demand analysis as regards fundamental ideas and chief methods. We shall now present some results obtained on the basis of Swedish statistics. Our aim here being to make a quick survey of the material, reference is made to Part V for details and further results.

The Swedish family budget data of 1913, 1923 and 1933 were briefly referred
to in Ch. 1·2. Table 1 is based on this material, showing the size of the samples,
the average of the yearly income for the various family classes (in 1933, $1 =
3.60 Sw. crowns), and the average of the family expenditure as specified for
10 groups of budget items. Food, including stimulants, is the main item,
covering more than a third of the budget for workers' and low grade employees'
families. Other leading items are housing, clothes, and taxes and professional
unions. In the course of time, food has decreased in relative importance
in the budget. The higher percentage for item group VIII in middle-class families is due to the progressive tax system.

Table 2 shows some of the income elasticities that have been calculated from
the family budget data. For example, the first figure 0.44 is based on data from
1913, workers' and low grade employees' families with no children (113 families);
the figure is the income elasticity obtained for food. For illustration we may
refer to Fig. 1·2·2. To recapitulate the procedure [for further details, see Ch. 14],
the 113 families have been grouped in four classes according to income. The
average income and average food expenditure in the four classes have then
been transformed to logarithms. The regression (1·5·6b) has been applied to the
data thus prepared. This has led to a system of normal equations of type
(1·5·3). Solving the system, we have obtained $E = 0.44$. Thus, according to the
general interpretation of elasticities [Ch. 1·1–2], the conclusion is that in the
family group considered an increase (decrease) of income of 1% is on the average accompanied by an increase (decrease) in food expenditure of 0.44 %.

The first row in Table 2 shows food elasticities calculated for the four
family types in the 1913 material. The value $E = 0.45$ in the fifth column is
the food elasticity for the aggregate group of families; using formula (6·4·2)
this elasticity has been obtained as a weighted average of the food elasticities
of the four subgroups. The first row further gives the food elasticity for 1933,
$E = 0.53$; this elasticity has been calculated in the same way, on the basis of
nine subgroups. Table 2 finally gives elasticities for workers and low grade
employees (1923) and for middle class families (1923 and 1933); these elasticities have been obtained directly from the aggregate material, without
separate treatment of different family types (the figures for workers and employees have been subjected to a correction deduced from the results for 1913
and 1933).

For each of the 10 item groups of the budget, Table 2 gives income elasticities
derived in the same manner as for food. According to the interpretation of
demand elasticities [cf Chs. 1·1 and 5·1], the higher an income elasticity, the
more rapid the change of expenditure with income. The lowest elasticities have
been obtained for food. Thus demand for food is relatively well satisfied in the
lower income classes, and shows only a moderate increase for higher incomes.

TABLE 1·6·1. *Family budget data. Expenditure on ten groups of budget items, in per cent of yearly income.*

Item group	Industrial workers and low grade employees			Middle class families		Small farmers	Farm and forestry workers
	1913	1923	1933	1923	1933	1933	1933
I Nourishment..........	45.1	41.8	33.9	26.1	22.4	42.7	50.6
II Housing..............	11.9	10.1	14.3	11.2	14.3	9.9	8.9
III Fuel, cleaning	5.7	5.7	5.2	5.1	4.7	5.8	6.5
IV Furniture	4.2	4.2	4.4	5.9	5.0	3.2	3.8
V Clothing..............	12.7	14.0	12.4	12.0	11.3	11.7	12.5
VI Hygiene..............	1.6	2.0	2.7	2.3	2.6	2.7	2.5
VII Education, etc.	4.5	5.4	5.9	7.6	7.6	3.8	3.5
VIII Taxes, unions.........	9.4	13.0	13.8	17.7	17.7	9.5	7.0
IX Domestic help	.9	.4	.3	3.5	2.6	.4	.4
X Other expenditures	2.8	3.7	5.6	9.1	8.0	5.1	3.4
I–X All expenditures	98.8	100.3	98.5	100.5	96.2	94.8	99.1
Yearly income per consumer unit; Sw. cr. ...	744	1232	1236	2692	2341	577	504
Sample size (number of families)	1355	1192	1050	208	195	331	440

Similarly, demand is inelastic for item III (fuel, laundry, etc.). As is quite natural, the highest elasticities have been obtained for relative luxuries, such as domestic help, recreation, etc. A striking feature is the change in the demand for housing in workers' and employees' families; from 1913 to 1933 income elasticity has risen from 0.76 to 1.28.

The row I–X at the bottom of Table 2 shows the income elasticity of total expenditure. The balance between income and total expenditure is savings and cash. The elasticities of total expenditure approach unity closely, a result in agreement with the fact that almost all income is spent on the various budget items. The value obtained for 1913 is somewhat lower than for 1933, which shows that saving was more of a luxury in 1933 than in 1913.

Starting from the fact that the whole equals the sum of its parts it is easy to show that the income elasticity of total expenditure is a weighted average of the income elasticities of the separate budget items [cf Ch. 6·2]. The next but last row of Table 2 shows total elasticities that in this way are based on the first ten rows of the table. As expected, these weighted averages approximate very closely to the total elasticities as calculated directly and given in the row I–X. The close agreement may be regarded as a test and a check on the statistical method adopted. Later on we shall see that there are other methods that are rejected by this test [Ch. 14·2].

TABLE 1·6·2. *Family budget data. Income elasticities for ten groups of budget items.*

Item group	Industrial workers and low grade employees, 1913				Workers and low grade employees			Middle class	
	Family size (consumer units)				All family sizes			All family sizes	
	1.8	1.9–2.2	2.3–2.9	3.0–	1913	1923^a	1933	1923	1933
I	.44	.44	.47	.45	.45	.51	.53	.46	.44
II	.70	.76	.73	.81	.76	1.12	1.28	.81	.79
III	.60	.87	.76	.78	.74	.77	.67	.82	.86
IV	1.85	1.80	1.77	2.03	1.85	1.58	1.41	1.28	.94
V	1.12	1.21	1.14	1.16	1.17	1.13	.96	.61	.93
VI	1.77	1.58	1.03	1.12	1.31	1.38	1.09	.84	.91
VII	1.41	1.47	1.72	2.05	1.70	1.89	1.88	.69	.81
VIII	1.02	1.54	1.44	1.46	1.44	1.45	1.24	1.44	1.26
IX	—$^\beta$	5.63	5.33	4.09	5.20	3.00	1.73	2.35	1.94
X	1.63	1.63	2.04	1.93	1.82	1.85	1.83	1.57	1.46
I-X	.86	.91	.89	.89	.89	.96	.97	.92	.91
Average	.88	.94	.88	.87	.90	.99	1.01	.95	.91
Sample size	113	465	448	329	1355	1 192	824	208	195

^{a} Corrected values, see the text. $^\beta$ Data not sufficient for elasticity calculation.

If savings and cash balance were included in the expenditures, income elasticity of total expenditure would equal unity exactly. The elasticities of the separate items would then be distributed so as to have unity for weighted average. In passing we note that this explains the current convention that elasticity in demand is called under-, over- or normally elastic, respectively, according as income elasticity is <1, >1 or $=1$.

Each of the budget items I–X covers a more or less varied set of sub-items. The sub-items will in general have different income elasticities, and as before we may infer that the elasticity of any budget item is a weighted average of the elasticities of its sub-items [cf Chs. 5·6 and 6·4]. The family budget data specify the expenditure in great detail, for food (item I) in particular.

Table 3 sums up, in rounded figures, the demand elasticities obtained for a few basic foods. The table gives both price and income elasticities. Some of the estimates are rather tentative, and have been put within brackets.

Column 1 of Table 3 gives income elasticities derived from family budget data. These results refer to the same family groups as the seventh column of Table 2. As remarked above, the food elasticity 0.53 should be regarded as an average of the elasticities for specific foodstuffs. In agreement herewith, the elasticities in Table 3, col. 1, cover a wide range about the average. For flour

TABLE 1·6·3. *Demand elasticities for certain foods; between-war period.*

Food items	Income elasticity		Price and cross elasticities		
	Workers and employees	Aggregate for Sweden	Cooperative stores Stockholm	Aggregate for Sweden	
			Price elasticity	Price el.	Cross el.
	(1)	(2)	(3)	(4)	(5)
Milk and cream	.25	.00	—	.30	—
Milk	.20	.00	.25	.20	—
Butter and margarine	.25	.60	.45	.70	—
Butter................	.40	(.55)	a) 1.45 b) .75	(.90)	(−.35)
Cheese.................	.35	(.50)	—	.20	—
Eggs	.50	.60 or .70	1.0	—	—
Meat and pork	.25	.30	.7	.30	—
Meat	(.30)	.30	—	.50	−.30
Pork	.10	.30	—	.45	−.15
Flour.................	−.50	−.55	—	.15	−.55
Sugar	.25	.30	—	.35	—
Potatoes...............	—	−.20	—	(−.20)	—

the elasticity is very low, − 0.50, which shows that expenditure is greatest for low incomes, flour being substituted by baked bread and other foods in higher income classes. Fresh milk is in Sweden one of the cheapest foods; its central place in the consumption is brought out by the low income elasticity obtained.

The price elasticities in Table 3, cols. 3–5, are derived from market statistics. As outlined in Ch. 1·3–5, the elasticities have been obtained by regression analysis on the basis of formula (1·5·7). The explanatory variables have been (a) real price of the food considered, (b) real income, and, if necessary, (c) the real price of some substitute. For butter and margarine, as well as meat and pork, the price of the aggregate commodity has been calculated as an average price of the constituents.

Col. 3 refers to data from cooperative stores in Stockholm, 1922–39. These price elasticities are somewhat higher than the corresponding income elasticities in col. 1. This is in agreement with a general theorem to the effect that, for ordinary food and other necessities, price elasticity is higher than income elasticity [cf Ch. 6·5]. For butter, two results are given. The elasticity $e = 1.45$ is based on the assumption that butter price varies, but margarine price is kept constant. The elasticity 0.75 refers to the situation where the two prices vary in the same proportion.

Cols. 4 and 5 refer to the total consumption in Sweden. The analysis has here been based on data compiled or revised within the State Agricultural Marketing Board. Thanks to the completeness and accuracy of these data it has been possible to carry through the analysis for most of the principal foods.

It has also been possible to obtain estimates for *cross elasticities*. For the demand of butter, for example, the elasticities w.r.t. (= with respect to, an abbreviation we shall often find useful) butter price and margarine price are 0.90 and − 0.35, respectively. Both of these estimates refer to the situation where the other price is kept constant. The elasticity 0.90 thus corresponds to the value 1.45 in col. 3. The deviations between cols. 3 and 4 are largely due to the fact that the markets under analysis are not the same.

Col. 2 gives income elasticities referring to the whole of Sweden. The data employed are the same set of market statistics as for cols. 4 − 5. As regards the estimates in col. 2 regression analysis has worked under less favourable conditions, for the changes in demand caused by income are partly blurred by factors which during the period considered have been correlated with the income changes, notably the general levelling of incomes in Sweden and the migration from rural to urban districts. One or two of the estimates in col. 2 are therefore adjusted values. As explained in detail in Ch. 17, the adjustment has mainly taken into consideration the income elasticities calculated from family budget data for different social classes.

The elasticities in Tables 2–3 are on the whole in line with the results of demand analysis as reported from other countries. It would carry us too far, however, to enter upon a detailed comparison. To be satisfactory, a comparison between demand elasticities must pay regard to type differences in the social environment and level differences in the income, and further, the comparison should include an appraisal of the quality of the statistical data and an examination of the regression methods employed, in all a big task that would require a volume for itself. As for specific references, the standard works of Allen and Bowley (1935) and Schultz (1938) have been mentioned in the preface.[1] The main difference between these earlier works and the present study is that here — as well as in the initial 1940 report — family budget data and market statistics have been coordinated for the purpose of demand analysis. The same general approach has been adopted by R. Stone and associated research workers in the series of demand studies made in the Department of Applied Economics, Cambridge.[2]

Most demand studies are limited to one or two decades. The only investigation I know of that covers a longer period refers to the Greenland Eskimos, a study based on the detailed records kept by the Danish company that had the trading monopoly with this abortive civilization of the polar region. Fig. 1 is borrowed from this highly interesting study.[3] We see that, on the introduction of Western goods, coffee soon became a necessity, with a very low income elasticity.

The empirical results thus far considered refer to the basic object of demand analysis, that of estimating demand functions and demand elasticities. We shall now turn to some practical applications of the results obtained. Two

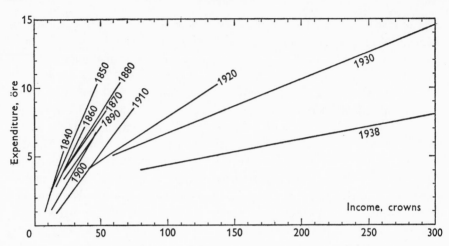

Fig. 1·6·1. Coffee demand as a function of income; Greenland 1840–1938 (after P. P. Sveistrup). Individual budget data; 1 crown = 100 öre.

examples will be outlined, both drawn from investigations made by Mr. L. Juréen as part of his work with the State Agricultural Marketing Board. The political background of these applications is on the one side the endeavours of the Swedish government towards a planned economy for the agricultural sector, on the other side the system of rationing and price control introduced during World War II.

In the inter-war period, consumption was entirely free from rationing in Sweden, except that liquor was under control. With the outbreak of war in 1939, from which Sweden was spared, foods were soon subjected to rationing, and it was not until 1947–1949 that the restrictions were gradually abandoned. Thus all of the foods specified in Table 4 were rationed during the war, except potatoes. In 1942, after two years of bad harvest, consumption reached its lowest point, as shown in col. 4. Then production went upwards, and in 1946, as seen from cols. 3 and 5, consumption was not very different from the general level of the peace period. Disregarding the balance between butter and margarine, the differences keep within a margin of about 10%. Thus, on the whole, rationing had been successful in balancing demand and supply so as to avoid violent changes in the actual consumption. On the other hand, the government had worked with rather substantial changes in real prices. Moreover, real income per capita had risen by no less than some 30% from 1936 to 1946. Under such circumstances it was an open question how the consumers would react if released from rationing. Would the balance between demand and supply be so upset as to make continued rationing necessary? In particular it was an open question whether the severe reduction of consumption during the first

TABLE 1·6·4. *Food consumption in Sweden, kilograms per capita, according to forecast and observation.*

Foods	Real price, öre/kg.		Consumption, kg./cap.			Consumption 1949/50 kg./cap.	
	1930/39	1949/50	1930/39	1942	1946	Forecast	Observed
	(1)	(2)	(3)	(4)	(5)	(6)	(7)
Milk and cream......	—	—	256	254	274	273	262
Milk	13.6	12.6	207	244	247	210	220
Butter and margarine	134	162	19.4	18.1	19.4	21.6	24.4
Butter	172	211	10.7	11.8	15.8	11.5	13.7
Margarine	88	98	8.7	6.3	3.6	10.1	10.7
Cheese	126	130	6.8	2.4	6.6	7.7	7.6
Eggs................	101	127	8.1	5.6	9.5	8.6	(11.5)
Meat and pork.......	99	126	46.3	30.6	41.1	46.9	47.5
Meat..............	97	134	24.3	15.2	21.9	23.5	21.2
Pork	102	120	22.0	15.4	19.2	23.4	26.3
Flour (wheat, rye) ...	23	25	89.1	79.0	81.8	79.2	80.3
Sugar (refined).......	29	34	42.3	43.1	37.0	47.4	46.9
Potatoes	7.9	10.0	125	152.1	133	116	117

war years had influenced the demand habits systematically, or whether the demand would resume the pattern known from the peace period.

Parallel with the final abolishment of rationing in 1949, Mr. Juréen made the forecast experiment shown in Table 4, cols. 6 and 7. The forecast refers to the production year 1.IX.1949–31.VIII.1950, and is based on the tentative assumption that on the abolishment of rationing the demand would resume the structure of the inter-war period 1930/39. Specifically, his forecast is in the main based on the following material:

(i) The consumption figures for 1930/39, that is, col. 3 of Table 4.

(ii) The prices for 1930/39 (given in col. 1), the prices for 1949/50 as fixed by the government, the known income for 1930/39 and the estimated income for 1949/50.

(iii) The hypothesis that the demand functions are of type (1·1·1–4), with price and income elasticities as given in Table 3, cols. 2, 4 and 5.

As seen from cols. 5 and 6, the forecast gave an indication of consumption changes that are rather great if compared with the consumption during 1946, when rationing was still in force. The change predicted was greatest for margarine, but quite substantial also for butter, sugar, potatoes, meat and pork. The last column in Table 4 refers to the actual consumption as observed in 1949/50. On the whole it may be said that the forecast was successful. Specifically, we see that the agreement between forecast and actual consumption is fairly close if regarded against the background of the consumption in 1942 and in the peace period 1930/39. If we follow up the comparison with the peace period we find, however, a certain discrepancy. Thus if the total consumption for 1930/39 is 100, the forecast for 1949/50 is 103.2 whereas the actual consumption is 107.3. A substantial part of the discrepancy, about 50%, refers to the egg consumption, the only item for which the forecast was clearly unsatisfactory. Behind this failure lies the fact, known beforehand, that the consumption statistics for eggs are less reliable than for the other items. What remains of the discrepancy can also to a large extent be explained by other factors known in advance, notably the change in the income distribution within the Swedish population, and certain changes in the food market, for example that certain edible fats have vanished from the stores.

Proceeding to our second example of applied demand analysis, we shall consider a forecast referring to the balance between production and consumption. After several decades of gradual increase in agricultural production, Sweden has in the 'forties reached the point where her actual consumption of food is essentially covered by home production, provided this is supported by phosphates and other fertilizers. Real income per capita is fairly high, and it may be expected that its steady trend upwards will continue. Such is, in all brevity, the economic background of the agricultural planning policy. According to the general programme, as set forth in 1947 and supported by all of the political parties, the agricultural sector is planned with a double purpose: on the one hand to maintain a home production sufficient to secure a standard of nourishment adequate from the viewpoint of public health, and on the other to raise agricultural incomes and wages to the same level as in other production sectors.[4] The main instrument of the planning is a system of price regulation by which the agricultural prices are kept independent of the international price movements. The price regulation is administrated by the State Agricultural Marketing Board. The Research Bureau of the Board makes investigations into technical questions that have a bearing upon the agricultural planning. Thus on the production side the Board has made a thorough investigation of the development of Swedish agriculture, with special regard to the effect of fertilizers. On the demand side we note a detailed study of the actual consumption and how it compares with modern standards of nutrition, particularly as regards its content of calories, fats and proteins. A third group of investigations is concerned with consumer demand and its future trend under reasonable assumptions about the agricultural prices and other influencing factors, primarily the population figures and the national income. A comprehensive report on these investigations has been submitted by Mr. Juréen (1952).

Some of the results obtained under the third heading are shown in Table 5. We see that the consumption as evaluated in calories per day and inhabitant

TABLE 1·6·5. *Consumption in Sweden of chief foodstuffs, in calories per capita and day.*

Food items	1876/85	1906/13	1930/39	1940/47	1970
Main cereals	1730	1990	1730	1690	1620
Animal foods................	550	990	1370	1280	1660
Cereals and animal foods	2280	2980	3100	2970	3280

has stabilized at a saturation level from 1900 and onwards. A gradual shift has taken place in the composition of the diet, the cheaper cereals having been replaced by the more health-protective animal foods. According to the forecast given in the last column, cereals and animal foods will in 1970 contribute about equally to the total supply of calories. If we make use of a supplementary forecast of population figures, the per capita estimates can be transformed into a forecast of the national totals of consumption.

The forecast in Table 5 is based on the assumption that the national income will in the future increase about as before, i.e. by 2% per capita and year. This gives a fairly large increase in the real income per inhabitant, so large indeed that the resulting change in demand can hardly be expected to conform to formula (1·1·1b), i.e. to the simple assumption of a constant income elasticity. The forecast has therefore been based on Törnqvist's demand functions, his formula (1·1·5a) for the demand for necessities having been fitted to the 1930/39 statistics. The forecast has been carried through separately for each of the food items given in Table 5. As regards the prices, the real prices have been assumed to be the same as during the period 1930/39. A general increase of agricultural prices would accordingly make the shift to animal foods less rapid than indicated by the forecast.

The above examples may serve as sufficient evidence of the practical importance of demand analysis. By way of conclusion we shall stress one point: Tables 2–3 display the demand structure as something fairly stable. Changes are there, it is true, but if economic conditions are stable the changes in demand take place gradually, and for ordinary commodities it seems that they can safely be ignored when studying the limited period of a few decades. This is of course a good thing from the viewpoint of the practical application of demand analysis; specifically, we note that efficient forecasts can be made provided reliable empirical data are at our disposal.

Chapter 2.

LEAST-SQUARES REGRESSION
UNDER DEBATE

1. Controversial issues. – In empirical demand analysis as it has gradually developed during the last four or five decades, the main statistical method employed has been ordinary regression analysis, that is, multiple regression analysis based on the principle of least squares. By way of straightforward adaptation, this classical device was carried over to the analysis of economic demand from other fields of application, where regression analysis had long served and still serves as a fundamental tool of statistical inference. As briefly outlined in Ch. 1 the traditional approach has also been followed in the empirical studies reported in the present volume. Now, as everybody knows, the method of least-squares regression has not escaped criticism, and in particular it has been stressed that the device is not foolproof if applied uncritically; everybody also knows that such cautions have not been uncalled for. Specifically, an intense discussion was opened up by Yule's classical paper of 1926, "Why do we sometimes get nonsense-correlations between time-series?" In the later development, several methods alternative to least-squares regression have been suggested. Well-known innovations are the confluence analysis of R. Frisch (1934), and the work on structural systems that was initiated by T. Haavelmo (1943, 1944) and carried further by the Cowles Commission research group [see Ref. 7: Tj. Koopmans, ed. (1950)].

The discussion of regression analysis has mainly centered around four controversial issues, viz. (a) the choice of regression line, (b) the bias resulting from observational errors, (c) the rationale of regression analysis in the case of time-series data, (d) complications due to simultaneous relationships. These issues, referring to the very foundations of regression analysis, have to be faced in each and every application, and some standpoint or other has to be taken. The literature having steadily brought forward new material, an endeavour is made in the present chapter towards a comprehensive survey of the situation. The endeavour is made in the feeling that the material is now becoming sufficiently mature for a definite appraisal. A main difficulty in this task has been that most of the earlier authors have not been very explicit on the rationale of regression methods. Not that any deep arguments are called for in the interpretation and logical foundation. Rather the basic issues are usually treated as if not requiring an explicit treatment, the arguments being given incidentally or not at all, so that they have to be inferred by reading between the lines. This being so, the author feels so much the more a desire to acknowledge how much he has profited from studies where the basic issues have really been taken up for treatment, and would wish to refer specifically to contributions by J. Tinbergen (1939), W. Shewhart (1939), Ch. Eisenhart (1939) and F. Anscombe (1948).

To get the controversial issues in proper perspective, it is necessary to keep in mind that regression analysis is a special application of a device of general scope, the principle of least squares. Backed by fruitful applications in the most varied fields of empirical analysis, this classical device is quite simple and natural. Stated in words, it is a conventional principle for approximate representation, the convention being that the accuracy of the approximation is evaluated as an average of the squared deviations [cf (1˙5˙2)]. The principle of least squares is the logical basis of several methods that are in current use in many fields of statistical analysis. Besides regression analysis we note e.g. the periodogram method for the search of hidden periodicities, and the least-squares fitting of polynomial or other trends. From the viewpoint of approximate representation, of course, the principle of least squares belongs to mathematics in general, not only to statistics [cf Ch. 12˙1–2]. First introduced by Legendre (1806), the method of least squares became rapidly known, and was soon familiar in various fields of applied mathematics. The theory of the general method is associated with the names of Laplace and Gauss.[1] The specific method of least-squares regression is of more recent date, being primarily due to Galton, K. Pearson, Yule and Fisher.

Briefly stated, the author's standpoint is that the traditional methods of regression analysis are essentially sound, and that much of the confusion around the controversial issues can be removed simply by bringing out more explicitly the basic logical principles behind the regression methods. This conclusion was arrived at in the 1940 report, in which the traditional methods were scrutinized without prejudice. Additional arguments to their support have been adduced by the author in later papers. The present chapter being confined to certain general issues, regression questions more specific to demand analysis will be dealt with in Chs. 14–15.

2. The choice of regression. – When making use of regression analysis to answer a given problem, different regression relations will in general be obtained if different variables are treated as dependent in forming the regression. From the very beginning, in the pioneering works of Galton, K. Pearson and Yule, this plurality has been stressed as a characteristic feature of regression analysis in contradistinction to the functional relations of mathematical analysis. As is typical for statistical literature, however, the formal aspects of the plurality were brought out more clearly than its implications for applied regression analysis. In particular, the question of which regression should be used in different types of application was treated by means of special examples rather than by giving general and explicit rules. This is one of the reasons why there has remained an air of vagueness and doubt around regression analysis. At the same time, regression analysis served as an indispensable tool in the hands of research workers who had learnt how to make use of it by experience.

The unsatisfactory state of things was keenly stressed by R. Frisch (1928, 1934). Arguing that there is a formal symmetry between the alternative regressions, Frisch suggested that some compromise regression should be used, such as the orthogonal or the diagonal regression. In an empirical study on the demand for milk in Norway, Frisch and Haavelmo (1938) applied the diagonal regression (modified by a correction factor) to family budget data to calculate the income elasticity for milk. Confronted with the same problem H. Schultz (1938) chose instead to calculate two demand elasticities, the one formed with quantity, the other with price as dependent variable. This dualism, which is present all through Schultz's great work on demand analysis, was referred to in our preface [Fig. 2].

To discuss the situation we must first specify the purpose for which the regression in question is to be used. We shall confine ourselves to the two main purposes of regression analysis:

A. To *estimate* or *predict* one variable, given one or more other variables.

B. To obtain a *causal explanation* of one variable as a function of one or more other variables.

In formal respects the procedure of regression analysis is the same in the two situations. The difference lies in the type of question put to the statistical material, and in the interpretation of the regression relation. In situation A the regression is used to estimate an unknown variable in terms of one or more known variables, and the primary concern is in making the estimate as accurate as possible. In situation B the regression is used as a tool for subject-matter analysis, serving to explain the variations in one variable as the effect of variations in one or more cause variables. Thus in case B the regression will form a *hypothetical explanation* of the effect variable, or, in other words, we try to establish the regression relation as a *theoretical model* for the phenomenon under analysis.

The controversial issues in regression analysis chiefly refer to situation B. This being the type of situation encountered in demand analysis, we have therefore a double reason to concentrate on this case. As is sufficient for our purpose, we shall in the main confine ourselves to the case of linear regression. For the empirical regressions dealt with we shall use the general notation

$$(1) \qquad x_\nu^{(0)} = b_0 + b_1 x_\nu^{(1)} + \cdots + b_h x_\nu^{(h)} + z_\nu \qquad\qquad \nu = 1, \ldots, n$$

where n is the number of observations.

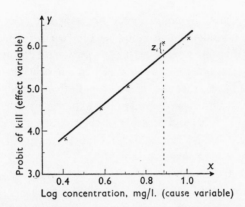

Fig. 2·2·1. Relationship between dosage of rotenone and probit of kill of *M. Sanborni*, showing probit regression line (= regression of y on x). After D. J. Finney.

Commencing with situation A, the proper device to be used here is well known from the textbooks:[1] In forming the estimate we must use the regression in which $x^{(0)}$ is the unknown variable and $x^{(1)}, \ldots, x^{(h)}$ are the known variables. The difference from situation B is that we do not necessarily require the regression relation to allow a causal interpretation.

The estimation method must in practice be handled with caution and judgement, as always in regression problems. Generally speaking, the difficulty is that the value to be estimated will in some respect or other appear as an extrapolation beyond the set of observations from which we derive the regression that is used for the estimation. Hence the method cannot be expected to work satisfactorily unless we are reasonably sure that the extrapolation does not involve any relevant change in the distribution of the variables dealt with. This qualification, which is easy to overlook, is usually covered by an assumption of 'ceteris paribus'. For a theoretical discussion of certain estimation problems, reference is made to Ch. 12·5–6.

Let us now turn to situation B. In the brief account of regression analysis given in Ch. 1·2–5 we have stressed the causal, subject-matter interpretation of a regression relation. Our concern will now be to emphasize the general scope of the arguments. The salient point is the reference to controlled experiments. This being the usual term for ordinary scientific experiments, the dosage-mortality experiment illustrated in Fig. 1 is a typical instance.[2] What is essential from the present viewpoint in the experimental case is (a) any experiment has for its purpose to study a causal dependence, (b) it is obvious from the design of the experiment which variable is causally dependent, and which variables are controlled or independent, and (c) the relationship under investigation is brought out by the regression of the dependent variable on the set of independent variables. In other words, the symmetry between the regression lines is merely formal, not real, for the causal structure of the experiment singles out the variable that should be taken as dependent in the regression. We see that the confusion is partly a matter of terminology, the terms dependent and independent being used in two different contexts. On the one hand they refer to the formal distinction between left-hand and right-hand variables in any least-squares regression (1), on the other hand to the subject-matter distinction between cause variables and effect variables in a controlled experiment. Now in the case of controlled experiments the two distinctions coincide, for here the left-hand member of the regression is an effect variable, this being approximated by the right-hand member which is built up linearly in terms of the controlled cause variables.

As regards nonexperimental data, and in particular demand analysis data, we have stressed in Ch. 1·2–3 that the causal interpretation of regression analysis is the same as in the case of experiments. There is the difference, however, that the subject-matter distinction between cause and effect variables is no longer obvious from the design of an experiment, but has to be justified otherwise, by experience in general or by theoretical inference. It may well happen, of course, that a given set of variables does not allow such a causal interpretation. For example, as pointed out in Ch. 1·3 it seems realistic to regard demand as causally dependent on price, provided the data refer to an ordinary retail market, but in a wholesale market there is also an opposite tendency of demand to influence price. We have suggested *unilateral causal dependence* as a general term of reference for the case when one variable is singled out as causally dependent on the other variables.[3] Thus under the hypothesis of unilateral dependence the choice of dependent variable will be strictly analogous to the case of experimental data.

Summing up, regression analysis as applied to experimental data has here been framed as a *logical prototype* for regression analysis in general. This stressing of the experimental situation, of course, should not be regarded as a novel interpretation in regression analysis. Even if it has not been explicitly formulated in textbooks or other literature, the interpretation is in line with what is current practice in regression analysis in its many fields of application.

Thus far, the reference to ordinary experiments has helped us to clear up the question of the choice of regression line. But this is not all. In the literature on regression analysis the notion of causal dependence is in general used rather vaguely or not used at all, as though to avoid what might evoke philosophical associations. By the above interpretation the notion has been specified so as to refer to the clear-cut relationship between cause and effect in a controlled experiment, and by way of analogy this specification has been extended to the regression analysis of nonexperimental data. This gives a precise meaning to the notion of causal dependence as used in regression analysis, and we need not bother about the deeper epistemological implications of causality [cf Ch. 3·5].

For another thing, the reference to experiments helps us to master the terminology of regression analysis. One difficulty is that the distinction between dependent and independent variables is in regression analysis used in two different meanings, none of which is the same as independence in the sense of probability theory. On the one hand the notions refer to variables involved in a unilateral causal dependence; alternative terms are here effect (=dependent) variable and cause or explanatory (=independent) variables. We see that this is a subject-matter distinction that has to be based on nonstatistical considerations. On the other hand the notions are used in a formal sense for the different variables in a regression relation, the left-hand variable being called dependent, the right-hand variables independent. To avoid the ambiguity, we shall never use the terms independent and dependent variable in regression analysis, but in the first situation speak of *cause* (or *explanatory*) and *effect* variables, in the second of *regressor* and *regressand*.[4]

There is further the distinction between *random* variables in the sense of statistics and probability, and *non-random* variables in the usual mathematical sense. In regression analysis the regressand is always treated as random, but the regressors may be random or non-random in accordance with circumstances. Specifically, the controlled variables of an experiment are as a rule to be regarded as non-random variables subject to purposive variation, and so may also be the case with the stratified variables of nonexperimental data, such as the income variable of family budget statistics. If we are dealing with nonexperimental data that have not been stratified, such as the time-series data of economic statistics, the regressors will in general be treated as being random. [See Ch. 13·2.]

The threefold distinction between variables may be a little confusing to the beginner, but it lies in the very nature of regression analysis, and is not a matter of terminological artificiality. If we always adhere to the experimental interpretation, directly or by analogy, the meaning of the terms should be clear from the context. Thus we need not enter upon the more elaborate terminologies of recent years, e.g. predictand, predictor, estimand, estimator, or variables determined, predetermined, predicated, instrumental, and so on, terms that have been introduced with the best of intentions to remove obscurities, but resulting rather in an 'embarras de richesses' where the issues may have become even more bewildering to the beginner.

In discussing the choice of regression in situation B we have thus far dealt with the question of which variable should be taken for regressand. Logically, this is the primary question, and it brings us at once in medias res, by giving rise to the distinction between experimental and nonexperimental data. The choice of regressors will be considered in the next section. We have now two final remarks.

(i) The above reference to the experimental situation is an argument of general type for the choice of regressand, but it is often possible to verify the conclusions by other arguments. Thus in situation B we may state as a general principle that, since the regression is regarded as a theoretical relation, we should be able to operate with the relation as forming part of our theory of the phenomena under analysis.[5] In the comment on Table 1·6·2 we have already made an application of this principle. By a simple theoretical argument the income elasticity for all expenditures is a weighted average of the elasticities of the separate items, so according to our principle this relation should also hold good for the elasticities calculated from the empirical data. The relation thus gives us a check or test on the regression adopted, and as seen from Table 1·6·2 the regression has passed the test. The situation is examined in some detail in Ch. 14·2 [cf also Ex. IV, 23]. Thus if we consider some other regression, say the diagonal or the orthogonal regression [lines L' and L'' in Fig. 1·2·1b], these fail to pass the test, the conclusion being that they over-estimate the elasticity. Incidentally, this explains why Frisch and Haavelmo in the above-mentioned work have obtained income elasticities for milk as high as between 0.85 and 3.14.

(ii) The upshot of our discussion is that the choice of regression line is rather obvious once we specify its purpose in the application dealt with. This being so, we may add the negative conclusion that when we have derived a regression relation for a specified purpose, we must stick to this purpose, and not use the regression outside of its proper sphere of application.

Suppose the regression (1·5·1) has been formed on the hypotheses of model (1·4·1). The regression relation arrived at, say $d_t = a + b p_t$, will then serve as an empirical approximation to the theoretical demand function $d_t = D(p_t)$. The regression may accordingly be dealt with just as an ordinary demand function. Specifically, the regression may be inverted so as to answer the same question as (1·4·2). As stressed in the comment upon model (1·4·1) the inverted relation must not be mixed up with the price relation (1·4·1c), and now we must also take care not to confuse the inverted relation with the regression of price upon demand, say $p_t = a^* + b^* d_t$. The regression of price on demand answers an estimation problem which is of restricted scope, and which must be kept apart from the inversion problem answered by (1·4·2).[6]

The fact that on inverting the regression of demand on price we do not obtain the regression of price on demand is of course nothing else than the plurality of regression relations that was referred to in the beginning of this section. Considering for example three variables x, y, z let

(2) $$x = R_1(y, z) \qquad y = R_2(x, z) \qquad z = R_3(x, y)$$

be the regressions of x on y, z, of y on x, z, and of z on x, y, respectively. Then if the first relation is solved for y, say $y = R(x, z)$, this will in general not coincide with $y = R_2(x, z)$, and similarly for the other regressions. This is a familiar consequence of the fact that regressions like (2) are not exact relations; they give the expected or average value of one variable as a function of the two others. On the other hand, suppose x, y, z stand in functional relationship, say

(3) $$f(x, y, z) = 0.$$

Being an exact relation, (3) may be solved for any variable in terms of the two others, say

(4) $x = f_1(y,z)$ $y = f_2(x,z)$ $z = f_3(x,y)$

and each of these relationships is the same as (3); for example, if $x = f_1(y,z)$ is solved for y, we obtain $y = f_2(x,z)$. In this sense, a functional relationship is *reversible*, whereas regression relations are in general *irreversible*.

3. The choice of regressors. Regression residuals. — Which variables of a given regression problem should be taken into account as regressors? This is, like the choice of regressand, essentially a question for subject-matter considerations. What can be stated in this respect by way of guiding principles of general scope is necessarily vague and nonoperational. Thus it can be said that regression analysis as traditionally applied aims at obtaining residuals that are *small* and *irregular*. Small, for in the regression arrived at the residuals play the part of a remainder that is left unexplained by the analysis. Irregular, for any trace of regularity in the residuals may in principle be regarded as a systematic tendency which is likewise left unexplained.

To discuss the situation more in detail we shall follow up the distinction made in Ch. 2·2 between prediction and causal analysis. As regards prediction or estimation [situation A], the basic arguments are again familiar from the textbooks. The regression relation gives us the estimate as a linear expression in the regressors. The deviation between the unknown and its estimate constitutes the regression residual; i.e. the residual is the *estimation error*. By the general properties of least-squares approximation, the residual has zero for average value, and its variance is the smallest that can be obtained with the regressors employed [Ch. 12·1–2]. In this sense the estimation or prediction given by least-squares regression is unbiased and of optimal efficiency. From the viewpoint of estimation we may thus conclude that if we have obtained a small residual variance it is reasonable to rest content with the regression arrived at, and not try to improve it by the introduction of more regressors.

It is further a general property of least-squares regression that the residual is uncorrelated with each of the regressors [Theorem 12·1·2]. Now, if there is correlation between the residual and a tentative additional regressor it is clear that the residual variance will become smaller on the introduction of this regressor. On the other hand, even if there is no such correlation it is still possible that the regressor will reduce the residual variance [cf Theorem 12·3·2].

We are now coming to regression relations that are formed for the purpose of causal analysis [situation B]. As before, the regression will provide an estimate for the regressand, but the analysis now goes further, the primary purpose being to measure how the regressand is influenced by the regressors. As a consequence, it is the regression coefficients rather than the residuals that come into the foreground of the analysis. Further there enters a dualism in the interpretation of the residuals. Just as in the case of estimation, the residual deviations indicate the accuracy of the regression, but at the same time they are interpreted as *disturbances* that sum up the influence of causal factors that have not explicitly been taken into account as regressors. Here it is again relevant to distinguish between experimental and nonexperimental data.

As regards experimental data, we have in Ch. 2·2 stated as a plain fact that the regression of the effect variable with the controlled variables as regressors will bring out the causal dependence that the experiment is intended to establish. For this to be so, however, the uncontrolled influences must be neutralized by a suitable design of the experiment. The classical device is R. A. Fisher's general method of *randomization*.[1] As briefly explained in Ch. 1·2, the uncontrolled factors are here neutralized by arranging so that their influence enters as a disturbance which is approximately independent or uncorrelated with the controlled variables. Thus in the case of one controlled variable, if $y = bx + z$ is the regression obtained, bx indicates the average influence of the controlled variable x, and z is the joint influence of the uncontrolled variables. For an important case we may once more refer to biological experiments [cf Fig. 2·2·1]. Whether we deal with animals, plants or other organisms their response to the experimental treatment will display individual differences, so-called biotype differences, irregularities that cannot be brought back to explicit causal factors but have to be summed up in an unspecified disturbance.

In the case of nonexperimental data, the causal dependences are more or less hypothetical, more or less tentative. In other respects the interpretation of the regression is the same as in a controlled experiment. Thus the chief interest is usually confined to one or two causal variables and their regression coefficients (for example, the income variable in family budget data, the regression coefficient here giving the income elasticity of demand). There is one important difference, however. Causal factors of secondary interest must in nonexperimental data be taken as they come, and their possible disturbing effect cannot be neutralized by the randomization design of controlled experiments. Such factors will be referred to as *secondary factors*. The traditional device in this situation is to include the secondary factors among the regressors. In other words, to obtain a regression relation in which the regression coefficients give a correct picture of the causal influence of the factors of primary interest, the set of regressors is enlarged by the secondary factors. The main dilemma of this method is that the secondary factors usually are numerous, whereas in practice the regression analysis must be confined to a limited number of regressors. The principle traditionally followed to meet this difficulty is to include those variables as regressors that according to experience and a priori theory are believed to be the main causal factors of the regressand. Experience shows that the method gives more reliable results than might perhaps be expected in view of the difficulties involved.[2]

Having stressed the primary importance of subject-matter considerations in the choice of regressors, we may now turn to certain statistical properties of regression relations that have a bearing upon the choice. Reference may in the first place be made to what will be called the *proximity theorem* of regression analysis [Theorem 12·1·3]. It is obvious that the regression coefficients are unbiased either if the disturbance factors are negligible (so that the residuals are small), or if they are uncorrelated with the regressors. The proximity theorem shows that the two conditions strengthen each other, to the effect that if they are fulfilled up to magnitudes that are small of the *first* order the bias of the regression coefficients will be small of the *second* order.

Illustration. Supposing that y is linearly dependent upon x, let the theoretical and empirical regression relations be written

$$y = \beta x + z^* \qquad y = b x + z \qquad \text{with} \quad E x = E y = 0.$$

In symbols easily understood, if then $\sigma(z^*) = \dfrac{1}{5}\sigma(x)$ and $r(x, z^*) = \dfrac{1}{5}$, we obtain

(1) $$E(b) \sim \frac{E(xy)}{E(x^2)} = \beta + \frac{E(xz^*)}{E(x^2)} = \beta + r(x,z^*) \cdot \frac{\sigma(z^*)}{\sigma(x)} = \beta + \frac{1}{25}.$$

The bias in the empirical coefficient thus is only about 0.04.

There are several reasons why in practice a regression relation is not specified so as to include among the regressors all factors that have causal influence on the effect variable under analysis. For one thing, the regression sets out to give a theoretical explanation, and so it is a quite legitimate endeavour to make the theory as simple as possible, taking into explicit account only the causal factors of main importance. Secondly, a frequent situation is that the statistical data available cover only a few of the causal factors, and it may even occur that data are lacking for highly relevant factors. Finally we note the difficulty that the causal factors may be highly intercorrelated, which brings difficulties in the technical treatment of the regression, a point that will be taken up for discussion in Ch. 2·6.

Whatever the reason for the limited number of regressors, the proximity theorem shows that the validity of the regression arrived at depends upon the disturbance factors and their correlation properties. Still considering the linear regression (2·2·1), we note a few related theorems that have a bearing upon the choice of regressors [see Theorems 12·3·1–3].

(i) If one more regressor is introduced in (2·2·1), say $x^{(h+1)}$, all regression coefficients b_i will remain the same, provided $x^{(h+1)}$ is uncorrelated with every $x^{(1)}, ..., x^{(h)}$. More generally, b_1 will remain the same if $x^{(h+1)}$ is uncorrelated with the residual in the regression of $x^{(1)}$ on $x^{(2)}, ..., x^{(h)}$.

(ii) If we introduce an arbitrary variable $x^{(h+1)}$ with given variance, the coefficient b_1 will change, say to the value b, and we can find an $x^{(h+1)}$ such that b will assume an arbitrarily prescribed value between $-\infty$ and $+\infty$.

(iii) If we classify the variables $x^{(h+1)}$ in two groups according as b is greater or smaller than b_1, the two groups will in a certain weak sense display a quantitative mutual symmetry.

These remarks combine with the proximity theorem to support the traditional manner in which least-squares regression is applied for the purpose of causal analysis of nonexperimental data. Thus (i) shows that the presence of residuals is not necessarily accompanied by a bias in the regression. We note that (i) further provides a simple argument for the method of randomization, since this device makes the controlled variables of an experiment approximately uncorrelated with the disturbance factors. According to (ii), it will always remain possible that a neglected, non-randomized factor — even if its variance is small — may entirely upset the regression picture. On the other hand, if we may argue from the symmetry established by (iii), the introduction of more regressors has no tendency to change the coefficients in a certain direction, either upwards or downwards.

4. Observational errors. — Thus far we have tacitly assumed that there are no observational errors, i.e. that the statistical data dealt with are based on measurements that are exact. Fortunately, this assumption is more realistic for the data used in demand analysis than for many other sectors of economic statistics. At least it is so as far as the present study is concerned; from all we know about our data, except for one or two specified series, notably the national totals of the egg consumption, it seems that the errors are so small that they can safely be neglected. The reason why we take up observational errors for comment is rather that the topic has some bearing upon the interpretation of regression relationships.

Several authors from C. H. Kummell (1879), K. Pearson (1901) and onwards have dealt with regression analysis from the viewpoint of observational errors.[1] Let us consider the case of one regressor, say

(1) $\qquad x = X + \varepsilon_1; \qquad y = Y + \varepsilon_2; \qquad Y = a + \beta X; \qquad y = a + bx + z,$

where x, y are the observed variables, ε_1, ε_2 are the observational errors, (1c) is the relation between the error-free variables X, Y, and (1d) the least-squares regression of y on x. Then, in easily understood symbols,[2]

(2) $\qquad b \cong \dfrac{1}{1+\lambda^2} \cdot \beta \qquad$ with $\quad \lambda^2 = \sigma^2(\varepsilon_1)/\sigma^2(X) \geq 0$

so that the observed regression coefficient b equals the "true" coefficient β multiplied by a reduction factor $1/(1+\lambda^2)$. An essential assumption underlying formula (2) is that the errors ε_1, ε_2 are uncorrelated with each other and with the error-free variables X, Y.

In the subsequent comments we shall consider (1) as well as the corresponding approach in the multivariate case. We write

(3) $$a + \beta_0 X^{(0)} + \beta_1 X^{(1)} + \cdots + \beta_h X^{(h)} = 0$$

for the hypothesis that in the general case forms the counterpart to (1c).

There are a number of points in (1)–(3) that call for comment.

(i) If (1c) is substituted in (1b), we obtain the first of the relations

(4) $$y = a + \beta X + \varepsilon_2 \qquad\qquad y = a^* + \beta^* x + z^*.$$

Let (4b) be a theoretical relation between x and y, with z^* for disturbance.

On top of the cautions stressed in Ch. 2·2 (ii) comes the danger of confusing (4a) and (4b). Both approaches assuming a linear relation behind the observed statistical scatter, the essential difference lies in the subject-matter hypotheses. In (4a) the spread of the scatter is assumed to be entirely due to observational errors, whereas x and y are in (4b) assumed to be measured without errors, so that the spread is due to the disturbance factors summed up in z^*. On the other hand (4a) and (4b) will be formally equivalent if x is free from errors, so that $x = X$, for then z^* may sum up the observational error of y as well as the disturbance factors. In such a case (2) gives $b \simeq \beta$, showing that the least-squares regression is unbiased.[3]

Approach (1)–(3) is the basis for certain methods alternative to least-squares regression, among them the orthogonal regression of K. Pearson (1901), the related method of weighted regression,[4] and the confluence analysis of R. Frisch (1934). According to the above such methods are called for when the theoretical relation (1c) is exact, and both variables are subject to observational errors. Such a situation is sometimes encountered in practice. For example, when determining a comet's orbit on the celestial globe from a set of latitude-longitude observations, the coordinate measurements will be subject to error, and the orbit may be treated as an exact relation between the error-free coordinates.[5] Reference is made to D. V. Lindley (1947) for a thorough treatment of the problem of estimating an exact relationship, and for a penetrating discussion of related regression problems.

As stressed in Ch. 2·2 the hypothesis of an exact relation is not adequate in biological experiments. We have here to introduce a disturbance to account for the influence of causal factors that are not included among the explanatory variables. The situation is similar in the social and economic sciences by and large, owing to regional and individual variation. Specifically, this holds true for demand analysis, whether based on family budget data or market statistics. It stands to reason that in the analysis of statistical relationships it is on the whole exceptional that the relation under investigation may be regarded as exact. We may therefore conclude that the methods just mentioned are of narrow scope as alternatives to least-squares regression, and that economic statistics in general and demand analysis in particular do not belong to their proper field of application.[6]

(ii) In approach (1)–(3) the exact relation between the error-free variables is usually written in the symmetric form (3). The symmetric form of (3) would indicate that the relation is not intended to answer the same types of question as in a causal analysis. Let us consider two types of question.

A. *On the hypothesis that $x^{(0)}$ is dependent upon $x^{(1)}, \ldots, x^{(h)}$ by a linear relationship, what are the numerical coefficients of the relation?*

B. *On the hypothesis that there exists a linear relationship between $x^{(0)}, x^{(1)}, \ldots, x^{(h)}$, what are the numerical coefficients of the relation?*

The first is the question put to the material when forming the least-squares regression of $x^{(0)}$ on $x^{(1)}, \ldots, x^{(h)}$. As stressed in Ch. 2·2, the regression method works in the same manner whether applied for the purpose of prediction or for causal analysis, whereas the resulting relations differ as regards their subject-matter interpretation.

Proceeding to question B, the phrasing is here in agreement with a symmetric treatment of the variables. Now, what is the operational meaning of this question, and how should it be treated statistically? To examine the situation we shall distinguish between exact and disturbed relationships.

a. In the theory of gases, Boyle-Mariotte's law

(5) $\quad \log P + \log V = C + \log T \quad$ (P = pressure, V = volume, T = temperature)

is a relationship that for the purpose of this discussion may be regarded as exact. We note that (5) as well as any other exact relation may be used for the estimation or prediction of one variable, given the values of the other variables.

An exact relation is reversible in the *functional* sense, as indicated in (2·2·4). Now if the exact relationship is causal, it may or may not be reversible in the *causal* sense. Causal reversibility, as is well known, is confined to a very narrow sector of the natural sciences. Thus for example the physical laws referring to diffusion and conduction of heat are irreversible.[7] As regards relation (5) it is possible to arrange experiments with T and V for controlled variables and P for effect variable, or P and T for controlled variables and V for effect variable, but it is not possible to make P and V controlled variables and T the effect variable. In other words, (5) is causally reversible in P and V, but not in T.

b. Still considering question B, suppose next that the relationship asked for is not exact. It is clear that, if the relation is to be employed for prediction or causal analysis, we are not in a position to apply ordinary regression analysis unless further information is available. In fact, we know that it is essential in regression analysis to use the proper regression line, but question B in itself gives no indication of which variable should play the part of regressand. In other words, question B is too vague, is not sufficiently specified to allow a statistical treatment.

In this last argument we have referred to prediction and causal analysis when specifying the question put to the statistical material. These are the main purposes of regression analysis, it is true, but it is essential to make clear that causal dependences are not the only type of theoretical relationship. Question B has such a general phrasing as to cover any theoretical relation. Thus in economic applications the relationship asked for may be a causal dependence, an equilibrium relation, a definitional identity, or any relation the economist works with. A special type of hypothesis is approach (1)–(3), where it is assumed that the relationship refers to the variables as freed from observational errors, and that the relation is exact; in this case it need not be specified whether or not the relation stands for a causal dependence.

Summing up, question B is less specified than A, but its more general phrasing has turned out to be deceptive. If the relation asked for is exact, the two questions are equivalent from a statistical viewpoint. If the relation is not exact, and this is the usual situation in statistical inference, question B gives us no indication of how to employ the relation asked for, nor is it specified so as to indicate which method should be used for its statistical treatment.

(iii) The term *structural relation* was introduced by R. Frisch (1934) to denote the exact relation that is assumed to subsist between the error-free variables of approach (1)–(3). Extending its usage, T. Haavelmo (1944) and T. Koopmans (1945) have adopted the term for relations between the observed variables. At the same time a causal interpretation of the relations was disregarded or purposively avoided.[8] If the author has understood correctly, the structural relations will then have the general meaning indicated in the previous paragraphs, i.e. they are any relations with which we operate in the theoretical analysis. It is a good thing to have a special term for this purpose, but a new terminology is never without dangers. We may conclude from our previous remark that a structural relation will in general need further specification in order to be applied in practice, and further specification is also needed when it comes to the choice of method for its statistical treatment. We shall return to this matter in Ch. 2·7.

In the literature on structural relations it is customary to distinguish between 'errors in the variables' and 'errors in the equations' according as the hypothetical relationship is an exact relation between the error-free variables or a disturbed relation between the observed variables. Alternative terms are 'error model' and 'shock model'. In both cases the second term conforms with a symmetric treatment of the variables, thus giving no association with a causal interpretation of the relationships.[9] It would appear that this terminology has contributed to the confusion about ends and means in regression analysis, and in particular it may explain the persistent confusion between observational errors on the one hand and the disturbances in a causal relation on the other.[10]

(iv) After this digression to other types of theoretical relationship, let us return to causal dependences and their estimation by least-squares regression. Approach (1)–(3) covers the case when the deviations from an exact relation are entirely due to observational errors, whereas the traditional regression applies when the deviations are due to disturbance factors not specified, including observational errors in the effect variable. What is often met in practice is something intermediate. That is, we encounter both disturbances in the effect variable and observational errors in the cause variables. It is therefore always necessary to be on the lookout for observational errors in the data under analysis.

By examining the various sources of error it is sometimes possible to form an idea of their magnitude.[11] If the errors are not negligible, we may try one of the following devices to neutralize their biasing effect. Firstly, the statistical data may be corrected before applying the regression. Such corrections will be more or less hypothetical, so it is desirable to work with several alternative hypotheses.[12] This is a pedestrian device, it is true, but it has the advantage of introducing the corrections explicitly, so that we can see what we are doing. Another method would be to make use of general formulae of type (2). As is well known, a fundamental difficulty of this approach is that such formulae involve the error variances, and in point of principle these cannot be estimated from the sample. Further we note that the observational errors are subjected to some hypothesis or other as regards randomness and noncorrelation, assumptions that are quite specific, and in practice requiring just as much verification as the hypothesis of no errors at all.

There is further the danger of systematic errors. Here it is out of the question to devise general formulae for the correction. Suffice it to refer to Millikan's measurements [preface, Fig. 1]. Although excellent they cannot in themselves give any indication of the systematic error. In regression analysis we are even more at a loss in the treatment of systematic errors. Specifically, it would be purely arbitrary to suppose that systematic errors are governed by noncorrelation hypotheses of the type that lie behind formula (2). We may therefore draw the moral that if the data available are suspected or known to be unreliable because of systematic errors it is sometimes wise not to touch the data, but instead to try to secure better observations before starting the regression analysis. After all, the statistical expert is not a magician, capable of extracting reliable results from unreliable data.

5. Tests of significance. – The traditional method for testing significance in regression analysis is based on K. Pearson's (1901) and G. U. Yule's (1907) formulae for the standard error of a regression coefficient. As applied to a least-squares regression with one regressor, the procedure is as follows,

$$(1) \qquad y = a + b x + z; \qquad E(b) = \beta; \qquad d(b) \sim \frac{s_z}{s_x} \cdot \frac{1}{\sqrt{n}}; \qquad \lambda = \frac{b - \beta}{d(b)}.$$

Here z is the regression residual, β the theoretical regression coefficient, and $d(b)$ the standard error of b. The s_x, s_z are the observed standard deviations of x and z, and n is the number of observations. Finally, λ is the significance criterion. By way of a large-sample approximation, λ is treated as following a normal distribution with zero mean and unit variance.

If viewed against the universal scope of regression analysis, this being a useful tool with any sort of statistics — regional data or time-series, experimental or nonexperimental data — the assumptions that underlie method (1) are rather narrow. The traditional hypotheses used to establish (1) are that the joint distribution of x, y is normal, and that the n observations are mutually independent. As is well known, method (1) can then be developed into a small-sample device, by the use of the t-distribution.[1] We shall limit ourselves to considering large-sample methods, thus requiring that the number of observations, n, is fairly large. As a large-sample device, method (1) is known to be valid under somewhat wider conditions. Referring to Ch. 13·2 for a detailed review of the situation, we note that the following conditions are sufficient:

(a) the regression is strictly linear,

(b) the observations are independent.

Condition (a) gives an additional argument for the employment of transformations that make the regression strictly linear [Ch. 1·5 (i)]. As regards the case of curvilinear regression, it is still possible to make use of a linear regression, provided this is interpreted as a linear graduation of the hypothetical curvilinear regression. Such a graduation, which we shall call *moment regression*, will be of relevance as a well-defined concept, provided the regressor is a variable with a specified distribution [cf Ch. 13·1]. We note that the formula for $d(b)$ given by (1 c) will in general not be valid in this case [cf Ex. IV, 13].

Condition (b) is well suited for applications to experimental data, for if carefully designed the replication pattern of the experiment will make for independence, sometimes completely, but often only approximately. In field trials, for example, there will usually be some intercorrelation between observations from neighbouring plots. With nonexperimental data, however, the independence cannot so often be accepted as a realistic assumption, and specifically it is inadequate for time-series data, owing to the tendency towards correlation between observations adjacent in time.

As regards time-series regression, it has of course always been known that the assumption of independence (b) is not satisfactory.[2] Methods of type (1) have nevertheless remained in use, for lack of anything better. Being a weak point in the theory, this state of things has given rise to much of the criticism and doubt about the method of regression analysis.

The modern theory of stochastic processes gives us the tools appropriate for dealing with the interdependence between time-series observations. Making use of this theory it is a straightforward matter to establish a large-sample test of type (1) under hypotheses that go some way to meet the needs of time-series applications. The following formulae refer to such a test,[3]

$$(2) \quad E(b) = \beta; \quad d(b) \sim \frac{s_z}{s_x} \cdot \frac{1}{\sqrt{n}} \cdot f; \quad f = \sqrt{1 + 2\,r_1\varrho_1 + 2\,r_2\varrho_2 + \cdots}; \quad \lambda = \frac{b - \beta}{d(b)}.$$

The main hypothesis behind (2) and corresponding tests in the case of several regressors is that the regression is strictly linear. For a detailed statement of the hypotheses, as well as for the proofs, reference is made to Ch. 13·4. In words, we see that the regression coefficients remain unbiased under the generalized hypotheses. Their standard deviation, however, is subject to a certain correction factor, f. The correction involves two sets of autocorrelation coefficients, or two *correlograms*, viz. the correlograms r_ν and ϱ_ν of the regressor x and the residual z.

A few comments:

(i) Formulae (2) imply a substantial extension in the scope of the classical regression test (1). In the classical case of independence, all r_ν and all ϱ_ν vanish, giving $f = 1$, so that (2) reduces to (1). Now for (2) to reduce to (1) it is clearly sufficient that *either* all r_ν *or* all ϱ_ν vanish. Thus for example the classical test remains valid even if there is autocorrelation in the regressors, provided autocorrelation is absent in the residual z.

(ii) The test (2) is based on the first term only in an asymptotic expansion with respect to n, the length of the time-series. Since the terms of higher order may still be substantial even if n is fairly large, we must warn that (2) must not be expected to give more than a very rough indication of the significance of a regression coefficient. For another thing, the test involves the correlograms r_ν and ϱ_ν. These will as a rule have to be estimated from the given time-series, a procedure that necessarily involves a margin of uncertainty [cf Ch. 15·2]. It may well happen, for example, that assumptions extreme in one direction give $f = 1.4$, whereas the other extreme gives $f = 1.1$. The consequence of all this uncertainty is that the correction called for in (1) is in practice subject to a considerable margin of indeterminacy.

(iii) The above reveals that, with regression based on time-series, questions of significance lie much deeper than questions of bias. On the assumption of strictly linear regression, the regression coefficients have in fact turned out to be unbiased for very general types of time-series, whereas their standard errors have been found to depend on the autocorrelation properties of the time-series dealt with. The theorems of Ch. 13·4 cover the case when the time-series under analysis are stationary, but the arguments are shown to extend over large classes of evolutive series. With evolutive time-series the standard error of a regression coefficient displays even greater variation. Here it may very well occur that the standard error is not of the usual order of $1/\sqrt{n}$; for example, it is easy to find cases where the standard error is of order $1/n$ or $1/n\sqrt{n}$. [Cf Ex. IV, 14.]

Summing up, the least-squares regression coefficients will be unbiased under very general conditions, whereas it is necessary to make detailed assumptions about the structure of the time-series under analysis if we wish to supply the coefficients with standard errors, confidence intervals, significance levels, etc. As always in time-series analysis, however, it is in practice difficult to choose between the theoretical models available, and in addition their parameters can be determined only with wide margins of indeterminacy. We see that the situation is very different from the clear-cut treatment of experimental data. Here the replication and randomization procedure assures the approximate validity of the classical assumptions of independence. It should be clear from the above, however, that the difficulties encountered in the significance problems of time-series regression are not due to the method of least squares; they are present in time-series analysis generally. It should also be clear that the author does not wish to exaggerate the capacity of general formulae of type (2) as a means of establishing standard errors and confidence intervals. Their main importance lies rather in that they bring out so clearly the fact that we cannot expect much in the way of exactness when asking for confidence intervals on time-series regression coefficients.

(iv) Formulae (2) make allowance for autocorrelation in time-series, but how about the corresponding question for spatial series? Can a similar method be devised so as to account for the tendency to intercorrelation between observations adjacent in space? We see that the problem lies still deeper than with time-series, for one thing because time-series run in time, a medium of only one coordinate, but perhaps even more so because time-series may be taken to be equidistant, whereas spatial series usually display an irregular clustering.[4] Leaving this problem open, we point out in passing that this order of ideas has an interesting point of contact with the recent work of J. S. Duesenberry (1949). [See Chs. 3·1 and 7·6.]

(v) Having seen that significance tests in terms of standard errors, confidence intervals and the like often carry relatively little weight in regression analysis, other means for testing the validity of the numerical results come so much the more to the foreground. Here, theoretical as well as empirical tests come into consideration.

In an empirical investigation that involves scores or hundreds of regression calculations, such as that reported in Part V of this volume, the individual regression coefficients obtained will be like pieces of a puzzle; they should combine to display a consistent total picture. Thus by comparing the demand elasticities as derived by regression analysis for different commodities, different family types, and so on, it will be possible to judge whether the results are plausible. Such scrutiny and checking will clearly amount to a sort of significance test. Much of the comment in Part V is based on this type of argument. What makes the device particularly efficient is that we may here make use of economic theory, by testing the empirical elasticities for relationships that should subsist on theoretical grounds. The a priori relations between elasticities will accordingly form an important requisite for the empirical analysis. The reader is referred to Chs. 6 and 7, where a number of such relations are deduced on the basis of the economic theory of consumer behaviour.

The ultimate and supreme test of the results obtained, however, is empirical. Are they useful in practice? Specifically, can the results be used to obtain realistic and efficient forecasts, forecasts that turn out to agree with the actual development? Such confrontation with fresh evidence, this much is clear, is the real touchstone for results derived by regression analysis, just as for any statistical inference. As indicated in Ch. 1·6 the present study includes a forecast test [Ch. 18·2]. Referring to 1949/50 and based on 1930/39 results, the forecast spans the war period with its compulsory changes in the consumption. Nevertheless the forecast has turned out to be rather satisfactory.

6. Multicollinearity. – This term, introduced by R. Frisch in his *confluence analysis* (1934), refers to the situation where the variables dealt with are subject to two or more relations. We may here distinguish between at least two cases. One is the degenerate situation in regression analysis where the regressors are highly intercorrelated so as to be themselves subject to a linear relationship; this case will be discussed in the present section. Another is the situation encountered in formulae (1·4·1). Here the variables are a priori regarded as subject to a system of relationships, the purpose of the empirical analysis being to estimate one or more relations of the system; this case will be considered in the next section.

Let us consider a regression with two regressors, say

$$(1) \qquad y_\nu = a + b_1 x_\nu^{(1)} + b_2 x_\nu^{(2)} + z_\nu \qquad \nu = 1, \ldots, n.$$

The method of least squares gives a system of normal equations for the regression coefficients a, b_1, b_2. Now, if the regressors stand in an exact linear relationship, say

(2) $$c_0 + c_1 x_\nu^{(1)} + c_2 x_\nu^{(2)} = 0 \qquad\qquad \nu = 1, \ldots, n,$$

the normal equations become indeterminate. More precisely, we can then fix an arbitrary value for one parameter, say $b_2 = b_2^*$, and on insertion of b_2^* in the normal equations these will determine b_1 [see Theorem 12·3·2 D]. The resulting b_1 will of course be a function of b_2^*. We see that the situation will be much the same if the relation (2) is not exact, but only almost exact, i.e. if the correlation coefficient between $x^{(1)}$ and $x^{(2)}$ comes near ± 1. The relation (1) is then in fact practically indeterminate; specifically, the residuals z will turn out almost the same, whether the coefficient b_2 be freely chosen a priori or calculated from the normal equations.[1]

As convincingly stressed by Frisch, the indeterminacy of regression relations is a frequent situation in practice, especially in economic applications. Compared with Frisch's treatment, however, the problem has in the present section been given a somewhat different twist. In Frisch's confluence analysis the multiple relations are of type (2·4·3), i.e., they involve non-observed variables and are assumed to be exact. Relation (1), on the other hand, refers to observed variables y, $x^{(1)}$, $x^{(2)}$, and need not necessarily be exact; other causal factors are here taken into account, being summed up in the residual z. From the present viewpoint the main conclusion in Frisch's analysis is that the presence of multicollinearity may be obscured if the data contain observational errors.[2]

To examine a special case of multicollinearity, let (1) be a demand relation to be estimated from market statistics on quantity y, price $x^{(1)}$, and income $x^{(2)}$. Further let the variables be given as logarithms, so that b_1, b_2 may be interpreted as demand elasticities. Then suppose price and income are highly intercorrelated, as they often will be since both variables reflect the business cycle. An indeterminacy will then come into the picture, the normal equations not being sufficient to determine uniquely the price and income elasticities. We see that the indeterminacy can be remedied if one of the elasticities is known a priori. This is the case if the income elasticity b_2 has been estimated beforehand, say from family budget data. The coefficient b_2 can then be regarded as a priori known in (1), whereupon the least-squares method can be used for determining b_1. This device will be referred to as regression analysis with *side conditions on the parameters*, or briefly *conditional regression analysis*.[3]

(i) The device of conditional regression analysis is clearly of general scope. If the normal equations do not provide determinate estimates of the coefficients sought for, this means that the statistical data do not contain sufficient information for the purpose. The empirical material must then be supplemented by information from other sources. Sometimes, as in our example, information on one or more coefficients may be drawn from other empirical data; in other cases we may utilize theoretical information. In demand analysis the situation is rather fortunate in this respect. In fact, as stressed in Ch. 2·5 (v), the theory of consumer demand gives us several relationships that a priori should subsist between demand elasticities, and any such relationship may be utilized for settling an indeterminacy that arises from multicollinearity.

(ii) The indeterminacy in question is nothing peculiar from the viewpoint of classical regression theory. In fact, considering a regression with nonvanishing residual, if we use a formula of type (2·5·1) to calculate the standard error of an indeterminate regression coefficient, the standard error will turn out to be large or infinite. The indeterminacy is, in other words, nothing else than the degenerate case when the regression coefficient has a very large confidence interval [cf Ex. IV, 10]. Conversely, the above device of removing the indeterminacy will reduce the standard error and the confidence interval. The simplest case is when the supplementary information gives us a priori values for one or more regression coefficients. The standard error will then be given by the ordinary type of formula, and this remark applies to the classical case of independence (2·5·1) as well as to the more general formula (2·5·2).

7. Simultaneous relationships. – In Ch. 1·4, formulae (1·4·1), a demand function was regarded as forming part of an economic model, a system of hypothetical relationships. We shall now turn to certain general questions that arise in the statistical treatment of such systems.

Early attempts towards a statistical analysis on the basis of economic models are due to H. L. Moore (1919, 1925). His approach in demand analysis, which has influenced much of the later development, is that of *moving equilibrium*. Briefly stated, the idea behind Moore's approach is that if we form a scatter diagram using market data on the quantities transacted, say q_t, and the prices of the commodity considered, say p_t, each point in the scatter (q_t, p_t) will be the intersection between a demand curve and a supply curve. The spread of the scatter is regarded as being due to shifts in the demand and supply curves, and according to an argument suggested by E. J. Working (1927) the nature of these shifts will determine from case to case how to carry out and interpret the statistical analysis. Thus, if the shifts in the supply curve dominate, the scatter (q_t, p_t) will give a picture of the demand curve, something like Fig. 1·4·2 a, and the demand curve may then be estimated by the regression of quantity on price. If on the other hand the demand shifts dominate, (q_t, p_t) will form a scatter like that of Fig. 1·4·2 b, and the regression of quantity q_t on price p_t will then give a supply curve.

In the approach of Moore and Working, the purpose is to estimate just one relation, and the system of relations enters by way of a theoretical requisite in support of the statistical method adopted. In Tinbergen's studies (1939) in the mechanism of the business cycle we find for the first time a genuine coordination between economic models and statistical analysis. Here the model system as a whole is studied, and statistical methods are used in order to estimate the various relations of which it is composed. Reference is further made to A. Hanau's study (1927) of the cycle of hog prices, a work of great interest from the viewpoint of economic models. These contributions will be further discussed in Ch. 3·2.

A common feature in the approaches mentioned is that the relationships of a system are estimated by ordinary regression analysis. The traditional method was adopted more or less uncritically, with an interesting discussion of the causal aspects of the method [cf Ch. 3·2], but without establishing its rationale for the purpose. Now with reference to applications of this type, regression analysis was vigorously attacked by R. Frisch (1928, 1934) and T. Haavelmo (1943; 1944). According to Haavelmo's argument the traditional method is a 'single-equation' approach, and it will in general give biased estimates when applied to a system of simultaneous relationships.[1] We see that Haavelmo's argument is potentially of general scope, for any single relation may be conceived of as forming part of a system, and so there would be a risk that the bias would creep in everywhere in regression analysis.

According to the theorem behind (2·5·2), least-squares regression will under general conditions be unbiased when applied to a single relation. The essential condition of the theorem is that the disturbance is a priori uncorrelated with the explanatory variables [cf Ch. 13·4]. However, there is nothing in this theorem that is invalidated if the relation under analysis is a member of a system of relationships. We may accordingly infer as a corollary to our 'single-equation' theorem that it applies as well to a system of relationships. More precisely, the time-series being regarded as generated by a stochastic process which is defined by the hypothetical system, we need only assume that the system has the form of a set of a priori regression relationships. It is easy to see that this type of system is nothing else than the *recursive system* defined in ·Ch. 1·4. Thus, as pointed out in Ch. 1·4, regression analysis is applicable without bias to the relations of a recursive system. In the special case illustrated in Fig. 1·4·2 it is therefore not by accident that the regression lines give a good approximation to the relationships (1·4·3) known a priori.[2]

The general situation is brought out in the formulae below. These refer to the case of linear relationships, and for the sake of further simplicity each system is confined to three relations. With these restrictions, (1) is the general formula for a recursive system. Formulae (2)–(3) give systems of the type considered in the approach that was initiated by T. Haavelmo and has been carried further by A. Wald, T. Koopmans and others.[3] The fundamental hypothesis is (2), which is referred to as a *structural system*. System (3), obtained from (2) by solving for $y_t^{(1)}, y_t^{(2)}, y_t^{(3)}$, is known as the *reduced form* of (2).

First an auxiliary notation:

$$L_t^{(i)} = b_i +$$
$$+ b_{i0}^{(1)} x_t^{(1)} + b_{i1}^{(1)} x_{t-1}^{(1)} + b_{i2}^{(1)} x_{t-2}^{(1)} + \cdots + b_{i0}^{(2)} x_t^{(2)} + b_{i1}^{(2)} x_{t-1}^{(2)} + b_{i2}^{(2)} x_{t-2}^{(2)} + \cdots + b_{ih}^{(p)} x_{t-h}^{(p)}$$
$$+ c_{i1}^{(1)} y_{t-1}^{(1)} + c_{i2}^{(1)} y_{t-2}^{(1)} + \cdots\cdots\cdots + c_{i1}^{(2)} y_{t-1}^{(2)} + c_{i2}^{(2)} y_{t-2}^{(2)} + \cdots + c_{ih}^{(3)} y_{t-h}^{(3)}$$

All $x^{(k)}, y^{(k)}$ are variables given as time-series. The linear expression $L_t^{(i)}$ contains *lagged* values of the $y^{(k)}$, *lagged* or *non-lagged* values of the $x^{(k)}$. The maximal lag present in $L_t^{(i)}$ has been denoted by h. In current terminology, $x^{(1)}, \ldots, x^{(p)}$ are *exogenous* and $y^{(1)}, y^{(2)}, y^{(3)}$ *endogenous* variables. Thus the $y^{(k)}$ are variables that the economic model sets out to explain, whereas the $x^{(k)}$ are regarded as outside influences that are left unexplained.

With these notations, we may write the systems as follows.

$$(1) \quad \begin{cases} y_t^{(1)} = \quad 0 \quad + \quad 0 \quad + L_t^{(1)} + z_t^{(1)} \\ y_t^{(2)} = c_{20}^{(1)} y_t^{(1)} + \quad 0 \quad + L_t^{(2)} + z_t^{(2)} \\ y_t^{(3)} = c_{30}^{(1)} y_t^{(1)} + c_{30}^{(2)} y_t^{(2)} + L_t^{(3)} + z_t^{(3)} \end{cases}$$

$$(2) \quad \begin{cases} y_t^{(1)} = \quad 0 \quad + c_{10}^{(2)} y_t^{(2)} + c_{10}^{(3)} y_t^{(3)} + L_t^{(1)} + z_t^{(1)} \\ y_t^{(2)} = c_{20}^{(1)} y_t^{(1)} + \quad 0 \quad + c_{20}^{(3)} y_t^{(3)} + L_t^{(2)} + z_t^{(2)} \\ y_t^{(3)} = c_{30}^{(1)} y_t^{(1)} + c_{30}^{(2)} y_t^{(2)} + \quad 0 \quad + L_t^{(3)} + z_t^{(3)} \end{cases}$$

$$(3) \quad \begin{cases} y_t^{(1)} = L_t^{(1)} + z_t^{(1)} \\ y_t^{(2)} = L_t^{(2)} + z_t^{(2)} \\ y_t^{(3)} = L_t^{(3)} + z_t^{(3)}. \end{cases}$$

We have now a few remarks on recursive and structural systems, remarks on common properties as well as dissimilarities.

(i) Both in recursive and structural systems, the endogenous variables at time t, that is $y_t^{(1)}, y_t^{(2)}, \ldots$, may be regarded as *jointly dependent* upon the variables that constitute the linear forms $L_t^{(1)}, L_t^{(2)}, \ldots$

In a recursive system (1) each relation is assumed to describe a *unilateral causal dependence* in the sense of Ch. 1·2–4. Thus in the ith relation $y_t^{(i)}$ is the effect variable, whereas $y_t^{(1)}, \ldots, y_t^{(i-1)}$ and the variables in $L_t^{(i)}$ are the cause variables. What makes the causal interpretation possible is that the coefficients $c_{i0}^{(k)}$ form a triangular scheme, so that $y_t^{(1)}$ may appear as cause variable for $y_t^{(2)}$, both $y_t^{(1)}$ and $y_t^{(2)}$ as cause variables for $y_t^{(3)}$, all of $y_t^{(1)}, y_t^{(2)}, y_t^{(3)}$ as cause variables for $y_{t+1}^{(1)}$, and so on. The notion of unilateral dependence thus being extended from a single relation so as to apply to a system of relationships, we may say that the endogenous variables of system (1) form a *recursive causal chain*.[4]

Formally, the recursive systems (1) are a subclass or special type of structural systems (2). We note that (1) cannot be generalized in the direction of (2) without losing the possibility of a strict causal interpretation. In fact, if $y_t^{(i)}$ and $y_t^{(k)}$ are singled out as effect variables in the ith and kth relations of (2), respectively, we see that in the ith equation $y_t^{(i)}$ would appear as effect and $y_t^{(k)}$ as cause variable, whereas the kth equation would have $y_t^{(k)}$ for effect and $y_t^{(i)}$ for cause, which is a causal contradiction.[5] Judging from an authoritative exposition by T. Koopmans (1949), the explanation is that structural systems are intended to cover not only causal dependences but also other types of theoretical relation, notably definitional identities. The situation is not very clear, however, for the reason that the literature on structural systems is almost exclusively concerned with their formal aspects.

As regards the applications there are several vague or obscure points in the literature on structural systems. It would seem that the vagueness is primarily due to the disregard of a causal interpretation of the relationships. Thus a structural system can be questioned using the same arguments as in Ch. 2·4 (ii). Can a relation in the system be used for estimating one variable in terms of the other ones? If it can, the estimable variable must be specified, for unless statistical relations are exact they cannot be treated as reversible; i.e. they can by no means be used for estimating every variable in terms of the other ones. If it cannot, for what purpose can the structural system then be used? For another thing, the passage from a structural system (2) to its reduced form (3) is a purely formal operation, the economic significance of which is not immediately obvious from the viewpoint of the applications.

In Ch. 2·2 (ii) we have touched upon regression analysis as used for the purpose of prediction. We note that if we are interested only in formal prediction, without entering upon a causal analysis, systems (1) have no advantage over systems of the special type (3), for the prediction variance will have the same minimum in the two systems [cf Ex. IV, 9]. Thus we see that systems (1) are of more general scope than (3) from the viewpoint of causal analysis, but as regards prediction they are equivalent. It is in view of this fact that we have in Ch. 1·4 adopted the terminology that a system (1) is not recursive unless each relation serves to describe a causal dependence. In particular, a system (3) will be called recursive if all its relations are causal.

(ii) In both of the systems (1) and (2), and in each of their relations, say the ith, the disturbance $z_t^{(i)}$ is assumed to be uncorrelated with the variables of the linear form $L_t^{(i)}$ of the same relation. In (1), but not in (2), it is further assumed that $z_t^{(i)}$ is uncorrelated with $y_t^{(1)}, \ldots, y_t^{(i-1)}$.

It is a general property of the residuals of a least-squares regression that they are uncorrelated with the regressors, but not with the regressand. In recursive systems the assumed noncorrelation between the disturbance $z_t^{(i)}$ and the explanatory variables in the ith relation will therefore assure that least-squares regression is applicable without bias.

In a structural system, on the other hand, the disturbance $z_t^{(i)}$ is allowed to be correlated with $y_t^{(1)}, y_t^{(2)}, \ldots$, that is with all of the endogenous variables at time t. As a consequence, the method of least-squares regression will in general give biased estimates for the parameters if applied to a relation in a structural system. This is Haavelmo's argument for the type of bias referred to in the beginning of this section. Ordinary regression thus not being consistent for the estimation of the parameters of a structural system, the maximum likelihood method has been adapted for the purpose.[6] A much-discussed difficulty met in this approach is the *identification problem*; we note that this problem does not arise in the case of recursive systems, at least not if they are estimated by the use of regression analysis.

Contrary to Haavelmo's statement that least-squares regression in general is biased when applied to a system of simultaneous relationships, we have seen that the regression is unbiased in the case of recursive systems. A first theorem in this direction was given in a joint paper by R. Bentzel and the author (1946). The present treatment is more general, inasmuch as normality is not assumed, nor zero inter- and auto-correlation between the disturbances.[7]

Thus when it comes to the statistical treatment of the theoretical model, the correlation properties of the disturbances are essential, or rather their noncorrelation properties. This much is obvious, however, that as a rule very little is known a priori about the correlation properties of the disturbances. In models (1) or (2), accordingly, their noncorrelation with the explanatory variables may be regarded as a working hypothesis chosen ad hoc so as to conform with the statistical method adopted, rather than as a hypothesis well-founded on the joint basis of theory and experience. Such hypotheses, nonetheless, are quite natural since we wish to obtain relations in which the disturbances are small and irregular [cf Ch. 2·3].

It is interesting to distinguish here between different types of noncorrelation. Thus in one and the same relation the consecutive disturbances form a time-series, say $\ldots, z_{t-1}^{(i)}, z_t^{(i)}, z_{t+1}^{(i)}, \ldots$. In economic applications experience has shown, by and large, that time-series are autocorrelated, and specifically that there is a ubiquitous tendency to persistency and hysteresis. It is therefore a great advantage of the method of least-squares regression that such autocorrelation will in general cause no bias [Ch. 2·5]. If on the other hand we consider the disturbances that refer to the same time point, but to different relations of the model, say $z_t^{(1)}, \ldots, z_t^{(q)}$, the situation is rather different. If correlation is present between such simultaneous disturbances, at least if the correlation is strong, this is an important trace of regularity that is left unexplained by the model, a feature that in itself makes the model unsatisfactory. Correlation of this simultaneous type is related to the notion of identifiability in the sense of T. Koopmans.[8] It would fall outside the scope of the present work to enter upon this order of ideas. Suffice it to note that some recursive models (1) have the property that the postulated noncorrelation between a disturbance and the corresponding right-hand variables implies that there will be no correlation between simultaneous disturbances. In other cases, the postulated non-correlation is compatible with simultaneous correlation. [See Exs. IV, 27–28.]

(iii) Recursive systems (1) and corresponding nonlinear systems are of a very general scope. If the author is not mistaken, they cover all of the models actually used in dynamic economic analysis, except for the approach of structural systems (for this statement to be correct, of course, we must in certain models use divided differences instead of differentials, sums instead of integrals, and so on). The traditional adherence to systems of type (1) is quite natural in view of the simple fact pointed out in (i), viz. that if a dynamic approach aims at explaining the variables in terms of a chain of causation the system must necessarily be recursive.

From the viewpoint of dynamic analysis, a structural system is a mixed type of approach, since static hypotheses are permitted in the form of equilibrium relations. This in itself is no disadvantage, quite the contrary. By introducing other types of relation than causal dependences the approach becomes more flexible, and therefore opens up new possibilities for econometric analysis. From the viewpoint of the applications, however, the questions raised under (i) throw some doubt upon the approach in its present stage of development. Maybe these questions can be cleared up. Anyhow, it is not intended to enter here upon an appraisal of the approach of structural systems. In the author's opinion, this cannot be done until more material is available, as regards the theory as well as the application of structural systems. Besides, such a discussion would not belong to the present topic, the rationale of least-squares regression.

In conclusion we stress two fundamental and simple properties of recursive systems: they are the most general form of a theoretical model that is constructed as a chain of causation, and under general conditions their relations may be estimated without bias by ordinary regression analysis. Meriting special attention because of these properties, the recursive systems will be taken up for further consideration in the present survey [Ch. 3·2].

8. Efficiency aspects of least-squares regression. – Thus far in this chapter, regression analysis has primarily been examined from the viewpoint of whether the regression coefficients are unbiased, i.e. whether they are unbiased estimates for the parameters of the theoretical relation that has been adopted as basic hypothesis for the analysis. It has turned out that asymptotically for large samples they actually are, under very general conditions. Further we have found that the standard errors of the regression coefficients will under general conditions be of order $1/\sqrt{n}$, where n is the sample size, so that the estimates are also consistent [Ch. 2·5]. But how about the efficiency of the estimates; will their standard errors be the smallest possible?

On the classical assumptions of independence the answer is in the affirmative. The primary reference is here to Gauss' *Theoria combinationis*, the main result of which is also known as Gauss-Markov's theorem.[1] To review the situation, let us consider the case of one regressor, writing

$$(1) \qquad y_\nu = \beta x_\nu + z_\nu \quad (\nu = 1, \ldots, n); \qquad b = \frac{\Sigma x_\nu y_\nu}{\Sigma x_\nu^2}$$

where (1a) is the theoretical regression and b is the least-squares regression coefficient; the y_ν and x_ν are measured from their means in the sample. The approach of the Theoria combinationis is based on three assumptions, viz. (a) the regression is formed for repeated independent samples, each comprising n pairs of observation (x_ν, y_ν); (b) the observations $x_1, \ldots, x_n$ of the regressor are *fixed*, being the same in each sample; (c) the disturbances $z_1, \ldots, z_n$ are observations of n random variables ζ_ν that are independent, have zero expectation, and the same variance for $\nu = 1, \ldots, n$. We see that b as given by (1b) is *linear* in $y_1, \ldots, y_n$, and since the x_ν are treated as constants it is also seen that b is an *unbiased* estimate of the parameter β. Further, as is readily verified, *the least-squares regression coefficient b is that unbiased linear estimate which is of optimal efficiency*; i.e., its standard error is the smallest possible. This and the corresponding theorem in the case of several regressors is the main result of the Theoria combinationis [see Ch. 13·3].

Next we recall the extension of the Theoria combinationis that has been given by A. C. Aitken (1935). Dropping the assumption under (c) that the disturbances $\zeta_1, \ldots, \zeta_n$ are independent, Aitken assumes that their second-order moments are known, say $E(\zeta_i \zeta_k) = \lambda_{ik}$, where the disturbances may be normed so as to make $\lambda_{11} = \cdots = \lambda_{nn}$, and solves the problem of finding that linear and unbiased estimate of β, say b^*, which is of optimal efficiency [cf Ex. IV, 16]. The resulting b^* coincides with the least-squares estimate b if $\lambda_{ik} = 0$ for all $i \neq k$; otherwise, the estimates will in general differ, and b^* be of higher efficiency. Reference is further made to an interesting paper by D. Cochrane and G. H. Orcutt (1949) on time-series regression. Considering the case when the disturbances ζ_ν form an autoregressive series, their calculation of the estimate b^* is brought over to the case of independence by subjecting the given time-series to an autoregressive transformation before the regression coefficients are calculated.

Thus in estimating the parameters of a theoretical regression relation we have a parting of the ways.

On the one hand we may follow the least-squares principle, making square sum of the regression residuals a minimum. On the other hand we may adopt the principle of optimal efficiency. According to the Gauss-Markov theorem the two ways do not part until we leave the domain of independent disturbances ζ_ν. What happens outside this classical domain is a question that has only recently been opened up for research. Thus in the direction of least-squares regression we have the author's results of type (2·5·2), showing that the parameter estimates given by the least-squares principle will remain unbiased. On the other side we have Aitken's and Cochrane-Orcutt's results on optimal-efficiency estimates. It will be noted that we cannot expect much by way of improvement if instead of least-squares regression we adopt the principle of optimal efficiency. For one thing, in fact, a parameter estimate b^* of Aitken's type and the corresponding least-squares estimate b will have standard errors of the same order, that is $1/\sqrt{n}$, and so the difference between b^* and b will at most be of order $1/\sqrt{n}$. For another thing, the situation is much the same as in our proximity theorem [see (2·3·1)]; thus if the disturbances are small and their interdependence moderate, we can be confident that the difference between the two estimates is negligible. Further we note that if nonetheless we wish to follow the principle of optimal efficiency we shall in the practical applications encounter the difficulty that an estimate of type b^* involves the disturbance covariances λ_{ik}, and these will in general have to be estimated from the sample. There is the same difficulty as regards Cochrane-Orcutt's device, of course, for there the coefficients of the autoregressive transformation will have to be estimated.[2]

A few final remarks:

(i) The above discussion refers to the special case when the theoretical regression is strictly linear. As pointed out in Ch. 2·5 the least-squares regression is unbiased also in the case of moment regression, i.e. when the theoretical regression (1a) is regarded as a linear graduation of a curvilinear relationship. To the author's knowledge, questions of efficiency have not been investigated in the case of moment regression.

On the other hand it will be observed that the above discussion involves no assumption of normality. Now if (1a) is specified so that the disturbances ζ_ν are independent and normally distributed, the analysis can be pushed further. The least-squares regression coefficients will then be maximum likelihood estimates, a classical result which in essence is embodied in Gauss' *Theoria motus* discussion of least-squares approximation.[3] As a consequence, the coefficients will then have the properties of consistency, efficiency and sufficiency that according to Fisher's theory of estimation are the privilege of maximum likelihood estimates.[4] Furthermore — another of Fisher's fundamental results — the regression coefficients will follow Student's distribution, which accordingly may be employed for a small-sample test of the significance of regression coefficients.[5]

(ii) We are now in a position to see the fundamental advantage of the least-squares regression in the treatment of nonexperimental data: it works with a minimum of assumptions. More refined methods require specification of the properties of the disturbances; thus, to obtain estimates of optimal efficiency we must specify their covariances, and to apply a small-sample test of significance we must even specify their joint distribution. Such specification, however, requires some prior experience and knowledge about the disturbances to be expected, and in this respect the statistician is not in a favourable situation when working outside the sphere of experimental data. The same general argument was stressed in Ch. 2·5 (iii) and 2·7 (ii). Thus we note that when regression analysis is applied to economic or social statistics, the introduction of a new regressor is often highly tentative, and in particular very little if anything is known a priori about the resulting change in the regression residuals and their joint distribution. As a consequence, the statistical inference based on the residuals will also be tentative. Or to state a constructive conclusion: In order to extend the refined methods to the field of nonexperimental data, it is a prerequisite that the regression residuals obtained in the analysis of such data should be systematically studied, so as to collect experience about different types met with, their possible regularities, and their distribution properties. [Cf Ch. 15·2 (v).]

We have said that least-squares regression works with a minimum of assumptions. In essence, the only assumption required is that the disturbance factors should be uncorrelated with the regressors, and this is a minimal requirement for the validity of the approach, since the regression residuals will automatically be uncorrelated with the regressors. Thus in contrast to the maximum likelihood method the approach is distribution-free w.r.t. the regression disturbances, and in contrast to Aitken's method the approach is even covariance-free. On the other hand we note that since the noncorrelation assumptions are dictated by the method, and cannot be dispensed with, it is the more important to use the regression approach with discretion and caution in applications to nonexperimental data. Thus as stressed earlier in this chapter, the relationship under analysis should be in line with prior knowledge, and the resulting conclusions should be checked and tested by the use of other evidence, empirical and theoretical. Or in the words of Ch. 2·5 (v), an isolated piece of regression analysis may be questionable, but the conclusions gain in significance and validity if several regression relations combine so as to display a consistent total picture.

(iii) Generally speaking, statistical methods aim at *accuracy*. The unbiasedness, efficiency and sufficiency assured in large samples by the maximum likelihood method are three aspects of accuracy, and a fourth is the exactness attained in tests of significance of the small-sample type. Statistical methods being more or less satisfactory as regards the different aspects of accuracy, the choice of method will often involve a compromise between different viewpoints. What is of primary importance in practice is to attain a reasonable compromise between unbiasedness and efficiency.[6] The refined methods of modern statistics aim at a high degree of accuracy from all of the four viewpoints mentioned, the maximum likelihood method even at an optimal degree. However, the modern methods have largely been devised for the purpose of experimental applications, and there they have won great triumphs, but as pointed out under (ii) it is by no means a straightforward matter to extend their application to non-experimental data. For small-sample tests, in particular, the accuracy attained will as a rule be illusory, since such tests require a full specification of the distribution of regression residuals and other erratic elements. For the analysis of nonexperimental data we may accordingly state the conclusion, at first sight paradoxical, that when dealing with a small sample we must as a rule rest content with the rough inference drawn by the use of large-sample methods, whereas in the analysis of a large sample we may sometimes be in a position to apply more refined methods, making use of the sample to estimate the auxiliary parameters involved in the method.

9. Conclusions. – In the literature on least-squares regression there is no phase of the method that has escaped objection, so in our investigation it has been necessary to examine the method throughout, from its very foundations up to technical points in the traditional procedure. Thus, in sections 2·2–3 and partly in 2·4 we have examined the method from the viewpoint of the logical and causal interpretation of regression relationships. In 2·4–6 we have considered certain technical difficulties that arise in the practical applications. Whereas 2·2–6 have largely been concerned with the proper use of regression analysis, we have in 2·7–8 met with more radical arguments, by which the regression method itself is called into question.

To find our way through the controversial field we have repeatedly made use of three guiding principles. The first is that regression analysis as applied in a controlled experiment rests on the solid ground of sound theory as well as varied experience, and that such applications by way of analogy serve as a conceptual prototype for the regression analysis of nonexperimental data. Against this background it is an easy matter to distinguish the main purposes of regression analysis, viz. to obtain forecasts and to establish causal relations.

What has been the main source of controversy is the analysis of causal relationships. Briefly stated, most of the controversies spring from a failure to realize that in each and every application the hypothesis of a causal dependence has to be indicated and supported by nonstatistical considerations. As regards demand analysis, in particular, the regression analysis has to be directed by economic arguments. This stressing of subject-matter considerations as a prerequisite and a supplementary tool in regression analysis underlies the exposition in Ch. 1·2–4, and is the second main principle followed in Ch. 2·2–7. Specifically, such considerations have been the salient point in discussing the interpretation of regression relations, the choice of regression line, and the analysis of systems of relationships. Generally speaking, it has turned out that the least-squares regression as traditionally used is a sound method, and especially it is legitimate for the purpose of demand analysis. At the same time we have stressed the limitations of the traditional methods. The methods cannot be applied blindly. In particular, the economic sector under analysis must satisfy certain qualifying conditions if the regression coefficients obtained are to be interpreted as genuine demand elasticities.

The third line of argument refers to the lack of a priori knowledge about the properties of regression residuals in the case of nonexperimental data. In a controlled experiment, the residuals are a variation of more or less random nature, being the total effect of a large number of uncontrolled factors. In plant experiments, for example, soil differences and biotype variation between different individuals of the same species are the main sources of uncontrolled variation. By replication of experiments and by experience in general the random variation is rather well known a priori as regards size and distribution. This knowledge is utilized by statistical methods in various ways, and in particular we note that the refined methods of modern statistics are based on a more or less detailed specification of the random variation. This argument goes some way to explain why the modern methods have been epoch-making in their application to experimental data, which is the sphere where they originated, and may also explain their success in certain other applications, for example the quality control of industrial production. In social and economic statistics, on the other hand, the situation is different. Here we are far from possessing any reliable knowledge about the nature of the residual variation, and the statistical inference based on the specification of its distribution will therefore be hypothetical and involve a large amount of arbitrariness. This point was stressed in Ch. 2·5 as regards tests of significance and in Ch. 2·8 as regards the maximum likelihood principle and related methods.[1] Being distribution-free, the method of least-squares regression is not open to the same critical argument. Further the conclusion is that in regression analysis of non-experimental data the formal tests of significance, however refined, carry little weight as compared with the non-formal and non-quantitative significance that is embodied in results derived from independent sources, provided these results support one another and form an organic whole.

The three principles now reviewed are main lines of argument which are essential for the understanding of the approach of the present work. As stated in advance in Ch. 2·1 they do not involve much by way of new ideas. Compared with other treatments of regression methods there is rather a shift in emphasis, the primary stress being laid on the purpose and the logical interpretation of regression analysis, whereas formal aspects have been pushed into the background. In one or two passages the shift of emphasis has given rise to novel theoretical considerations, notably in sections 2·3, 2·5 and 2·7.

Summing up our discussion of least-squares regression, we have found that part of the criticism of the traditional methods is unfounded, being due to vague notions about the ends and means of regression analysis. The discussion has helped us to get a more clear understanding of the scope and limitation of the regression approach in general. Its proper field of application is estimation and prediction in the general sense of Ch. 2·2. The analysis of causal dependences may be regarded as a special type of application within this field. Another part of the criticism reveals certain shortcomings of the traditional methods. Thanks to the flexibility of the approach, however, these deficiencies can to a great extent be remedied without diverging from the general frame of regression analysis, and without losing the attractive simplicity of the method. In the end there does not really remain much to be said against the method, except perhaps that it does not always come up to optimal efficiency. Much of the recent criticism of regression methods has no doubt been inspired by a desire to extend the triumphs of modern statistical methods to the fields of economic and social statistics. We have seen, however, that such a programme meets great difficulties, for in applications to nonexperimental data we lack the experience and knowledge required for the proper specification of disturbances and residuals. This does not exclude the possibility that better methods may exist or can be devised. When it comes to the practical applications, however, their advantages will always have to be balanced against the substantial advantages of the least-squares method of being highly flexible as regards the underlying assumptions and very simple as regards the numerical computations. For the present the theoretical and practical evidence available in this direction is not strong enough to warrant the abandonment of the traditional methods.

The final conclusion must be, no doubt, that the regression analysis as traditionally applied is essentially sound. In demand analysis, at least, it can still be safely recommended.

Chapter 3.

THE THEORETICAL REQUISITES OF DEMAND ANALYSIS

1. The Paretoan theory of preference fields. – Demand analysis is a composite subject in which many threads run together, the approach being a coordination between theoretical and empirical analysis, with ideas and methods taken from several branches of science. Parts II–IV give a detailed account of the methods and theoretical requisites of demand analysis in the sciences of economics, probability theory and statistics. The present chapter will serve as an introduction, the purpose being at the same time to stress the connexion between demand analysis and general ideas and lines of development in the three sciences.

Pareto's theory of preference fields, the main topic of Part II, is a psychological approach to the analysis of economic behaviour. The first attempts in this direction were hedonistic, and based on the notion of utility. We may distinguish three phases in the development.[1] In the original approach of Gossen (1854), followed up by Jevons (1871) and Walras (1874), utility was regarded as a measurable quality of any commodity, and further it was assumed that utility is an *additive* quality. Thus the total utility, say U, of specified quantities $q_1, ..., q_n$ of n commodities is given by the sum of the separate utilities, in symbols

(1) $$U = U_1(q_1) + U_2(q_2) + \cdots + U_n(q_n).$$

The second phase is associated with the names of Edgeworth (1881), G. B. Antonelli (1886) and I. Fisher (1892). The basic assumption is that utility is a quality that in general is non-additive, in symbols

(2) $$U = U(q_1, ..., q_n).$$

If we interpret $q_1, ..., q_n$ as a point in a Euclidean space R_n, the relation

(3) $$U(q_1, ..., q_n) = c$$

represents the locus of points of equal utility, $U = c$. Assuming $U(q_1, ..., q_n)$ to be a sufficiently regular function, locus (3) will be an $(n-1)$-dimensional surface in R_n, called an *indifference surface*. The family of such surfaces obtained by allowing c to vary is called an *indifference map*. If $n = 2$, which case is illustrated in Fig. 1, the surfaces of the map become ordinary curves.

The third phase is the approach of Pareto (1906). The basis is formally the

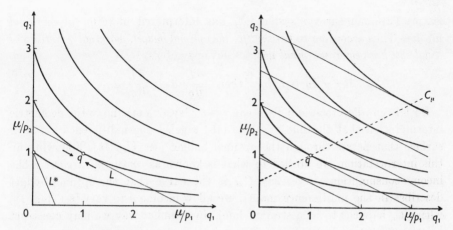

Fig. 3·1·1. Indifference map for two commodities. Preference index $U = q_2 \cdot q_1 + q_2$.
a. A balance line L and its optimal   b. An income-consumption curve C_μ.
     budget q.

same as (2)–(3), but with a change in the interpretation. The salient point is
that for the main results of the theory it is only the shape of the indifference
map that matters, and that the map can be defined on a psychological-behaviouristic basis, without making use of the concept of measurable utility.
Briefly stated, it is assumed that the consumer considered has a scale or
field of *ordered preferences*. This enables him to compare any two budgets
$q = (q_1,\ldots,q_n)$, $q' = (q_1',\ldots,q_n')$ and to decide whether q is preferred, disfavoured,
or equivalent relative to q'. The indifference surface that passes through a
given point q is then defined as the locus of points q' that are equivalent to q.
As before the indifference surfaces will allow the representation (3), but,
having lost its significance of measurable utility, U is now interpreted as a
preference index-function.

In Part II, the Paretoan theory is developed on an axiomatic basis, following
an earlier work of the author (1943–1944).

A fundamental proposition in pre-Paretoan as well as Paretoan theory is
that if prices are fixed, say $p_1,\ldots,p_n$, the consumer will spend his income, μ, on
a well-defined optimal budget, $q_1,\ldots,q_n$. Being functions of $\mu,p_1,\ldots,p_n$, the
optimal q_i are, in modern terminology, the consumer's *demand functions*, say
$q_i = Q_i(\mu,p_1,\ldots,p_n)$. Analytically, the demand functions are deduced by making
$U(q_1,\ldots,q_n)$ a maximum, subject to the side condition that expenditure cannot exceed income, that is $p_1 q_1 + \cdots + p_n q_n \leq \mu$. This gives the optimal
$q_1,\ldots,q_n$ as the solution of the classical system

$$(4) \qquad \frac{\partial U/\partial q_1}{p_1} = \cdots = \frac{\partial U/\partial q_n}{p_n}; \qquad p_1 q_1 + \cdots + p_n q_n = \mu.$$

In pre-Paretoan theory, system (4) was interpreted in terms of *marginal utilities*. Thus according to Gossen: *for the optimal budget, marginal quantities of equal cost have equal marginal utilities*, or, in symbols,

$$\text{if} \quad p_i \, dq_i = p_k \, dq_k \quad \text{then} \quad \frac{\partial U}{\partial q_i} \cdot dq_i = \frac{\partial U}{\partial q_k} \cdot dq_k.$$

Both in pre-Paretoan and Paretoan theory, system (4) allows the geometric interpretation that the line or plane (4b) touches the indifference curve or surface that passes through the optimal budget [see Fig. 1a]. Following up this interpretation, we are led to what is known as *consumption curves*. The income-consumption curve, say C_μ, is the curve that the optimal budget describes in the indifference map if we allow income μ to vary [see Fig. 1b, where C_μ happens to be a straight line]. In a similar way we may construct price-consumption curves [Ch. 5·2].

The primary purpose of Paretoan theory is to provide a psychological-behaviouristic interpretation of the concept of demand function, and to establish the general properties of demand functions [Chs. 4–7]. The applications of Paretoan theory further include the analysis of barter [Ch. 8·2] and the modern theory of consumer price indexes [Ch. 8·3]. On the whole it would seem that the Paretoan approach has not as yet been fully exploited by economic theory. In the theory of wage systems, for example, further results of relevance can no doubt be obtained by following up — theoretically and empirically — the approach in which indifference maps are used for the analysis of the balance between leisure and paid work time [cf Ch. 8·1].

Part II concentrates on those aspects of Paretoan theory that are of importance for empirical demand analysis, primarily the relations between demand elasticities [Chs. 6 and 7]. As regards the elasticity relations, these may serve as theoretical checks or tests on the empirical elasticities. Alternatively, in case the empirical material is not sufficient for the estimation of all the elasticities involved, such a relation can be employed as supplementary information in the empirical analysis. Devices of this type have been referred to in Chs. 2·2 (i) and 2·6 (i).

It was only gradually that Pareto came to realize that the theory of consumer demand could dispense with the idea of measurable utility, and his own work (1906) gives but the first elements of the ensuing theory of preference fields. An important contribution to the theory is due to E. Slutsky (1915), who deduced a set of general formulae for the change in the optimal budget w.r.t. infinitesimal changes in prices $p_1, \ldots, p_n$ and income μ. These formulae can be directly transformed to price and income elasticities [Ch. 4·5]. On this basis he deduced what has come to be known as Slutsky's relation [Ch. 5·3].

The later development of the theory has been somewhat disturbed and hampered by the confusing discussion of the so-called *integrability condition*.

Thus by a misunderstanding in its interpretation it has been argued that the integrability condition has something to do with the order in which the constituents $q_1, \ldots, q_n$ of the optimal budget are actually consumed by the consumer. As a consequence, the theory has given rise to a number of alternative approaches [Ch. 4·6]. On the one hand we note Pareto's outline of a theory of 'open cycles', and the related approach by Hicks and Allen which is based on the concept of marginal substitution. Another type of theory, which includes the approach of G. Cassel and, as a variation, P. A. Samuelson's theory of 'revealed preference', starts directly from the concept of demand function. Now, a correct subject-matter interpretation of the integrability condition shows it to be a fundamental theorem in the theory of preference fields, and further it follows that all of the alternative approaches become self-contradictory unless the integrability condition is included in the hypothetical set-up [Theorem 4·6·1]. Since the incorporation of the integrability condition makes the different approaches logically equivalent to the classical theory, we see that the resolution of the controversial issue has led to a unified theory of consumer demand, and that in the ensuing synthesis any of the approaches in question can be taken as a basis for the theory.

Pareto's theory provides us with a general theory of consumer demand. The three axioms from which the theory is developed in Part II are very simple, and seem quite natural as basic principles of economic behaviour [Ch. 4·2]. We note that the fundamental concept of an indifference map is established in a more direct way than would be possible from the alternative hypotheses just mentioned. As regards the demand function approach, this would be less appropriate for the additional reason that there are certain applications of preference field theory where demand functions play no part (in barter analysis, for example). The assumptions introduced in connexion with the axioms serve to simplify the theory. A first set of assumptions [Ch. 4·3] is such that the theory can be developed along classical lines, by the ordinary methods of infinitesimal calculus. A set of relaxed assumptions [Ch. 4·7] has for its purpose the generalization of classical theory so as to dismiss certain objections that are sometimes raised. Thus in reality, many, if not most, commodities appear in natural units, such as pieces of furniture, suits, etc., whereas they are in the theory subjected to infinitesimal changes. For another thing, the classical theory may seem to be over-rationalistic in its hypothesis of a preference field that rigorously and in minute detail rules the consumer's economic transactions. It turns out that the assumption of divisible units involves but a slight approximation in the structure of the preference field [Theorems 4·7·2–3]. Further it is shown that the main results of the theory remain valid if interpreted not as individual laws but as average tendencies in a group [Ch. 7·2; see also Ch. 7·6]. On the relaxed hypotheses, the theory will largely have to make use of geometric methods. As elsewhere in this volume, however, the assumptions do not aim at the greatest possible generality.

Pareto's theory of consumer demand is essentially a static approach: its primary purpose and natural scope are the analysis of stable patterns of behaviour. In Part II the theory is developed under strict adherence to static principles of analysis. As regards the development of a dynamic theory, reference is made to the recent work of J. S. Duesenberry (1949).[2] This is a theoretical and empirical study of savings, a theme where dynamic considerations come into the foreground, breaking the frame of a static approach. Since dynamic methods fall outside the programme of the present monograph, we shall not enter upon Duesenberry's analysis of savings, which is highly interesting in its constructive and unconventional approach. We note, however, that a main argument in his criticism of the classical theory of preference fields is not to the point. Thus he states that for the classical theory it is an essential hypothesis that the individual preferences are independent.[3] However, we show in Ch. 7·6 that interdependence can be assumed without impairing the general results of classical theory. Incidentally, this brings certain repercussions into the statistical analysis of family budget data, for as remarked in Ch. 2·5 (iv) the interdependence tends to invalidate the traditional tests of significance for regression coefficients.

Some further remarks on the scope and limitation of the theory of preference fields will be given in Ch. 3·5, the section entitled 'Theory and empiricism.'

2. Dynamic systems of the recursive type. – From the Cournot-Walras equilibrium up to the modern approaches of Keynes and others, the builders of economic theory have more and more set forth their ideas in terms of systems of theoretical relationships. Such systems are known as *economic models*. In Chs. 1·4 and 2·7 we have made acquaintance with economic models as a requisite in demand analysis, and in particular we have stressed the importance of models that have the form of recursive systems. It is characteristic of the approach based on recursive systems that it has come forth by a gradual process, by a sequence of contributions where economic and statistical ideas have been developed and coordinated, and where the basic principles and the general scope of the approach have only been brought out step by step. The present section attempts to give a brief survey of the many lines that run together in the approach of recursive systems.[1]

For a start, we shall consider three economic models in which demand functions are involved. Referring to (1·4·1) for the notations, the systems are

(1) $d = D(p)$ $s = S(p)$ $D(p^*) = S(p^*)$ (Cournot equilibrium);

(2) $d_t = D(p, a)$ $s_t = S(p, \beta)$ $d_t = s_t$ (moving equilibrium);

(3) $d_t = D(p_t)$ $s_t = S(p_{t-1})$ $d_t = s_t$ (cobweb theory).

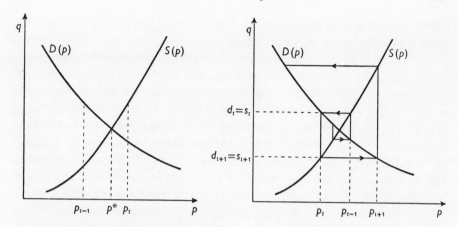

Fig. 3·2·1. Cournot's static equilibrium and related dynamic models.
a. Cournot's model (1) and the recursive   b. The cobweb model (3).
    model (1·4·1).

Relation (1c) determines the price $p=p^*$ for which demand and supply are in equilibrium [see Fig. 1a]. The model of Cournot (1838) was extended by Walras (1874) so as to give a static equilibrium system for all commodities in the market considered, with demand and supply functions assumed to be dependent upon the whole set of prices. The Cournot-Walras approach is a static theory, devised to explain the general experience that in a market of free competition we find, on the whole, stable prices and a stable balance between consumption and production. Here and in the following, the terms *static* and *dynamic* are taken in the traditional sense adopted from the natural sciences. Thus both types of approach are concerned with the active forces behind variable phenomena, and static theories deal with the special case when the phenomena are in a state of equilibrium.[1a]

Models (2)–(3) belong to approaches that foreshadow a fullfledged dynamic analysis. As mentioned in Ch. 2·7, the moving equilibrium model (2) is essentially due to H. L. Moore (1919), whereas model (3) germinates from A. Hanau (1927).[2] In (2) the demand and supply functions are variable, the parameters α, β shifting from period to period. In (3) the demand and supply functions are stable. For the interpretation of (3a–b) reference is made to the model (1·4·1), in which the demand and supply functions have been borrowed from this simple case of cobweb theory. Relations (2c) and (3c) are of the same type as (1c). Whereas (1c) does not specify the time required for reaching the equilibrium, (2)–(3) assume an *instantaneous* adjustment to equilibrium within each period t.

Models (3) and (1·4·1) are in agreement with the conclusion stated in Ch. 1·6, viz., that our empirical results invite us to regard the demand functions as a static element in a dynamic system. The difference between the two models lying in the third relation, we note that the substitution of (3c) by (1·4·1c) has improved the model in three respects. Firstly, as is well known from cobweb theory, the price development in model (3) will converge towards equilibrium or diverge with increasing oscillations according as the demand function is steeper or less steep than the supply function (the divergent case is illustrated in Fig. 1b). However, since increasing price oscillations have never been recorded in empirical observations, model (3) cannot be accepted as realistic. In model (1·4·1) the divergent case has been removed, for as illustrated in Fig. 1a it is easy to see that, whatever the slopes of the demand and supply functions, a sufficiently small γ will make the development converge towards the Cournot equilibrium, that is $p_t \to p^*$ as $t \to \infty$. Secondly, in (3) just as in (1)–(2) the relation (3c) determines price p_t implicitly as an *equilibrating variable*, while (1·4·1c) is an explicit relation that serves to explain the price movement. We see that the step from (3) to (1·4·1) is in line with the general device of P. A. Samuelson (1941; 1947) for the dynamization of equilibrium systems of the Cournot-Walras type. According to classical theory, an equilibrium like (1c) is reached by price adjustments, called forth by discrepancies between demand and supply. The classical theory makes no specified hypothesis about the adjustment process, but in Samuelson's theory the process is described explicitly by means of a formula. Samuelson considers infinitesimal price adjustments, whereas (1·4·1c) uses the finite difference $p_t - p_{t-1}$ for the same purpose.

The third advantage of model (1·4·1) is that all relations are causal. The difference lies in the third relation, which in all of models (1)–(3) is an equilibrium relation, and thus does not allow a causal interpretation. We have seen in Ch. 1·4 that model (1·4·1) may be taken to describe how the consumers, producers and retailers react to the changes in the explanatory variables. The three groups thus being regarded as the active forces behind the variable phenomena, we note that it is this interpretation that brings (1·4·1) to its full significance as a dynamic model.[3]

After these introductory distinctions between models of different type, let us turn to the general development of dynamic analysis.

In the years around 1930 a new epoch had begun for dynamic analysis in economics. The potentialities of a dynamic approach were first recognized in monetary theory. Foreshadowed by K. Wicksell's analysis of a cumulative process in interest theory (1898), the contributions of D. H. Robertson (1926) and E. Lindahl (1929; 1930) are among the pioneering works.[4] Cobweb theory, with its analysis of (3) and similar models, also did its part to display the advantages of dynamic systems. Thus started, dynamic approaches soon came into fashion, and further progress was made both applications and in methods. The typical device was to frame the analysis in terms of equation systems that are recursive in the sense of Ch. 1·4. This approach is in economics known under the name of *sequence analysis* or *process analysis*.[5] Of great importance are the works in which recursive models are used for a dynamization of Keynes' systems.[6]

The formal pattern of recursive models is clear from system (2·7·1). Referring to Tinbergen's arrow scheme [cf Fig. 1·4·1], the general pattern involves on the one hand lagged dependences, illustrated by arrows that point from the left to the right, either upwards, downwards, or horizontally, on the other hand non-lagged dependences, illustrated by arrows that point vertically downwards.

The logical pattern of recursive models is simple and natural. The relevant points are clear from the special cases in Ch. 1·4 and the comment in Ch. 2·7. Each relation of a recursive system is the formal representation of a unilateral causal dependence. The relations that constitute the system link the endogenous variables together into a *recursive causal chain* [Ch. 2·7 (i)]. Each link of the chain may further involve exogenous variables as causal factors. The causal factors not explicitly allowed for in a relation are summed up in a disturbance [cf (1·4·3)]. We note that a recursive system may include one or more relations that are exact by definition, for example

(4) $S_t = I_t - C_t,$ where S = savings, I = income, C = consumption.

According to the form of this relation, S is regarded as the dependent variable, the hypothesis being that S is causally generated as a remainder or residual between income and consumption.

A causal relation is ready for use as it stands; it enables us to estimate the effect variable when the explanatory variables are given. In the same sense, recursive systems are ready for use, since all of their relations are causal dependences. This is a fundamental point, for statistical relations in general are not exact, and we know that a disturbed relation does not permit an arbitrary choice if applied for estimating one of its variables in terms of the other ones [cf Chs. 2·2 (ii); 2·4 (ii) and 2·7 (i)]. Hence the causal interpretation is essential for making a relation fit for application.

As regards the notion of causal relation, some essential features were stressed by J. Tinbergen (1939), with special reference to economic relationships. A variable explained by a causal relationship should always refer to a distinct subject or group of subjects in the economic sphere, the purpose of the relation being to describe how the group reacts to changes in the explanatory variables. Such a group is called a *behaving unit*.[7] Furthermore, the relations involved in an economic model should be *autonomous* in the sense that the behaving units should be able to shift their reaction pattern without the shift necessarily changing the other relations of the system. For example, in the system (1·4·1) the three relations refer to the consumers, the producers, and the retailers, these behaving units being more or less autonomous in a market of free competition. If we consider a monopolistic market, we may replace (1·4·1 b) and (1·4·1 c) by relations that describe the monopolistic price and production policy, whereas (1·4·1 a) remains the same as for a free market.

Summing up, we see that the causal interpretation of recursive systems in terms of autonomous behaving units is of essential relevance from the viewpoint of theory as well as applications. On the one hand, it specifies the active forces to which the system refers as a dynamic model; on the other, it specifies how the system can be used for the purpose of estimation and prediction.

The concept of causality is involved in highly controversial questions in philosophical literature: the questions about its general scope, its relation to free will, etc. It is indeed remarkable what a mess the human mind has been able to make of the answers. The causal interpretation of economic-statistical relationships, however, is by no means burdened by implications in this direction. All we need is a definition of causality that refers to the clear-cut relationship between the controlled variables and the effect variable in ordinary scientific experiments. In Ch. 3·5 we shall return to this point for a few remarks from the viewpoint of the general theory of knowledge.

If in econometric literature the idea of causal interpretation of the theoretical relationships has sometimes been disregarded on purpose, as in the approach of structural systems [cf Ch. 2·4 (iii) and 2·7 (i)], it seems possible that part of the explanation lies in a sound desire to keep away from philosophical notions which are controversial and of doubtful relevance. As we have seen, however, this would be to throw away the baby with the bath-water.

Having now examined the recursive systems from the viewpoint of their logical structure and operational meaning, we turn to the contributions that have their source in the theory of probability. The primary reference is here to the works of G. U. Yule (1927) and E. Slutsky (1927). The common starting point is that variation and cycles in time-series can be generated as the cumulative effect of random disturbances or 'shocks'. A special case of Yule's approach is

$$(5) \qquad\qquad y_t = b_1 y_{t-1} + b_2 y_{t-2} + z_t \qquad\qquad t = 0, \pm 1, \pm 2, \ldots$$

Here y_t is the autoregressive series, this being generated by the series z_t, which is supposed to be a purely random sequence. Yule gives the instructive illustration in which y_t describes the movement of a pendulum that is kept swinging by a stream of random shocks z_t. Generally speaking, y_t will follow the natural swings of the pendulum, but the random shocks will produce gradual shifts in amplitude and phase. Yule applies his scheme to the irregular 11-year cycle of sunspot intensity, and his general conclusions stress the wide scope of the approach and the possibility of application in other fields [see Ch. 10·4]. The first explicit reference to economic applications is due to

R. Frisch, who in an influential paper (1933) emphasized Yule's approach as a theoretical model for the business cycle.

Yule's autoregressive scheme (5) is formally of the same type as the recursive relations (2·7·1). In a study by the author (1938), the autoregressive scheme was linked up with the theory of stochastic processes of the stationary type. These matters will be dealt with more in detail in Chs. 10 and 12·6–7. Among the results along this line we note a theorem on the 'resolving power' of linear recursive systems [Theorem 12·7·1]. This theorem displays the general scope of such systems. We have seen in the above discussion that the causal interpretation of theoretical relations places the economist under the onus of building his models in accordance with recursive systems (2·7·1) or corresponding nonlinear systems. Now according to the theorem on resolving power, this onus in itself is not heavy. In fact, given *any* set of stationary time-series, we can to any desired degree of approximation use a suitable linear recursive system for the formal representation of the given series, and the representation can be arranged in agreement with the usual noncorrelation hypotheses on the disturbances.

It must be stressed that the representation yielded by the resolving power theorem is a formal one, which does not necessarily correspond to the causal structure of the phenomena under analysis. Specifically, a realistic model of the causal structure may involve bi- or multilateral interdependence, nonlinear relationships, fractional lags, and so on. All of these complications require special attention in the application of the recursive systems to empirical data.

Turning finally to the statistical aspects of dynamic analysis, the coordination between theoretical and empirical inference will in practice be systematic and complete to a varying degree. As in Cournot's equilibrium theory, the empirical substance may enter by way of general experience, in setting the theoretical problem and confirming the theoretical conclusions. On the other hand there are approaches which are mainly empirical, such as Mitchell's business cycle approach, which have for their programme the establishment of statistical regularities, with a minimum of theoretical treatment. From the viewpoint of statistical theory, the ideal is that the economic analysis is framed in a system of hypothetical relationships, and that statistical data are used for testing the hypotheses and estimating their numerical parameters.[8] The investigations of Tinbergen (1939; 1940) referred to above are pioneering endeavours to coordinate theory and empiricism in line with this ideal programme. A characteristic feature of Tinbergen's approach has already been mentioned: his models are recursive in the sense of Ch. 1·4, the relations thus in the linear case being of type (2·7·1), and each relation being interpreted as representing a causal dependence. As regards the statistical technique, Tinbergen adopts the traditional method of least-squares regression.

Tinbergen's studies have not escaped criticism. The great ambition manifested is beyond praise, but some doubts have been raised as regards results and conclusions. Thus it has been argued that the hypothetical relationships are highly tentative, and that the statistical material is too weak as a basis for estimating the very large number of relations and parameters involved. However, it would fall outside the scope of the present survey to enter upon a general appraisal of Tinbergen's investigations.[9] Our interest is here limited to the rationale of the statistical method he has adopted, the question being whether regression analysis is legitimate for investigations of this kind.

Having dealt with this question in detail in Ch. 2·7, we shall not dwell further on the matter. It will only be repeated that in the application of least-squares regression it is not of relevance whether the relation under analysis is single or a member of a system, provided the system is recursive. For the regression to give unbiased estimates the essential condition is in any case that the disturbance of the hypothetical relation is uncorrelated with the explanatory variables.

Our survey of recursive systems has now come to an end. We have seen that there are several features that combine to make the recursive systems a most natural tool for dynamic analysis. Logically, they are the general form for models that are constructed as a chain of causation. Formally, they are of very general scope, and in particular they are applicable to any set of stationary time-series. As regards the applications, they require no further specification, it being immediately obvious how they should be used for the purpose of estimation and prediction. Statistically, they are simple to handle, since unbiased and consistent estimates for their parameters can be obtained by ordinary regression analysis. In view of these properties it is no wonder that the approach of recursive systems is the traditional method of dynamic analysis in economics and econometrics. This does not imply, of course, that the recursive systems should be used under all circumstances. Thus in Ch. 1·2–3, for example, we have seen cases where a unilateral causal dependence is more or less blurred by a tendency to a bi- or multilateral interdependence, and in Ch. 2·7 we have touched upon the possibility of constructing a mixed model by combining causal dependences and equilibrium relations. With reference to these situations a few supplementary approaches will be considered in Part IV by way of exercises [Exs. IV, 30–32].

3. Probability theory. Stochastic processes. – In demand analysis, probability theory forms one of the fundamental mathematical tools in much the same way as infinitesimal calculus. Specifically, probability arguments are employed in the following contexts. (A) In the theory of consumer demand, to widen the scope of the theory of preference fields. (B) In the theory of economic models, and in particular in the theory of recursive systems. (C) In the sampling theory of least-squares regression. The present section will briefly outline the nature of the probability arguments that come into play.

What is referred to in (A) is the possibility of making allowance for random features in consumer behaviour [Ch. 7·6]. The argument is that owing to the law of large numbers the individual randomness will under general conditions become negligible when forming market totals, with the result that the main theorems of the Paretoan approach will hold good in the sense of average laws for the entire market. As a consequence, when in Paretoan theory the basic psychological assumptions are stated with reference to an individual consumer, as done in Ch. 4·2, the minute rationalism postulated is not essential for the theory. It does not require much experience to see that approximations of this type are frequent in the applications of mathematical analysis. The arrangement is legitimate because the individual randomness is of secondary interest, and because great advantages are gained as regards mathematical convenience as well as in making the approach clear and simple.

The issues under (B) and (C) have been dealt with in some detail in Chs. 2·5, 2·7 and 3·2. We have seen that in the study of these matters a fundamental part is played by the theory of stochastic processes. What is of relevance is primarily certain aspects of processes of the stationary type. A brief survey of the field being given in Part III and Chs. 12·5–6 and 13·4, we shall here make a few introductory comments.

In accordance with the general theory of statistical inference, we may distinguish between three problems in the analysis of time-series data, (a) the specification of hypotheses, (b) the testing of hypotheses, and (c) the estimation of parameters. Generally speaking, the hypotheses specify a probability model for the given data. In time-series analysis, the probability models take the form of stochastic processes.

What makes time-series analysis a specialized branch of statistics is that with different types of time-series the questions put to the data are entirely different, and so are the statistical methods for their treatment. This fact is reflected in the probability models, the various types of stochastic process being fundamentally different. Hence the specification of hypotheses comes into the foreground of interest, and the primary concern is to reveal the structure of the time-series under analysis. It will be observed that this makes a shift in emphasis as compared with other fields of statistical inference. In time-series analysis it is an essential prerequisite to have a working knowledge of the main types of stochastic process that may possibly serve as hypotheses for the phenomenon under consideration, and in particular we must know which types of question can be answered by the data on the basis of the alternative hypotheses.

The modern development of probability theory as founded on Kolmogorov's system of axioms (1933) has provided the proper tools for dealing with time-series problems. Ch. 9·2 recalls the definition of a stochastic process with discrete time-parameter, briefly a *discrete* process. This being the general probability model for time-series given as observations at equidistant time points, we shall limit our attention to discrete processes. For the applications it involves no restriction not to allow time to vary continuously. Stochastic processes, however, become much simpler to deal with if time is regarded as a discrete variable. We see that the situation is different from calculus, where infinitesimals are often simpler to handle than finite differences.

The discrete process is simply a joint probability distribution which specifies not a finite number of random variables but an infinite sequence of variables. In this generalization none of the fundamental properties of ordinary probability distributions are lost. Specifically, formulae (9·1·10) for conditional expectations remain the same. A *realization* of a process is what corresponds to a single sample value of a random variable or a single sample vector of an n-dimensional probability distribution. An observed time-series thus is conceived of as a realization of the theoretical process.

Time-series may be roughly classified in two broad categories, *stationary* or *evolutive*. In stationary series, the fluctuations up and down may seem random or show tendencies to regularity, but on the whole the structure of the variations is the same in different sections of the series. In evolutive series, different sections are dissimilar in one or more respects; e.g., a logistic curve passing from one level to another is evolutive.

Ch. 9·3 gives the general definition of a *stationary* process. In correspondence with the empirical concept of stationarity, the theoretical definition (9·3·2) requires that time should play the passive role of a medium in which the realizations develop. The fundamental types of stationary process are reviewed in Ch. 10. First we have the *purely random process*. This is formed by a sequence of independent random variables with the same distribution; e.g. a sequence of dice throws will give a realization of such a process. A number of classical theorems in probability theory give information on the purely random process. Next we have the process which is defined as a *moving summation* on the basis of a purely random process. The process of moving summation covers two important types of process, special cases of which were first considered by G. U. Yule (1921, 1926, 1927), viz. on the one hand any finite moving summation of a purely random process, on the other hand the autoregressive process [cf (3·2·5)]. Finally we note the *harmonic process*; here each realization allows the functional representation as a sum of ordinary sine waves.

The stationary process thus displays a number of special types which are of undamentally different structure. As a consequence, the theory of the stationary process provides a unified treatment of a number of approaches in time-series analysis that have earlier been isolated. This is perhaps surprising at first sight, since the definition of stationarity (9·3·2) may seem to imply a severe limitation on the structure of the observational time-series. In Ch. 12·5–7 the situation is examined from the viewpoint of linear prediction. At the one extreme we have the purely random process, which is perfectly non-deterministic in the sense that the past development of a realization gives no clue whatever for the prediction of its future path. At the other extreme is the harmonic process, which is perfectly deterministic inasmuch as the entire future development can be forecasted with complete exactness. For the process of moving summation, forecasts of limited efficiency can be obtained.

From the viewpoint of linear prediction, the special processes considered in Ch. 10·1–3 exhaust the scope of the stationary process. This is seen from Theorem 12·6·1, which will be referred to as the theorem of 'predictive decomposition'. According to this theorem, any stationary process can be split up into the sum of two uncorrelated processes, called the *nondeterministic* and the *deterministic components*, which as far as linear prediction is concerned are similar to the process of moving summation and the harmonic process, respectively. The decomposition theorem is closely related to the theorem on the 'resolving power' of recursive systems that was referred to in Chs. 2·7 and 3·2 [Theorem 12·7·1]. As a matter of fact, the first step in the decomposition theorem makes use of regression analysis with the past variables as regressors, and a similar application of regression analysis to a system of stationary processes gives immediately the 'resolving power' theorem.

Each of the two theorems mentioned can be obtained in two versions, the one referring to the sequence of random variables that constitute the process dealt with, the other one referring to a single realization of the process. The dualism between the two versions is a feature which is of general scope in the theory of stationary processes. The simplest case in point is the double interpretation of a mean value. Thus on the one hand we have the 'phase average' that is formed as an average for a single realization, on the other hand the 'space average' given by the mathematical expectation of the random variable that is associated with a specified time point. The two averages may or may not be equal. They are so if the process considered is *ergodic*. This again is an important concept in the theory of stationary processes, since the properties of an ergodic process may be deduced from a single realization. Ch. 9·4 recalls the definition of ergodicity and gives a few comments.

In the analysis of time-series data, the theory of stochastic processes raises new problems under the headings of hypothesis testing and estimation of parameters. Several types of processes being available as probability models for a given series, we see that there is a great number of possible hypotheses and counter-hypotheses to explore. In view of the arbitrary number of parameters and the fundamental difference in structure between different processes, it is further clear that the problems are by no means easy. In the wide field thus opened up for investigation, several different approaches have been suggested, and the research is in rapid progress. Ch. 11 gives a brief account of the methods recently developed by P. Whittle (1951). In the present work, Whittle's methods have been applied to the correlograms employed in our general formula (2·5·2) for the standard error of a regression coefficient.

4. Statistical methods. – If we regard scientific research as a production process, the statistical methods enter among the prefabricates. To obtain a finished scientific product, the statistical methods have to be coordinated with other scientific material in much the same way as the different parts of an automobile are put together on the assembly line. Like an unspecified prefabricate, say a ball-bearing, every statistical method has its range of applications, and in each and every problem of statistical analysis the primary thing is to find a method that is appropriate for the specific purpose at issue.

In Ch. 2 we have discussed the rationale of the method of least-squares regression. We have seen that the method has a wide range of application, and in particular we have stressed its legitimacy for the purpose of establishing causal relationships, i.e. relations that explain one variable as a function of one or more other variables. We need not repeat that causal relations are of central importance in economic analysis, in theory as well as in the applications. Other types of relation, however, are also encountered in economic analysis, e.g. equilibrium relations, and here the least-squares regression in general does not apply, at least not in the same direct manner. It may be remarked that this limitation in the scope of regression analysis must not in itself be regarded as a disadvantage. To follow up the simile of a production process, the situation is analogous to the production of cars for different purposes. Causal relations forming the highway of economic analysis, it is a good thing that a method is available for this highway, just as there is great demand for ordinary cars but little demand for amphibious cars which have the advantage that they can make their way on land as well as water, but are inefficient in ordinary traffic.

With respect to the applications of regression analysis, the discussion in Ch. 2 is of general scope. When applied for the purpose of demand analysis, specific problems are encountered. Chs. 14 and 15 deal with a number of such questions. Thus in the treatment of family budget data we have several questions about the proper measurement of the variables: whether the income variable should be taken to be total expenditure or earned income; whether the specific items or item groups of the budget should be measured in quantities or in money expenditure; whether the family size should be measured in terms of consumer units, and what scale is appropriate for the purpose. As regards market statistics we note the question of whether trends should be removed before starting the regression analysis, the question of whether nominal or real prices should be used, and the distinction between demand reactions that take place immediately and those that manifest themselves only after a period of adjustment, briefly the distinction between short term and long term reactions. There is further the important problem of the coordination of income elasticities, viz., whether there is any systematic difference between income elasticities derived from family budget data and market statistics.

In Ch. 2·9 we stated as a final conclusion that least-squares regression as traditionally applied in demand analysis is essentially sound. The issues of Chs. 14 and 15 give us no reason to doubt this conclusion. On the contrary, they give further evidence of how naturally the least-squares method adapts itself to the different problems in question.

5. Theory and empiricism. – The theme of the present chapter has been to examine demand analysis from the viewpoints of economics, probability theory, and statistics, with special reference to how demand analysis stands in relation to the general methods and lines of approach in these sciences. In this final section we shall adopt a still wider perspective, giving a few comments on demand analysis from the viewpoint of the general theory of knowledge. The standpoint adopted will be that of *logical empiricism*.[1] We take this as a general name for the antimetaphysical approaches in modern theory of knowledge. These aim at a realistic description and analysis of how science actually works, in contradistinction to earlier philosophizing systems that tried to develop the theory of knowledge on the basis of principles metaphysical or suprascientific ('cogito ergo sum', 'das Ding an sich', and so on).

It is a fundamental principle in science to keep apart on the one side what is fact, empirical observations, and on the other side what is theory, speculative thoughts. First embodied in Euclid's geometry, the principle has in the modern era become appreciated and accepted as a norm in more and more branches of science. A case in point is the device of hypothesis testing in modern statistics. We have here on the one hand the theoretical hypothesis, on the other the empirical observations against which the hypothesis is tested. In logical empiricism the principle in question constitutes a cornerstone.

Euclidean geometry and Newtonian mechanics, to mention only two instances, are theories that appear in axiomatic form. In axiomatic theories the separation of theoretical and empirical elements is carried to the extreme. Thus in any axiomatic theory of empirical phenomena there are four main parts or phases: (a) the introduction, indicating in common-sense terms which category of phenomena is the object of the theory, (b) the axioms, a number of propositions adopted as a priori truths about the phenomena under analysis, (c) the theorems, which are deduced on the sole basis of the axioms, by the tools of logic and mathematics, (d) the testing of the theory, by confronting its results with empirical evidence. In the theories of empirical phenomena, the axioms may in general be regarded as having been abstracted from experience. We note that for one and the same theory the axioms can usually be chosen in different ways. Thus for example, as shown in Ch. 4·6, the Paretoan theory can alternatively be based on axioms that refer to the consumer's order of preferences, to his marginal substitution rates, or to his demand functions. Further we note that the deduction of theorems without any reference to empirical observations or findings is an expository arrangement that has nothing to do with the historical development of the theory. Actual research is a mixed and irregular process where empirical and theoretical approaches are used simultaneously, giving guidance and support to each other.

Exactness and clarity are obvious advantages of the axiomatic form of theory. A beautiful example is given by Kolmogorov's axioms (1933) for probability theory; on the firm basis thus established the theory has entered a phase of forceful expansion. Another important advantage of axiomatic theories lies in the economy of thought that is gained when seemingly different theories are *isomorphous*, i.e., mathematically equivalent. The two theories may then be regarded as two aspects of a general body of theorems, and any theorem in one of the theories may be obtained as an immediate corollary of a corresponding theorem in the other, simply by rephrasing in a different terminology. Kolmogorov's probability axioms are a striking instance, these being isomorphous with additive measure theory. The theory of Hilbert space exhibits many cases of isomorphism.[2] Two of these are employed in Ch. 12. Thus, the elementary formulae for least-squares approximation are developed in (real) Hilbert space and then reinterpreted in terms of probability distributions and statistical scatters, respectively, so as to give the familiar formulae of least-squares regression. Similarly, the isomorphism between a stationary process (10·1·1) and a stationary sequence of type (12·7·6) is utilized in Ch· 12·7 to obtain dual versions of the theorems on predictive decomposition and on the resolving power of recursive systems.

Axiomatic theory is an ideal, but to display its advantages in full the theory must be simple. When a theory has to make allowance for a great many factors of different nature in order to be sufficiently realistic, an axiomatic approach would become highly complex, and instead of clarity its exactness would lead to abstruseness and lack of perspicuity. For this reason it would be a hopeless task to develop an axiomatic system for the whole of a science like economics with its manifold of institutional features and interacting forces. In such cases the axiomatic approach may still be used with advantage for a limited sector of the field. For example, as shown in Part II, the Paretoan theory of consumer demand can be developed on the basis of three simple and natural axioms. As is well known, the theory of consumer demand is mathematically equivalent to the elements of the theory of production; it is easy to see how the axioms of Ch. 4·2 should be reinterpreted in order to bring out the equivalence as a genuine isomorphism [cf Ex. II, 60].[3]

Any theory has to be modified or discarded (a) if it is logically inconsistent, or (b) if it does not fit the observed facts. A case of inconsistency is pointed out in Ch. 4·6, it being shown that the integrability condition is an indispensable hypothesis if we choose to base the theory of consumer demand on the concept of marginal substitution rates, or alternatively on the concept of individual demand functions. As regards (b), the emphasis is on the authority of observations. Thus, if there are systematic deviations of theory from the facts, it is the theory that must give way, not the facts. Or in the words of Montesquieu: *"Les observations sont l'histoire de la physique, les systèmes en sont la fable."*

On the other hand, deliberate simplification is an essential feature of any theory. It is necessary to simplify in order to grasp and master the chaos of details that build up the real world. Every scientific approach, however refined, involves several types of theoretical simplification, such as the basic device of forming general empirical categories by disregarding the differences between individual elements, or at a higher level the more or less approximate theories set forth to explain the properties of these categories. Thus in regression analysis, for example, only the main factors that influence the phenomenon investigated are taken explicitly into consideration, and their influence is usually assumed to be linear in their effects. In some theories a high degree of accuracy is essential; in other cases we may rest satisfied with a simple theory although there are large, perhaps even systematic, deviations from the observations. The decisive test of the theory is whether in practice it actually works for the purpose for which it is intended. Thus, if a theory gives useful results, there is no point in criticizing it merely on the ground that a more refined theory is available. The road of improvement has no end. Even the refined theory can be made more elaborate by making allowance for features that have been disregarded.

Let us examine the axioms for the Paretoan theory which are given in Ch. 4·2. From the viewpoint of experimental psychology the axioms are meaningful in the behaviouristic sense. In fact, we see that in principle they can be tested by observing the consumer's actual reaction in different situations involving choice. A controlled experiment performed for the purpose may show that his order of preferences is subject to trends in time as well as random fluctuations. Anyhow, the axioms are natural as hypotheses concerning the consumer's behaviour in actual choice situations, and it is obvious that they form an approximation to reality. It is interesting to compare this approach with the system of axioms established by R. Frisch (1926) for the pre-Paretoan theory of demand. The essential axiom here is that the consumer has an order of preferences for alternative changes in the budget. Thus if we take an example from the theory in Ch. 8·1, let us consider on the one hand the change from a budget A of 100 units of consumption goods and 15 hours of leisure to a budget B of 125 units and 16 hours, on the other hand a change from C of 150 units and 16 hours to D of 180 units and 17 hours. Then the axioms of Ch. 4·2 refer to a choice between any two *budgets*, say between A and B, whereas Frisch's axiom assumes that the consumer is able to decide which of the two *changes* he would prefer. We see that Frisch's axiom is not meaningful in the behaviouristic sense, for the consumer cannot in the same experiment be in possession of two different budgets, and so in principle it is not possible to observe how he would actually choose between prescribed changes in the two budgets.[4] This being so, the theory will involve certain notions that in principle cannot be linked up with empirical observations. In pre-Paretoan theory of demand, this is the case with the notion of marginal utility, including the marginal utility of money. The conclusion is that Frisch's axiom is not a genuine approximation towards reality; it has instead the character of an arbitrary or gratuitous assumption.

Other things being equal, a theory that approaches reality is better than a theory based on gratuitous assumptions. This is not to say, however, that gratuitous assumptions make a theory void of interest or importance. Such a theory, especially if developed in axiomatic form, may have the didactic advantage of a clear and rigorous exposition. Further it may be of considerable interest if it displays the implications of seemingly innocent assumptions. As regards Frisch's axiomatic treatment of the pre-Paretoan theory, this has the distinct merit of having shown that the concept of measurable utility is implied in his axiom of alternative changes. We note that the situation is similar in the axiom system for preference fields given by J. von Neumann and O. Morgenstern (1944). The axioms are here behaviouristic, but the chance element introduced in the consumer's budget choices are subjected to arbitrary restrictions that make the theory of doubtful relevance from the viewpoint of the applications [Ch. 7·6]. Reference may further be made to the theories of welfare economics. Whether the theory is based on the concept of utility or we consider the modern approach in terms of welfare functions, the basic assumptions of welfare economics are not meaningful in the behaviouristic sense. Yet the theory is of interest, especially in the axiomatic form developed by K. J. Arrow (1951); not as an approximation towards reality, however, but rather because it gives a general device for the interpretation and logical scrutiny of ethical systems.[5]

In accordance with the introductory reference, the above remarks on the axiomatic approach are in line with the general theory of knowledge as embodied in logical empiricism. The same explicit reference applies to the whole of the present work, inasmuch as arguments of a common-sense nature are involved. Specifically, we have tried to adhere to the basic principles of logical empiricism in Ch. 2, in our critical examination of regression methods. There is one passage, however, where no guidance has been obtained from logical empiricism. This is the treatment in Ch. 2·2 of causal analysis, and in particular our specification of the term causal dependence.

In ordinary as well as scientific language there are a great many words that are related to the notion of causality, such as dependence, y is a function of x, influence, agent, and so on. In the philosophical literature the discussion of causality and related notions suffers from the fact that it is not based on an explicit definition of causality.[6] Now in regression analysis there is need for a clear-cut definition of causality that conforms with its actual usage in science and ordinary language. In the definition attempted in Ch. 2·2, the controlled experiment is taken as the reference situation in specifying the concept of causal dependence. The simplest types of controlled experiment are universally known, and the distinction between cause and effect is here clear enough to indicate the meaning of causal dependence. In principle, of course, our definition is not new, and in particular it is in agreement with current practice in regression analysis. It is clearly so in the analysis of experimental data, and as regards nonexperimental data we have seen in Ch. 2·2 that regression analysis by analogy follows the same logical pattern. Further we note that the definition suggested conforms with the notion of causality as used in the natural sciences,[7] and also, it would seem, with the common-sense meaning of the term in ordinary language.

It should here be remembered that thanks to R. A. Fisher's device of randomization the scope of controlled experiment as an instrument for causal analysis has been radically extended. The typical situation in the classical experiments is that the relation between cause and effect is exact or nearly exact in the functional sense. At a later stage (Legendre, Gauss), observational errors and random disturbances were allowed for so as to give statistical instead of functional relationships. By Fisher's randomization procedure, the wide sphere of biological variation was brought under the routine of controlled experiment.

In conclusion, it would seem that our definition of causal dependence is sufficiently precise for the purpose of regression analysis, and that the definition is in line with the traditional usage of the term in this field. It may be that the definition suggested has a much wider scope, and even that it can be accepted as a perfectly general definition of causality.

PART II

The Paretoan theory of consumer demand

Chapter 4.

INDIVIDUAL PREFERENCE FIELDS

1. Basic concepts.[1] – The economic concepts dealt with in this chapter are specified as follows.

a. There is a fixed number of different commodities (including services), say n, each of which is assumed to have a well-defined unit of measure.

b. The prices of unit measure of each commodity are, in terms of the monetary unit,

$$p_1, \ldots, p_n.$$

c. The prices are assumed to be positive,

(1) $$p_i > 0 \qquad\qquad i = 1, \ldots, n.$$

d. A budget alternative

$$q = (q_1, \ldots, q_n),$$

or briefly a *budget* q, is composed of specified quantities of the commodities. The q_i are called *budget components*, and are by definition nonnegative,

(2) $$q_i \geq 0 \qquad\qquad i = 1, \ldots, n.$$

It is often convenient to think of the budgets q as points in an n-dimensional Euclidean space, the *budget space*, denoted Ω. If two budgets $q^{(1)}$, $q^{(2)}$ satisfy the inequalities

$$q_i^{(1)} \geq q_i^{(2)} \qquad (i = 1, \ldots, n); \qquad q_1^{(1)} + \cdots + q_n^{(1)} > q_1^{(2)} + \cdots + q_n^{(2)}$$

we say that $q^{(1)}$ is *larger* than $q^{(2)}$, and that $q^{(2)}$ is *smaller* than $q^{(1)}$.

e. The budget alternatives refer to a fixed individual, called the *consumer*.

f. The budget alternatives cover a fixed period of time, called the *budget period*; for instance, the first week of October, 1950.

g. The consumer has a positive sum, called *income*, of say μ monetary units, at his disposal for purchases during the budget period. By definition,

$$\mu > 0.$$

2. Axioms of economic behaviour. – The following three axioms form the basis of the subsequent theory.[1]

Axiom of comparison. *The consumer has a definite order of preferences in the following sense. Letting $q^{(1)}$ and $q^{(2)}$ be two arbitrary budget alternatives, three cases are possible: $q^{(1)}$ is preferred to $q^{(2)}$, or $q^{(2)}$ is preferred to $q^{(1)}$, or $q^{(1)}$ and $q^{(2)}$ are equivalent ($=$ indifferent).*

Commodities as ruled by an order of preferences are called a *preference field*.

Axiom of transitivity. *The order of preferences is logically consistent in the following sense: If $q^{(1)}$ is equivalent (preferred, disfavoured) to $q^{(2)}$, and $q^{(2)}$ equivalent (pref., disf.) to $q^{(3)}$, then $q^{(1)}$ is equivalent (pref., disf.) to $q^{(3)}$.*

The set of budget alternatives that are equivalent to a budget q is called the *locus of indifference* of q. The loci of indifference constitute the *indifference map* of the consumer [cf Fig. 3·1·1].

Axiom of choice. *The consumer chooses a budget which is preferred to any other budget that he can obtain, provided such a budget exists.*

A budget preferred to any other alternative the consumer can obtain is called an *optimal budget*. A set of equivalent budgets preferred to any other budget he can obtain is called an *optimal budget set*.

3. Regularity assumptions.[1] – To be able to apply the ordinary tools of mathematical analysis we must require that the preference fields present some degree of orderliness, are not too irregular. We shall now impose three assumptions that allow us to develop the theory along classical lines. Later on we shall see that the main results of the theory can be established under considerably relaxed hypotheses [Ch. 4·7–8, Ch. 7·6].

A. Assumption of non-satiety. *A larger budget is always preferred to a smaller one.*

By this assumption, all loci of indifference reduce to $(n-1)$-dimensional surfaces, called *indifference surfaces*. Clearly we have

THEOREM 1. *Through every point q of the budget space there passes one, and only one, indifference surface.*

B. Assumption of continuity. *Let $q^{(1)}$, $q^{(2)}$, $q^{(3)}$ be any budgets such that $q^{(1)}$ is preferred to $q^{(2)}$, and $q^{(2)}$ to $q^{(3)}$. Let L be the line in the budget space that connects $q^{(1)}$ with $q^{(3)}$. Then L passes through a budget q that is equivalent to $q^{(2)}$.*

By this assumption we make sure that the loci of indifference will never take the form of surface fragments. As an immediate consequence we also obtain

THEOREM 2. *The indifference surface of an arbitrary budget q divides the budget space in one upper and one lower part, called the* preference *and* disfavour region *of q, the upper part being formed by budgets preferred to q, the lower by budgets disfavoured to q.*

Given a function $f(q_1, \ldots, q_n)$, the locus of points $q = (q_1, \ldots, q_n)$ such that

$$f(q_1, \ldots, q_n) = c,$$

where c is a constant, forms a well-defined point set in the budget space. The system of such loci obtained for different c-values is called the *level map* of f. We shall now prove

THEOREM 3. *Any indifference map allows the representation of a level map, say*

(1) $$U(q_1, \ldots, q_n) = c, \qquad briefly \quad U(q) = c,$$

where c ranges continuously from 0 to ∞, and U is a well-defined function that is continuous and increasing in each variable q_i.

To establish (1) we require merely a rule giving the value of $U(q)$ at every point q. Let L be that straight line through the origin of the budget space which forms equal angles with all coordinate axes. Now if $q = (q_1, \ldots, q_n)$ is an arbitrary budget in the budget space, there is according to Assumptions A–B one, and only one, budget q^* on L that is equivalent to q. Writing $c(q^*)$ for the distance from q^* to the origin, let $U(q)$ be defined by making

$$U(q_1, \ldots, q_n) = c(q^*), \qquad briefly \quad U(q_1, \ldots, q_n) = c.$$

The function $U(q)$ will clearly fulfil the requirements of the theorem, which thereby is proved.

Considering an arbitrary indifference map and the corresponding representation (1), let $\Psi(x)$ be any increasing function. Writing

(2) $$\Psi(U(q_1, \ldots, q_n)) = U^*(q_1, \ldots, q_n),$$

the same map allows the representation

$$U^*(q_1, \ldots, q_n) = c.$$

A function $U^*(q_1, \ldots, q_n)$ of type (2), of which (1) is a special case, is called a *preference index-function* of the consumer, or briefly a *preference function*.[2]

C. Assumption of differentiability. *The preference function $U(q)$ ·as defined by (1) has continuous derivatives of first and second order.*

We shall use the following notation for the derivatives,

$$\frac{\partial U}{\partial q_i} = U_i(q_1, \ldots, q_n); \qquad \frac{\partial^2 U}{\partial q_i \, \partial q_k} = U_{ik}(q_1, \ldots, q_n) \qquad i, k = 1, \ldots, n$$

or briefly U_i and U_{ik}. By Assumption A,

$$U_i > 0 \qquad\qquad i = 1, \ldots, n.$$

Summing up, Assumptions A–B imply that the loci of indifference form a system of $(n-1)$-dimensional surfaces that fills the entire budget space. By Assumption C, these surfaces will be twice differentiable. The first derivatives will be positive, but the second derivatives may have any sign.

4. Balance planes and optimal budgets.[1] – Given the prices $p_1, \ldots, p_n$, a consumer with income μ can afford to buy such budget alternatives as satisfy

(1) $$p_1 q_1 + \cdots + p_n q_n \leq \mu.$$

The plane

(2) $$p_1 q_1 + \cdots + p_n q_n = \mu$$

is called a *balance plane*.

If the region (1) contains an optimal budget, the consumer will, by the axiom of choice, buy this budget. If the region contains an optimal budget set, his purchase will be regarded as undetermined. We have

THEOREM 1. *Given an arbitrary preference field, the region (1) contains an optimal budget, or possibly an optimal budget set. This budget or these budgets lie in the balance plane (2).*

In fact, if a budget q lies in the region (1) but not in the plane (2), there will by Assumption A be a budget in (2) that is preferred to q. It remains to show that a maximum of $U(q)$ is actually attained at one or more points of (2). This, however, is a consequence of the facts that the balance plane according to (4·1·2) is a closed point set, and that $U(q)$ is a continuous function of every q_i.

THEOREM 2. *In order that a budget*

(3) $$q^0 = (q_1^0, \ldots, q_n^0) \quad with \quad q_1^0 > 0, \ldots, q_n^0 > 0$$

should be optimal in the region (1), or belong to the optimal budget set, it is necessary that the indifference surface that passes through q^0 should have (2) for tangent plane at q^0. For a budget q^0 where one or more q_i^0 are zero, the condition of optimality is the same, except that the notion of tangent plane then refers to the subspace formed by the nonvanishing q_i.

This theorem is an immediate consequence of the geometric interpretation of the loci of indifference. We note that the condition stated is necessary and sufficient for $U(q)$ to attain an extremum at q^0. The extremum may be a minimum, and since this does not make an optimal budget, the condition is necessary but not sufficient.

In analytical formulation the condition of optimality is that $U(q)$ should be a maximum, subject to the side condition (2). Hence, forming

$$U(q_1, \ldots, q_n) - \lambda(p_1 q_1 + \cdots + p_n q_n - \mu),$$

where λ is a Lagrange multiplier, the derivatives of this expression must vanish at q^0 if this is to be optimal. This gives the necessary conditions

$$U_i(q_1^0, \ldots, q_n^0) - \lambda p_i = 0 \qquad\qquad i = 1, \ldots, n$$

and so we have

THEOREM 3. *In order that a budget q^0 as specified by (3) should be optimal or belong to the optimal budget set it is necessary that q^0 should satisfy the relations*

(4) $\qquad p_1 q_1^0 + \cdots + p_n q_n^0 = \mu; \qquad \dfrac{U_1(q_1^0, \ldots, q_n^0)}{p_1} = \cdots = \dfrac{U_n(q_1^0, \ldots, q_n^0)}{p_n}.$

For a budget q^0 where one or more q_i^0 are zero the condition is the same, except that in (4 b) we must omit the ratios U_i/p_i for those i-values for which $q_i^0 = 0$.

We see that the condition stated in Theorem 3 is the same as in Theorem 2. In fact, the indifference surface passing through q^0 has

(5) $\qquad U_1(q_1^0, \ldots, q_n^0) \cdot (q_1 - q_1^0) + \cdots + U_n(q_1^0, \ldots, q_n^0) \cdot (q_n - q_n^0) = 0$

as tangent plane at q^0; thus (4b) requires that the planes (2) and (5) should have proportional direction coefficients. Since both pass through q^0, the two planes will coincide.

According to Theorems 2–3, a balance plane with q^0 for optimal budget will touch an indifference surface at q^0, except possibly in the case when q^0 lies on the border of the budget space, i. e. if one or more quantities in q^0 are zero. An illustration is given by Fig. 3·1·1. For line L, the optimal budget q^0 satisfies (3), and L touches an indifference curve at q^0. For L^*, on the other hand, the optimal budget does not satisfy (3), and in this case the line does not touch an indifference curve at the optimal budget.

The ratio U_i/U_k is called the marginal rate of substitution of the ith commodity for the kth. The obvious interpretation of this definition is that if in an arbitrary budget $q^0 = (q_1^0, \ldots, q_n^0)$ we reduce q_i^0 by Δ_i and increase q_k^0 by Δ_k, where Δ_i and Δ_k are infinitesimal quantities standing in the ratio

(6) $\qquad\qquad \dfrac{\Delta_k}{\Delta_i} = \dfrac{U_i}{U_k},$

then the modified budget will lie in the tangent plane (5), and will accordingly be equivalent to q^0 [see Fig. 1]. This definition allows us to state the optimum condition of Theorems 2–3 in a third equivalent form, viz.

THEOREM 4. A necessary condition for a budget q^0 to be optimal is that the marginal rates of substitution U_i/U_k equal the price ratios p_i/p_k for all i and k.

An indifference surface is said to be convex towards the origin at the point q, or simply convex at q, if the surface in the vicinity of q lies above its tangent plane at q. In the case of two commodities, $n = 2$, this definition allows the interpretation that if the indifference curve is convex at q the marginal rate of substitution will vary monotonically in the course of the substitution of one commodity for the other [see Fig. 1]. It will be observed that this is a symmetric property; that is, Δ_k/Δ_i is increasing with q_k if q_i is substituted by q_k, and Δ_i/Δ_k is increasing with q_i if q_k is substituted by q_i.

THEOREM 5. A sufficient condition for an indifference surface to be convex at q is that the following inequalities are fulfilled at q,

(7) $\qquad\qquad\qquad (-1)^k M^{(k)}(q_1, \ldots, q_n) > 0 \qquad\qquad k = 2, \ldots, n$

where $M^{(k)}$ is the determinant

$$(8) \qquad M^{(k)}(q_1, \ldots, q_n) = \begin{vmatrix} 0 & U_1 & U_2 & \cdots U_k \\ U_1 & U_{11} & U_{12} & \cdots U_{1k} \\ \cdot & \cdot & \cdot & \cdots \cdot \\ U_k & U_{k1} & U_{k2} & \cdots U_{kk} \end{vmatrix}.$$

If we disregard contacts of higher order than the second, the condition is also necessary.

In the usual notation of infinitesimal calculus,

$$(9) \qquad dU = U_1 dq_1 + \cdots + U_n dq_n$$

gives the variation of U as the components of q vary by $dq_1, \ldots, dq_n$. Now let the components vary in the tangent plane at q. Forming dU and d^2U we then have $dU = 0$, that is

$$(10) \qquad U_1 dq_1 + U_2 dq_2 + \cdots + U_n dq_n = 0,$$

whereas $d^2U \leq 0$ is a necessary condition for convexity at q, and $d^2U < 0$ a sufficient condition. Taking q_1 for dependent variable, we obtain from (9)

$$(11) \qquad d^2 U = U_1 d^2 q_1 + \sum_{i,k=1}^{n} U_{ik} dq_i dq_k,$$

while (5) gives q_1 as a linear function in $q_2, \ldots, q_n$, and so

$$(12) \qquad d^2 q_1 = 0.$$

We solve (10) for dq_1, and substitute in (11). Paying regard to (12), and writing

$$v_{ik} = U_{ik} - \frac{U_i}{U_1} U_{1k} - \frac{U_k}{U_1} U_{1i} + \frac{U_i U_k}{U_1^2} U_{11}$$

we obtain

$$(13) \qquad d^2 U = \sum_{i,k=2}^{n} v_{ik} dq_i dq_k.$$

Theorem 5 will be proved if we can show that (7) implies $d^2U < 0$, i.e. that the quadratic form (13) is negative definite. By a familiar theorem[2] the form will have this property if the determinant sequence

$$V_k = \begin{vmatrix} v_{22} \cdots v_{2k} \\ \cdot \cdot \cdot \cdot \cdot \\ v_{k2} \cdots v_{kk} \end{vmatrix} \qquad k = 2, \ldots, n$$

has alternating negative and positive signs. Now (7) implies that the latter condition is fulfilled, for we have

$$M^{(k)}(q_1, \ldots, q_n) = -U_1^2 \cdot V_k \qquad k = 2, \ldots, n$$

as seen if we take $i = 3, \ldots, k$ and reduce respectively the ith row and column of the left-hand determinant by the second row and column, multiplied by U_i / U_1. Theorem 5 is proved.

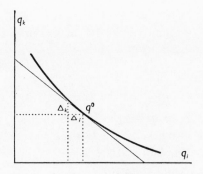

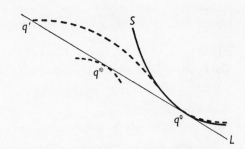

Fig. 4·4·1. The marginal rate of substitution.

Fig. 4·4·2. The existence of an optimal budget in the case of convex indifference maps.

THEOREM 6. *Given an indifference map satisfying Assumptions A–C, let (2) be an arbitrary balance plane. The condition that the map be convex everywhere in the budget space is sufficient to ensure that (a) the balance plane should contain one, and only one, optimal budget, and (b) the optimal budget should be given by the system (4), or if this has no solution, by a system (4) reduced by making one or more $q_i = 0$. The condition remains sufficient if requiring only that the map be convex either at all points of the balance plane, or at all points of the indifference surface that passes through the optimal budget.*

Proof: By Theorem 1 there exists at least one budget, say q^0, that is preferred or equivalent to all other budgets in (2). By Theorem 2 the indifference surface that passes through q^0, say S, has (2) for tangent plane at q^0. By hypothesis, S is convex at q^0, so that q^0 is preferred to those budgets in (2) that lie in the infinitesimal vicinity of q^0. Now if S is everywhere convex, S bends away upwards from the balance plane, and so the statements (a)–(b) will hold true [see Fig. 2, which shows how an arbitrary plane that passes through q^0 and the origin ω of Ω intersects the plane (2) along the line L and the surface S along the full curve indicated by S]. It remains to verify (a)–(b) on the assumption that the map is convex at all points of (2). Disregarding contacts of higher order, we thus have $d^2U < 0$. Now suppose on the contrary that there is a budget q' farther away in (2) that is equivalent to q^0 [see Fig. 2, where the plane of the page now passes through ω and the straight line L that connects q^0 and q', whereas the intersection with the surface S is the broken curve through q^0 and q']. Allowing q to vary along L from q^0 to q', the function $U(q)$ will be decreasing in the vicinity of q^0 and increasing in the vicinity of q'. Accordingly, by a familiar theorem, there is a point q^* between q^0 and q' where $U(q)$ attains an absolute minimum. At this point we have $dU = 0$ and $d^2U \geq 0$. Since this contradicts our initial hypothesis $d^2U < 0$, the assumption that q' is equivalent to q^0 must be false.

5. Demand functions. – We shall now allow the prices p_i and the consumer's income μ to vary. The optimal budget as determined by (4·4·4) may then be represented as a function of income and prices, say

(1) $$q_i = Q_i(\mu, p_1, \ldots, p_n) \qquad\qquad i = 1, \ldots, n.$$

The function Q_i is called the consumer's *demand function* for the ith commodity.[1]

THEOREM 1. *For the demand functions (1) to be well-defined for an income-price constellation μ, $p_1, \ldots, p_n$ it is necessary and sufficient that the balance plane (4·4·2) should contain an optimal budget, not an optimal budget set.*

Theorem 1 is an immediate corollary of Theorem 4·4·1.

THEOREM 2.[2] *The demand functions (1) satisfy*

(2) $$p_1 Q_1(\mu, p_1, \ldots, p_n) + \cdots + p_n Q_n(\mu, p_1, \ldots, p_n) = \mu,$$

called the balance relation, *and*

(3) $$Q_i(\lambda\mu, \lambda p_1, \ldots, \lambda p_n) = Q_i(\mu, p_1, \ldots, p_n) \qquad i = 1, \ldots, n$$

where $\lambda > 0$ is arbitrary, called the proportionality relation.

In this simple and fundamental theorem, (2) expresses the fact stated in Theorem 4·4·1 that the optimal budget lies in the balance plane. The relation (3) follows from the same theorem, since the two income-price constellations

$$\mu, p_1, \ldots, p_n \qquad\qquad \lambda\mu, \lambda p_1, \ldots, \lambda p_n$$

define the same balance plane, and accordingly give the same optimal budget.

In words, (3) states that the optimal budget will remain unchanged if income and prices are multiplied by the same factor. In other words, the components q_i of the optimal budget are functions of relative income and relative prices, i.e., relative with respect to either income or one of the prices. Hence

(4) $$q_i = Q_i^*\left(\frac{p_1}{\mu}, \ldots, \frac{p_n}{\mu}\right) = Q_i^{(k)}\left(\frac{\mu}{p_k}, \frac{p_1}{p_k}, \ldots, \frac{p_{k-1}}{p_k}, \frac{p_{k+1}}{p_k}, \ldots, \frac{p_n}{p_k}\right),$$
$$i, k = 1, \ldots, n$$

where Q_i^* and $Q_i^{(k)}$ are well-defined functions.

Proceeding, let us consider all balance planes that pass through a fixed budget q. It is seen that three cases are possible:

(A) At least one balance plane is such that all budgets that are equivalent to q lie above the plane.

(B) There is no balance plane with the above property, but at least one that lies wholly below the preference region of q.

(C) There is no balance plane that lies wholly below the preference region of q.

Let this classification be applied to all budgets q of the budget space. We see that a budget q belongs to category (A) if and only if there is an income-price constellation μ, $p_1, \ldots, p_n$ such that q is preferred to all other budget alternatives the consumer can afford. The category (A) will accordingly be said to form the *purchase region* of the budget space.

Next a few notations. We write

$$\varkappa = \varkappa(\mu, p_1, \ldots, p_n)$$

for the equal quotients obtained when inserting the functions (1) in the numerators of (4·4·4 b), so that

(5) $\qquad\qquad U_i - p_i \cdot \varkappa(\mu, p_1, \ldots, p_n) = 0 \qquad\qquad i = 1, \ldots, n$

[cf Ex. 59]. Further, let M denote the determinant $M^{(n)}$ defined by (4·4·8), and let $M_{ik} = M_{ki}$ denote the cofactor of the element U_{ik} of M.

THEOREM 3.[3] *In the interior of the purchase region, the derivatives of the demand functions* (1) *are given by*

(6) $\qquad\qquad \dfrac{\partial Q_i}{\partial \mu} = \dfrac{\varkappa}{M} M_{0i} \qquad\qquad i = 1, \ldots, n$

(7) $\qquad \dfrac{\partial Q_i}{\partial p_k} = \dfrac{\varkappa}{M}(M_{ki} - q_k M_{0i}), \qquad where \ \ M_{ki} = M_{ik} \qquad i, k = 1, \ldots, n.$

Formulae (6)–(7) come out by straightforward calculation if we take $\varkappa$, $q_1, \ldots, q_n$ for dependent variables, differentiate the $n+1$ relations (4·4·2) and (5) with respect to one of the variables μ, $p_1, \ldots, p_n$, and finally solve the resulting linear system. E.g., differentiating with respect to p_1 we obtain

$$p_1 \frac{\partial q_1}{\partial p_1} + \cdots + p_n \frac{\partial q_n}{\partial p_1} = -q_1$$

$$-p_1 \frac{\partial \varkappa}{\partial p_1} + U_{11} \frac{\partial q_1}{\partial p_1} + \cdots + U_{1n} \frac{\partial q_n}{\partial p_1} = \varkappa$$

$$-p_m \frac{\partial \varkappa}{\partial p_1} + U_{m1} \frac{\partial q_1}{\partial p_1} + \cdots + U_{mn} \frac{\partial q_n}{\partial p_1} = 0, \qquad \text{where } m = 2, \ldots, n.$$

Hence,

$$\frac{\partial q_i}{\partial p_1} = \frac{\Delta_i}{\Delta} \qquad \text{with } \Delta = \begin{vmatrix} 0 & p_1 & \cdots & p_n \\ -p_1 & U_{11} & \cdots & U_{1n} \\ \cdots\cdots\cdots\cdots\cdots \\ -p_n & U_{n1} & \cdots & U_{nn} \end{vmatrix} = -\frac{M}{\varkappa^2}$$

and $\Delta_i = -\dfrac{1}{\varkappa}(M_{1i} - q_1 M_{0i})$, in agreement with (7).

6. The integrability condition. Alternative approaches. – The theory of

preference fields as developed in this chapter has followed traditional lines, the basic hypotheses in sections 1–3 having been chosen so as to be in agreement with the classical approach of V. Pareto (1906). In section 5 we have reached the first main result of the theory, viz. that the consumer will have a well-defined set of demand functions, i.e. that his purchases will be determined by the prices and his income. What differs from other expositions is notably our stressing of one point, viz. that in the budget choice the consumer makes a simultaneous comparison between all budget alternatives he can afford, not only between alternatives in the vicinity of the optimal budget. The point is apparent in Theorem 4·4·6. It is not sufficient to require, as is done in several earlier treatments, that the indifference surface should be convex in the vicinity of the tangent point q^0, for as indicated in Fig. 4·4·2 it may then occur that there are budgets farther away in the balance plane that are preferred to q^0.

The point in question has repercussions in other parts of demand theory as well, in the first place those to be dealt with in the present section.

(i) The integrability condition. – In the pre-Paretoan theory of consumer demand, every budget alternative is supposed to have a measurable utility $U(q_1, \ldots, q_n)$, which the consumer seeks to make a maximum. On this assumption the optimum conditions (4·4·4) were established by F. Y. Edgeworth (1881). It was pointed out by G. B. Antonelli (1886), in a paper largely overlooked in later literature, that if $n \geq 3$ the partial derivatives U_i that appear in (4·4·4b) cannot be replaced by n arbitrary functions, say $R_i(q_1, \ldots, q_n)$. The corresponding remark was made by V. Volterra (1906) on Pareto's theory of preference fields. In fact, we should have $U_i = \lambda \cdot R_i$, where $\lambda = \lambda(q_1, \ldots, q_n)$ is a suitable function, and so the R_i have to satisfy the conditions

$$U_{ik} = \frac{\partial}{\partial q_k}(\lambda \cdot R_i) = \frac{\partial}{\partial q_i}(\lambda \cdot R_k) = U_{ki} \qquad i, k = 1, \ldots, n.$$

These may be shown to be equivalent to the following relations, known as the *integrability condition*,

$$(1) \qquad R_i\left(\frac{\partial R_j}{\partial q_k} - \frac{\partial R_k}{\partial q_j}\right) + R_j\left(\frac{\partial R_k}{\partial q_i} - \frac{\partial R_i}{\partial q_k}\right) + R_k\left(\frac{\partial R_i}{\partial q_j} - \frac{\partial R_j}{\partial q_i}\right) = 0,$$

where i, j, $k = 1, \ldots, n$ [cf Exs. 16 and 26].

The integrability condition allows a simple interpretation.[1] As regards the case $n = 2$ let $R_1(q_1, q_2)$ and $R_2(q_1, q_2)$ be arbitrary functions. Then (4·4·10) gives us the differential equation

$$R_1(q_1, q_2)\, dq_1 + R_2(q_1, q_2)\, dq_2 = 0.$$

It is a familiar fact that this can under general conditions of regularity be solved, giving a family of indifference curves which allow the representation

$$U(q_1, q_2) = c \quad \text{with} \quad U_1 = \lambda \cdot R_1,\ U_2 = \lambda \cdot R_2.$$

Considering now the case $n = 3$ [see Fig. 1a], suppose first that the consumer has a well-defined preference field. Given an arbitrary budget $a = (a_1, a_2, a_3)$, let the indifference surface that passes through a be intersected by the planes

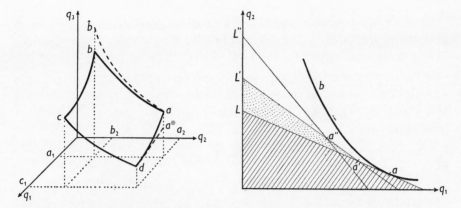

Fig. 4·6·1. The necessity of the integrability condition, and the equivalence between Paretoan theory and other approaches in the theory of consumer demand.

    a. The marginal substitution approach.   b. The demand function approach.

$q_1 = a_1$, $q_2 = b_2$, $q_1 = c_1$, $q_2 = a_2$, giving a segment of the surface that is bordered by the four curves ab, bc, cd, da. By construction, all budgets along these four curves are equivalent to a. On the other hand, dropping the explicit assumption about the existence of an indifference map, suppose the partial derivatives U_i of the function U are arbitrarily given. Then (4·4·10) forms a partial differential equation for determining the function $U(q_1, \ldots, q_n)$, i.e., for determining the surface $U(q_1, \ldots, q_n) = c$. Starting as before in the point a, we can use (4·4·10) consecutively for determining a curve ab in the plane $q_1 = a_1$, a curve bc in $q_2 = b_2$, a curve cd in $q_1 = c_1$, and finally a curve da^* in the plane $q_2 = a_2$. In fact, for determining each of these plane curves (4·4·10) will reduce to an ordinary differential equation, just as in the case $n = 2$, which ensures that the curves will be well-defined. By construction, each of the four curves will be an indifference curve, and so all budgets along the chain will again be equivalent to a. Now according as the integrability condition is satisfied or not we shall have $a = a^*$ or $a \neq a^*$, that is $a_3 = a_3^*$ or $a_3 \neq a_3^*$. However, a and a^* being equivalent to the consumer, Assumption A implies that $a_3 = a_3^*$, and so we must require the integrability condition to be fulfilled.

A similar interpretation of the integrability condition is due to J. Ville (1946): allowing the budget to pass along a closed curve C, starting and ending in the same budget q, it is not possible that the budget all along will pass through increasing levels of preference. Ville further points out that it is sufficient to take this statement as an axiom (it is even sufficient to consider infinitesimal cycles C), together with axioms of the type of our axioms of transitivity and choice, in order to develop Pareto's theory of preference fields.

In reply to Volterra's remark, Pareto suggested his much-discussed theory of 'open cycles', an approach intended as a generalization of his theory of indifference maps.[2] Not requiring that the integrability condition be fulfilled, the theory of open cycles does not imply the existence of individual indifference maps. The situation is the same as in the marginal substitution approach examined below.

(ii) **Alternative approaches.** – Various attempts have been made to generalize Pareto's theory of preference fields. We shall now briefly consider two of these approaches.

a. *The marginal substitution approach.*[3] Given an arbitrary budget $q = (q_1, ..., q_n)$, formula (4·4·10) is said to define the *indifference segment* of q, that is, the locus of budgets $(q_1 + dq_1, ..., q_n + dq_n)$ in the infinitesimal vicinity of q that are equivalent to q.

The notion of indifference segment is the basis of the marginal substitution approach. To use other notation than that of Paretoan theory, let

(2) $$R_1(q_1, ..., q_n)\, dq_1 + \cdots + R_n(q_1, ..., q_n)\, dq_n = 0$$

be the formula for the indifference segment of an arbitrary q. In the marginal substitution approach it is assumed that $R_1, ..., R_n$ are nonnegative functions, but otherwise arbitrary. The quotients R_i/R_k are interpreted as marginal substitution rates, just as in (4·4·6).

Now if the functions $R_i(q_1, ..., q_n)$ satisfy the integrability condition (1), the relation (2) implies the existence of a system of indifference surfaces, and so the approach is equivalent to the theory of Pareto. If (1) is not fulfilled, the marginal substitution approach has been claimed to be more general than the indifference surface approach.[4] However, as is clear from the interpretation in Fig. 1a, or likewise from Ville's interpretation, the locus of indifference of q will then form not an $(n-1)$-dimensional surface, but an n-dimensional solid. More drastically, if we assume that the budgets above (below) the indifference segment (2) are preferred (disfavoured) to q, the approach will even be self-contradictory. In any case, only if the integrability condition is fulfilled the marginal substitution approach can be used as a basis for the theory of consumer demand.

b. *The demand function approach.* The basic assumption is that the consumer's demand functions are well-defined, say $Q_i(\mu, p_1, ..., p_n)$. Otherwise expressed, the assumption is that, if the prices and the consumer's income are given, the purchases $q = (q_1, ..., q_n)$ of the consumer will be determined. More or less explicitly, q is interpreted as preferred to all other budgets the consumer can afford.[5] As in (4·5·4) it is then seen that only relative prices p_i/μ will enter in the demand functions Q_i.

Under general conditions of regularity, we can solve (4·5·4) for the relative prices, say

(3) $$p_i/\mu = P_i(q_1, ..., q_n) \qquad\qquad i = 1, ..., n.$$

The P_i, known as the *price functions*, give the relative prices at which q is optimal. Writing (2) for the infinitesimal segment around q of the balance plane where q is optimal, the R_i will thus be replaced by the P_i. Then if we interpret (2) as an indifference segment it follows, as pointed out by H. Hotelling (1932), that if the price functions P_i satisfy the integrability condition (1) the demand function approach implies the existence of an indifference map. For $n = 2$, accordingly, the map will always exist [cf. (5·4·5-7) and Exs. 7 and 45].

On the other hand, suppose the P_i do not satisfy (1). Considering first the case $n = 2$ (see Fig. 1b), let L, L', L'' be balance lines with a, a', a'' for demanded budgets. Then a is preferred to all budgets on or below L, a' preferred to all budgets on or below L', and so on, so that a will be preferred to all budgets below any of the lines $L, L', L'', \ldots$. Choosing, $a, a', a'', \ldots$ arbitrarily, it follows that a is preferred to all budgets below a certain limiting curve ab. If we combine this argument with Fig. 1a, it follows that a is preferred to all budgets below the path $a - b - c - d - a^*$. The integrability condition not being fulfilled, a^* need not coincide with a, and so the path may be chosen so as to go downwards in a spiral. Our next step is to construct a similar path, say $a\hat{b}\hat{c}\hat{d}\hat{a}$, such that a is disfavoured to all budgets above the path. We see that this path must be the same as $abcda^*$. In fact, the situation would otherwise be as in Fig. 1a, with $\hat{b}$ above b, and this would contradict Assumption B, since the vertical through a would contain no budget equivalent to the budgets between b and $\hat{b}$. Thus $\hat{a} = a^*$, and so we arrive at the contradiction that a, lying above the path $a\hat{b}\hat{c}\hat{d}\hat{a}$, is disfavoured to itself.

Summing up, we obtain[6]

THEOREM 1. *The marginal substitution approach and the demand function approach are logically and mathematically equivalent to Pareto's theory of preference fields if the integrability condition is fulfilled, whereas each of the two approaches is self-contradictory if the integrability condition is not fulfilled.*

7. Relaxed assumptions.[1] – The Assumptions A–C of Ch. 4·3 are of wide scope, but nevertheless it is worth while to point out that they allow some generalization without impairing the essential results of the theory. This section and the next will consider the theory when extended as follows: (a) In line with the approaches of I. Fisher (1892) and others, Assumption A will be supplemented by the notion of satiety. (b) The preference level will be assumed to be nondecreasing, instead of increasing, as the budget is enlarged; this will notably permit us to treat the case of nondivisible commodity units. (c) The indifference surfaces need not be differentiable.

Adopting the three axioms 1–3 of Ch. 4·2 without change, we replace Assumption A of Ch. 4·3 by

Assumption A*. *If any component q_i in a budget is allowed to increase, starting from $q_i = 0$, the preference level is nondecreasing up to a certain point $\hat{q}_i$, called the satiety point, above which the preference levels are not higher than at $\hat{q}_i$.*

This assumption allows the loci of indifference to swell from $(n-1)$-dimensional surfaces to n-dimensional solids. To avoid ambiguity about end-points, we agree that, if the preference level remains constant as q_i varies in an interval, this will always include its lower end-point.

The budgets q with $q_i \leq q_i^*$ for every q_i are said to form the *scarcity region*, denoted Ω^*. The highest preference level attainable belongs to Ω^*, and is called the *total satiety level*. We see that the border of Ω^* is a surface which approaches monotonically towards the coordinate planes in the sense that if two coordinates are allowed to vary in the surface, say q_i and q_k, then q_i is monotonically nonincreasing for increasing q_k.

THEOREM 1. *The purchase region is contained in the scarcity region* Ω^*.

A budget q in which all components q_i have integral values is called a *lattice point* of Ω. If the preference level changes only for integral values of the budget components, we shall say that the preference field is a *lattice field*. The case when the commodities appear in natural units that are not divisible can be studied by the use of lattice fields.[2] Without proof we state the following two theorems, which show that the case of indivisible units does not bring in any appreciable change in the demand structure. The assumption about divisibility is chiefly a matter of making the mathematics more convenient.

THEOREM 2. *Given a preference field* **F** *satisfying Assumptions A–C, let* L^* *be any balance plane such that the optimal budget is a lattice point. Then there exists a lattice field* **F*** *such that every* L^* *has the same optimal budget in the two fields.*

The field **F*** in general will not be continuous in the sense of Assumption B of Ch. 4·3.

THEOREM 3. *Given a lattice field* **F*** *such that every lattice point* q^* *is the optimal budget of at least one region* $(4·4·1)$; *then there exists a preference field* **F** *satisfying Assumptions A–C, such that to every* q^* *there corresponds a balance plane which has* q^* *for optimal budget in both of the fields.*

Proceeding, we let Assumption B remain the same, with notation B*.

THEOREM 4. *Given a preference field that satisfies Assumptions* A^*–B^*, *Theorems* $4·3·1$–3 *hold good in the scarcity region, with the qualifications that* (a) *instead of the term* indifference surface *we must use* locus of indifference, (b) *the parameter* c *in* $(4·3·1)$ *may be discontinuous, and range from* 0 *to a finite value, and* (c) *the function* $U(q_1, \ldots, q_n)$ *may be discontinuous.*

Let L^* be a straight line which makes positive angles with all coordinate axes and connects the origin ω with a point at the total satiety level. Then Theorem 4 follows immediately if we use L^* in the same manner as L in Theorem $4·3·3$, except that since L^* may contain an interval where all budgets q^* are equivalent we must define $c(q^*)$ as the distance from ω to that point in the interval which is *nearest* to ω.

THEOREM 5. *On Assumptions A^*-B^*, Theorem 4·4·1 remains valid, with the qualification that part of the optimal budget set may lie below the balance plane.*

The proof of Theorem 5 is the same as for Theorem 4·4·1.

Assumption C^*. *In the scarcity region, with the possible exception for a finite number of surfaces or curves of dimension $n-1$ or lower, the preference function $U(q_1, \ldots, q_n)$ has continuous derivatives of the two first orders, and those of first order are positive,*

$$U_i > 0 \qquad\qquad i = 1, \ldots, n.$$

This gives, as needs no comment,

THEOREM 6. *Given an indifference map that satisfies Assumptions $A^* - C^*$, Theorem 4·4·2 remains valid for budgets q^0 in the interior of the scarcity region, with the qualifications that (a) the balance planes considered should cut across the scarcity region, and (b) the notion of tangent plane should include any plane that has one, and only one, point in common with the surface touched. Theorems 4·4·3–6 remain valid with the qualifications (a) and (c) : q^0 must not belong to the exceptional curves or surfaces of Assumption C^*.*

8. A general budget classification.[1]

– It is the purpose of this section to examine the geometric structure of indifference maps, notably with regard to convexity. The analysis involves a budget classification that has the advantage of not making use of Assumptions C or C^*.

First a definition. Given $m+1$ budgets

$$q, q^{(1)}, \ldots, q^{(m)} \qquad\qquad 2 \leq m \leq n$$

that lie in a balance plane, suppose q is a weighted average of the $q^{(i)}$, say

(1) $$q_i = w_1 q_i^{(1)} + \cdots + w_m q_i^{(m)} \qquad\qquad i = 1, \ldots, n$$

where

(2) $$w_k \geq 0 \ (k = 1, \ldots, m); \qquad w_1 + \cdots + w_m = 1.$$

Then q is called a *compromise* between the m budgets $q^{(i)}$. This definition requiring $m \geq 2$, we shall in this section disregard budgets q that contain but one nonvanishing component q_i.

Thus prepared we shall examine a preference field that satisfies Assumptions A^*-B^*. Let a budget q be arbitrarily given in the scarcity region. Then one of the following statements (A)–(C) is true, and it is seen that the three cases are mutually exclusive, so that they define three sets of budgets q that are non-overlapping and fill up the entire scarcity region.

Considering all balance planes that pass through q, there is in cases (A) and (B) at least one plane, say L, such that if $q^{(1)}, \ldots, q^{(n)}$ are arbitrary budgets in L that have q for compromise then

(A) q is preferred to every $q^{(i)}$. The budgets q of this type form the *region of compromise*, or, with another term, the *region of both-and*.

(B) q is preferred or equivalent to every $q^{(i)}$, without q being of type (A).

(C) There is at least one plane L such that L contains at least one set of n budgets $q^{(1)}, \ldots, q^{(n)}$ which have q for compromise, and all of which are preferred to q. If in such case all other budgets in L are preferred to q, we shall say that q belongs to the *region of either-or*.

If the indifference surfaces are convex towards the origin, as e.g. in Fig. 3·1·1, every budget in the map will clearly be of category (A). In Fig. 3·1·1a the situation of compromise is brought out by the arrows that point towards the optimal budget of the balance line L. Case (C) is illustrated in Fig. 1. Fig. 1a shows a case of either-or with $n = 2$; the indifference curves are here concave towards the origin, and the point of contact q is disfavoured to neighbouring budgets, as indicated by the arrows. Fig. 1b refers to a case (C) with $n = 3$. The tangent plane L at q is here the plane of the page, which intersects the indifference surfaces along a family of hyperbolas.

THEOREM 1. *For budgets q in the scarcity region, the above classification (A)–(C) is equivalent to the classification (A)–(C) of Ch. 4·5. Specifically, the purchase region coincides with the region of both-and.*

It is obvious that the two versions of (A) are equivalent. As to (B)–(C) we note a lemma which shows that the first version is implied in the second:

If q is a compromise between m budgets $q^{(1)}, \ldots, q^{(m)}$, all of which are preferred or equivalent to q, then q does not belong to the purchase region of the indifference map considered.

For the proof of the lemma, and of the fact that the second version of (B) is implied in the first, reference is made to the author's earlier review of Paretoan theory (1943–44). It remains to show that the first version of (C) implies the second. This can be done as follows.[2]

Let us examine the case $n = 3$. Given a budget q, let its preference region be denoted $P(q)$. We shall consider those balance planes every point of which lies below $P(q)$. Supposing that the first version of (C) is true, none of these planes passes through q. For one of the planes, say L^*, the distance to q is accordingly a minimum. The plane L^* may be supposed to touch $P(q)$ at 3 points, say b_1, b_2, b_3. The second version (C) will be true if we can show that the orthogonal projection of q into L^* cannot fall outside of the triangle $b_1 b_2 b_3$. Now if it did, say as in Fig. 2 (where the plane L^* is viewed perpendicularly), we could shift L^* by bringing b_3 slightly towards the origin, retaining the contact with $P(q)$ in the vicinity of b_1 and b_2. If infinitesimal, such a movement may be regarded as a rotation around the axis $b_1 b_2$. This rotation,

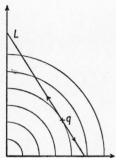 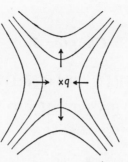 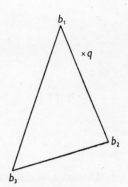

Fig. 4·8·1. Budget classification in terms of
both-and and *either-or*.
a. A case of *either-or*.   b. Neither *both-and* nor *either-or*.

Fig. 4·8·2.
Illustration to the
proof of Theorem 4·8·1.

however, would bring L^* nearer to q, which would be in contradiction to the assumption that L^* is at a minimal distance from q. The assertion is now proved for $n = 3$, and the same argument applies for any $n > 3$.

The following theorem, which is stated without proof, gives an application of the classification (A)–(C).

THEOREM 2. *Given a preference field that satisfies Assumptions A^*–B^*. In order that a balance plane should contain one optimal budget, and only one, it is sufficient that the region of both-and should contain the whole of the balance plane.*

The classification (A)–(C) may be modified by requiring that the extremal budgets $q^{(1)}, \ldots, q^{(n)}$ should lie in the infinitesimal vicinity of the budget q considered. For illustration, reference may again be made to Figs. 1 a–b and 3·1·1. The two parts of the budget space thus defined in analogy to (A) and (C) will be termed the regions of *local both-and* and *local either-or*. We see that the region of local both-and contains (a) the region of both-and, and a fortiori the purchase region, and (b) the points q at which the indifference map is convex in the sense of Ch. 4·4. The notion of local both-and is accordingly a generalization of the notion of convexity. The following theorem, stated without proof, is therefore more general than Theorem 2 and the first part of Theorem 4·4·6.

THEOREM 3. *The condition stated in Theorem 2 remains sufficient if we replace the region of both-and by the region of local both-and.*

Chapter 5.

THE SPECIFICATION OF DEMAND
PATTERNS

1. Demand elasticities.[1] – Given a function $f(x, y, \ldots, v)$, its *elasticity* with respect to the variable x is defined as plus or minus its logarithmic derivative w.r.t. x. We denote the elasticity by $E_x f$ or $e_x f$ according to the sign, thus

(1) $$E_x f = \frac{\partial \log f}{\partial \log x} = \frac{x}{f} \frac{\partial f}{\partial x} \qquad e_x f = -\frac{\partial \log f}{\partial \log x} = -\frac{x}{f} \frac{\partial f}{\partial x}.$$

In graphical interpretation, if the curve of f is drawn with logarithmic scale for f as well as for x, the gradient of the curve will equal the elasticity $E_x f$.

The advantage of using elasticities instead of ordinary derivatives $\partial f/\partial x$ is that they are independent of the measuring units. In fact, for any transformation of the type $F = k_1 f$, $X = k_2 x$, where k_1, k_2 are any constants, we have

$$\log F = \log k_1 + \log f \qquad \log X = \log k_2 + \log x$$

which shows that the gradient of $\log F$ on $\log X$ is the same as for $\log f$ on $\log x$.

The elasticity of a demand function is called a *demand elasticity*. In this introductory section, the demand functions considered will be perfectly general; thus it makes no difference whether or not they refer to a preference field.

Forming the elasticities of a demand function $Q(\mu, p, p_1, \ldots, p_n)$ of a commodity G, the elasticity with respect to income μ is briefly called the *income elasticity* of G, the elasticity w.r.t. the price p of G is called the *price elasticity* of G, and the elasticities w.r.t. the prices p_i of other commodities are called *cross elasticities*. Let us agree to use the positive sign in (1) for income elasticities, the negative sign for price and cross elasticities, thus[2]

$$E_\mu Q = \frac{\mu}{Q} \frac{\partial Q}{\partial \mu} \qquad e_p Q = -\frac{p}{Q} \frac{\partial Q}{\partial p} \qquad e_{p_i} Q = -\frac{p_i}{Q} \frac{\partial Q}{\partial p_i}.$$

For demand functions referring to a preference field, the partial derivatives that appear in these formulae are given by Theorem 4·5·3.

If income rises (falls) by 1 %, demand will increase (fall) by E %, and if price rises (falls) by 1 %, demand will fall (increase) by e %. This interpretation of demand elasticities involves a slight approximation, and if we say that an increase of income by a % (or a fall of price by a %) will increase the demand by $a \cdot E$ % (or by $a \cdot e$ %) the approximation error will be appreciable if the percentage $a \cdot E$ or $a \cdot e$ is as large as 10 or 15. If a function $f(x)$ is of constant elasticity for all x between x_0 and x_1, the exact formula for the elasticity is

$$(2) \qquad E = -e = \frac{\log f_1 - \log f_0}{\log x_1 - \log x_0}$$

where we have written $f(x_0) = f_0$, $f(x_1) = f_1$. If $f(x)$ is an arbitrary function, (2) gives what is known as *arc elasticity*.[3] We note that if $f(x)$ has a continuous derivative, but is otherwise arbitrary, the arc elasticity will equal the elasticity of $f(x)$, as defined by (1), for some x intermediate betweeen x_0 and x_1. A convenient formula that gives the arc elasticity with good approximation is

$$(3) \qquad E_x f = -e_x f \sim \frac{f_1 - f_0}{f_1 + f_0} \cdot \frac{x_1 + x_0}{x_1 - x_0}.$$

Illustration. Suppose demand increases by 30 % as income increases by 10 %. The income elasticity as given by (2) and the approximate formula (3) are, respectively,

$$E = \frac{\log 1.3}{\log 1.1} = 2.753 \qquad\qquad E \sim \frac{0.3}{2.3} \cdot \frac{2.1}{0.1} = 2.739.$$

The error of the latter value is 0.014, which is only $\frac{1}{2}$ % of E. [See Ex. 2.]

Demand is called *over-* or *under-elastic* according as the elasticity is greater or smaller than plus one; if equal to plus one, elasticity is called *normal*. For income elasticities this terminology is natural in view of Theorem 6·2·1, which states that a weighted average of the income elasticities equals unity. For price elasticities, on the other hand, the interpretation is that if elasticity is normal a change in the price will be balanced by a reverse change in demand, so that the expenditure on the commodity will remain constant. In fact, writing X for expenditure we have

$$(4) \qquad X = p \cdot Q \qquad e_p X = -\frac{d \log X}{d \log p} = -1 - \frac{d \log Q}{d \log p} = e_p Q - 1,$$

so if $e_p Q = 1$. then $e_p X = 0$. Similarly, relation (4b) shows that if demand is under-elastic with respect to price the expenditure will increase (decrease) as price rises (falls), whereas in case demand is over-elastic w.r.t. price, the expenditure will decrease (increase) as price rises (falls). An instructive example is supplied by Gregory King's law: "The smaller a crop, the greater its money value"; we see that this famous 'law' of the 17th century may be interpreted as an empirical proposition to the effect that the price elasticity of cereals is under-elastic. [See Ex. 1.]

The rules for calculating with ordinary derivatives can easily be translated into rules for calculating with logarithmic derivatives, i.e. with elasticities.[4] For instance, the derivative of a sum of functions is the sum of the derivatives of the terms; in symbols

$$(5) \qquad f(x) = f_1(x) + \cdots + f_n(x); \qquad \frac{d}{dx} f(x) = \frac{d}{dx} f_1(x) + \cdots + \frac{d}{dx} f_n(x).$$

Transforming to elasticities, this gives

$$E_x f = \frac{f_1 \cdot E_x f_1 + \cdots + f_n \cdot E_x f_n}{f_1 + \cdots + f_n}; \qquad e_x f = \frac{f_1 \cdot e_x f_1 + \cdots + f_n \cdot e_x f_n}{f_1 + \cdots + f_n}.$$

In words,

THEOREM 1. *The elasticity of a sum is a weighted average of the elasticities of the terms of the sum, with weights proportional to the terms.*

2. Consumption curves. Giffen's paradox. – Returning to the Paretoan theory, let us consider a preference field that satisfies Assumptions A–C. According to (4·4·4) the individual demand for a commodity is a more or less complicated function of income and prices, and in general the consumer will have different demand functions for different commodities. The consumption curves referred to in Ch. 3·1 provide a useful graphical interpretation of the demand functions and their properties.

Keeping the prices $p_1, \ldots, p_n$ fixed, and allowing the income μ to vary, the optimal budget (4·5·1) will describe a curve C_μ in the budget space, called the *income-consumption curve*. In geometric interpretation [see Fig. 3·1·2, where $n = 2$], the budget plane (4·4·2) will move by parallel translation, and C_μ is the locus of points where the moving plane touches the indifference curves. Similarly, if we keep the income μ and all prices but one fixed, say p_i, the optimal budget will for varying p_i describe a curve C_i, called the price-consumption curve for the component q_i, or briefly the ith *price-consumption curve*. Geometrically, the budget plane will now move so that for any $k \neq i$ its intersection with the q_k-axis remains the same, μ / p_k, whereas its intersection with the q_i-axis, μ / p_i, is variable. Otherwise expressed, if we interpret (4·5·1) as a point $Q = (Q_1, \ldots, Q_n)$ in the budget space, the consumption curves are the loci of Q for varying μ and for varying p_i, respectively.[1]

For the same map as in Fig. 3·1·2, we see in Fig. 1 the consumption curves C_μ, C_1, C_2 that pass through the budget q^0. A variation in income μ brings the optimal budget from q^0 to a; similarly, a variation in p_1 or p_2 brings the budget from q^0 to b or c, respectively. Fig. 2 shows a map where the price-consumption curves C_1 are more sophisticated, having kinks along the line $B e f g$.

We note a few properties of the consumption curves that follow directly from the definition. Through every point q in the purchase region there passes one price-consumption curve for each budget component and one income-consumption curve, in all $n + 1$ curves. All curves intersect the balance plane that has q for optimal budget. For the income-consumption curve the passage through q will be from below upwards if income μ is *rising*, whereas for the ith price-consumption curve the passage will be from below upwards if p_i is *falling*. Otherwise, any direction is possible in the passage. Thus in Fig. 3, which refers to the case $n = 2$, the lines a–e indicate possible directions for any consumption curve C_μ, C_1 or C_2 that passes through the budget q.

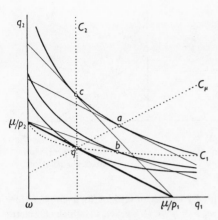

Fig. 5·2·1. Consumption curves.   Fig. 5·2·2. Giffen's paradox.

The following theorem, illustrated for $n = 2$ in Fig. 4, gives some information on the course of the consumption curves relative to each other.

THEOREM 1.[2] *The price-consumption curves that pass through a budget q form an n-dimensional corner on each side of that balance plane in which q is optimal. The income-consumption curve that passes through q is situated in the interior of this corner.*

The first statement is implied in the previous comments. As to the second, suppose q lies in the balance plane (4·4·2), say L [see Fig. 4]. We shall examine how the corner in question is intersected by the plane L^* obtained by the infinitesimal substitution of $\mu + d\mu$ for μ. We note that if μ is retained, and all the prices in (4·4·2) are simultaneously replaced by $p_1 + dp_1, \ldots, p_n + dp_n$, this substitution will lead to a balance plane that coincides with L^* in the vicinity of q, provided

$$(1) \qquad d\mu = -q_1 dp_1 - \cdots - q_n dp_n.$$

The intersection of L^* with the income-consumption curve will, according to (4·5·6), be the point $(q_1 + dq_1, \ldots, q_n + dq_n)$ given by

$$(2) \qquad dq_i = \frac{\partial Q_i}{\partial \mu} d\mu = \frac{\varkappa}{M} M_{0i} d\mu \qquad\qquad i = 1, \ldots, n.$$

On the other hand, (1) will be satisfied if we make $dp_k = -d\mu/q_k$ for any fixed k, and $dp_i = 0$ for $i \neq k$. Writing $(q_1 + dq_1^{(k)}, \ldots, q_n + dq_n^{(k)})$ for the intersection between L^* and the kth price-consumption curve, we infer, making use of (4·5·7),

$$(3) \qquad dq_i^{(k)} = \frac{\partial Q_i}{\partial p_k} dp_k = \frac{\varkappa}{M}\left(M_{0i} - \frac{1}{q_k} M_{ki} \right) d\mu \qquad\qquad i, k = 1, \ldots, n$$

[in Fig. 4, α is the point (2), whereas β and γ are the two points (3)]. Now, Theorem 1 will be true if $dq_1, \ldots, dq_n$ allow the representation

$$(4) \qquad dq_i = w_1 dq_i^{(1)} + \cdots + w_n dq_i^{(n)} \qquad\qquad i = 1, \ldots, n$$

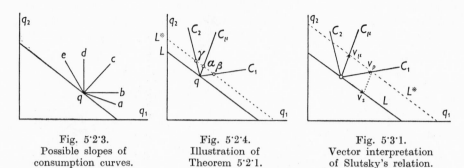

Fig. 5·2·3.	Fig. 5·2·4.	Fig. 5·3·1.
Possible slopes of	Illustration of	Vector interpretation
consumption curves.	Theorem 5·2·1.	of Slutsky's relation.

with weights w_i satisfying (4·8·2). If we substitute by the use of (2) and (3), a simple reduction shows that (4) will be satisfied if we make $w_k = p_k\, q_k/\mu$, $(k = 1, \ldots, n)$, which completes the proof of Theorem 1.

Next some comments on the direction of the consumption curves. If the consumer's income rises, his expenditure on the various commodities will, on the whole, increase. For one or more commodities the demand may decrease, but not for all, since the total expenditure equals income. This means that a commodity with falling demand will at higher income levels be replaced by better qualities or superior commodities, e.g., margarine being replaced by butter. Hence commodities may be classified as *inferior* if their income elasticity is negative.

A fall in the price of a commodity will likewise, on the whole, increase the demand for the various commodities. Again there may be exception for one or more of the commodities, but not for all. It may even occur that demand decreases for that commodity the price of which is falling; this possibility is known as *Giffen's paradox*.[3] Following Marshall's interpretation, Giffen's paradox may occur for basic foods like bread or potatoes if their price is low and income is so low that the consumer has to spend the larger part thereof on the basic foods. A rise in the price of the basic foods may then have the effect that, in order to maintain a minimum supply of calories, the consumer is forced to reduce his demand for the more expensive foods and increase his demand for the basic foods, these still being cheaper in spite of their increased price.

Illustration. Fig. 2 shows the indifference map defined by

$$(q_1 - 1)/(q_2 - 2)^2 = c \qquad \text{for } q_1 > 1, \quad q_2 \leq 1.6,$$

and by straight lines parallel to the q_2-axis for other parts of the budget space. Fixing income $\mu = 1$ and price $p_2 = 1/3$, and allowing p_1 to decrease from ∞ to 0, the budget line will turn around the point $q_1 = 0$, $q_2 = 3$. The optimal budget will describe the curve $\omega abcdefg$, which accordingly is a price-consumption curve of type C_1. The segment cde is obtained as p_1 decreases from 2/3 to 2/5. The component q_1 being here decreasing, we have before us Giffen's paradox.

The following theorem, which is stated without proof, makes clear that Giffen's paradox is an exceptional phenomenon.

THEOREM 2.[4] *A region where Giffen's paradox occurs can at most form a finite part of the budget space.*

In Fig. 2, for instance, the paradox is confined to the rectangle $A\,b\,B\,f$, and does not occur if p_1 is fixed $\geq 1/2$. Thus for $p_1 = \frac{1}{2}$ the curve C_1 is $\omega A f g$.

3. Slutsky's relation and its interpretation. – For the demand functions (4·5·1) of an individual consumer we have, making use of (4·5·6–7),

$$(1) \qquad \frac{\partial Q_i}{\partial p_k} = -q_k \frac{\partial Q_i}{\partial \mu} + s_{ki}, \quad \text{with} \quad s_{ki} = \frac{\varkappa}{M} M_{ki}; \qquad i, k = 1, \ldots, n.$$

Now suppose that the price of the kth commodity changes by the infinitesimal amount dp_k. This making a shift of the balance plane, we infer from (5·2·1) that in the neighbourhood of the optimal budget the same shift is obtained if income changes by the amount

$$(2) \qquad d\mu = -q_k\,dp_k.$$

The amount $q_k\,dp_k = -d\mu$ will be referred to as the *price compensation* in the income. Now (1) gives, inserting (2),

$$(3) \qquad \frac{\partial Q_i}{\partial p_k}\,dp_k = \frac{\partial Q_i}{\partial \mu}\,d\mu + s_{ki}\,dp_k \qquad\qquad i, k = 1, \ldots, n.$$

This is known as *Slutsky's relation*. It may be interpreted as follows.[1]

In (3) to the left we have the effect on the demand for the ith commodity of a rise (fall) in the price of the kth commodity. To the right this is split up in two terms, called the *income effect* and the *substitution effect*. To buy the same quantities as before the price change, the consumer would require a price compensation in the income. Without the compensation, the consumer contracts (expands) his demand in the same way as for a decrease (increase) in his income; this is the income effect. The budget reached in this way, however, will not be preferred to all other alternatives he can afford after the change of the price p_k; the resulting change in the demand is the substitution effect.

As pointed out by E. Cansado (1950), the relation (3) allows a simple vector interpretation. Considering a reduction in price p_k, the left-hand members of (3) will for $i = 1, \ldots, n$ give the components of an infinitesimal vector, v_p, called the *price vector*, directed from q along the price-consumption curve for q_k that passes through q. The right-hand members give this vector as the sum of two other ones, called the *income vector* and the *substitution vector*. The income vector, v_μ, is directed from q along the income-consumption curve that passes through q, whereas the substitution vector, v_s, is situated in the balance plane that passes through q. By (2), the length of the price vector determines the length of the income vector; the substitution vector is then obtained as the difference between the price vector and the income vector.

Figs. 1–2 show for $n = 2$ the vector interpretation of a reduction in the price p_1. In Fig. 1 the consumption curves are the same as in Fig. 5'2'4. In Fig. 2 we have an instance of Giffen's paradox; in fact, forming the projection g of the price vector on the q_1-axis, we see that g in this case goes in the negative direction.

A few simple properties of the substitution effect are summed up in

THEOREM 1.[2] A. *The substitution effect is always negative for the demand of a commodity w.r.t. a change in the price of the same commodity, that is* $s_{kk} < 0$.

B. *In the case of two commodities,* $n = 2$, *the substitution effect is always positive, that is* $s_{12} > 0$.

C. *The substitution effect is symmetric,* $s_{ik} = s_{ki}$, *that is for the demand for a commodity* G_i *w.r.t. the price of a commodity* G_k *the substitution effect is the same as for the demand for* G_k *w.r.t. the price of* G_i.

Proof: $\varkappa$ is always positive, and (4'4'7) implies $M_{kk}/M < 0$. Hence (1) gives $s_{kk} < 0$. Next, making $n = 2$ we obtain $M_{12} = U_1 U_2 > 0$, and since $M > 0$, $\varkappa > 0$, we infer $s_{12} > 0$. For any n, finally, (4'5'7) gives $M_{ki} = M_{ik}$, and so $s_{ik} = s_{ki}$. For later reference we note that $s_{ik} = s_{ki}$ implies, as seen from (1),

$$(4) \qquad \frac{\partial Q_i}{\partial p_k} + q_k \frac{\partial Q_i}{\partial \mu} = \frac{\partial Q_k}{\partial p_i} + q_i \frac{\partial Q_k}{\partial \mu} \qquad i, k = 1, \ldots, n.$$

As shown in Fig. 2, Theorem 1 A–B allows a simple graphic interpretation. Considering a reduction of price p_1 in the case $n = 2$, let the substitution vector v_s in its turn be decomposed into two vectors, say a and b, making a parallel with the q_1-axis and b with the q_2-axis. Then a will have the direction of the positive q_1-axis [Theorem 1 A], and b will be directed as the negative q_2-axis [Theorem 1 B]. For a graphic interpretation of statement C, see Ex. 9.

Following E. Slutsky (1915) and J. R. Hicks (1939) we call the ith and kth commodities *competitive, independent,* or *complementary* according as the substitution effect as defined by (3) is positive, zero, or negative. This distinction is relevant only for $n \geq 3$, for by Theorem 1 B the commodities are necessarily competitive if $n = 2$. Which case is present for $n \geq 3$ depends on the structure of the indifference map at the budget point q considered. The following theorem, which is illustrated by Fig. 3, gives a geometric interpretation in terms of the indifference curves (surfaces) that form the intersection between the balance plane and the indifference map.

THEOREM 2. *Given an indifference map satisfying Assumptions A–C, let* q^0 *be the optimal budget of an arbitrary balance plane. In the case* $n = 3$ *the loci of indifference in the balance plane will in the vicinity of* q^0 *form a system of concentric and similar ellipses. For a change in the price* p_i *the substitution vector*

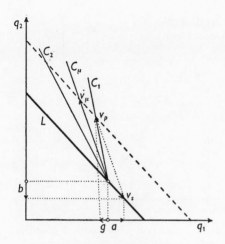

Fig. 5·3·2. Vector interpretation
of Giffen's paradox.

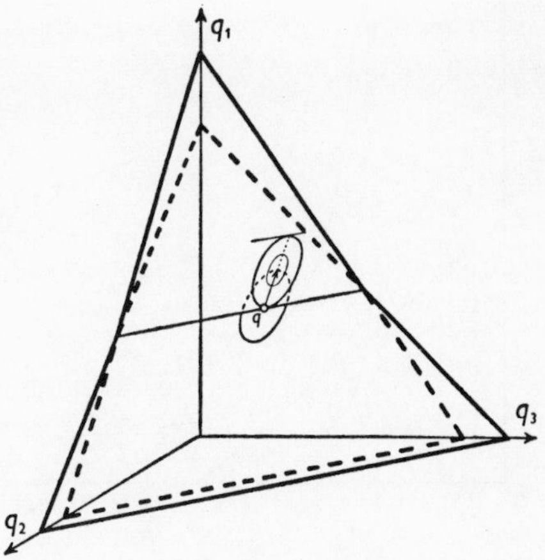

Fig. 5·3·3. Illustration
of Theorem 5·3·2.

goes in the direction where the ellipses *have their maximal* q_i-*coordinate; i.e., the vector is conjugate to the* line *along which the plane is intersected by the plane* $q_i = q_i^0$. *For* $n > 3$ *the same statements hold true, only for* ellipses *and* line *one should read* $(n-1)$-dimensional ellipsoids *and* $(n-2)$-dimensional plane, *respectively.*

For the proof of this theorem, as well as for corollaries, reference is made to E. Cansado and H. Wold (1950).

4. Demand functions with constant elasticity. – If a function $f(x)$ has constant elasticity, say $e_x f = \alpha$, we have by (5·1·1)

$$(1) \qquad d \log f = -\alpha \cdot d \log x; \qquad \log f = c - \alpha \log x; \qquad f(x) = C x^{-\alpha};$$

where c and C are arbitrary constants. Thus if a commodity has constant price elasticity e, or constant income elasticity E, respectively, its demand function will be given by the formulae (1·1·1 a–b), where c_1 is independent of price p, and c_2 is independent of income μ.

Fig. 1·1·1 shows 18 demand curves with constant elasticity. Their equations are given by formulae (1·1·1), with c_1 and c_2 equal to 2, 1, 1/2 for the curves passing through the points a, β, γ. The elasticity is $E = -e = 1$, $E = -e = 2$, $E = -e = 1/2$, respectively, for the full, the broken, and the dotted curves.

The deduction (1) extends to the case when demand is a function of several variables. Thus if E, e_1, e_2, ..., e_n are the constant elasticities of demand with respect to income, w.r.t. the price p_1 of the commodity considered, and w.r.t. other prices $p_2, ..., p_n$, the demand function will be

$$(2) \qquad q = C \mu^E p_1^{-e_1} p_2^{-e_2} \cdots p_n^{-e_n}.$$

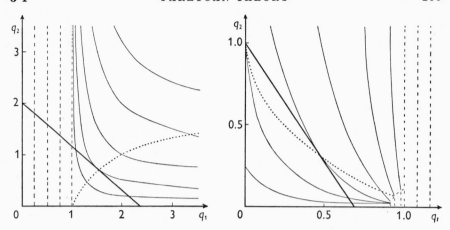

Fig. 5·4·1. Indifference maps that have a demand function with constant elasticity,
$$q_1 = A \mu^a p_1^{-a}.$$
a. Elasticity $\alpha = \frac{1}{2}$.   b. Elasticity $\alpha = 2$.

Considering now a preference field for n commodities, suppose the demand function for the first commodity is of the form (2). The function (2) must then allow the representation (4·5·4), and so we infer

(3) $$E = e_1 + e_2 + \cdots + e_n.$$

In words: Income elasticity equals the sum of price and cross elasticities. We note that this is a special case of the Slutsky-Schultz theorem of Ch. 6·1.

If we ask whether a demand function of the type (2)–(3) can result from an individual preference field, it is easy to see that the answer is partly in the negative, inasmuch as if one or more of the elasticities differ from unity such a function cannot satisfy the balance relation (4·5·2) in the whole range of the variables involved. For part of the field, however, it is perfectly possible to yield a demand function of the general type (2)–(3).

Illustration.[1] Let us construct an indifference map with $n = 2$ for which

(4) $$Q_1 (\mu, p_1, p_2) = A \mu^a p_1^{-a}   A > 0.$$

Inserting this function in the balance relation (4·5·2) we obtain

(5) $$Q_2 (\mu, p_1, p_2) = \frac{\mu}{p_2} \left[1 - A \left(\frac{p_1}{\mu} \right)^{1-a} \right].$$

Solving for the relative prices, (4)–(5) give

(6) $$p_1/\mu = A^{1/a} q_1^{-1/a}   p_2/\mu = (1 - A^{1/a} q_1^{(a-1)/a})/q_2.$$

These being the price functions as defined by (4·6·3), we obtain the following differential equation of type (4·6·2) for the map sought for,

(7) $$\frac{A^{1/a} q_1^{-1/a}}{1 - A^{1/a} q_1^{(a-1)/a}} dq_1 + \frac{1}{q_2} dq_2 = 0.$$

The integration is elementary, and gives the equation of the map in the form $U(q_1, q_2) = c$. It turns out that the solution gives the demand function desired, but for $a \neq 1$ only in a certain region of the map. This region is different for $a < 1$ and $a > 1$. We indicate below (a) the equation of the map in the form $U(q_1, q_2) = c$, (b) the range for the relative price p_1/μ where the demand function of q_1 is given by (4), and (c) the region of the map where the optimal budget is given by (4)–(5).

Under-elastic demand, $a < 1$:

$$\frac{q_2}{q_1}[q_1^{(1-a)/a} - A^{1/a}]^{a/(1-a)} = c; \qquad \frac{p_1}{\mu} \leq A^{-1/(1-a)}; \qquad q_1 \geq A^{1/(1-a)}.$$

Fig. 1a shows the map of this type obtained for $a = 1/2$, $A = 1$. In the region where the solution does not correspond to the problem, the map has been completed by lines parallel to the q_2-axis.

Over-elastic demand, $a > 1$:

$$q_2[1 - A^{1/a} q_1^{(a-1)/a}]^{-a/(a-1)} = c; \qquad \frac{p_1}{\mu} \geq A^{1/(a-1)}; \qquad q_1 \leq A^{-1/(a-1)}.$$

Fig. 1b shows this map for $a = 2$, $A = 1$. In the vicinity of the point $q_1 = 1$, $q_2 = 0$ the map has been modified in order to avoid having the indifference curves run together (otherwise the preference level at $q_1 = 1$, $q_2 = 0$ would not be well-defined).

Normal-elastic demand, $a = 1$:

$$q_1^A q_2^{1-A} = c, \qquad \text{where } A < 1; \quad 0 < p_1 < \infty; \quad 0 < q_1 < \infty.$$

Here the case $A = 1$ is trivial, giving a map formed by lines parallel to the q_2-axis.

5. Törnqvist's system of demand functions.[1] – The system was briefly introduced in Ch. 1·1 [cf Fig. 1·1·3]. Devised for the analysis of family budget data, the system refers to demand as a function of income. The Törnqvist system has the great merit of being constructed so as to be applicable over a wide range of income. Nevertheless it is very simple. When applied to family budget data from Finland and Sweden the system has given an excellent fit.

Törnqvist's demand functions, here denoted by $d(\mu)$, are of three types, referring to commodities classified as necessities, relative luxuries, and luxuries. It will be observed that the parameters can be specified as involving price p in such manner that $d(\mu)$ takes the form (4·5·4). [Cf also Ex. 13.] Writing $d(\mu) = p \cdot q$, we can, further, as done below, interpret $d(\mu)$ as the consumer's expenditure on the commodity considered.

Necessities:

$$(1) \qquad d(\mu) = d(\infty) \frac{\mu}{\mu + \beta}, \qquad\qquad \beta > 0.$$

With $d(\mu)$ interpreted as expenditure, $d(\infty)$ is the finite amount the consumer spends on the commodity considered if his income is very high.

Relative luxuries:

$$(2) \qquad d(\mu) = d(\infty) \frac{\mu - \mu_0}{\mu + \beta}, \qquad\qquad \mu_0 > 0, \beta > -\mu_0.$$

The amount μ_0 is the income level below which the consumer has no demand for the commodity in question.

Luxuries:

$$(3) \qquad d(\mu) = \alpha \mu \frac{\mu - \mu_0}{\mu + \beta}, \qquad \alpha > 0, \mu_0 > 0, \beta > -\mu_0.$$

For very high levels of income, the consumer tends to spend the fraction α of his income on the commodity considered. In fact, $d(\mu)/\mu \to \alpha$ as $\mu \to \infty$. We note that if $d_1(\mu)$ is of type (1) the function

$$d_3(\mu) = \mu - d_1(\mu)$$

will be of type (3). Thus Törnqvist's system is logically consistent in the following sense: Let the items of the consumer's budget be lumped together in two aggregates, and suppose that the demand function of the first aggregate is of type (1); then the demand function for the second aggregate will be of type (3).

Functions (1)–(3) being increasing, we see that an adaptation of the parameters will make them decreasing, so as to be applicable to inferior goods. We note two cases.

Inferior commodities:

$$(4) \qquad d(\mu) = d(\infty) \frac{\mu}{\mu - \beta} \qquad d(\mu) = d(\infty) \frac{\mu - \mu_0}{\mu - \beta}$$

with $\mu > \beta > 0$ and $\mu > \beta > \mu_0$, respectively,

6. Aggregate commodities. Leontief–Hicks' theorem. – As stated in Ch. 4·1 (a) the commodities dealt with in demand theory are regarded as well-defined and distinct. This, however, is a simplifying abstraction such as is met in any theory about real phenomena. Almost every commodity is the group label of a more or less vague aggregate of different items and qualities. In practice, what makes it realistic to disregard the group character of the commodities is the general experience that price changes within an aggregate are approximately uniform. We shall now examine the situation in some detail, and in particular we shall bring home a point stressed by J. R. Hicks (1939), viz. that in the theory of consumer demand an aggregate can be dealt with as a single commodity, provided all price changes within the aggregate are proportional.[1]

The first difficulty about aggregate consumption is its measurement. Assuming that the aggregate is formed by a group of m different commodities, referred to as sub-items, each with a well-defined measuring unit, we shall consider three different measures for the aggregate.[2]

a. For the aggregate, a quantity q_i is defined as the direct sum of the sub-item quantities,

(1) $$q_i = q_{i1} + \cdots + q_{im}.$$

This measure may be used if the sub-items are not too different; it is legitimate e.g., for butter and margarine.

b. An aggregate quantity q_i^* is defined as a weighted sum of the sub-item quantities, say

(2) $$q_i^* = w_1 q_{i1} + \cdots + w_m q_{im}$$

with weights w_i satisfying $w_i > 0$. This measure covers the frequent case when a more or less conventional measuring unit has been devised for the specific purpose of comparing and summing up the sub-items, e.g., when measuring the various crops in terms of harvest units.

c. An aggregate expenditure x_i is defined as the sum of the sub-item expenditures,

(3) $$x_i = x_{i1} + \cdots + x_{im} = p_{i1} q_{i1} + \cdots + p_{im} q_{im}.$$

This measure is adequate if the sub-items are widely different, as they often are in family budget data, for instance.

Let us now consider a preference field where the first commodity is a group label for m sub-items. We shall suppose that all prices within the aggregate vary in proportion, say

(4) $$p_{11} = \lambda_1 p_1, \quad \ldots, \quad p_{1m} = \lambda_m p_1 \qquad \text{with } \lambda_1 > 0, \ldots, \lambda_m > 0$$

where $\lambda_1, \ldots, \lambda_m$ indicate the fixed ratios of the sub-item prices. Then we have

THEOREM 1. *Suppose that within a certain group of commodities all price changes are proportional. In the theory of consumer demand such a group can be treated as a single commodity.*

This will be referred to as *Leontief-Hicks' theorem.*[3] In the notation (4), its precise meaning is

$$\sum_{k=1}^{m} \lambda_k Q_{1k}(p_{11}, \ldots, p_{1m}, p_2, \ldots, p_n, \mu) = Q_1^*(p_1, \ldots, p_n, \mu)$$

$$Q_i(p_{11}, \ldots, p_{1m}, p_2, \ldots, p_n, \mu) = Q_i^*(p_1, \ldots, p_n, \mu) \qquad i = 2, \ldots, n$$

where the demand functions Q refer to the given preference field in $n + m - 1$ quantities, whereas the functions Q^* refer to a field in the n quantities

$$q_1 = \lambda_1 q_{11} + \cdots + \lambda_m q_{1m} \quad \text{and} \quad q_2, \ldots, q_n.$$

For a proof we shall consider the case $n = 2$, $m = 2$, as is sufficient, since the argument is perfectly general. Let $U(q_{11}, q_{12}, q_2)$ be the preference function of the given field. Then if we consider the entire family of balance planes, their intersections with an arbitrary plane of type $q_2 = c$ will on the assumption (4) be a set of parallel lines L, the slope of which is determined by the fixed price ratio λ_1/λ_2 for the sub-items. It follows that on each line L there is at most

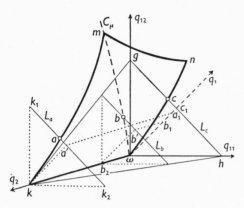

Fig. 5·6·1. Illustration of
Leontief-Hicks' theorem.

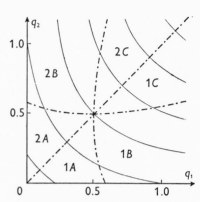

Fig. 6·5·1. Illustration of
Theorem 6·5·2 and Exercise 33.

one point, say $q^* = (q_{11}^*, q_{12}^*, q_2^*)$, that can appear as optimal, irrespective of how p_1, p_2 and μ vary. The locus of points q^* is the purchase region [Ch. 4·5], and since there is only one q^* on each line L the purchase region will reduce to a surface, say S. It is only the budgets q^* of this surface that will matter in the demand structure; in other words, the relevant preference field will be in two dimensions only. In this field we may take $q_1 = \lambda_1 q_{11}^* + \lambda_2 q_{12}^*$ and q_2 for quantity variables, so that q_1 will be an aggregate measure of type (2). The corresponding indifference map will be given by

$$U^*(q_1, q_2) = c,$$

where U^* is the function obtained by inserting in $U(q_{11}, q_{12}, q_2)$ the expressions $q_{11}^* = f_1(q_1, q_2)$, $q_{12}^* = f_2(q_1, q_2)$ that make $U(q_{11}, q_{12}, q_2)$ a maximum, subject to the side condition $\lambda_1 q_{11} + \lambda_2 q_{12} = q_1$.

Illustration. In Fig. 1 we have made $\lambda_1 = \lambda_2 = 1$. Hence all lines L make equal angles with the q_{11}-and q_{12}-axes, and the bisector of these axes is the q_1-axis. The balance plane $g h k$ has b for optimal budget. Thus b is a point of the surface S. The q_1- and q_2-coordinates of $b = (b_{11}, b_{12}, b_2)$ are ωb_1 and ωb_2, where ωb_1 equals the perpendicular $b_2 b'$ from b_2 to the line $L = L_b$ that passes through b. The broken curve C_μ is the income-consumption curve through b. Thus C_μ is a curve in the surface S. The surface $\omega k m n$ is a fragment of S. The graph finally shows the q_1- and q_2-coordinates of a and c, two other points of S. The curve $k m$ is the intersection between S and the plane of the page, $k k_1 k_2$. Hence a is the optimal budget in some balance plane that intersects the plane of the page along $k_1 k_2$. Similarly, c is the optimal budget in some balance plane through $g h$.

Given the preference index of Ex. 6, that is $U(q_{11}, q_{12}, q_2) = (q_{11} q_{12} + q_{11}) q_2$, suppose $p_{11} = p_{12}$, so that $\lambda_1 = \lambda_2 = 1$. Then $q_1 = q_{11} + q_{12}$, and $q_{11}^* = f_1(q_1, q_2) = \frac{1}{2}(q_1 + 1)$, $q_{12}^* = f_2(q_1, q_2) = \frac{1}{2}(q_1 - 1)$, which gives the preference index $U^*(q_1, q_2) = \frac{1}{4}(q_1 + 1)^2 \cdot q_2$.

Chapter 6.

RELATIONS BETWEEN INDIVIDUAL
DEMAND ELASTICITIES

1. One commodity, all elasticities. – Throughout this chapter we shall be concerned with a system of demand functions (4·5·1) referring to an individual consumer. Unless explicitly stated otherwise we shall assume once and for all that the demand structure of the consumer is ruled by a preference field, and that Assumptions A–C of Ch. 4·3 are satisfied. After the detailed theorems of Ch. 4·7–8 it will be clear that the results of the present chapter, with little qualification, remain valid on Assumptions A*–C* of Ch. 4·7.

THEOREM 1. *For the individual demand of any commodity, the income elasticity equals the sum of price and cross elasticities, or in symbols*

$$(1) \qquad E_\mu Q_i = e_{p_1} Q_i + \cdots + e_{p_n} Q_i \qquad\qquad i = 1, \ldots, n.$$

This will be referred to as *Slutsky-Schultz' relation.*[1] Transforming to derivatives, it reads

$$(2) \qquad \mu \frac{\partial Q_i}{\partial \mu} + p_1 \frac{\partial Q_i}{\partial p_1} + \cdots + p_n \frac{\partial Q_i}{\partial p_n} = 0.$$

For the equivalent relations (1)–(2) we shall first give Slutsky's proof. Making use of formulae (4·5·6–7), we form the left side in (2). Omitting the factor $\varkappa/M$, we obtain

$$\mu M_{0i} + \sum_{k=1}^n p_k M_{ki} - M_{0i} \sum_{k=1}^n p_k q_k \qquad \text{which is the same as} \qquad \frac{1}{\varkappa} \sum_{k=1}^n U_k M_{ki},$$

as seen from (4·5·2) and (4·5·5). The last sum is zero, equalling the determinant obtained from (4·4·8) by replacing the $(i+1)$st column by the first.

A second proof is to differentiate the identity (4·5·3) with respect to λ, and then set $\lambda = 1$; this simple device leads directly to (2). It will be observed that the second proof is nothing else than Euler's theorem on homogeneous functions as applied to the demand functions Q_i, these by (4·5·3) being homogeneous of order zero.[2]

2. One elasticity, all commodities. – The theorem of the previous section being implied in the fundamental relation of proportionality (4·5·3), we shall now see that the equally fundamental balance relation (4·5·2) implies

THEOREM 1. *Taking the expenditures for weights, the weighted average of a consumer's income elasticities is unity, or in symbols*

(1)
$$\frac{p_1 Q_1 \cdot E_\mu Q_1 + \cdots + p_n Q_n \cdot E_\mu Q_n}{p_1 Q_1 + \cdots + p_n Q_n} = 1.$$

Taking the same weights, the average of his demand elasticities with respect to the price of a fixed commodity equals the proportion of his income spent on this commodity, or

(2)
$$\frac{p_1 Q_1 \cdot e_{p_i} Q_1 + \cdots + p_n Q_n \cdot e_{p_i} Q_n}{p_1 Q_1 + \cdots + p_n Q_n} = \frac{p_i Q_i}{\mu} \qquad i = 1, \ldots, n.$$

We shall refer to (1)–(2) as the *Hicks-Allen relations*.[1] The first is an immediate consequence of Theorem 5·1·1 as applied to (4·5·2). Similarly, differentiating (4·5·2) with respect to p_i we obtain

$$p_1 \frac{\partial Q_1}{\partial p_i} + \cdots + p_n \frac{\partial Q_n}{\partial p_i} = -Q_i$$

which on transformation to elasticities gives (2).

3. A pair of cross elasticities. – Let us first restate Slutsky's relation (5·3·4) in terms of elasticities:

(1)
$$x_i \left[e_{p_k} Q_i - \frac{x_k}{\mu} E_\mu Q_i \right] = x_k \left[e_{p_i} Q_k - \frac{x_i}{\mu} E_\mu Q_k \right] \qquad i, k = 1, \ldots, n.$$

As before, x_i stands for the consumer's expenditure on the ith commodity.

THEOREM 1. *Suppose two commodities are such that (a) the consumer's expenditure on each is but a small fraction of his income, and (b) their mutual cross elasticities are of the same (or larger) order of magnitude as their income elasticities. Then the two cross elasticities stand, approximately, in inverse proportion to the consumer's expenditures on the two commodities, or in symbols*

(2)
$$\frac{e_{p_i} Q_k}{e_{p_k} Q_i} \sim \frac{x_i}{x_k} \qquad i, k = 1, \ldots, n.$$

On the conditions stated, (2) is, in fact, an immediate consequence of (1). We shall refer to (2) as *Hotelling-Juréen's relation*.[1]

4. Aggregate elasticities.[1] – In this section we may drop the assumption that the demand functions belong to a preference field.

Each of the aggregate expressions (5·6·1–3) can be taken as a basis for calculating elasticities with respect to income and prices. The deductions are elementary, and it is seen that Theorem 5·1·1 covers the simplest cases. Thus for income elasticities we obtain

$$(1) \qquad E_\mu q_i^* = \frac{w_1 q_{i1} E_\mu q_{i1} + \cdots + w_m q_{i\,m} E_\mu q_{i\,m}}{w_1 q_{i1} + \cdots + w_m q_{i\,m}}$$

$$(2) \qquad E_\mu x_i = \frac{x_{i1} E_\mu q_{i1} + \cdots + x_{i\,m} E_\mu q_{i\,m}}{x_{i1} + \cdots + x_{i\,m}}.$$

In words,

THEOREM 1. *The income elasticity of aggregate demand is a weighted average of the income elasticities of the sub-items. If the aggregate is measured by the quantity sum (5·6·1) or the factorized sum (5·6·2), the weights are the (factorized) quantities of the sub-items; if measured by the expenditure (5·6·3) the weights are the expenditures on the sub-items.*

Making the aggregate embrace the whole budget, so that $x_i = \mu$, we obtain as an immediate corollary (6·2·1), which we repeat as

THEOREM 2. *If all items of the consumer's budget are measured by the expenditures, their income elasticities have unity for weighted average. The weights of the average equal the expenditures of the various budget items.*

For demand as measured by a quantity sum Theorem 1 extends to price and cross elasticities. For (5·6·1) we have, as is easily verified,

$$(3) \qquad e_p q_i = \frac{q_{i1} e_p q_{i1} + \cdots + q_{i\,m} e_p q_{i\,m}}{q_{i1} + \cdots + q_{i\,m}} \qquad \begin{cases} p = p_{i1}, \ldots, p_{i\,m} \\ p = p_k \quad (k \neq i) \end{cases}$$

and similarly for (5·6·2). For demand as measured by (5·6·3) the corresponding formula is more complicated [cf Ex. 32].

As to price changes, the case of main interest is when all prices within the aggregate vary in proportion. Then if we write $p_i = \mathfrak{P}_i$ for any price index referring to the prices $p_{i\,m}$ within the aggregate, we have

$$(4) \qquad \frac{d p_{i1}}{p_{i1}} = \cdots = \frac{d p_{i\,m}}{p_{i\,m}} = \frac{d p_i}{p_i},$$

provided the index p_i satisfies the proportionality criterion (8·3·8). Letting $f(p_{i1}, \ldots, p_{i\,m})$ denote an arbitrary function of the sub-item prices, we obtain

$$df = \frac{\partial f}{\partial p_{i1}} d p_{i1} + \cdots + \frac{\partial f}{\partial p_{i\,m}} d p_{i\,m} = \left(\frac{\partial f}{\partial p_{i1}} p_{i1} + \cdots + \frac{\partial f}{\partial p_{i\,m}} p_{i\,m} \right) \cdot \frac{d p_i}{p_i}.$$

Transforming to elasticities, this gives

$$(5) \qquad e_{p_i} f = e_{p_{i1}} f + \cdots + e_{p_{i\,m}} f$$

where each term to the right is an elasticity of the ordinary type, i.e. referring to a change in the price of one of the sub-items, the other prices remaining constant. In words,

THEOREM 3. *Assuming that all prices within an aggregate vary in proportion, let p_i be a price index for the aggregate that satisfies the proportionality criterion $(8\cdot3\cdot8)$. Then any elasticity with respect to p_i equals the sum of the sub-item elasticities with respect to their prices.*

Applying Theorem 3 to the quantity sum $(5\cdot6\cdot1)$, we obtain

(6) $e_{p_i} q_{i\nu} = e_{p_{i1}} q_{i\nu} + \cdots + e_{p_{im}} q_{i\nu}, \ (\nu = 1, \ldots, m); \ \ e_{p_i} q_i = e_{p_{i1}} q_i + \cdots + e_{p_{im}} q_i.$

We transform $(6\,b)$ by the use of (3), and pay regard to $(6\,a)$. This gives

(7) $$e_{p_i} q_i = \frac{q_{i1} e_{p_i} q_{i1} + \cdots + q_{im} e_{p_i} q_{im}}{q_{i1} + \cdots + q_{im}}$$

and similarly for $(5\cdot6\cdot2)$. For $(5\cdot6\cdot3)$ the same argument gives

(8) $$e_{p_i} x_i = \frac{x_{i1} e_{p_i} x_{i1} + \cdots + x_{im} e_{p_i} x_{im}}{x_{i1} + \cdots + x_{im}}.$$

It will be observed that the elasticities to the right in (6)–(8), but not in (3), refer to assumption (4), i.e. to a proportional change in all sub-item prices. On the assumption (4), any elasticity with respect to p_i is of course the same as with respect to any of $p_{i1}, \ldots, p_{im}$.

Expressing (7)–(8) in words:

THEOREM 4. *On the assumptions of Theorem 3, the elasticity of aggregate demand is a weighted average of the elasticities of the sub-items, all elasticities being formed with respect to the price index p_i.*

5. Price and income elasticities. – The analysis in section 4 has shown that the theory of demand is applicable to aggregate commodities, provided prices and quantities are interpreted as suitable price indexes and quantity indexes. The notion of aggregate commodities will be used in this section for the study of preference fields referring to two commodities, $n = 2$. The case $n = 2$ is of importance not merely for providing instructive illustration of results valid for arbitrary fields; it will turn out that results of independent interest are obtained. For one thing, grouping the commodities in the two broad categories of necessities and luxuries, light is shed on the interdependence in the demand for these two categories. Another application refers to an arbitrary commodity as singled out against the aggregate of all other commodities.

THEOREM 1.[1] *Considering a preference field for two commodities, $n = 2$, suppose the price elasticity of one commodity is greater (less) than unity. Then the income elasticity of the other commodity is less (greater) than its price elasticity.*

Following Törnqvist (1941), we make $n = 2$ in $(6\cdot1\cdot1)$ and $(6\cdot2\cdot2)$,

(1) $E_\mu Q_2 = e_{p_1} Q_2 + e_{p_2} Q_2; \qquad x_1 . e_{p_1} Q_1 + x_2 . e_{p_1} Q_2 = x_1.$

Solving the second relation for $e_{p_1}Q_2$, and inserting in the first,

(2)　　　$e_{p_1}Q_2 = \dfrac{x_1}{x_2}(1 - e_{p_1}Q_1);$　　　　　$E_\mu Q_2 = e_{p_2}Q_2 + \dfrac{x_1}{x_2}(1 - e_{p_1}Q_1).$

By analogy,

(3)　　　$e_{p_2}Q_1 = \dfrac{x_2}{x_1}(1 - e_{p_2}Q_2);$　　　　　$E_\mu Q_1 = e_{p_1}Q_1 + \dfrac{x_2}{x_1}(1 - e_{p_2}Q_2).$

The expenditures x_1, x_2 being nonnegative, the second relation in (2)–(3) completes the proof of Theorem 1.

Commenting upon the relations (2)–(3), Törnqvist groups the commodities into "necessities" and "luxuries", with price elasticity below and above unity, respectively. This leads to the conclusion that, *as a rule, income elasticities of necessities are smaller than their price elasticities, whereas income elasticities of luxuries are greater than their price elasticities.*

The cautious formulation of this assertion pays regard to the fact, brought out in our next theorem, that (6·2·1) has no analogue for price elasticities. The theorem shows that if a single commodity, or a commodity group, is considered against the aggregate of all other commodities it is possible that both of the price elasticities lie below unity, or both above unity.

THEOREM 2.[2] *In a preference field for two commodities, $n = 2$, there are 6 possible constellations of the demand elasticities, viz.*

1 A.	$E_\mu Q_1 \leq 1 \leq e_{p_1}Q_1;$	$1 \leq E_\mu Q_2 \leq e_{p_2}Q_2;$	$e_{p_1}Q_2 \leq 0;$	$e_{p_2}Q_1 \leq 0;$
1 B.	$E_\mu Q_1 \leq e_{p_1}Q_1 \leq 1;$	$1 \leq e_{p_2}Q_2 \leq E_\mu Q_2;$	$e_{p_1}Q_2 \geq 0;$	$e_{p_2}Q_1 \leq 0;$
1 C.	$e_{p_1}Q_1 \leq E_\mu Q_1 \leq 1;$	$e_{p_2}Q_2 \leq 1 \leq E_\mu Q_2;$	$e_{p_1}Q_2 \geq 0;$	$e_{p_2}Q_1 \geq 0;$
2 A.	$1 \leq E_\mu Q_1 \leq e_{p_1}Q_1;$	$E_\mu Q_2 \leq 1 \leq e_{p_2}Q_2;$	$e_{p_1}Q_2 \leq 0;$	$e_{p_2}Q_1 \leq 0;$
2 B.	$1 \leq e_{p_1}Q_1 \leq E_\mu Q_1;$	$E_\mu Q_2 \leq e_{p_2}Q_2 \leq 1;$	$e_{p_1}Q_2 \leq 0;$	$e_{p_2}Q_1 \geq 0;$
2 C.	$e_{p_1}Q_1 \leq 1 \leq E_\mu Q_1;$	$e_{p_2}Q_2 \leq E_\mu Q_2 \leq 1;$	$e_{p_1}Q_2 \geq 0;$	$e_{p_2}Q_1 \geq 0.$

First we infer from (6·2·1) that if $E_\mu Q_1 \leq 1$ then $E_\mu Q_2 \geq 1$, and conversely. Considering the first alternative, 1 A–C are the three logical possibilities for $e_{p_1}Q_1$. As to 1 A it follows from the second relation in (3) that $1 \leq e_{p_2}Q_2$, and from the second relation in (2) that $E_\mu Q_2 \leq e_{p_2}Q_2$; further, the first relations in (2)–(3) imply $e_{p_1}Q_2 \leq 0$ and $e_{p_2}Q_1 \leq 0$. The cases 1 B and 1 C can be settled in the same manner. The cases 2 A–C, finally, are symmetrical to 1 A–C.

To complete the proof of Theorem 2 we must make sure that preference fields can be constructed so as to display the six cases. As shown in Fig. 1, p. 110, which refers to Ex. 33, the six cases not only exist, they can even occur in one and the same indifference map.

6. Nominal and real elasticities. – When representing demand as a function of prices and income, the variables may be specified either as *nominal*, i.e. prices and income as actually observed, or *real*, i.e. the nominal values divided by a consumer price index. In empirical demand analysis it is customary to work with real prices and income. As regards the rationale of this device it will be remembered, as indicated in Ch. 4·1 (b), that the theory of consumer demand rests on the assumption that money is a well-defined scale of measure. According to this approach, the inflationary and deflationary trends may be regarded as changes in the monetary unit. Thus, when assuming demand to be a function of real prices and incomes, this specification serves, by way of a first approximation, to allow for changes in the monetary unit. We shall return to this matter in Ch. 15·4.

The distinction between real and nominal values will now be examined with particular regard to demand elasticities. We have

THEOREM 1. *Elasticities with respect to real prices and income, say p_i and μ, are equal to the corresponding elasticities w.r.t. nominal prices and income, say p_i' and μ'.*

For a proof we need only reflect that the proportionality relation (4·5·3) gives, for $i = 1, \ldots, n$,

$$Q_i\left(\mu', p_1', \ldots, p_n'\right) = Q_i\left(\frac{\mu'}{\mathfrak{P}}, \frac{p_i'}{\mathfrak{P}}, \ldots, \frac{p_n'}{\mathfrak{P}}\right) = Q_i\left(\mu, p_1, \ldots, p_n\right),$$

where $\mathfrak{P}$ is a price index, and the three Q_i are identically the same demand function.

A notion related to the elasticity w.r.t. real price p_i is the elasticity formed w.r.t. nominal price p_i' on the assumption of a *compensating change in nominal income* μ'. Denoting this elasticity by $e_{p_i}^*$, a simple deduction gives

$$(1) \qquad\qquad e_{p_i}^* Q_k = e_{p_i} Q_k - \frac{x_i}{\mu} E_\mu Q_k \qquad\qquad i, k = 1, \ldots, n.$$

Similarly we may form the elasticity w.r.t. nominal price p_i' on the assumption of a compensating change *in another price*, say p_k'. Writing $e_{p_i}^{**}$ for this elasticity, we obtain

$$e_{p_i}^{**} Q_k = e_{p_i} Q_k - \frac{x_i}{x_k} e_{p_k} Q_k \qquad\qquad i, k = 1, \ldots, n.$$

We note that this is a reinterpretation of a formula given by L. Törnqvist (1941), who presents $e_{p_i}^{**} Q_i$ as the real price elasticity of Q_i. In the author's opinion, Törnqvist's interpretation is not correct, for according to Theorem 1 the real and nominal elasticities are equal.

Chapter 7.

MARKET DEMAND

1. Homogeneous markets. – The passage from individual demand to market demand is a chapter in demand theory where several approaches may be distinguished. The simplest device is perhaps to deal with the market in terms of a 'typical consumer', which is taken to represent the demand structure of the whole market. Strictly speaking, the assumptions underlying this approach are (a) that all consumers in the market have the same indifference map, and (b) that they have the same income. It is plain that on these assumptions all results of Chs. 4–6 apply to market demand. Specifically, the theorems of Slutsky-Schultz, Hicks-Allen, and Hotelling-Juréen allow such interpretation. We state this simple fact as

THEOREM 1. *Suppose a market is homogeneous in the sense that all consumers have the same preferences, and the same income. Interpreting quantities, incomes, expenditures, etc., as market averages, all theorems of Ch. 4–6 will apply to market demand.*

2. Demand elasticities for individuals and markets. – In economic theory ever since Walras (1874) a customary device for dealing with market demand and supply is to form market totals by summation over the individuals. This approach will be reviewed in this section and the next. The fundamental point is that if demand functions for the individuals are established on the assumption of individual preference fields, no further argument is required to establish a demand function for the market.[1]

In Ch. 4·1 we specified the basic concepts underlying our analysis of individual demand. In point of principle, the same concepts will be used for the analysis of market demand. Specifically, the market analysis refers to n commodities, and a fixed budget period. Otherwise, the following points will be sufficient to indicate the assumptions adopted in the passage from individual to market demand.

a. The prices $p_1, \ldots, p_n$ are the same over the entire market.

b. The market consists of s consumers, each with a well-defined preference function that satisfies Assumptions A–C and is denoted by

$$(1) \qquad\qquad U^{(k)}(q_1, \ldots, q_n) \qquad\qquad k = 1, \ldots, s.$$

More generally, the market is assumed to consist of s sections or strata that are homogeneous in the sense of Theorem 7·1·1.

    c. The individual incomes, or the total incomes of the s market sections, are $\mu^{(1)}, \ldots, \mu^{(s)}$ or in vector notation $\mu = [\mu^{(1)}, \ldots, \mu^{(s)}]$. The total market income, say μ, is accordingly given by the sum

$$(2) \qquad \mu = \mu^{(1)} + \cdots + \mu^{(s)}.$$

As a special case we introduce the assumption

    c*. The individual or sectional incomes vary in the same proportion,

$$(3) \qquad \frac{d\mu^{(1)}}{\mu^{(1)}} = \cdots = \frac{d\mu^{(s)}}{\mu^{(s)}} = \frac{d\mu}{\mu},$$

which assumption is the same as

$$\mu^{(k)} = \alpha_k \cdot \mu, \quad \text{with} \quad \alpha_1 + \cdots + \alpha_s = 1.$$

To avoid a new series of subscripts and other symbols, we shall use much the same notation for market totals as we used earlier for individual quantities, demand functions, etc. Symbols referring to individuals or market sections will be indicated by superscripts, as in (1)–(3). In the verbal treatment we shall usually refer to market sections, since this interpretation not only covers individual variation as a special case but also is of greater relevance in the applications, of course.

Until further notice, we may drop the assumption that the individual demand functions have reference to preference fields. The fundamental relation is that market demand for any commodity is the total of the sectional demand, in symbols

$$(4) \qquad Q_i(\mu, p_1, \ldots, p_n) = \sum_k Q_i^{(k)}(\mu^{(k)}, p_1, \ldots, p_n) \qquad i = 1, \ldots, n.$$

Here, as in the rest of this chapter, the sum over k runs from 1 to s. The market demand functions $Q_i(\mu, p_1, \ldots, p_n)$ will involve the sectional incomes as independent variables, except under assumption c*.

The following three theorems are easily derived from (4), making use of Theorem 5·1·1.

THEOREM 1. *For the market demand of any commodity, the elasticity with respect to any price is a weighted average of the corresponding sectional elasticities; the weights are given by the quantities demanded by the market sections. In symbols,*

$$(5) \qquad e_{p_k} Q_i = \frac{Q_i^{(1)} \cdot e_{p_k} Q_i^{(1)} + \cdots + Q_i^{(s)} \cdot e_{p_k} Q_i^{(s)}}{Q_i^{(1)} + \cdots + Q_i^{(s)}} \qquad i, k = 1, \ldots, n.$$

Elasticities with respect to income are in general more complicated because we have assumed that the market is homogeneous w.r.t. price changes, but in general not w.r.t. income changes. To begin with, we note that (2) gives

$$d\mu = d\mu^{(1)} + \cdots + d\mu^{(s)}.$$

Further we note the formula

$$(6) \qquad E_\mu \mu^{(k)} = \frac{\mu}{\mu^{(k)}} \cdot \frac{d\mu^{(k)}}{d\mu} \qquad\qquad k = 1, \ldots, s$$

which gives the elasticity of a sectional income with respect to the total income. If the sectional incomes vary in the same proportion (assumption c*), it is seen that (6) reduces to

$$E_\mu \mu^{(k)} = 1 \qquad\qquad k = 1, \ldots, s.$$

THEOREM 2. *For the income elasticity of market demand we have*

$$(7) \qquad E_\mu Q_i = \frac{Q_i^{(1)} \cdot E_\mu \mu^{(1)} \cdot E_{\mu^{(1)}} Q_i^{(1)} + \cdots + Q_i^{(s)} \cdot E_\mu \mu^{(s)} \cdot E_{\mu^{(s)}} Q_i^{(s)}}{Q_i^{(1)} + \cdots + Q_i^{(s)}}; \qquad i = 1, \ldots, n.$$

If the sectional incomes vary in the same proportion, we have

$$(8) \qquad E_\mu Q_i = \frac{Q_i^{(1)} \cdot E_{\mu^{(1)}} Q_i^{(1)} + \cdots + Q_i^{(s)} \cdot E_{\mu^{(s)}} Q_i^{(s)}}{Q_i^{(1)} + \cdots + Q_i^{(s)}}.$$

The average (8) is seen to be of the same type as (5).

Our third theorem refers to market expenditure as defined by

$$x_i = x_i^{(1)} + \cdots + x_i^{(s)} = p_i (Q_i^{(1)} + \cdots + Q_i^{(s)}).$$

THEOREM 3. *Theorems 1–2 remain valid if sectional and market quantities $Q_i^{(k)}$ and Q_i are replaced by expenditures $x_i^{(k)}$ and x_i; for instance, the analogue to (8) reads*

$$(9) \qquad E_\mu x_i = \frac{1}{x_i} \sum_k x_i^{(k)} \cdot E_{\mu^{(k)}} x_i^{(k)} = \frac{1}{x_i} \sum_k x_i^{(k)} \cdot E_{\mu^{(k)}} Q_i^{(k)} \qquad i = 1, \ldots, n.$$

Let us now resume the assumption that the individual demand functions are of the special type that is obtained from preference fields. Then in immediate consequence of Theorem 4·5·2 we obtain

THEOREM 4. *The market demand functions satisfy the balance relation*

$$(10) \qquad p_1 \cdot Q_1(\mu, p_1, \ldots, p_n) + \cdots + p_n \cdot Q_n(\mu, p_1, \ldots, p_n) = \mu,$$

and the proportionality relation

$$(11) \qquad Q_i(\lambda \mu, \lambda p_1, \ldots, \lambda p_n) = Q_i(\mu, p_1, \ldots, p_n) \qquad \lambda > 0; i = 1, \ldots, n.$$

3. Relations between market elasticities. – We shall now examine whether the relations between individual elasticities given in Ch. 6 can be extended to market elasticities. Clearly all relations of Ch. 6 will allow this generalization if there exists an indifference map that corresponds to the market demand functions as defined by (7·2·4). Now in general such a map will not exist, for the reason that the integrability relation (4·6·1) is not additive with respect to the individual functions $R_i^{(s)}$ [cf Ex. 27]. As a consequence it may occur that a relation of Ch. 6 has no exact analogue in the case of market demand. Most of the relations in Ch. 6, however, do allow an extension to market demand. We have, in fact,

THEOREM 1.[1] *The relations between individual demand elasticities given in Ch. 6 are valid also for market demand. The only exceptions are the Slutsky relation (6·3·1), the Slutsky-Schultz relation (6·1·1) and the theorems of Ch. 6·5. Whereas (6·3·1) has no direct analogue for market demand, (6·1·1) and the theorems of Ch. 6·5 are valid if the sectional incomes vary proportionately (assumption c^*). Otherwise, the income elasticities involved refer to independent sectional incomes, in agreement with (7·2·6).*

The theorem referring to some ten relations, the proofs of which are elementary and follow the same pattern, it suffices to verify the theorem for one of the relations. Choosing (6·4·1), and considering the case of direct summation, the market demand for the aggregate commodity is given by

$$Q_i = \sum_k Q_{i1}^{(k)} + \cdots + \sum_k Q_{im}^{(k)} .$$

Hence,

$$dQ_i = \sum_k \frac{\partial Q_{i1}^{(k)}}{\partial \mu^{(k)}} d\mu^{(k)} + \cdots + \sum_k \frac{\partial Q_{im}^{(k)}}{\partial \mu^{(k)}} d\mu^{(k)} .$$

Transforming to elasticities, and making use of (7·2·7) as applied to $Q_{i1}, \ldots, Q_{im}$, we obtain

$$Q_i \cdot E_\mu Q_i = \sum_k Q_{i1}^{(k)} \cdot E_{\mu^{(k)}} Q_{i1}^{(k)} \cdot E_\mu \mu^{(k)} + \cdots + \sum_k Q_{im}^{(k)} \cdot E_{\mu^{(k)}} Q_{im}^{(k)} \cdot E_\mu \mu^{(k)}$$

$$= Q_{i1} \cdot E_\mu Q_{i1} + \cdots + Q_{im} \cdot E_\mu Q_{im}$$

which is the same as (6·4·1) when all $w_i = 1$, as was to be verified.

4. The stratification approach. Roy's theorem. – Part of the analysis in Ch. 4–7 is more general than the rest in that no use is made of the notion of indifference map. Such are notably the additive relations between separate and aggregate commodities [Ch. 6·4], and between individual and market demand [Ch. 7·2–3]. This kind of approach will now be followed up for market demand by specifying the market sections or market strata in terms of distribution functions that depend on a parameter, a device which will be referred to as *the stratification approach*. The method is so simple and flexible, however, that it should perhaps not be given a name of its own. As to its origin we note that it was employed by Pareto (1895).

Beginning with a particular case, let us consider the market demand for a certain commodity. Suppose

(i) individual demand is a function of income μ, say of Törnqvist's first type,

(1) $$q(\mu) = \alpha \frac{\mu}{\mu + \beta} ;$$

(ii) the consumers are distributed with respect to income μ in accordance with a frequency function depending on a parameter a, say Pareto's law

(2) $$f(\mu, a) = (a-1) c^{a-1} \mu^{-a} \quad \text{for } \mu > c; \qquad f(\mu, a) = 0 \quad \text{for } \mu \leq c.$$

Then the average market income M and the average market demand Q may be expressed as functions of a,

(3) $$M(a) = \int_0^\infty \mu \cdot f(\mu, a)\, d\mu \qquad Q(a) = \int_0^\infty q(\mu) \cdot f(\mu, a)\, d\mu.$$

Thus prepared, suppose the income distribution changes in such manner that there is a shift in the parameter a. For an infinitesimal shift, the market income and the market demand will change by amounts given by

(4) $$dM(a) = \int_0^\infty \mu \frac{\partial}{\partial a} f(\mu, a)\, d\mu\, da; \qquad dQ(a) = \int_0^\infty q(\mu) \frac{\partial}{\partial a} f(\mu, a)\, d\mu\, da.$$

We see that $f(\mu, a)$ may in (3)-(4) be interpreted as an arbitrary income distribution with a for parameter. Hence,

THEOREM 1. *Suppose that the individual demand for a certain commodity is a function $q(\mu)$ of income μ, and that the consumers' income distribution has $f(\mu, \lambda)$ for frequency function. Then the elasticity of market demand with respect to such an income change as is due to a shift in the parameter λ is given by*

(5) $$E_M Q = \frac{M(\lambda)}{Q(\lambda)} \frac{dQ(\lambda)}{dM(\lambda)}$$

where the right-hand member is obtained from (3)-(4) on substitution of λ for a.

Illustrations. From the empirical findings in Part V we quote the following demand function for animal foodstuffs in Sweden,

$$q(\mu) = 5660 \frac{\mu}{\mu + 66.67}.$$

The function $q(\mu)$ refers to a consumer with income μ, giving his yearly demand for animal foods, measured in units of 10^9 calories. The income variable μ is an income index, normed so as to give $\mu = 100$ for the period 1930-39.

To illustrate Theorem 1, let us specify (1) to be the above function, setting $\alpha = 5\,660$, $\beta = 66.67$. For $f(\mu, \lambda)$ we take the Pareto distribution (2) with $a = 2.5$ and $c = 33.33$, which makes the average income equal 100. For the parameter λ and its variation, we shall consider three alternatives.

(A) Let λ be the exponential parameter a in Pareto's distribution (2). Letting λ vary, keeping $c = 33.33$ fixed, formulae (3) then give $M(\lambda)$ and $Q(\lambda)$. In Fig. 1 the heavy curve shows $\log Q(\lambda)$ against $\log M(\lambda)$. Finally, making use of (5), this curve gives $E_M Q$ as a function of λ. For $\lambda = a = 2.5$ we obtain

$$M = 100 \qquad\qquad E_M Q = 0.1415.$$

(B) Suppose that all incomes are raised by an additive constant $\lambda > 0$. Writing $f(\mu)$ for the income distribution before the shift, Theorem 1 applies with

$$f(\mu, \lambda) = f(\mu - \lambda) \text{ for } \mu > \lambda; \qquad f(\mu, \lambda) = 0 \text{ for } \mu \leq \lambda.$$

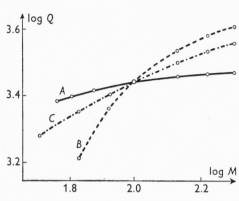

Fig. 7·4·1. The stratification approach. Relationships between total demand $Q(\lambda)$ and total income $M(\lambda)$.

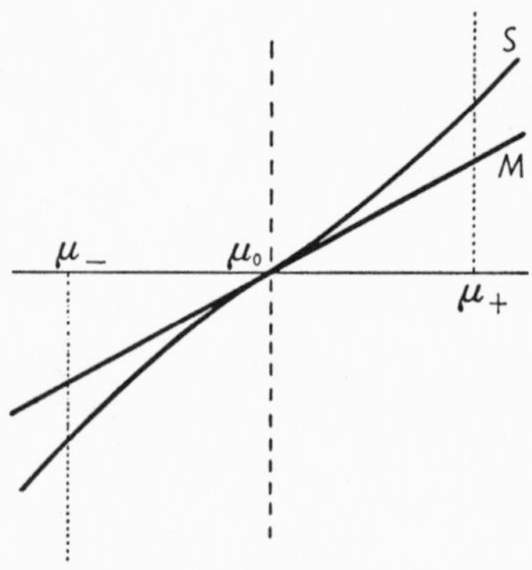

Fig. 7·6·1. Subjective evaluation (S) versus mathematical expectation (M) of risks and chances.

Again taking $f(\mu)$ to be Pareto's law with parameters 2.5 and 33.33, we have obtained the broken curve in Fig. 1. Again this curve gives $E_M Q$. For $\lambda = 0$ we obtain

$$M = 100 \qquad\qquad E_M Q = 0.872 .$$

(C) Supposing that all incomes change by a multiplicative constant $\lambda > 0$, Theorem 1 applies with

$$f(\mu, \lambda) = f(\mu/\lambda)/\lambda \qquad\qquad M(\lambda) = \lambda \cdot M(1) .$$

With the same specification as in (A)–(B) we have obtained the stippled curve in Fig. 1. For $\lambda = 1$ this gives

$$M = 100 \qquad\qquad E_M Q = 0.473 .$$

Summing up, we have in (A)–(C) obtained three different elasticities for the income elasticity of animal foods, all of which refer to a parametric shift in the income distribution. The elasticities are directly comparable, since the values of the parameters λ for which the elasticity has been evaluated give one and the same income distribution, viz. Pareto's law (2) with $a = 2.5$ and $c = 33.33$. Comparing the elasticities, we see that the demand is very sensitive for an additive increase in all incomes, and rather sensitive for a proportionate change in all incomes, whereas demand is not much affected by a shift in the exponential parameter of the Pareto distribution. These results are rather natural in view of the fact that the demand function $q(\mu)$ dealt with is of a type that is appropriate for necessities.

The flexibility and the general scope of the stratification method should be clear from the above applications.[1] We shall now briefly consider one or two applications referring to price elasticities.

Suppose that the individual demand for a certain commodity is a known function $q(p, \xi)$ of price p and a stratifying variable ξ. Further let the consumers be distributed over the strata in accordance with the frequency function $f(\xi)$. Then the market demand is given by

$$(6) \qquad\qquad Q(p) = \int q(p, \xi) f(\xi) \, d\xi$$

and its derivative with respect to price p by

$$\frac{\partial Q}{\partial p} = \int \frac{\partial}{\partial p} q(p, \xi) \cdot f(\xi) \, d\xi.$$

Inserting these expressions in

(7) $$e_p Q = -\frac{p}{Q(p)} \frac{\partial Q}{\partial p}$$

we obtain the price elasticity of market demand.

Formula (7) may be specified so as to give a theorem due to R. Roy (1930).[2] Let G be a group of commodities, referred to as 'first necessities'. Suppose that for every consumer the demand for G is satiated when reaching a certain quantity s, and that all his income is spent on G as long as the demand for G is not satiated.[3] Writing p for the price of G, the demand function for G will then be

(8) $$q(p, \mu) = \mu/p \text{ for } \mu/p < s; \qquad q(p, \mu) = s \text{ for } \mu/p \geq s.$$

We are now in a position to apply (6)–(7), taking income μ to be the parameter ξ. The market demand will be given by

(9) $$Q(p) = \int_0^{sp} \frac{\mu}{p} f(\mu) \, d\mu + s \int_{sp}^{\infty} f(\mu) \, d\mu = Q_1 + Q_2,$$

where Q_1 is the unsatiated and Q_2 the satiated demand. Multiplying in (9) by p, the second member reduces on differentiation, giving

$$p \frac{\partial Q}{\partial p} + Q(p) = s \int_{sp}^{\infty} f(\mu) \, d\mu = Q_2.$$

Hence

(10) $$e_p Q = -\frac{p}{Q} \frac{\partial Q}{\partial p} = 1 - \frac{Q_2}{Q} = \frac{Q_1}{Q_1 + Q_2},$$

which is Roy's theorem. In words,

THEOREM 2. *For an aggregate of 'first necessities' as defined by (8), the price elasticity is the ratio between the unsatiated and the total demand.*

As a final illustration we shall consider a case of price discrimination.[4] Suppose that price p is discriminated between the strata, say as a function $p = p(\xi, \lambda)$, where λ is another parameter. Then $q(p, \xi)$ becomes a function of ξ and λ, say $q^*(\xi, \lambda)$. The market demand will be given by

(11) $$Q(\lambda) = \int q^*(\xi, \lambda) f(\xi) \, d\xi.$$

If the price discrimination is modified, in accordance with an infinitesimal change in the parameter λ, the effect on market demand will be given by an elasticity formula analogous to (7).

5. Rationed commodities. Malmquist's theorem. – When commodities are rationed, demand analysis is confronted with special problems. In Sweden, for instance, alcoholic liquors have been rationed since 1920, the purchase of distilled liquors being limited to some 3 litres per month. The rich statistical material collected by the rationing authorities has recently been subjected to a detailed statistical analysis by S. Malmquist (1948). From the theoretical part of his analysis we shall now restate the main theorem.

Considering a commodity G with price p, suppose that its price elasticity is the same function of p for all consumers, say $e(p)$. The individual demand function for G will then allow the representation [cf Ex. 3]

$$(1) \quad q(p) = q_0 \cdot d(p), \quad \text{with } d(p) = \exp\left(-\int_{p_0}^{p} \frac{e(p)}{p}\, dp\right), \quad \text{and } q(p_0) = q_0,$$

where the consumption q_0 at price p_0 varies from one individual to another. Suppose further that we know the distribution of the consumers with respect to q_0, say that the frequency function is $f(q_0)$. If there is no rationing, the average market demand for G will then be given by

$$(2) \quad Q(p) = \int_0^{\infty} q_0 \cdot d(p) \cdot f(q_0)\, dq_0 \qquad \text{with } e_p Q = e(p) = -\frac{p}{d(p)} d'(p).$$

Now suppose that the commodity is rationed, say with a maximum purchase of R measuring units per budget period. Writing $Q^*(p)$ for the rationed market demand, let us examine $Q^*(p)$ for prices p in the infinitesimal vicinity of p_0 (as is clear from (1), p_0 is arbitrary). We have

$$Q^*(p) = \int_0^{R} q_0\, d(p)\, f(q_0)\, dq_0 + R\int_R^{\infty} f(q_0)\, dq_0 = Q_1^* + Q_2^*, \qquad \text{provided } p \sim p_0,$$

where Q_1^* and Q_2^* represent unrestricted and restricted demand, i.e. those parts of the total consumption disposed of by consumers that do not or do purchase the whole ration R. Differentiating, and making use of (2),

$$dQ^*(p) = d'(p)\, dp \cdot \int_0^{R} q_0 f(q_0)\, dq_0 = -\frac{d(p)}{p} e(p)\, dp \cdot \int_0^{R} q_0 f(q_0)\, dq_0.$$

This gives

$$e_p Q^* = -\frac{p}{Q^*}\frac{dQ^*}{dp} = \frac{Q_1^*}{Q_1^* + Q_2^*} e(p),$$

which is Malmquist's theorem. In words,[1]

THEOREM 1. *On the assumptions indicated, the price elasticity of rationed demand is a fraction of the price elasticity of unrationed demand; the fraction equals the ratio between the unrestricted part and the total of the rationed demand.*

We see that there is a certain formal analogy with Roy's theorem (7·4·10), but clearly the assumptions underlying Malmquist's theorem are of a much wider scope.

6. Probabilistic approaches. – The demand theory thus far presented may seem unrealistic in being too precise and rigorous, in making no allowance for random features in the consumers' behaviour. This rigour, however, has not the character of an arbitrary assumption; rather it will under fairly general conditions approximate reality. To bring home this assertion, we may regard the individual budget choice as involving a chance element, say

$$(1) \qquad\qquad q_i^* = q_i + \Delta_i \qquad\qquad i = 1, \ldots, n$$

where $q_1, \ldots, q_n$ is the optimal budget of Ch. 4·4, and Δ_i is a random variable with zero expectation and finite variance,

$$(2) \qquad\qquad E(\Delta_i) = 0 \qquad E(\Delta_i^2) < \infty \qquad i = 1, \ldots, n.$$

Now let us consider a market where the consumers' demand patterns follow the scheme (1)–(2), in general with individual differences between the preference fields. Let us further assume that the random components referring to different consumers are independent in the sense of probability theory, in symbols

$$(3) \qquad \Delta_1^{(i)}, \ldots, \Delta_n^{(i)} \quad \text{independent of} \quad \Delta_1^{(k)}, \ldots, \Delta_n^{(k)} \qquad i, k = 1, \ldots, s.$$

The market demand for the ith commodity will then be Σq_i^*, where the sum runs over the s consumers. By the law of large numbers as referring to multi-dimensional distributions, it then follows that the market demand Σq_i^* will for every i approximate Σq_i, the random term $\Sigma \Delta_i$ being of smaller order of magnitude. Briefly expressed, the individual randomness may be neglected when forming market totals.[1]

For the exact conditions under which the multidimensional law of large numbers is valid, reference is made to the relevant theorems of probability [for a treatment well suited for the present applications, see A. Khintchine (1933)]. We note that the random components $\Delta_1^{(i)}, \ldots, \Delta_n^{(i)}$ that refer to the same consumer should in general be regarded as interdependent.

In Ch. 7·2, when applying Pareto's theory to a group of consumers, no assumption whatever is made about the structure of the individual preferences. They may be equal or different, and further we note that since the approach is static the theory need not consider how the preferences have arisen. Specifically, the theory remains valid whether we assume that the consumers influence each other or whether they are independent in forming their behaviour patterns. Now in the theory based on the more general assumptions (1)–(3), condition (3) requires that the consumers are independent as regards the random element in their transactions. It will be noticed that (3) may be somewhat weakened, but that some degree of independence between the consumers is essential for establishing that the random components $\Sigma \Delta_i$ become negligible relative to Σq_i for s large.[2] Interdependence between the demand patterns may be due to some common factor, a typical example being the fluctuating dictates of fashion. Hence the argument is in line with the fact that the more a commodity involves an element of fashion the less stable is the demand.

As remarked in Ch. 3·1 it has been argued by J. S. Duesenberry (1949) that Paretoan theory requires the individual preferences to be independent. Whether independence is taken in a causal or a probabilistic sense, the above analysis shows that Duesenberry's argument is not correct. As a matter of fact, in stressing the social milieu as a relevant factor in the formation of behaviour patterns he is entirely in line with classical theory. An interpretation along such lines is indeed essential for a realistic understanding of the theory of preference fields.[3] To avoid misunderstanding we should like to add explicitly that, if Duesenberry's treatment makes the scope of classical theory too narrow, this does not in any respect invalidate his constructive approach towards a dynamic theory.

There are many economic matters that can be treated adequately only in terms of probability arguments. Such is, for instance, the fact that there is a lottery market, i.e., that people are willing to pay a surplus for a lottery ticket over its mathematical expectation of gain. Approaches towards an economic theory of chance and risk have been made, but as yet the theory is on the whole rather vague and tentative. A fundamental feature is the distinction between mathematical expectation on the one hand, and the subjective evaluation of chances and risks on the other. The traditional idea about the subjective attitude is that chances for great gain are taken more willingly, but risks of great loss less willingly, than indicated by the mathematical expectation. The typical attitude would be as shown in Fig. 1, p. 122. For a man on income level μ_0, the subjective evaluation follows a curve like S. Thus for a small chance to reach the higher level μ_+ he is willing to pay a surplus over the mathematical expectation M, while if confronted with the risk of falling down to level μ_- the amount M will not suffice to induce him to take the risk.

The above approach has been pursued by L. Törnqvist (1945) in a highly interesting study of lottery economics. His results include a quantitative estimation of the upper branch of the curve S, which refers to an increase of the income.

In their interesting work on the theory of games, J. von Neumann and O. Morgenstern (1944) have developed a theory of consumer demand on a probabilistic basis. Their approach leads to the notion of *measurable utility*, and is therefore less related to the Paretoan theory than to the pre-Paretoan theory, especially in its axiomatic form as given by R. Frisch (1926). [Cf Ch. 3·5.] In Frisch's theory the salient axiom refers to a simultaneous comparison of two budget changes, say from $q^{(a)}$ to $q^{(b)}$ and from $q^{(a)}$ to $q^{(\beta)}$, it being assumed that the consumer is able to decide which of the two shifts he prefers. Instead of this device, the Neumann-Morgenstern theory makes use of comparisons involving a chance element, assuming for example that the consumer is able to decide whether he prefers a 50 % chance of being supplied with three pounds of coffee to a certain supply of one pound of tea. Combining this type of hypothesis with the assumption that the preferences involved are additive functions of the mathematical expectations, von Neumann and Morgenstern show that the consumer's preferences can be expressed in terms of a quantitative utility scale.[4]

Like Frisch's axioms, those of von Neumann-Morgenstern play the rabbit trick with the Paretoan theory, the rabbit of a measurable utility being smuggled into the empty hat of a preference field. At first the author thought that the rabbit was hidden in the postulated additivity of the probability choices, but what is also active in playing the trick is the seemingly innocent assumption that the choices compared are mutually exclusive [see H. Wold (1952)]. The argument does not affect the Neumann-Morgenstern approach as a theory of monetary games and of chance evaluations of money sums, and here, as pointed out by M. Friedman and L. J. Savage (1948), the theory is able to explain the existence of such phenomena as lottery markets as well as insurance.[5] For the chance evaluation of different commodities, however, the axioms involve a severe restriction on consumer behaviour. The author's argument here leads to the double conclusion that the theory cannot be used for a static approach, and that in a dynamic approach the theory would be nonoperational in the sense that it cannot be tested empirically.

7. The psychological foundations. – In Chs. 3·1 and 3·5 the Paretoan theory of consumer demand was commented upon with regard to the underlying psychological hypotheses, and we have stated that these hypotheses are acceptable from the viewpoint of experimental psychology. We shall now follow up these remarks by a brief discussion.

Thanks to the specific nature of its fundamental principles and methods, economics is separated from other sciences by a fairly clear-cut line of demarcation. At the same time there are close interrelations across the frontiers, in the first place with the other social sciences and with psychology. As is fairly natural in view of the short history of economics, its border fields have to a large extent been neglected in the scientific analysis. As regards psychology it is only recently that the contacts with economics have been taken up for systematic study by the professional psychologists. Reference should here be made to the programmatic work by G. Katona (1951), in which general principles for the analysis of economic behaviour are outlined from the viewpoint of experimental psychology. The economic topics discussed by Katona include consumer behaviour, with special regard to spending and saving. The indifference map approach is touched upon very briefly, and Katona gives no explicit indication of whether he accepts the principles of Paretoan theory or no. In the subsequent remarks it is argued that the Paretoan theory, as based on the hypotheses or axioms of Ch. 4·2, is in line with the general principles of experimental psychology.

Psychological analysis of economic behaviour is directed towards motives and attitudes. The analysis need not be pursued down to the 'molecular' behaviour units of muscle contractions, gland secretion, and so on. As stressed by Katona [p. 29] it is perfectly legitimate that the units are higher mental processes, the essential thing being that such 'molar' units of behaviour are well defined from a starting point to an end point. It seems clear (a) that the choice-situations specified in Ch. 4·1–2 fulfil the requirements of a molar unit, and (b) that the hypotheses in Ch. 4·2 are in agreement with the basic scheme of psychological analysis: situation — intervening variable — overt behaviour. The term 'intervening variable' is used by Katona [p. 31] to denote those factors or constructs that are not directly observable by recording situations and responses but are postulated to explain behaviour. As regards the third axiom in Ch. 4·2 we note that this is, moreover, in agreement with the following general remark by Katona [p. 49]: "The psychologist does not acknowledge the occurrence of behavior that is not eventually understandable. The only meaning he can give to the concept of rational behavior is based on its description as the weighing of different alternative courses of action and of choosing deliberately among them, according to some principle."

In the axioms of Ch. 4·2 no restrictions whatever are imposed upon the intervening variables that may influence the consumer choice. The axioms thus give the psychologist an entirely free hand when analyzing the influences in terms of motives and attitudes.[1] As regards the statistical methods for the analysis, the introduction of a psychological element has no specific implications. Thus, for example, considering Katona's investigation of spending and saving on the basis of consumer survey data, his statistical analysis runs in terms of cross tabulations of the same type that is used in the present work in the analysis of family budget data.

It is a fundamental principle in the present volume that econometric analysis should be laid out along causal lines, in terms of autonomous behaving units. Our theoretical framework is in agreement with this principle, the main issues in point being the axioms of Ch. 4·2 and the general recursive system [cf Chs. 2·7 and 12·7]. Since the framework is quite general it will in each and every application have to be specified with regard to the requirements of the data under analysis. Here the psychological methods come in, deepening the causal approach by investigating the motives and attitudes of the behaving units. In such investigations, of course, joint research work across the frontiers of economics, statistics and psychology is highly desirable.

Chapter 8.

SOME FURTHER APPLICATIONS OF
PREFERENCE FIELDS

1. Income-leisure balance. – We shall in this section examine the balance between leisure and paid work time. In point of principle, leisure can be dealt with as an ordinary commodity, so that the balance can be studied by the use of preference field theory. The specific feature of this application is that the time at disposal for leisure and work adds to a constant, 24 hours a day, and that from the viewpoint of the earner-consumer the leisure hours are on the demand side, the work hours on the supply side.

Following the customary approach, we take the daily income μ of the earner-consumer to be the ordinate μ of a Euclidean system [see Fig. 1], and his daily leisure time to be the abscissa t. The approach being static, income μ is interpreted as total expenditure or aggregate consumption. Now regarding the points $q = (\mu, t)$ as budget alternatives in the sense of Ch. 4·1, suppose that the alternatives q are subject to an order of preferences in the sense of Ch. 4·2-3. This gives [see Fig. 1a] an indifference map that allows the representation (4·3·1), and which may be taken as a basis for the analysis of the demand for leisure and the supply of work hours.

The demand-supply pattern of leisure-work will depend on the wage system. Let us first consider the case when the wage is proportional to the working time, say p_1 monetary units per hour. The daily income will then be

(1) $$\mu = p_1(24 - t).$$

We are now in a position to apply the axiom of choice, inferring that the alternative (μ, t) chosen will make the preference function $U(\mu, t)$ a maximum, subject to the condition (1). The hourly wage p_1 being fixed, (1) may be interpreted as a balance line, viz.

(2) $$\mu + p_1 \cdot t = 24\,p_1$$

[see Fig. 1a]. It follows that the optimal budget, say (μ_1, t_1), will be determined by a system of type (4·4·4).

If we allow the hourly wage to vary, the optimum (μ_1, t_1) will describe a curve known as the *offer curve* of work. Since a variation of p_1 in (2) is equivalent to a variation in the price of aggregate consumption, i.e. of μ, we obtain

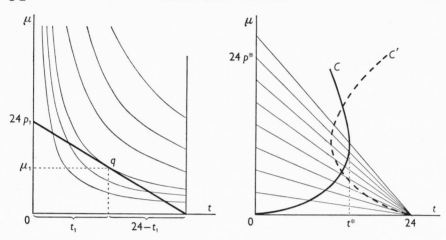

Fig. 8·1·1. Paretoan analysis of the income-leisure balance.
Wage system: Earnings proportional to work time.

a. Optimal balance between income, μ,   b. Offer curves, giving leisure as a
   and leisure, t.   function of hourly wage p_1.

THEOREM 1. *If the earnings are proportional to the work time, the offer curve of work coincides with a price-consumption curve of the aggregate consumption.*

The offer curves found in the literature are sometimes drawn as the curve C in Fig. 1b. This has a turning point at a certain time t^*, so that if the hourly wage is low and rises up to a certain level p^* the leisure time will increase up to t^* and the work time decrease down to $24-t^*$, while if the hourly wage rises above p^* the leisure time will decrease and the work time increase. It may well be that such a trend of the offer curve is realistic, but unfortunately there is an almost total lack of empirical data to indicate the typical tendency. Another type found in the literature is the curve C' in Fig. 1b. We note that the indifference maps of Figs. 5·2·1–2 give offer curves of still other types. Specifically, it is not necessary that the curve should have a turning point. Quite generally the offer curve will for rising wage p_1 have one of the gradients shown in Fig. 5·2·3. The gradients c, d, e correspond to the curve C in Fig. 8·1·1 for hourly wages below p^*, equal to p^*, and above p^*. The indifference map may also give gradients like b or a. In case b, the propensity to increase the leisure is so great that an increase in the hourly wage leads to such a marked decrease in the work time that the daily income remains constant. In case a, finally, the decrease in the work time is even more marked, leading to a decrease in the daily income. It will be observed that case a is what in the present application corresponds to Giffen's paradox [cf Fig. 5·2·2].

Let us now consider a wage system such that part of the daily income μ is constant, the other part proportional to the work time, say

$$(3) \qquad\qquad \mu = a + p_2(24 - t), \qquad\qquad \text{with } a > 0.$$

THEOREM 2. *If an established wage system (1) is changed so that the total amount of wages is distributed in accordance with system (3), other things being equal, the work time will become shorter and the daily income will fall.*

Referring to Fig. 2 for illustration, let t_1 be the optimal work time under wage system (1), and let p_2 in (3) be adjusted so that for work time t_1 the daily income is the same in the two systems. Since $a>0$, we have $p_2<p_1$. It follows that for $t>t_1$ the line (3) will pass through higher preference levels than the line (1). The optimal work time of (1), that is $24-t_1$, will accordingly be shorter than the optimal work time of (3), say $24-t_2$. Since $p_2>0$, the daily income at t_2 is lower than at t_1, which completes the proof of Theorem 2.

The work time in modern society is mostly a matter of collective agreement. The relevance of the above analysis therefore does not lie in the individual determination of work time, but rather in the interpretation of group tendencies. Referring once more to Fig. 1b, suppose for example that the curve C refers to the demand structure of a group of workers with work time $24-t$ fixed by collective agreement. For a certain interval of the hourly wage, the map indicates a tendency to reduce the work time. If the collective agreement is not changed, this tendency may materialize otherwise, e.g., in an increased number of absence days.[1]

2. Barter. – The analysis of barter is a classical application of the theory of preference fields. We are here concerned with one producer-consumer A of a commodity G_1, and one producer-consumer B of a commodity G_2, their exchange of the products being a matter of bargaining. The specific feature of barter is that the ratio of exchange, i.e. the relative prices of the two commodities, is not fixed beforehand, and it may even change in the course of the barter. As compared with a modern retail market with fixed prices, barter is a primitive market form, but still it is not necessary to go as far as Oriental bazaars to find similar bargaining conditions.

Suppose A starts the barter with the quantity a_1 of G_1 and a_2 of G_2, and B with b_1 of G_1 and b_2 of G_2. The course of the barter may be illustrated in the familiar manner of Fig. 1. The quantities of G_1 and G_2 held by A are indicated along the axes $\omega_1 k_1$ and $\omega_1 k_2$, the quantities held by B along $\omega_2 k_1$ and $\omega_2 k_2$. With the same sets of axes, Fig. 1 further shows the indifference map of A (full curves) and B (broken curves). The barter starting at the point q^0, we infer that both A and B disfavour q^0 to any point q in the region between the two indifference curves L_A and L_B that pass through q^0. The curve C, known as the *contract curve* of the barter, is the locus of points where an indifference curve of A's is touched by an indifference curve of B's. We see that, if the barter comes to a point q' that does not lie on the contract curve, both A and B will be able to reach a higher preference level by a continued barter (or by a continued trial, if q' was merely a trial bargain), if necessary at a modified rate of exchange. Hence

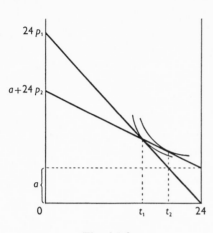

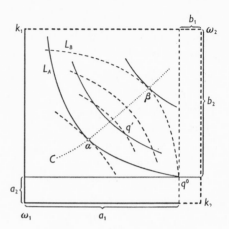

Fig. 8·1·2.
Illustration of Theorem 8·1·2.

Fig. 8·2·1.
Paretoan analysis of barter.

THEOREM 1.[1] *Barter ends in equilibrium when reaching a point q^* on the contract curve C. The equilibrium is indeterminate, in so far as q^* may be any point of the segment $\alpha\beta$ of C that lies between the two indifference curves L_A and L_B that pass through the point q^0 where the barter starts.*

In which point q^* of $\alpha\beta$ the barter actually ends will depend on the skill of A and B. If A (or B) is the stronger bargainer, he will be able to lead the barter to a point near β (or α, respectively).

It will be noticed that the above conclusions involve some qualification of barter theory as developed by A. L. Bowley (1924). If the author has understood correctly, Bowley does not allow the barter to proceed in steps, with different rates of exchange. The assumption of a uniform rate of exchange, however, applies to an ordinary market, but is not realistic in pure barter. It would seem that Bowley has adopted this assumption because barter is dealt with by way of introduction, as a first step in his analysis of market exchange.[2]

3. Consumer price indexes. – In empirical demand analysis, an important point is the distinction between nominal (=ordinary) prices and real prices, i.e. ordinary prices divided by a price index [cf Ch. 6·6]. Price indexes used in demand analysis are of the type known as *consumer price indexes*, which serve to measure the changes in the cost for maintaining a certain standard of living. The theory of consumer price indexes, which is one of the best-developed fields of econometric analysis, is of relevance for an understanding of ends as well as means in demand analysis. The brief outline in this section is limited to some of the groundwork only.[1]

(i) Some price index formulae. — Let us first consider the fundamental case when the price index refers to n commodities for which two sets of prices are given, say $p_1^0, \ldots, p_n^0$, called the *reference prices*, and $p_1^1, \ldots, p_n^1$, called the *comparison prices*. The price ratios

$$\mathfrak{P}_1 = \frac{p_1^1}{p_1^0}, \qquad \mathfrak{P}_2 = \frac{p_2^1}{p_2^0}, \qquad \ldots, \qquad \mathfrak{P}_n = \frac{p_n^1}{p_n^0}$$

being more or less irregular, a price index has for its purpose to express the general tendency of the n ratios in the form of one single number. We shall denote index numbers by $\mathfrak{P}$, with subscripts and superscripts for the variants.

We are going to consider two general types of index, (a) weighted averages of the price ratios, (b) chain indexes.

a. *Weighted averages of the price ratios.* The main types of weighted average are the *arithmetic, geometric* and *harmonic* averages, in symbols

$$\mathfrak{P}_A = w_1\,\mathfrak{P}_1 + \cdots + w_n\,\mathfrak{P}_n; \qquad \mathfrak{P}_G = \mathfrak{P}_1^{w_1} \cdot \ldots \cdot \mathfrak{P}_n^{w_n}; \qquad \mathfrak{P}_H = 1 : \left(\frac{w_1}{\mathfrak{P}_1} + \cdots + \frac{w_n}{\mathfrak{P}_n} \right)$$

where $w_1, \ldots, w_n$ are suitable weights satisfying (4·8·2). As is well known,[2]

$$(1) \qquad\qquad\qquad \mathfrak{P}_A \geq \mathfrak{P}_G \geq \mathfrak{P}_H.$$

Letting $q = (q_1, \ldots, q_n)$ be a fixed budget, to be called the *reference budget*, two sets of weights are defined by the formulae

$$w_i^0 = \frac{p_i^0 q_i}{p_1^0 q_1 + \cdots + p_n^0 q_n}; \qquad w_i^1 = \frac{p_i^1 q_i}{p_1^1 q_1 + \cdots + p_n^1 q_n}; \qquad (i = 1, \ldots, n).$$

We see that the weights are proportional to the expenditures for the reference budget at the two price sets. Inserting these weights in $\mathfrak{P}_A$ and $\mathfrak{P}_H$, respectively, the two indexes reduce to the same formula,

$$(2) \qquad\qquad \mathfrak{P}_A^0 = \mathfrak{P}_H^1 = \frac{p_1^1 q_1 + \cdots + p_n^1 q_n}{p_1^0 q_1 + \cdots + p_n^0 q_n}.$$

The index thus defined is seen to equal *the ratio between the total amounts of expenditure required to buy the reference budget at the two price sets.*

We shall now turn to Laspeyres' and Paasche's formulae, the fundamental formulae for the construction of index numbers. These are obtained from (2) by alternative specifications of the reference budget. The reference budget is intended to be representative, in some sense or other indicating or measuring the standard of living to which the index refers. In actual index calculations, the reference budget is usually compiled from empirical observations of the type known as family budget data [Ch. 1·2].

Laspeyres' index. This is obtained from (2) by specifying the reference budget so as to correspond to the reference price set, thus

$$(3) \qquad q_1 = q_1^0, \ldots, q_n = q_n^0; \qquad \mathfrak{P}_L = \frac{p_1^1 q_1^0 + \cdots + p_n^1 q_n^0}{p_1^0 q_1^0 + \cdots + p_n^0 q_n^0}.$$

Paasche's index. This is analogous to Laspeyres' index, except that the reference budget corresponds to the comparison price set,

$$(4) \qquad q_1 = q_1^1, \ldots, q_n = q_n^1; \qquad \mathfrak{P}_P = \frac{p_1^1 q_1^1 + \cdots + p_n^1 q_n^1}{p_1^0 q_1^1 + \cdots + p_n^0 q_n^1}.$$

Let us consider formulae (3)–(4) as applied to price data given in the form of n time series, say

$$p_1^{(t)}, \ldots, p_n^{(t)} \qquad\qquad (t = 0, 1, \ldots, T).$$

The period $t = 0$ is called the *base period* for the index. The Laspeyres index $\mathfrak{P}_L^{(t)}$ as defined by (3) indicates the cost at the time period t of the reference budget $q_1^0, \ldots, q_n^0$. The Paasche index $\mathfrak{P}_P^{(t)}$, on the other hand, makes use of a variable budget $q_1^1 = q_1^t, \ldots, q_n^1 = q_n^t$, and indicates the cost of this reference budget relative to the prices $p_1^0, \ldots, p_n^0$ of the base period.

In times when price changes are rapid and large, or generally when the time series data extend over long periods (say two or three decades), the index construction should make allowance for changes in the consumption pattern. It would therefore be unrealistic to use the same reference data for the whole period, i.e., the same reference budget in Laspeyres' index or the same reference prices in Paasche's index. The customary device for meeting this difficulty is to revise the reference data from time to time. The fragmentary index series thus obtained are then spliced so as to give one series covering the whole period. The formula usually employed for the splicing is, in easily understood symbols,

$$(5) \qquad \mathfrak{P}_0^{(t)} = \mathfrak{P}_0^{(t_1)} \cdot \mathfrak{P}_{t_1}^{(t)}, \qquad \text{briefly} \quad \mathfrak{P}_0^{(2)} = \mathfrak{P}_0^{(1)} \cdot \mathfrak{P}_1^{(2)},$$

where t_1 is the period for the revision of the reference data.

b. *Chain indexes.* In this type of index the revision and splicing is made at regular intervals, for instance, every year for a monthly index. Thus

$$(6) \qquad \mathfrak{P}_0^{(t+\varDelta)} = \mathfrak{P}_0^{(1)} \cdot \mathfrak{P}_1^{(2)} \cdot \cdots \cdot \mathfrak{P}_{t-1}^{(t)} \cdot \mathfrak{P}_t^{(t+\varDelta)} \qquad\qquad 0 \le \varDelta < 1$$

gives the chain index for an arbitrary instant $t + \varDelta$, with $t = 0$ for base period. Using Laspeyres', Paasche's, or some other index formula to calculate the consecutive factors in (6), we get as many variants of chain index.

An interesting type of chain index is due to F. Divisia (1925–26). Considering a price change from $p^0 = (p_1^0, \ldots, p_n^0)$ to $p^1 = (p_1^1, \ldots, p_n^1)$ and the corresponding change in the quantities from $q^0 = (q_1^0, \ldots, q_n^0)$ to $q^1 = (q_1^1, \ldots, q_n^1)$, suppose that the changes take place by infinitesimal steps. The index is then defined by the differential equation

$$\frac{d\mathfrak{P}}{\mathfrak{P}} = \frac{\Sigma q_i \, dp_i}{\Sigma q_i p_i}$$

where the sums extend over the n commodities, and $q = (q_1, \ldots, q_n)$ as well as $p = (p_1, \ldots, p_n)$ are regarded as functions of time. By integration we obtain the following formula for Divisia's chain index,

$$(7) \qquad \mathfrak{P}_D = \mathfrak{P}_D^0 \cdot \exp \left(\int_C \frac{\Sigma \, q_i \, dp_i}{\Sigma \, q_i \, p_i} \right)$$

where $\mathfrak{P}_D^0$ is the index for the initial prices $p^0 = (p_1^0, \ldots, p_n^0)$, and C is the path described by price p when changing from p^0 to p^1. Without loss of generality, we may take p^0 to refer to the base period, making $\mathfrak{P}_D^0 = 100 \,\%$.

(ii) Index criteria. – On common sense grounds, certain properties stand out as desirable for a price index, properties that may be taken as tests or criteria on the practical usefulness of a specified index formula. This is the line of approach in I. Fisher's classical work on index numbers (1922). At first sight very attractive, this approach has the weak point that on a formal basis it is logically impossible to construct an index such that certain reasonable criteria are satisfied simultaneously [see Ex. 40]. Among the great number of formal index criteria we note the following two.

The proportionality criterion. This requires that if all prices change in the same proportion the index should also change in this proportion, in symbols

$$(8) \qquad \mathfrak{P}(\lambda p_1^0, \ldots, \lambda p_n^0) = \lambda \cdot \mathfrak{P}(p_1^0, \ldots, p_n^0).$$

As readily verified, the index formulae (2)–(4) satisfy the proportionality criterion, and so does the chain index (6), provided the links $\mathfrak{P}_{t-1}^{(t)}$ are calculated by a formula that satisfies this criterion.

The cycle criterion. This requires that if all prices at $t = t_0$ are the same as at $t = t_1$ the index should take the same value for t_0 as for t_1, or in symbols:

$$(9) \qquad \text{If} \quad p_1^{(t_0)} = p_1^{(t_1)}, \ldots, p_n^{(t_0)} = p_n^{(t_1)} \quad \text{then} \quad \mathfrak{P}_0^{(t_0)} = \mathfrak{P}_0^{(t_1)}.$$

This criterion is clearly satisfied by Laspeyres' index as long as the reference data remain unchanged. For a revised and spliced index (5), however, and a fortiori for a chain index (6), the cycle criterion will in general not be satisfied.

(iii) The preference field approach. – Index theory can be considerably deepened by arguments derived from the theory of consumer demand. The basic idea of this approach, first suggested by A. Konyus (1924), is that the reference budget should be interpreted as the optimal budget in a preference field. An index allowing this interpretation will be called a *preference field index* or alternatively a *Konyus index*.

We shall next state a few elements from the theory of preference field indexes as applied to the situation of an individual consumer.[3] Until further notice, we shall assume that the nominal income of the consumer is constant, say μ.

A. *A Konyus price index is 100% if the optimal budget of the reference price set lies on the same indifference level as the optimal budget of the comparison price set.*

Referring to Fig. 1a for illustration, suppose that for income μ the reference and comparison prices give the balance lines A_0 and C_1, respectively. Since these lines touch the same indifference curve, S_0, the Konyus index is 100%.

B. *A Konyus index may be uniquely defined if taken to refer to a specified indifference level.* We distinguish between a Laspeyres-Konyus index *and a* Paasche-Konyus index, *according as the indifference level is specified by the optimal budget of the reference prices or by the optimal budget of the comparison prices.*

Again referring to Fig. 1a, suppose now that the balance lines A_0, A_1 are based on the reference and comparison prices, respectively, and on the same income μ. At the price change, the optimal budget of the consumer will shift from q^0 to q^1. The Laspeyres-Konyus index is the ratio by which income μ should be multiplied if the consumer when buying an optimal budget is to maintain the same indifference level S_0 as at the reference prices. This gives

$$(10) \qquad \mathfrak{P}_{LK} = \frac{\Sigma\, p^1 q^{(0)}}{\Sigma\, p^0 q^0} = \frac{\Sigma\, p^1 q^{(0)}}{\Sigma\, p^1 q^1} = \frac{\omega\, c_1}{\omega\, a_1}.$$

The Paasche-Konyus index is obtained if the two price situations are compared by way of a Laspeyres-Konyus index with p^1 for reference prices and p^0 for comparison prices. The Paasche-Konyus index thus is the ratio by which income μ should be *divided* so as to give the income that at prices p^0 enables the consumer to attain the preference level S_1 he reaches with income μ at prices p^1. In symbols,

$$(11) \qquad \mathfrak{P}_{PK} = \frac{\Sigma\, p^1 q^1}{\Sigma\, p^0 q^{(1)}} = \frac{\Sigma\, p^0 q^0}{\Sigma\, p^0 q^{(1)}} = \frac{\omega\, a_0}{\omega\, c_0}.$$

C. *Laspeyres' index (3) is at least as high as the Laspeyres-Konyus index (10), while Paasche's index (4) is lower than or equal to the Paasche-Konyus index (11), or in symbols*

$$(12) \qquad \mathfrak{P}_L \geq \mathfrak{P}_{LK} \qquad\qquad \mathfrak{P}_{PK} \geq \mathfrak{P}_P,$$

and the equality signs will hold if the two price sets compared are proportional.

On the same assumptions as under B, Laspeyres' index (3) is given by

$$\mathfrak{P}_L = \Sigma\, p^1 q^0 / \Sigma\, p^0 q^0 = \Sigma\, p^1 q^0 / \Sigma\, p^1 q^1 = \omega\, b_1 / \omega\, a_1.$$

Since the balance line C_1 touches the indifference curve that passes through q^0, the point b_1 must lie above c_1, which verifies the first part of statement C. Similarly, Paasche's index (4) is $\omega a_0 / \omega b_0$, and here b_0 lies above c_0.

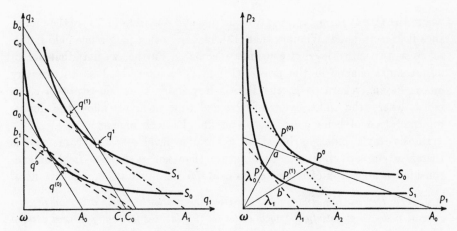

Fig. 8·3·1. Preference field interpretation of indexes in a situation of falling prices.
a. The geometry of budget space.[4]   b. The geometry of price space.

Given the reference and the comparison prices, the indifference level to which a preference field index refers may be specified by the consumer's income μ. We conclude:

D. *The Laspeyres-Konyus and Paasche-Konyus indexes will in general depend upon consumer income. If the reference budget is chosen so as to be optimal, the same holds true of the Laspeyres and Paasche indexes.*

Illustration. The map used in Fig. 1a for illustrating the four indexes in (12) is the same as in Fig. 3·1·1, or $q_1 q_2 + q_2 = c$. On the basis of the same map the four indexes have been calculated for different levels of consumer income, μ, for a change in prices from $p_1 = p_2 = 1$ to $p_1 = 2$, $p_2 = 1$. Fig. 2 shows that the indexes are four different functions of income. We see that if this map holds good for all consumers the price rise will appear greater, the greater the consumer's income. This would indicate that commodity q_1 is a luxury as compared with q_2.

E. *For infinitesimal price changes, the Laspeyres-Konyus and Paasche-Konyus indexes will lie between the Laspeyres and Paasche indexes, and the differences between the four indexes will be infinitesimal of the second order.*

The proof is immediate if we use the price space for a geometric interpretation [see below, p. 139]. Explicit formulae are given in Exs. 49–50.

Divisia's chain index (7) forms a most natural basis for the construction of a preference field index.[5] We have then only to interpret $q = (q_1, ..., q_n)$ as the optimal budget at prices $p = (p_1, ..., p_n)$. The resulting index will be called the *Divisia-Roy index* and denoted $\mathfrak{P}_{DR}$. Setting $\mathfrak{P}_{DR}^0 = 100\%$, the index thus is given by

(13) $$\mathfrak{P}_{DR} = \exp \left(\int_C \frac{\Sigma Q_i \, dp_i}{\Sigma Q_i p_i} \right)$$

where the $Q_i = Q_i(\mu, p_1, \ldots, p_n)$ are the demand functions (4·5·1) of the preference field considered. We note that (13), like any other preference field index, refers to a specified level of consumer income, μ. Further we note that, for an infinitesimal change in the prices, (13) may be interpreted as an ordinary index. Paying regard to E, the Divisia-Roy index thus constitutes a chain index where the links over infinitesimal time intervals allow the double interpretation of being both Laspeyres and Paasche indexes.

Divisia-Roy's index is based on a variable level of real income and is therefore, in principle, of other nature than the preference field indexes considered above. Referring to Exs. 51–55 for illustration, we also note[6]

F. *The Divisia-Roy index (13) satisfies the proportionality criterion (8). In general it does not satisfy the cycle criterion (9), but the following relaxed version of the cycle criterion is always satisfied: If prices change from p^0 to p^1 along a certain path C and then return to p^0 via the same path, the index will return to its initial value at p^0.*

To prove the first statement, suppose that all prices p_i vary proportionately, so that they allow the representation $p_i = \lambda p_i^0$, where the p_i^0 are constant and λ varies, say between 1 and $\lambda_0 \geq 1$. Then $dp_i = p_i^0 d\lambda$, and so $\Sigma q_i p_i = \lambda \Sigma q_i p_i^0$ and $\Sigma q_i dp_i = d\lambda \cdot \Sigma q_i p_i^0$. Hence

$$\int_C \frac{\Sigma q_i \, dp_i}{\Sigma q_i \, p_i} = \int_1^{\lambda_0} \frac{d\lambda}{\lambda},$$

which gives $\mathfrak{P}_{DR}(p_1, \ldots, p_n) = \lambda_0$, in agreement with (8), as stated.

Finally we turn to the case when the consumer's nominal income μ changes simultaneously with the price change. Reflecting that a price index has for its purpose, among other things, to transform nominal income changes into real income changes, we conclude that the real income change should be disregarded in the index construction. Hence,

G. *If nominal income changes from μ_0 to μ_1, real income changes in the ratio*

(14) $$\mu_1 / \mathfrak{P} \cdot \mu_0$$

where $\mathfrak{P}$ is a price index calculated without regard to the change in real income.

We note that, if income changes at the same time as the prices, we must specify whether the price index should refer to the income level before or after the change. It is natural to base the Laspeyres index variants on the income *before* the change, the Paasche variants on the income *after* the change.

It is instructive to examine situations where index $\mathfrak{P}$ may be specified so as to make the ratio (14) equal unity, indicating that real income remains constant. Suppose for example that the balance lines in Fig. 1a are given by

$$A_0 : p_1^0 q_1 + p_2^0 q_2 = \mu_0; \qquad A_1 : p_1^1 q_1 + p_2^1 q_2 = \mu_0; \qquad C_1 : p_1^1 q_1 + p_2^1 q_2 = \mu_1.$$

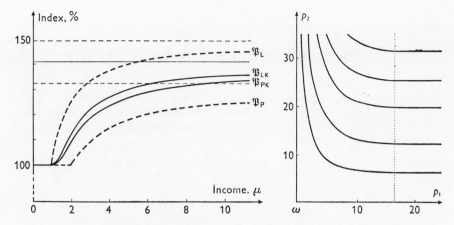

Fig. 8·3·2. Illustrations referring to the indifference map of Fig. 3·1·1.

a. Price indexes as functions
of income.

b. The indifference map of
price space.

Making $\mu = \mu_0$, the Laspeyres-Konyus index will be given by $\omega c_1 / \omega a_1 = \mu_1 / \mu_0$. We see that ratio (14) will then equal unity, provided $\mathfrak{P} = \mathfrak{P}_{LK}$, where $\mathfrak{P}_{LK}$ refers to income level $\mu = \mu_0$, that is the income before the change. Similar illustrations can be given for the cases when $\mathfrak{P}$ is specified as a Laspeyres index (3) or as the Paasche variants (4) and (11).

Following up the argument, let $\mu(t)$ represent consumer income as a function of time, and let $\mathfrak{P}_{LK}(t)$ be Laspeyres-Konyus' index as formed on the basis of the fixed income $\mu(0)$. Then $\mathfrak{P}_{LK}(t)$ may be interpreted as a *price compensation index*, inasmuch as the variable income $\mu^*(t) = \mu(0) \cdot \mathfrak{P}_{LK}(t)$ will leave real income constant.[7] Further we see that $\mu(t) / \mu^*(t)$ may be interpreted as an *index for the change in real income*. Otherwise expressed, writing

$$\mu(t) - \mu(0) = [\mu^*(t) - \mu(0)] + [\mu(t) - \mu^*(t)],$$

the income change is split up as the sum of two components: the *price compensation* and the *change in real income*.

If we consider the price constellations $p = (p_1, \ldots, p_n)$ as points in a Euclidean space, the *price space*, this can be used in much the same way as the budget space for the geometric illustration of demand theory.[8] Specifically, the notion of indifference map has a parallel in the price space. The price space is particularly well suited for the illustration of index theory. Reference is made to Exs. 41–44 and 59, where index theory is examined from this viewpoint.

The inequalities (12) giving one-sided index limits, we shall consider the much-discussed problem of obtaining two-sided limits. Let the four indexes in (12), with and without asterisks, be defined for two income levels μ^* and μ, respectively. Regarding μ as fixed, it is possible to determine $\mu^* = \mu^*(\mu)$ so that $\mathfrak{P}^*_{PK} = \mathfrak{P}_{LK}$. Writing $\mathfrak{P}_K$ for the common value, (12) gives[9]

H. *For the Konyus index* $\mathfrak{P}_K$ *defined by* $\mathfrak{P}_K = \mathfrak{P}_{LK} = \mathfrak{P}^*_{PK}$ *we have*

(15) $$\mathfrak{P}_L \geq \mathfrak{P}_K \geq \mathfrak{P}^*_P.$$

EXERCISES FOR PART II.[1]

1. To illustrate his proposition "the smaller the crop, the greater its money value," Gregory King (1699) used the figures reproduced in the three first columns below.[1] Interpret King's law in terms of demand functions and price elasticities, and make use of (5'1'2–3) to verify the elasticities in the two last columns.

Crop	Price	Value of crop	Price elasticity of demand Exact	Price elasticity of demand Approximate
100	100	100		
			0.40	0.40
90	130	117		
			0.36	0.36
80	180	144		
			0.36	0.37
70	260	182		
			0.41	0.41
60	380	228		
			0.49	0.50
50	550	275		

2 (Wold, 1940). Disregarding terms of higher order, the approximation error of the elasticity formula (5'1'3) is

$$(\Theta^2 - \delta^2)\frac{E}{12}, \qquad \text{with } \Theta = \frac{x_1 - x_0}{x_0}, \qquad \delta = \frac{f_1 - f_0}{f_0}.$$

Hint: Make use of Taylor expansions.

3. Given the elasticity $E_x f = -e_x f$ of an arbitrary function $f(x)$, verify the formula

$$f(x_1) = f(x_0) \cdot e^{\int_{x_0}^{x_1} \frac{E_x f}{x} dx} = f(x_0) \cdot e^{-\int_{x_0}^{x_1} \frac{e_x f}{x} dx}.$$

4. Given $E_x f = E = -e$, the elasticity formula (5'1'3) can be used for the approximate calculation of f_1 in terms of x_0, x_1, f_0, the result being

$$f_1 \sim \frac{x_1 + x_0 + (x_1 - x_0)E}{x_1 + x_0 - (x_1 - x_0)E} \cdot f_0.$$

5. Verify that the indifference map given by $xyz/(xy + xz + yz) = c$ satisfies the three axioms and the three assumptions of Ch. 4'2–3. Establish the demand function

$$Q_x(\mu, p_x, p_y, p_z) = \frac{\mu}{(\sqrt{p_x} + \sqrt{p_y} + \sqrt{p_z})\sqrt{p_x}}, \qquad \text{and similarly for } Q_y \text{ and } Q_z.$$

6. Given the preference function $U(x, y, z) = (xy + y)z$, the demand functions are

$$Q_x = (\mu - 2p_x)/3p_x \qquad Q_y = (\mu + p_x)/3p_y \qquad Q_z = (\mu + p_x)/3p_z.$$

Further verify that relations (4'5'2–3) are satisfied.

7 (Guiraúm, Tena and Wold, 1950). For an indifference map for two commodities, suppose that the demand function for q_1 is independent of (a) income μ, or (b) price p_1, or (c) price p_2. Show that the general formulae for such maps are, respectively,

$$q_2 = f(q_1) + c \qquad q_2 = f(q_1) + c \cdot q_1 \qquad q_2 = c \cdot f(q_1),$$

where the functions f and the constants c are arbitrary.

Hint: If all income-consumption curves are given, or all price-consumption curves, the indifference map can be reconstructed by solving a differential equation.

8. Given the prices p_1, p_2 and the income μ, let L be the balance line $p_1 q_1 + p_2 q_2 = \mu$, and let μ^* be the section of L that lies between the q_1- and q_2-axes. Let x_1^*, x_2^* be the two sections in which μ^* is divided by an arbitrary point $q^* = (q_1^*, q_2^*)$ on L, so that q_1^* and q_2^* are projections of x_1^* and x_2^* on the respective axes. Verify

$$x_1^* : x_2^* : \mu^* = x_1 : x_2 : \mu,$$

where $x_1 = p_1 q_1^*$ and $x_2 = p_2 q_2^*$ are the expenditures for the budget q^*.

Generalize this relation to balance planes in three or more dimensions.

9. Given an indifference map for two commodities, let L be an arbitrary balance line, $q = (q_1, q_2)$ the optimal budget on L, and C_μ, C_1 and C_2 the consumption curves that pass through the point q [see Fig. 5˙2˙4]. Cutting the curves C by a balance line L^* that is parallel to L and lies above L at infinitesimal distance, let $x_1^* = \alpha\beta$ be the segment of L^* that lies between C_μ and C_1, and $x_2^* = \alpha\gamma$ the segment between C_μ and C_2. Show that

(1) $$x_1 : x_2 = x_1^* : x_2^*$$

where x_1, x_2 are the segments of L that lie between the point q and the q_1- and q_2-axes, respectively.

Hint: Relation (1) is equivalent to Theorem 5˙3˙1 c.

10. If $f(x)$, $g(x)$ are two arbitrary functions, the elasticities of their product and quotient are given by the rules for logarithmic derivatives, in symbols

$$E_x(f \cdot g) = E_x f + E_x g \qquad\qquad E_x(f/g) = E_x f - E_x g$$
$$e_x(f \cdot g) = e_x f + e_x g \qquad\qquad e_x(f/g) = e_x f - e_x g.$$

As an application, verify formula (14˙3˙1b).

11. Letting $f(u)$, $u(x)$ be arbitrary functions, verify

$$E_x f = E_u f \cdot E_x u \qquad\qquad e_x f = e_u f \cdot e_x u.$$

12. Show that Törnqvist's demand functions (1˙1˙5 a–c) have for asymptotes, respectively,

$$d = a \qquad\qquad d = a \qquad\qquad d = a\mu - a(\beta + \gamma).$$

How is it that the demand function for luxuries goes above its asymptote in Fig. 1˙1˙3 a, but below its asymptote in Fig. 1˙1˙3 b?

Further show that the income elasticities of Törnqvist's functions are given by

$$E = \frac{\beta}{\mu + \beta} \qquad E = \frac{(\beta + \gamma)\,\mu}{(\mu + \beta)\,(\mu - \gamma)} \qquad E = \frac{\mu^2 + 2\,\mu\beta - \beta\gamma}{(\mu + \beta)\,(\mu - \gamma)}.$$

13 (Guiraúm, Tena and Wold, 1950). Specifying the parameters a, β, γ as functions of prices p_i, show by way of various examples that each of Törnqvist's functions may take the form (4˙5˙4).

Considering the case $n = 2$, and norming so that $p_2 = 1$, let $(1\cdot1\cdot5\,\text{a})$ be specified by making $\alpha = a$, $\beta = b\,p_1$. Verify that the corresponding preference index is given by

$$U\,(q_1,\, q_2) = q_1^a\,q_2^{\,b-a}\,(q_1 + b - a)^{-b}.$$

14 (Samuelson, 1947). It is a fundamental proposition by Pareto that the demand functions are not affected if the given indifference map $U(q_1, \ldots, q_n) = c$ is instead defined by an arbitrary preference function $(4\cdot3\cdot2)$, say $\Psi(U) = c$. Give an analytic proof that the transformation Ψ does not affect the demand function derivatives $(4\cdot5\cdot6\text{--}7)$.

15. For a commodity q_i, let the scale of measurement be subjected to a linear translation, say $q_i = a_i\,q_i^* + b_i$. Show that the condition of convexity $(4\cdot4\cdot7)$ is invariant to any such changes in the measurement.

16. Making use of the relations $U_{ik} = U_{ki}$, verify the integrability condition $(4\cdot6\cdot1)$ for $n = 3$ and for general n.

17. An indifference map will be called a *Gossen map* if there exists a preference function $U(q_1, \ldots, q_n)$ of the additive form $(3\cdot1\cdot1)$, or, which is the same, if the map allows the representation

$$U_1\,(q_1) + \cdots + U_n\,(q_n) = c.$$

Show that the indifference map of Ex. 6 is a Gossen map.

18 (Allen, 1938). Three goods are said to be 'independent' in consumption if the ratios of the consumer's marginal rates of substitution $1 : R_1 : R_2$ are of the form $f(x) : g(y) : h(z)$, where f, g and h are functions of the variables named. Show that the integrability condition is always satisfied and indicate the form of the preference index. Illustrate when

$$1 : R_1 : R_2 = (x - a) : (y - b) : (z - c).$$

19. For an indifference map to be a Gossen map it is necessary and sufficient that the commodities are independent in the sense of the preceding exercise.

20 (Wold, 1940). Let M be the indifference map of a commodity q_1 as considered against the aggregate of all other commodities, so that $n = 2$. If M is a Gossen map, and if the expenditure on q_1 is a small fraction of total expenditure, the income elasticity of q_1 approximates its price elasticity, in symbols

$$E_\mu\,(q_1) \sim e_{p_1}\,(q_1), \qquad\qquad \text{briefly} \ \ E \sim e.$$

21 (Samuelson, 1947). Given a Gossen map, there exists a set of functions $h_{ij}(x, y, z)$ such that the demand functions $(4\cdot5\cdot1)$ will satisfy the identities

$$Q_i\,(\mu,\, p_1,\, \ldots,\, p_n) \equiv h_{ij}\,(p_i,\, p_j,\, p_i\,q_i + p_j\,q_j) \qquad i \neq j;\ i, j = 1, \ldots, n.$$

22 (Samuelson, 1947). In the notation of $(4\cdot6\cdot2)$, let $R(q_1, q_2) = R_1(q_1, q_2)/R_2(q_1, q_2)$ be the marginal rate of substitution for two commodities. Show that R belongs to a Gossen map if, and only if, we have the identity

$$R\frac{\partial^2 R}{\partial q_1\,\partial q_2} - \frac{\partial R}{\partial q_1}\,\frac{\partial R}{\partial q_2} = 0.$$

23. Given a Gossen map with $U_1(q_1) + \cdots + U_n(q_n)$ for preference function, let all quantities except q_i and q_k be held constant, and write $U(q_i, q_k) = U_1(q_1) + \cdots + U_n(q_n)$. Show that for arbitrary $q_i,\, q_k,\, a,\, b$

(1) $$U(q_i + a, q_k + b) - U(q_i + a, q_k) - U(q_i, q_k + b) + U(q_i, q_k) = 0.$$

Considering the case of two commodities, use this relation to establish the following geometric criterion for deciding whether or not a given indifference map is a Gossen map: Cutting any two indifference curves by an arbitrary horizontal, let x_0, x_1 be the abscissae of the points of intersection, and let y_0, y_1 be the ordinates when cutting by an arbitrary vertical. For the map to be a Gossen map, it is necessary and sufficient that the indifference curve through (x_0, y_1) should also pass through (x_1, y_0).
Apply the criterion to Figs. 3`1`1 and 6`5`1.

24. Construct a Gossen map for two commodities, given two of its indifference curves that lie at infinitesimal distance from each other.

Solution: Given the curves $y = f(x)$ and $y + dy = f(x) + f'(x) h(y) dx$, and writing $y = \varphi(x, c)$ for the map sought for, its differential equation is

$$\frac{d\varphi}{f'(f^{-1}(\varphi)) h(\varphi)} = \frac{dx}{h(f(x))}.$$

Special case: $f(x) = \sqrt{1 - x^2}$; $h(y) = 1/y$; $f^{-1}(y) = \sqrt{1 - y^2}$; $\varphi(x, c) = \sqrt{c - x^2}$.

25 (Allen, 1938). The marginal rates of substitution for n goods are defined by the differential equation

$$(a_1 + a_{11} q_1) dq_1 + (a_2 + a_{22} q_2) dq_2 + \cdots + (a_n + a_{nn} q_n) dq_n = 0,$$

where the a's are constants. Show that an indifference map exists, and verify that the demands of the consumer are stable, provided that $a_{11}, \ldots, a_{nn}$ are all negative. Show that the demand for each good depends linearly in income (prices fixed) and is a ratio of quadratic expressions in the prices (income fixed).

26 (Antonelli, 1886). Show that if the marginal substitution rates R_i in (4`6`2) are normed by making $R_1 = 1$, they allow the general representation

$$R_i = \frac{\partial f}{\partial q_i} \bigg/ \left[\frac{\partial f}{\partial q_1} + g(f, q_1) \right] \qquad i = 2, \ldots, n$$

where $f(q_1, \ldots, q_n)$ and $g(x, y)$ are two arbitrary functions.

27.[1] Form the market demand functions (7`2`4) for $s = 2$ individuals, A and B, supposing that A has income μ and preference function $(q_1 + 1) q_2 q_3$, and that B has income μ and preference function $q_1 q_2 (q_3)^2$.

a. Show that the market demand functions are

(1) $$Q_1 = \frac{7\mu - 8p_1}{12 p_1}, \qquad Q_2 = \frac{7\mu + 4p_1}{12 p_2}, \qquad Q_3 = \frac{5\mu + 2p_1}{6 p_3}.$$

b. Further show that the corresponding price functions (4`6`3), or $p_i / 2\mu$, are

(2) $$P_1 = \frac{7}{8(3q_1 + 2)}, \qquad P_2 = \frac{7(q_1 + 1)}{8 q_2 (3q_1 + 2)}, \qquad P_3 = \frac{10 q_1 + 9}{8 q_3 (3q_1 + 2)}.$$

c. Finally show that the functions (2) do not satisfy the integrability condition (4`6`1). Hence there exists no 'market preference function' which for given μ, p_1, p_2, p_3 could be maximized by the quantities (1).

28 (Wold, 1948). Make use of Ex. 7 (b) to verify Theorem $5\cdot2\cdot2$.

29. Give an analytic proof of Theorem $5\cdot3\cdot2$ for the case $n = 3$.

30. Verify Slutsky-Schultz' relation $(6\cdot1\cdot1)$ for each of the demand functions in Ex. 6.

31. For the indifference map of Ex. 5 the Hotelling-Juréen relation $(6\cdot3\cdot2)$ holds as an exact identity, viz.

$$e_{p_x} Q_y \big/ e_{p_y} Q_x = p_x Q_x \big/ p_y Q_y = \sqrt{p_x} \big/ \sqrt{p_y},$$

and similarly for x, z and y, z.

32 (Wold, 1943–44). Considering the case when the sub-item prices of an aggregate commodity need not vary proportionately, establish the formula

$$e_{p_{ik}} x_i = \frac{x_{i1} e_{p_{ik}} Q_{i1} + \cdots + x_{im} e_{p_{ik}} Q_{im}}{x_{i1} + \cdots + x_{im}} - \frac{x_{ik}}{x_{i1} + \cdots + x_{im}} \qquad k = 1, \ldots, m$$

for the elasticity of the aggregate expenditure $(5\cdot6\cdot3)$ w.r.t. a sub-item price.

33 (Wold, 1943–44). Show that the curve system $(2q_1 - c)(2q_2 - c) = 1$ defines an indifference map, and that the demand function for q_1 is

$$Q_1 = \frac{1}{p_1 + p_2} \left[\mu + \frac{p_2 - p_1}{2} \sqrt{\frac{p_2}{p_1}} \right]$$

and similarly for q_2. Verify that the map displays all of the six possibilities of Theorem $6\cdot5\cdot2$, as shown in Fig. $6\cdot5\cdot1$ (p. 110).

Hint: Find the boundaries between the six regions in question.

34. Find how the six possibilities of Theorem $6\cdot5\cdot2$ are distributed in the indifference maps of Figs. $3\cdot1\cdot1$ and $5\cdot4\cdot1$.

35. In Illustrations A–C of Ch. $7\cdot4$ we have, respectively,

$$M(\lambda) = \frac{\lambda - 1}{\lambda - 2} \cdot c; \qquad M(\lambda) = \lambda + \frac{a - 1}{a - 2} \cdot c; \qquad M(\lambda) = \lambda \cdot \frac{a - 1}{a - 2} \cdot c;$$

whereas the $Q(\lambda)$ must be calculated by numerical integration or development in series. Check one point on each of the three curves in Fig. $7\cdot4\cdot1$.

36 (Malmquist, 1948). If the market demand $(7\cdot5\cdot2)$ is subjected to rationing, with maximum purchase R, we have

$$E_R Q^* = Q_2^* \big/ (Q_1^* + Q_2^*).$$

In words: the demand elasticity w.r.t. the purchase limit equals the ratio between the restricted part and the total of the rationed demand.

37 (von Hofsten, 1952). The following table gives market statistics for butter and margarine in Sweden, for periods before and after the rise of prices on January 1, 1951.

	July–Nov. 1950		Febr.–April 1951		
	q^0	p^0	q^1	p^1	p^1/p^0
Butter	8.1	560	6.3	645	115
Margarine	4.7	260	5.9	345	133

Verify that (8'3'3–4) give

$$\mathfrak{P}_L = 118.9\%\qquad\qquad \mathfrak{P}_P = 120.5\%.$$

Assuming that the market is homogeneous in the sense of Ch. 7'1, argue from (8'3'12) that there has been *either* a change in real income *or* a shift in the preference field.

38 (I. Fisher, 1922). In addition to the index criteria of Ch. 8'3 (ii) we note the *commensurability test*: $\mathfrak{P}$ shall not change for a change in the measuring unit for any of the commodities involved; and the *determinateness test*: $\mathfrak{P}$ shall not become zero, infinite, or indeterminate if one of the prices or quantities becomes zero. Show that all of the indexes (8'3'2–7) satisfy these criteria.

39 (I. Fisher, 1922). *The circular test* refers to a revised and spliced index (8'3'5), and requires

(1) $$\mathfrak{P}_0^{(1)}\cdot\mathfrak{P}_1^{(2)}=\mathfrak{P}_0^{[2]}$$

where $\mathfrak{P}_0^{[2]}$ is formed without revision and splicing at the intermediate period t_1. It will be observed that criterion (1) differs from the cycle test, which by the definition in Ch. 8'3 (ii) does not necessarily refer to a revised and spliced index. The *time reversal test* is the special case of (1) when prices are the same at t_0 and t_2, that is

$$\mathfrak{P}_0^{(1)}\cdot\mathfrak{P}_1^{(0)}=1.$$

Show that Laspeyres' and Paasche's indexes (8'3'3–4) do not satisfy these tests. Further show that the time reversal test is satisfied by Fisher's *ideal index*, defined by

$$\mathfrak{P}_F=\sqrt{\mathfrak{P}_L\cdot\mathfrak{P}_P}.$$

40 (Frisch, 1930). Considering an index $\mathfrak{P}$ which is constructed by the use of constant quantities q_i, show that if $\mathfrak{P}$ satisfies the commensurability and determinateness tests, it cannot satisfy the cycle test.

41 (Hotelling, 1932). Given a preference function $U(q_1,\dots,q_n)$ and corresponding demand functions $Q_i(\mu, p_1,\dots,p_n)$, let $u(p_1,\dots,p_n)$ be the function obtained when fixing income μ and inserting $q_i=Q_i(\mu,p_1,\dots,p_n)$, $i=1,\dots,n$, in $U(q_1,\dots,q_n)$. For any increasing function $\Psi(x)$, the transform $\Psi(u)=u^*(p_1,\dots,p_n)$ is called a *price preference function*. Considering the price sets $p=(p_1,\dots,p_n)$ as points in a Euclidean space, the *price space*, the level map $u(p_1,\dots,p_n)=c$ is called *the indifference map of price space*.

As a function of income μ, any price preference function u^* allows the representation $u^*(p_1/\mu,\dots,p_n/\mu)$. Given the preference function $U(q_1,\dots,q_n)$, further show that the price functions (4'6'3) are given by[1]

$$P_i(q_1,\dots,q_n)=\frac{U_i}{U_1\,q_1+\cdots+U_n\,q_n}\qquad i=1,\dots,n.$$

Finally show that the indifference surfaces of price space are convex towards the origin (or possibly linear).

42. As illustrated in Figs. 3'1'1 and 8'3'2b, the preference function $U=q_1\,q_2+q_2$ gives us the price preference function $u=(\mu+p_1)^2/4\,p_1 p_2$ for $p_1\le\mu$ and $u=\mu/p_2$ for $p_1\ge\mu$.

43 (Roy, 1942). Given $p^0=(p_1^0,\dots,p_n^0)$ and μ^0, let q^0 be the corresponding optimal budget. Then

(1) $$q_1^0\cdot p_1+\cdots+q_n^0\cdot p_n=\mu^0$$

defines a plane in price space, called the *budget plane*, this being the locus of points $p = (p_1, \ldots, p_n)$ such that μ^0 is the cost of budget q^0.

Let S be the indifference surface in price space that passes through p^0. Show that (1) touches S at p^0. Considering any price set $p \neq p^0$ in plane (1) and the corresponding optimal budget q, further show that q is preferred to q^0.

44 (S. Malmquist[1]). Reconsidering the index theorems A–C of Ch. 8.3 (iii), make use of Fig. 8`3`1b for a geometric interpretation in price space. Let S_0 and S_1 be the indifference curves through p^0 and p^1, and let income μ be fixed.

A: For all prices p on S_0, any Konyus index is 100%. — B: Let $p^{(0)}$ be the point where S_0 is intersected by a straight line λ_0 through origin ω and p^1; then the Laspeyres-Konyus index is $\omega\,p^1/\omega p^{(0)}$. Similarly, the Paasche-Konyus index is $\omega p^{(1)}/\omega p^0$, where $p^{(1)}$ is the point in which S_1 is intersected by a line λ_1 through p^0. — C: Let a be the point where λ_0 is intersected by the tangent of S_0 at p^0; then Laspeyres' index is $\omega p^1/\omega a$, which verifies (8`3`12 a) since $\omega a < \omega p^{(0)}$. Similarly, Paasche's index is $\omega b/\omega p^0$, where b is the intersection between λ_1 and the tangent of S_1 at p^1; here $\omega b < \omega p^{(1)}$, which verifies (8`3`12 b).

Further make use of price space to illustrate situations where nominal income changes, but the ratio (8`3`14) of real incomes equals unity.

45 (Wold, 1943–44). The indifference surfaces of budget space Ω_q and price space Ω_p stand in the relationship of a point-tangent transformation, by which the purchase region of Ω_q is mapped onto the entire space Ω_p.

Given the demand functions (4`5`1) that belong to a preference field that satisfies Assumptions A^*-C^* of Ch. 4`7, show that it is possible to reconstruct in Ω_q the convex envelope of any locus of indifference.

Considering the case $n = 2$, further show that, if there is a curve S in Ω_p along which the indifference map presents corners, curve S corresponds to a region of Ω_q in which the indifference map is concave towards the origin (or linear).

46. Given a preference field, let $p^0 = (p_1^0, \ldots, p_n^0)$, $p^1 = (p_1^1, \ldots, p_n^1)$ be two arbitrary price constellations. Specifying the two income levels arbitrarily, let $q^0 = (q_1^0, \ldots, q_n^0)$, $q^1 = (q_1^1, \ldots, q_n^1)$ be the corresponding optimal budgets. Show by a geometric argument in the budget space that

(1) $$ \text{if} \quad \sum_i p_i^0\,(q_i^1 - q_i^0) \leq 0 \quad \text{then} \quad \sum_i p_i^1\,(q_i^1 - q_i^0) < 0. $$

This is known as *Samuelson's inequality*.[1] Similarly, considering the price space, show that

(2) $$ \text{if} \quad \sum_i q_i^0\,(p_i^1 - p_i^0) < 0 \quad \text{then} \quad \sum_i q_i^1\,(p_i^1 - p_i^0) < 0. $$

Adopting Samuelson's approach of 'revealed preference', show that (2) cannot be deduced from (1) unless the preferences constitute an indifference map, i. e. unless the price functions (4`6`3) satisfy the integrability condition (4`6`1).

47. Considering the case when q^1 and q^0 belong to the same preference level, and making $p_i^1 = p_i^0 + dp_i^0$ and $p_k^1 = p_k^0$ for $k \neq i$, Samuelson's inequality gives as an immediate corollary $dq_i/dp_i < 0$, which is the statement A in Theorem 5`3`1.

48. Check the curves in Fig. 8`3`2 a. Show that $\mathfrak{P}_{LK}$ and $\mathfrak{P}_{PK}$ have the same asymptote.

49 (Hicks, 1942). Considering the Laspeyres index variants for an infinitesimal change in prices, verify the relation

$$\mathfrak{P}_{LK} - \mathfrak{P}_L = \frac{1}{2\,\mu} \sum_{i=1}^{n} \sum_{k=1}^{n} s_{ik}\, dp_i\, dp_k \quad \text{with } s_{ik} = s_{ki} \text{ given by (5·3·1)}.$$

Further deduce a similar formula for the Paasche indexes.

50 (Vieno Rajaoja[1]). For an infinitesimal price change, we have

$$\mathfrak{P}_{LK} - \mathfrak{P}_{PK} = \sum_{i} \sum_{k} c_i\, c_k\, (E_\mu q_k - 1)\, \frac{dp_i}{p_i}\, \frac{dp_k}{p_k} \quad \text{with } c_i = p_i q_i / \mu.$$

51. The Divisia-Roy index involves a curve integral along the path C in price space. Consider a price fall from $p^0 = (p_1 = 1,\ p_2 = 1)$ to $p^1 = (p_1 = \frac{1}{2},\ p_2 = \frac{1}{2})$ along three paths defined as follows. C_1: Prices p_1, p_2 fall in the same proportion. C_2: First p_1 falls from 1 to $\frac{1}{2}$ while p_2 remains constant, then p_2 falls from 1 to $\frac{1}{2}$ while p_1 remains constant. C_3: Like C_2, but p_2 falls first and then p_1. Letting $\mathfrak{P}_i$ be the Divisia-Roy index for income $\mu = 1$ and path C_i, form $\mathfrak{P}_i$ for the preference field defined by $q_1 q_2 = c$, and verify $\mathfrak{P}_1 = \mathfrak{P}_2 = \mathfrak{P}_3 = 50\,\%$. Further show that the field defined by $q_1 q_2 + q_2 = c$ gives $\mathfrak{P}_1 = 50\,\%$, $\mathfrak{P}_2 = 54.0\,\%$, $\mathfrak{P}_3 = 45.4\,\%$.
Hence if C is the closed price cycle from p^0 to p^1 along C_2 and then back to p^0 along C_3, the first preference field gives $\mathfrak{P}_{DR} = 100\,\%$, the second $\mathfrak{P}_{DR} = 118.9\,\%$.

52. Referring to Fig. 8·3·1b, show that the Divisia-Roy index coincides with the Laspeyres-Konyus index if the path C goes from p^0 along S_0 to $p^{(0)}$ and then along λ_0 to p^1. Similarly, show that we obtain the Paasche-Konyus index if C goes from p^0 along λ_1 to $p^{(1)}$ and then along S_1 to p^1.
Generalize to an arbitrary number of commodities.

53 (Roy, 1935). Suppose that $q = (q_1, \ldots, q_n)$ and $p = (p_1, \ldots, p_n)$ vary in such manner that $p_i q_i = w_i \sum p_i q_i$, where $w_1, \ldots, w_n$ are constant. If we take these w_i for weights in the geometric average $\mathfrak{P}_G$ in (8·3·1), Divisia's chain index (8·3·7) will coincide with $\mathfrak{P}_G$.

54. Considering the Divisia-Roy index (8·3·13) in the case of two commodities, show that the condition of the previous exercise is fulfilled if the indifference map is given by

$$q_1^\alpha \cdot q_2^\beta = c.$$

Further show that this is the only type of map for which the Divisia-Roy index reduces to the geometric average index.
Hint: Make combined use of Exercises 7 (c) and 8.

55 (Ville, 1946). A preference function $U(q_1, \ldots, q_n)$ will be said to define a *Ville indifference map* if U is a homogeneous function, in symbols

$$U(\lambda q_1, \ldots, \lambda q_n) = f(\lambda) \cdot U(q_1, \ldots, q_n).$$

For an indifference map to be a Ville map, each of the following conditions is necessary and sufficient. (i) All indifference surfaces are equiform w.r.t. the origin. (ii) All income-consumption curves are straight lines that pass through the origin. (iii) The four index variants in (8·3·12) are independent of consumer income. (iv) For every closed price cycle C, the Divisia-Roy index satisfies the cycle criterion. (v) Supposing that all consumers in a market have the same indifference map, the market demand functions (7·2·4) reduce to functions of total market income, thus

$$\sum_{\nu} Q_i(\mu^{(\nu)}, p_1, \ldots, p_n) = Q_i\left(\sum_{\nu} \mu^{(\nu)}, p_1, \ldots, p_n\right).$$

Special cases: In Ex. 5 we have a Ville map, but not in Fig. $3\dot{}1\dot{}1$ and Exs. 6 and 33. [Cf also Ex. 51.]

56. Construct a Ville map, given one of its indifference surfaces.

Special case: For $n = 2$, given $xy + y = 1$ the Ville map is $y + \sqrt{y(4x + y)} = c$.

57. Making use of the data of Ex. 37, calculate aggregate quantities according to $(5\dot{}6\dot{}1{-}3)$. Further verify

$$\mathfrak{Q}_L = 87.9 \% \qquad \mathfrak{Q}_P = 89.1 \%$$

where $\mathfrak{Q}_L$ and $\mathfrak{Q}_P$ are volume indexes formed in analogy to Laspeyres' and Paasche's price indexes $(8\dot{}3\dot{}3{-}4)$.

58 (Divisia, 1925–26). Divisia's price index $\mathfrak{P}_D$ being defined by $(8\dot{}3\dot{}7)$, a corresponding volume index is given by

$$\mathfrak{Q}_D = \exp \left(\int_C \frac{\Sigma\, p_i\, dq_i}{\Sigma\, p_i\, q_i} \right).$$

Assuming that the $q_i = q_i(p_1, \ldots, p_n)$ are arbitrary functions of the p_i, verify the identity

$$\mathfrak{P}_D \cdot \mathfrak{Q}_D \equiv c\, \Sigma\, p_i q_i.$$

Thus if $\mathfrak{X} = \mathfrak{P}_D \cdot \mathfrak{Q}_D$ is interpreted as a chain index for expenditure, $\mathfrak{X}$ is exact in the sense of being proportional to actual expenditure.

59 (S. Malmquist[1]). To construct a price index is to introduce a *conventional metric* in the price space. In the case of a preference field index, the metric constitutes a metric relative to the indifference surfaces.

Laspeyres-Konyus' index $\mathfrak{P}_{LK}(t)$ may be regarded as a price compensation index; more precisely, $\mathfrak{P}_{LK}(t)$ can be interpreted as a chain index formed on the basis of a variable income $\mu^*(t)$, where $\mu^*(t)$ is income $\mu(0)$ when subjected to continuous price compensation. Further show that $\mathfrak{P}_{LK}(t)$, in contradistinction to Divisia-Roy's chain index, will always satisfy the circular test.

60. Establish an isomorphism between production theory and the theory of consumer demand by translating Ch. $4\dot{}1{-}3$ into a different terminology, viz. by interpreting the commodities as production factors, μ as total production cost, $U(q_1, \ldots, q_n)$ as total production volume, and $q_1, \ldots, q_n$ as quantities spent of the production factors.[1]

Since $U(q_1, \ldots, q_n)$ is now measurable, we see that production theory is strictly isomorphic with the pre-Paretoan theory of consumer demand, where utility $(3\dot{}1\dot{}2)$ was dealt with as a measurable quantity. Specifically, we note that $U(q_1, \ldots, q_n)$ will satisfy Frisch's axiom of *alternative changes* [Ch. $3\dot{}5$]. Further we note that the quotient $\varkappa$ in $(4\dot{}5\dot{}5)$ is the *marginal utility of money* in the pre-Paretoan theory and the *marginal productivity* in production theory, whereas $\varkappa$ has no concrete significance in Paretoan theory.

PART III

Some topics in the theory of stationary random processes

Chapter 9.

THE NOTION OF A STATIONARY PROCESS

1. Random variables.[1] – In statistics the dualism between empirical and theoretical notions takes the form of frequencies and observed distributions on the one side, probabilities and probability distributions on the other. From an intuitive standpoint, known as the *frequency interpretation*, a probability distribution is regarded as a hypothetical infinite population that can be specified in mathematical terms. For the exact treatment of probability theory we start from a set of abstract notions which are designed to conform to the frequency interpretation. The groundwork of probability analysis as applied in statistics is supposed to be known to the reader. Reference may be made to S. S. Wilks (1949), N. Arley and K. R. Buch (1950) and, for the advanced theory, H. Cramér (1945). By way of introduction we shall recall the notion of random variable, stressing those aspects that are of primary relevance when proceeding to stochastic processes.

The notion of a probability distribution in n dimensions is illustrated in Figs. 1–2. From the viewpoint of the applications such a distribution refers to a random phenomenon, every observation x of which comprises n measurements, say

(1) $$x = (x_1, x_2, \ldots, x_n).$$

The observations may for $n = 1$ be plotted as points on a coordinate axis [see Fig. 1a, where 4 observations are plotted], for $n = 2$ as points in a system of two axes [Fig. 1b]. For $n > 2$ it is convenient to imagine an observation x as a path joining the points x_i as plotted on n parallel axes [see Fig. 2, which shows 4 observations, each comprising $n = 9$ measurements].

Regarding an observation (1) as a point x in an n-dimensional Euclidean space Ω_n, a set S of points x is called an *event*, or a *random event*. The points x themselves are called *elementary events*. Thanks to the set interpretation of events, the notion of probability distribution can be defined with full

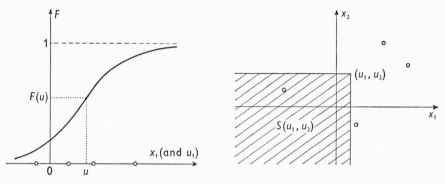

Fig. 9'1'1. Graphic representation of statistical observations.

a. Four observations (9'1'1), each comprising one measurement, x_1.

b. Four observations $x^{(1)}$, $x^{(2)}$, $x^{(3)}$, $x^{(4)}$, each comprising two measurements, $x^{(i)} = (x_1^{(i)}, x_2^{(i)})$.

mathematical rigour. The definition involves three elements $(\Omega, \mathfrak{S}, P)$, which in their totality are called a *probability field*.[2] Briefly stated, $\Omega = \Omega_n$ is the space of elementary events, $\mathfrak{S}$ is the family of events S to which probabilities $P(S)$ are assigned, and P is the set function $P(S)$. Quite generally, we may take the sets S of type

(2) $$S(u_1, \ldots, u_n) = (x_1 \leq u_1, \ldots, x_n \leq u_n)$$

for a basis, and build up $\mathfrak{S}$ as a Borel family of sets by including all sets obtained from the sets (2) by iterated use of set addition and set subtraction.

The probabilities of the basic sets (2), say

(3) $$F(u_1, \ldots, u_n) = P(x_1 \leq u_1, \ldots, x_n \leq u_n), \quad -\infty < u_1 < \infty, \ldots, -\infty < u_n < \infty$$

define the *distribution function* $F(u_1, \ldots, u_n)$ of the probability field. Given $F(u_1, \ldots, u_n)$, the probability $P(S)$ of any set S in $\mathfrak{S}$ can be determined by the elementary rules of probability. As an example could be mentioned the rule that if $S_1, S_2, \ldots$ are events no two of which can occur simultaneously, then the event $(S_1$ or S_2 or $\ldots)$ will have probability

$$P(S_1 \text{ or } S_2 \text{ or } \cdots) = P(S_1) + P(S_2) + \cdots.$$

The probabilities $P(S)$ thus determined by (3) include, in particular, any probability of the type

(4) $$\Delta_n F = P(a_1 < x_1 \leq b_1, \ldots, a_n < x_n \leq b_n).$$

It is known that any distribution (3) has the following properties,

(5a) $$0 \leq F(u_1, \ldots, u_n) \leq 1; \qquad \Delta_n F \geq 0; \qquad F(+\infty, \ldots, +\infty) = 1;$$

(5b) $$F(-\infty, u_2, \ldots, u_n) = \cdots = F(u_1, \ldots, u_{n-1}, -\infty) = 0.$$

Conversely, any function $F(u_1, \ldots, u_n)$ that satisfies (5) will define a probability field $(\Omega, \mathfrak{S}, P)$ in Ω_n.

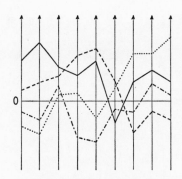

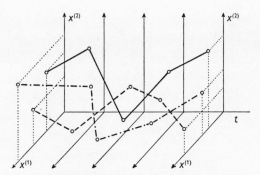

Fig. 9·1·2. Four observations, each with 9 measurements.

Fig. 9·2·1. Three time-series, each comprising two simultaneous observations.

Given a function $\zeta = \zeta(x_1, \ldots, x_n)$ of the elementary event x, suppose the events defined by

$$(6) \qquad \zeta(x_1, \ldots, x_n) \leq v \qquad\qquad -\infty < v < \infty$$

belong to the set family $\mathfrak{S}$ of the probability field considered. Then the distribution function of ζ, say $G(v)$, will be well-defined by

$$(7) \qquad G(v) = P(\zeta(x_1, \ldots, x_n) \leq v).$$

Any such function ζ is called a *random variable* in the field $(\Omega_n, \mathfrak{S}, P)$. Simple examples of functions ζ which constitute well-defined random variables are

$$(8) \qquad x_i, \quad x_i^2, \quad x_i \cdot x_k, \quad b_1 x_1 + \cdots + b_n x_n, \quad \mathrm{Max}\,(x_1, \ldots, x_n).$$

For a random variable $\zeta = \zeta(x_1, \ldots, x_n)$ it is often convenient to denote the arguments as random variables, thus $\zeta = \zeta(\xi_1, \ldots, \xi_n)$. For example, the two first variables in (8) may be denoted ξ_i and ξ_i^2, respectively.

As a straightforward generalization of the notion of random variable we may define a *random vector* $\zeta = (\zeta^{(1)}, \ldots, \zeta^{(m)})$ with m components $\zeta^{(i)} = \zeta^{(i)}(\xi_1, \ldots, \xi_n)$ that are functions of $\xi_1, \ldots, \xi_n$. In particular, the elementary event $(x_1, \ldots, x_n)$ is itself a random vector, $\zeta = (\xi_1, \ldots, \xi_n)$.

We recall that the random variables $\xi_1, \ldots, \xi_n$ are *independent* in the sense of probability theory if, and only if, their distribution function factorizes into

$$(9) \qquad F(u_1, \ldots, u_n) = F_1(u_1) \cdot \cdots \cdot F_n(u_n).$$

The same definition applies to the components of a random vector.

Reference is made to the text-books for further elements of probability theory, especially for the concepts of *mathematical expectation* and *conditional probabilities* and *expectations*. We note some fundamental formulae concerning conditional expectation,[3]

$$(10) \quad E(\xi) = E[E(\xi|\eta)]; \; E[f(\eta) \cdot \xi|\eta] = f(\eta) \cdot E(\xi|\eta); \; E[E(\xi|\eta, \zeta)|\eta] = E(\xi|\eta)$$

where ξ, η, ζ are arbitrary random variables, and $E(\xi|\eta)$ is the conditional expectation of ξ formed w.r.t. the condition that η is constant. Being a function of η, the expectation $E(\xi | \eta)$ is itself a well-defined random variable.

In our notation we shall usually follow H. Cramér (1945). Thus in particular

$$m = m_\xi = E\,\xi; \qquad \sigma_\xi^2 = D^2\,\xi = E\,(\xi - m)^2; \qquad \lambda_{ik} = \lambda_{ki} = E\,(\xi_i - m_i)\,(\xi_k - m_k)$$

denote, respectively, the mathematical expectation ($=$ mean) of a random variable ξ, the variance of ξ, and the covariance of two variables ξ_i, ξ_k with means m_i, m_k. With λ_{ik} defined as above we shall write

$$(11) \qquad \boldsymbol{\Lambda}_n = \begin{bmatrix} \lambda_{11} & \cdots & \lambda_{1n} \\ \cdot & \cdots & \cdot \\ \lambda_{n1} & \cdots & \lambda_{nn} \end{bmatrix} \qquad \Lambda_n = \begin{vmatrix} \lambda_{11} & \cdots & \lambda_{1n} \\ \cdot & \cdots & \cdot \\ \lambda_{n1} & \cdots & \lambda_{nn} \end{vmatrix}$$

for the *dispersion matrix* and the *dispersion determinant* of n variables $\xi_1, \ldots, \xi_n$. Any dispersion determinant is nonnegative; hence

$$(12) \qquad\qquad \Lambda_m \geq 0 \qquad\qquad m = 1, \ldots, n.$$

In what follows we shall often be concerned with random variables that are defined as linear functions of other variables. Considering the variable

$$\zeta = b_0 + b_1\,\xi_1 + \cdots + b_n\,\xi_n$$

we note that the distribution function of ζ, say $F(v) = \operatorname{Prob}(\zeta \leq v)$, may be interpreted geometrically in the space Ω_n of the variables $\xi_1, \ldots, \xi_n$ as giving for every v the probability mass situated in the half-space $b_0 + b_1 x_1 + \cdots + b_n x_n \leq v$. Letting L be a line that is orthogonal to the planes $b_0 + b_1 x_1 + \cdots + b_n x_n = v$, where v is arbitrary, we see that the probability distribution of ζ may be interpreted as the orthogonal projection into L of the probability mass contained in Ω_n. In the special case when $F(v)$ is a step-function with a saltus from $F = 0$ to $F = 1$, say for $v = a$, we have $\zeta = a$ with probability 1, that is $b_0 + b_1\xi_1 + \cdots + b_n\xi_n$ reduces to the constant a. If $a = 0$, the entire probability mass of the space Ω_n is then situated in the plane $b_0 + b_1 x_1 + \cdots + b_n x_n = 0$ and on projection into L the mass will be concentrated at a single point of L. If the probability distribution of $\xi_1, \ldots, \xi_n$ in this sense is contained in a linear subspace of Ω_n, the distribution is called *linearly singular*, or briefly *singular*. For the distribution to be singular it is necessary and sufficient that[4]

$$(13) \qquad\qquad \Lambda_n = 0.$$

2. Stochastic processes. – The notions of Ch. 9·1 are valid irrespective of the nature of the measurements (9·1·1). Specifically, they apply if (9·1·1) is a time-series, i.e. if the measurements refer to the development in time of a random phenomenon. A random variable thus being associated with each of the measurements, we see that this application requires an extension of the notion of n-dimensional probability distribution, for the observations in a time-series are in point of principle unlimited in number. Confining ourselves to the case of equidistant observations, it involves no loss of generality to take the observation interval as time unit, and so we are led to consider series of the type

(1) $x = (\ldots, x_{t-1}, x_t, x_{t+1}, x_{t+2}, \ldots)$

where t runs through all integers from $-\infty$ to $+\infty$. For the illustration of such series we may use a graph like Fig. 9·1·2, with one vertical for each time point. Thus Fig. 9·1·2 would represent 4 time-series which are recorded at 9 time-points.

The corresponding generalization of the notion of a random variable is known as a *stochastic process*, or simply a *random process*. To be precise, we should say process with *discrete time-parameter* t. To define such a process it is convenient to use the notion of a probability field $(\Omega, \mathfrak{S}, P)$. In this case, Ω is the space of all real sequences of type (1). Any such sequence x is an elementary event, also called a *realization* of the process. Any set S of realizations is an event. The events of type

(2) $S(t, n; u_1, \ldots, u_n) = (x_{t+1} \le u_1, \ldots, x_{t+n} \le u_n);$ $n > 0,\ -\infty < t < \infty$

are taken as the basis for generating $\mathfrak{S}$ as a Borel family of sets. The probabilities of the basic sets (2),

(3) $F(t, n; u_1, \ldots, u_n) = P(x_{t+1} \le u_1, \ldots, x_{t+n} \le u_n),$

form a system $\{F\}$ of distribution functions. Thus each F of the system satisfies all relations of type (9·1·5). Moreover, the functions F satisfy the following relations of mutual consistency,

(4) $F(t, m; u_1, \ldots, u_m) = F(t, n; u_1, \ldots, u_m, \infty, \cdots, \infty);$ $m < n,\ -\infty < t < \infty.$

According to a fundamental theorem of A. Kolmogorov (1933), the system $\{F\}$ determines uniquely the probabilities $P(S)$ of all events S in $\mathfrak{S}$. And conversely, any system $\{F\}$ of distribution functions will define a probability field $(\Omega, \mathfrak{S}, P)$, provided the functions satisfy the consistency relations (4).

In the special case when all functions F in (3) are normal (Gauss-Laplace) distribution functions, the stochastic process will be called a *Gaussian process*.[1]

From the viewpoint of applications there is an important difference between ordinary random variables [Ch. 9·1] and random processes. The random phenomenon considered will for ordinary variables generally supply a large or unlimited number of observations x of the type (9·1·1). For a random process the number of observational series x of the type (9·2·1) may be large, but the number may also be limited, it being even possible that the process does not supply more than just one series x. Fig. 9·1·2 may be taken to refer to a process where there are several observations, 4 series x being plotted. It will be noted that for stationary processes it is quite often the case that just one series x is available [for example, the price series p_t in Fig. 1·3·1a]. We shall return to this point in Ch. 9·4.

The notion of a stochastic process may be extended to the case when each observation element x_t in (1) consists of several measurements, say m in number,

$$x_t = (x_t^{(1)}, \ldots, x_t^{(m)}) \qquad\qquad -\infty < t < \infty.$$

Formulae (2)–(4) apply as before if we interpret x_t, u_t, etc., as vectors, which leads to the notion of an m-dimensional random process, or a *vector process* with m components. For illustration we refer to Fig. 1 (p. 151), which shows three realizations of a two-dimensional process. Again it may occur that the phenomenon considered does not provide more than one realization, as for example when the two observations $x_t^{(1)}$, $x_t^{(2)}$ at the instant t are the price and the quantity sold of a certain commodity in a certain market.

In analogy with the finite case (9˙1˙6–7), a stochastic process may be interpreted as an infinite sequence of random variables, say

(5) $$\{\xi_t\} = (\ldots, \xi_{t-1}, \xi_t, \xi_{t+1}, \ldots).$$

This notation covers also the case of a vector process. Alternatively, we shall for vector processes use the more elaborate notation

$$\{\xi_t^{(1)}, \ldots, \xi_t^{(m)}\}.$$

For a vector process $\{\xi_t\}$ the element associated with instant t forms an m-dimensional random variable $\xi_t = (\xi_t^{(1)}, \ldots, \xi_t^{(m)})$. On the other hand, the variables $\xi_t^{(k)}$ as defined for k fixed and $t = 0, \pm 1, \pm 2, \cdots$ will form a random process, $\{\xi_t^{(k)}\} = (\ldots, \xi_{t-1}^{(k)}, \xi_t^{(k)}, \ldots)$. Process $\{\xi_t^{(k)}\}$, called *the k:th component of* $\{\xi_t\}$, is well-defined by a system of distribution functions of the type (3), say $\{F^{(k)}\}$, where the $F^{(k)}$ are easily deduced from the system $\{F\}$ that defines the vector process.

The definition (9˙1˙9) of independence between random variables extends to the components $\{\xi_t^{(k)}\}$ of a vector process $\{\xi_t\}$. Thus the component processes are called independent if in the system $\{F\}$ that defines $\{\xi_t\}$ each function F splits up into factors referring to the m components, thus

(6) $$F(t, n; u_1, \ldots, u_n) = F^{(1)}(t, n; u_1^{(1)}, \ldots, u_n^{(1)}) \cdot \cdots \cdot F^{(m)}(t, n; u_1^{(m)}, \ldots, u_n^{(m)}).$$

Similarly, the correlation concepts extend to random processes. We note in particular that two component processes $\{\xi_t^{(i)}\}$, $\{\xi_t^{(k)}\}$ are mutually uncorrelated if the two variables $\xi_s^{(i)}$, $\xi_t^{(k)}$ are uncorrelated for all s, t.

When dealing with stochastic processes with a discrete time-parameter t, we can on the whole use the same methods as in the case of an ordinary multi-dimensional variable. Specifically, the notions of random function, mathematical expectation and conditional probability distribution allow a straightforward generalization to such processes. Let us examine the notion of random function. Given a stochastic process $\{\xi_t\}$, let ζ be a random variable defined as a function of the variables in $\{\xi_t\}$, in symbols

(7) $$\zeta = \zeta(\ldots, \xi_{t-1}, \xi_t, \xi_{t+1}, \ldots).$$

Then we may form a stochastic process $\{\zeta_t\}$ by setting $\zeta_t = \zeta$ and $\zeta_{t+n} =$

$\zeta(\ldots, \xi_{t+n-1}, \xi_{t+n}, \xi_{t+n+1}, \ldots)$, so that for n positive (negative) ζ_{t+n} is obtained from ζ_t by moving all variables ξ_t, simultaneously, n steps to the left (right). This device defines the process $\{\zeta_t\}$ as a function of the given process $\{\xi_t\}$. Interpreting this notion in terms of the spaces Ω of the two processes, say Ω_ξ and Ω_ζ respectively, the functional transform carries over each realization x in Ω_ξ into a realization z in Ω_ζ.

A fundamental type of functional transform is the one where $\zeta_t = \xi_{t+1}$ for all t; the process $\{\zeta_t\}$ thus defined will be denoted $\{\xi_{t+1}\}$. Considering a realization (9·2·1) of $\{\xi_t\}$, and letting this be denoted X_t, the corresponding realization of $\{\xi_{t+1}\}$, say X_{t+1}, is obtained from X_t by putting x_{t+1} in the place of x_t for all t; thus

(8) $\qquad X_t = (\ldots, x_{-1}, x_0, x_1, \ldots), \qquad X_{t+1} = (\ldots, x_0, x_1, x_2, \ldots).$

3. The stationary process. – Let

(1) $\qquad \{\xi_t\} = (\ldots, \xi_{t-1}, \xi_t, \xi_{t+1}, \xi_{t+2}, \ldots)$

be a stochastic process with discrete time-parameter as defined in (9·2·2–5). The process is called *stationary* if the distribution functions (9·2·3) satisfy

(2) $\qquad F(t, n; u_1, \ldots, u_n) = F(t+\nu, n; u_1, \ldots, u_n)$

for all $n > 0$, $-\infty < t < \infty$, $-\infty < \nu < \infty$ and $-\infty < u_i < \infty$ for $i = 1, \ldots, n$.

The general theory of the stationary process has been founded by A. Khintchine (1934).

Each ξ_t in (1) being an ordinary random variable, we shall for the processes considered in this chapter assume, once and for all, that each ξ_t has finite mean and finite standard deviation. The stationarity of the process implies that the expectation and the standard deviation are independent of t. Thus we can use the simple notation $m = E\xi$ and $\sigma = D\xi$, obtaining for all t

(3) $\quad m = E\,\xi_t = \int_{-\infty}^{\infty} u\,d_u F(t, 1; u); \quad \sigma^2 = E(\xi_t - m)^2 = \int_{-\infty}^{\infty}(u-m)^2\, d_u F(t, 1; u).$

The covariance and the correlation coefficient of ξ_t, $\xi_{t+\nu}$ will be finite, independent of t, and the same as for $\xi_{t-\nu}$, ξ_t; we write

(4) $\quad E(\xi_t - m)(\xi_{t+\nu} - m) = \lambda_\nu = \lambda_{-\nu}; \quad \varrho_\nu = \varrho_{-\nu} = \lambda_\nu/\sigma^2; \quad (\nu = 0, \pm 1, \pm 2, \ldots).$

The ϱ_ν are called the *autocorrelation coefficients*, and their totality

(5) $\qquad \varrho_0\,(=1), \varrho_1, \varrho_2, \ldots$

is the *correlogram* of the stationary process considered.

If $\{\xi_t\}$ is a general stochastic process (9·2·5) and $\lambda_{ik} = E(\xi_i - E\xi_i)(\xi_k - E\xi_k)$ its covariances, the λ_{ik} will form an infinite dispersion matrix, say

(6) $\qquad \boldsymbol{\Lambda} = [\lambda_{ik}] \qquad\qquad i, k = 0, \pm 1, \pm 2, \ldots$

Let Λ_{tn} be the dispersion matrix of the variables $\xi_{t+1}, \ldots, \xi_{t+n}$. Clearly Λ_{tn} is a principal minor of Λ. By (9·1·12), the corresponding determinant Λ_{tn} is nonnegative,

(7) $$\Lambda_{tn} \geq 0. \qquad n>0;\, t=0,\, \pm 1,\, \pm 2,\, \ldots$$

Now if the process $\{\xi_t\}$ is stationary, we have

(8) $$\lambda_{ik} = \lambda_{|i-k|} = \sigma^2 \cdot \varrho_{|i-k|} \qquad i,\, k = 0,\, \pm 1,\, \pm 2,\, \ldots$$

In the dispersion matrix Λ of a stationary process, the elements λ_{ik} will by (8) be equal along any NW–SE diagonal. Thus Λ reduces to what is known as a *Laurent matrix*.

A necessary and sufficient condition that a sequence $\varrho_0 = 1, \varrho_1, \varrho_2, \ldots$, should by (8) define a Laurent matrix (6) satisfying (7) is that we should have

(9) $$\varrho_\nu = \frac{1}{\pi} \int_0^\pi \cos \nu\lambda \cdot dW(\lambda) \qquad \nu = 0,\, 1,\, 2,\, \ldots$$

where $W(\lambda)$ is a nondecreasing function with $W(0)=0$, $W(\pi)=\pi$. Thus (9) gives a necessary and sufficient condition for the ϱ_ν to form the correlogram (5) of a stationary random process. Function $W(\lambda)$ and its derivative $W'(\lambda)$ are called the *spectral functions* of the process considered. Quite generally, $W(\lambda)$ may conversely be expressed in terms of the correlogram,

(10) $$W(\lambda) = \lambda + 2 \sum_{\nu=1}^{\infty} \frac{\varrho_\nu}{\nu} \sin \nu\lambda, \qquad 0 \leq \lambda \leq \pi,$$

which series is always convergent.[1]

The above definitions of stationarity may be generalized as follows:

(i) Given an arbitrary process $\{\xi_t\}$, suppose that its mean m, variance σ^2, and correlogram ϱ_ν as defined by (3)–(5) are independent of t. Then $\{\xi_t\}$ is said to be *stationary to the second order*. Clearly, a process that is stationary in the sense of (2) is stationary to the second order, but the converse is not necessarily true.

(ii) Let $\{\xi_t\} = \{\xi_t^{(1)}, \ldots, \xi_t^{(m)}\}$ be a vector process as defined in connection with (9·2·5). Interpreting each u_i as a vector $(u_i^{(1)}, \ldots, u_i^{(m)})$, the two definitions of stationarity extend immediately to the vector process.[2]

The following theorem is an immediate consequence of the definition (2).

THEOREM 1. *Given a process $\{\xi_t\}$ that is stationary in the sense of (2), let ζ be an arbitrary function (9·2·7), and let $\{\zeta_t\}$ be the corresponding functional transform of $\{\xi_t\}$. Then the process $\{\zeta_t\}$ will be stationary in the sense of (2), and this holds true also if $\{\xi_t\}$ and $\{\zeta_t\}$ are vector processes.*

4. Space averages and phase averages.[1] – The space Ω of the process (9·3·1) may be regarded as a universe of realizations of the type

(1) $$x = (\ldots,\, x_{t-1},\, x_t,\, x_{t+1},\, \ldots).$$

Holding t fixed, let us consider the component x_t of all realizations x of the universe. [In Fig. 9·1·2, the x_t considered lie on the same vertical.] The distribution of the x_t-values will then define the random variable ξ_t. The condition (9·3·2) of stationarity requires that this distribution is the same for all t. In this distribution, the average of x_t is $E\xi$. The expectation $E\xi$ may thus be described as a *space average* over Ω for fixed t.

On the other hand, forming

(2) $$M_{t_2-t_1+1}x = \frac{1}{t_2-t_1+1}\sum_{t=t_1}^{t_2} x_t; \qquad Mx = \lim_{\substack{t_1\to-\infty \\ t_2\to\infty}} M_{t_2-t_1+1}x$$

we have in Mx another type of average of the x_t, a *time* or *phase average* over a fixed realization x. The *ergodic theorem* of Birkhoff-Khintchine[2] states that, if the process $\{\xi_t\}$ is stationary in the sense of (9·3·2) and has a finite expectation $E\xi$, the phase average Mx will exist with probability 1, in other words, will exist for 'almost all' realizations x in the universe Ω considered.[3] In general, Mx will vary from one realization x to another. A necessary and sufficient condition that $Mx = E\xi$ for almost all realizations is given by

(3) $$\lim_{n\to\infty}\frac{1}{n}\sum_{\nu=1}^{n}\varrho_\nu = 0.$$

On this basis we arrive at the important notion of an *ergodic process:* Given a process $\{\xi_t\}$, let ζ be an arbitrary function (9·2·7). Then by Theorem 9·3·1 the process $\{\zeta_t\}$ is stationary in the sense of (9·3·2). Now suppose that the expectation $E\zeta$ is finite. Letting z denote a realization of the process $\{\zeta_t\}$, the phase average Mz will exist with probability 1, by the Birkhoff-Khintchine theorem. The process $\{\xi_t\}$ is then called *ergodic* if $Mz = E\zeta$ for all ζ such that $E\zeta^2$ is finite.[4]

Knowing from (3) that the phase average Mx will under certain general conditions equal the space average $E\xi$, we are led to ask what more a single realization x can possibly tell us about the structure of the entire process $\{\xi_t\}$ considered. To examine this question, we transform the realization x into another sequence z,

(4) $$z = (\ldots, z_{t-1}, z_t, z_{t+1}, \ldots) \quad \text{with} \quad z_t = z_t(x; u_1, \ldots, u_n)$$

by making

(5) $$z_t = 1 \text{ if } x_{t+1}\le u_1, \ldots, x_{t+n}\le u_n; \qquad z_t = 0 \text{ otherwise.}$$

Then Mz is well-defined according to (2). We may accordingly write

$$Mz = F_x(t, n; u_1, \ldots, u_n).$$

By construction, $F_x(t, n; u_1, \ldots, u_n)$ is the relative frequency of the event $\xi_{t+1}\le u_1, \ldots, \xi_{t+n}\le u_n$, a frequency defined as a *phase average* over the realization x. Forming the corresponding *space average*, we see that this is nothing else than the distribution function $F(t, n; u_1, \ldots, u_n)$ in the system $\{F\}$ that defines the process $\{\xi_t\}$. Now making $n = 1, 2, \ldots$ in (4)–(5) we obtain a system of functions $\{F_x\}$ of the type (9·2·3). Then if $F_x = F$ for each function in the two systems, that is if $\{F\}$ and $\{F_x\}$ coincide, the single realization x has revealed the entire probability structure of the process $\{\xi_t\}$.

THEOREM 1. *The system* $\{F_x\}$ *will coincide with* $\{F\}$ *for almost all realizations* x *if and only if the stationary process* $\{\xi_t\}$ *is ergodic.*

Briefly indicating the proof, it is seen that the functional transform defined by (4)-(5) is a special case of (9·2·7-8), and so the ergodicity of $\{\xi_t\}$ implies, with probability 1, that $F_x = F$ for every function in $\{F\}$. Conversely, if $\{F_x\}$ coincides with $\{F\}$ for almost all x, the relation $Mz = E\zeta$ will hold true not only for all transforms (4)-(5), but also for all functions ζ generated by linear combinations of transforms of the type (4)-(5). By a familiar approximation procedure the relation $Mz = E\zeta$ then extends to all functions ζ such that ζ^2 is measurable.[5]

Available criteria of ergodicity are of restricted scope. A fairly general result, due to G. Maruyama (1949), is that a Gaussian process is ergodic if and only if its spectral function (9·3·10) is continuous. The restriction to a Gaussian process is of course essential. [Cf Ex. 31.]

The autocorrelation coefficient ϱ_ν has in (9·3·4) been defined in terms of space averages. The corresponding phase average definition is, in obvious notation,

(6) $$\varrho_\nu^* = \varrho_{-\nu}^* = M(x_t - Mx)(x_{t+\nu} - Mx)/M(x_t - Mx)^2; \quad \nu = 0, 1, 2, \ldots$$

The ϱ_ν^* constitute the *correlogram* of the realization x; for ergodic processes we have, of course, $\varrho_\nu^* = \varrho_\nu$ for almost all realizations.

In a stationary process the structural elements of primary importance are the *mean*, the *variance*, and the *correlogram*. In (9·3·3-4) these notions have been introduced as theoretical concepts, and in the present section we have stressed their dual interpretation in terms of space averages and phase averages. We shall now recall the corresponding empirical notions. Writing

(7) $$x_1, \ldots, x_n \qquad \bar{x} = \frac{1}{n}\sum_{t=1}^{n} x_t \qquad s^2 = \frac{1}{n}\sum_{t=1}^{n}(x_t - \bar{x})^2$$

for a time-series and its observed mean and variance, the observed correlogram is defined by[6]

(8) $$r_\nu = r_{-\nu} = \sum(x_t - \bar{x}')(x_{t+\nu} - \bar{x}'')/\sqrt{\sum(x_t - \bar{x}')^2 \sum(x_{t+\nu} - \bar{x}'')^2} \qquad \nu = 0, 1, 2, \ldots$$

with $$\bar{x}' = \frac{1}{n-\nu}\sum x_t \qquad \bar{x}'' = \frac{1}{n-\nu}\sum x_{t+\nu},$$

all sums running over t from 1 to $n - \nu$.

Regarding the given time-series (7a) as part of a realization (1), we see that the phase average Mx in (2) may be interpreted as the limiting value of $\bar{x}'$ and $\bar{x}''$ if the number of observations, n, is allowed to increase indefinitely, and similarly for the variance and the correlogram.

For all correlograms we have $\varrho_0 = \varrho_0^* = r_0 = 1$, so that our correlogram formulae need only be given for $\nu > 0$.

Chapter 10.

FUNDAMENTAL TYPES OF STATIONARY PROCESSES

1. The purely random process.[1] – This is a stochastic process

(1) $$\{\varepsilon_t\} = (\ldots, \varepsilon_{t-1}, \varepsilon_t, \varepsilon_{t+1}, \ldots)$$

where all components ε_t are independent random variables with the same distribution function, say $F(u)$. By (9·1·9), the distribution functions (9·2·3) reduce to

(2) $$F(t, n; u_1, \ldots, u_n) = F(u_1) \cdot \cdots \cdot F(u_n).$$

The system $\{F\}$ defined by (2) is seen to satisfy the relations (9·2·4) and (9·3·2). The purely random process is accordingly a well-defined stationary process in the sense of (9·3·2).

For any purely random process (1), the independence between any two components ε_t implies that the correlogram (9·3·5) reduces to

(3) $$\varrho_0 = 1, \qquad \varrho_1 = \varrho_2 = \cdots = 0.$$

A group of classical theorems in probability theory center around averages and sums of independent random variables. Writing

(4) $$\alpha_t = (\varepsilon_1 + \varepsilon_2 + \cdots + \varepsilon_t)/t \qquad \Sigma_t = \varepsilon_1 + \varepsilon_2 + \cdots + \varepsilon_t$$

we may apply these theorems to the purely random process. In (i)–(iv) below, we restate some fundamental results on this line.[2] We shall here assume $m_\varepsilon = 0$, $\sigma_\varepsilon = 1$, which involves no loss of generality.

(i) The earliest theorem on the behaviour of averages and sums (4) is the *law of large numbers,* first stated and proved in a particular case by J. Bernoulli († 1705). According to this theorem,

(5) $$\lim_{t \to \infty} P(|\alpha_t| < \Theta) = 1 \qquad \lim_{t \to \infty} P(|\Sigma_t| < \Theta \cdot t) = 1$$

for any fixed, arbitrarily small $\Theta > 0$. As is well known, an elementary, general proof of (5) can be based on Chebyshev's inequality.

As in (5), any theorem on α_t gives as an immediate corollary a corresponding theorem on Σ_t, and conversely. In what follows we shall therefore consider the sums Σ_t only.

To interpret (5) we note that (4) defines an evolutive process

(6) $$\{\Sigma_t\} = (\varepsilon_1, \varepsilon_1 + \varepsilon_2, \varepsilon_1 + \varepsilon_2 + \varepsilon_3, \ldots).$$

Writing

$$e = (\ldots, e_{t-1}, e_t, e_{t+1}, \ldots), \qquad S = (S_1, S_2, S_3, \ldots)$$

for the realizations of the processes $\{\varepsilon_t\}$ and $\{\Sigma_t\}$, the definition (6) implies that the universe Ω_ε of e is transformed into the universe Ω_S of S by the relation

$$S_t = e_1 + e_2 + \cdots + e_t \qquad\qquad t = 1, 2, \ldots$$

Fig. 1 shows one realization S as plotted against t in a coordinate system $(Y; t)$. Such a path S runs irregularly up and down, in accordance with the purely random path of the realization e. Now if we consider the universe of paths S at a fixed instant, say T, there is a certain fraction of the universe such that S_T takes a value between $-\Theta T$ and $+\Theta T$. This fraction is $P(|\Sigma_t| < \Theta T)$. Thus (5) states that, for t large, nearly all of the realizations S will fall between $-\Theta t$ and $+\Theta t$.

(ii) The *central limit theorem*, first found in a particular case by de Moivre (1733), states that for t large the sum Σ_t tends to follow the normal (Gauss-Laplace) distribution with $m = 0$, $\sigma = \sqrt{t}$. Hence, in particular,

$$(7) \qquad \lim_{t \to \infty} P(|\Sigma_t| < \lambda \sqrt{t}) = \frac{1}{\sqrt{2\pi}} \int_{-\lambda}^{\lambda} e^{-x^2/2} \, dx.$$

Or in words [see Fig. 1]: In the universe of realizations S there is a fraction that at the instant t falls between the two branches of the parabola $Y = \pm \lambda \sqrt{t}$; for t large this fraction is asymptotically independent of t, and given by the right member of (7).

(iii) Whereas (i)–(ii) refer to the value of S_t at a given instant t, we shall now be concerned with the behaviour of S_t in a whole interval $T \leq t \leq T + \tau$. The first result in this direction is the *strong law of large numbers*, established by F. Cantelli (1917):

$$(8) \qquad \lim_{T \to \infty} \lim_{\tau \to \infty} P[|\Sigma_T| \leq \Theta T, \ |\Sigma_{T+1}| \leq \Theta(T+1), \ \ldots, \ |\Sigma_{T+\tau}| \leq \Theta(T+\tau)] = 1.$$

In words: Almost all realizations S of the universe are such that, for T large, S_t runs between the two lines $Y = \pm \Theta t$ for all t greater than T.

(iv) Among later improvements of (8) we note the famous *law of the iterated logarithm*, due to Khintchine (1923) and Kolmogorov (1929). This not only gives less divergent boundaries for the oscillations of the path S, but also indicates lower limits for the oscillations. Thus on the one hand (8) remains true if the boundaries $Y = \pm \Theta t$ are replaced by the curves

$$(9) \qquad\qquad Y = \pm (1 + \delta) \sqrt{2t \log \log t} \qquad (\delta = \text{const.} > 0)$$

[see Fig. 1]. On the other hand, the double limit (8) becomes zero if instead of (9) we make use of the curves

$$(10) \qquad\qquad Y = \pm (1 - \delta) \sqrt{2t \log \log t}.$$

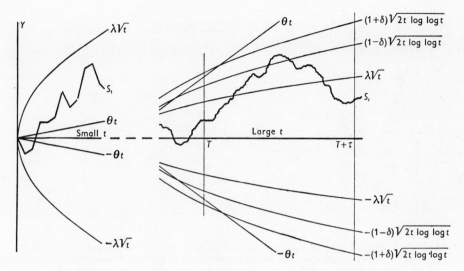

Fig. 10·1·1. Illustration of classical theorems on the sum of independent random variables.

2. Processes of moving summation. – Let $\{\varepsilon_t\}$ be a purely random process with zero expectation, $E(\varepsilon_t) = 0$. We form

$$(1) \qquad \zeta_t = a_0 \varepsilon_t + a_1 \varepsilon_{t-1} + a_2 \varepsilon_{t-2} + \cdots \qquad -\infty < t < \infty,$$

and in order to make the sum convergent we assume that $a_0^2 + a_1^2 + \cdots$ is finite. For the expectation and the variance of ζ_t we then obtain

$$(2) \qquad m_\zeta = E(\zeta_t) = 0; \qquad \sigma_\zeta^2 = E(\zeta_t^2) = (a_0^2 + a_1^2 + a_2^2 + \cdots) \cdot \sigma_\varepsilon^2.$$

By Theorem 9·3·1 the variables ζ_t defined by (1) constitute a stationary stochastic process $\{\zeta_t\}$. This is called the *process of moving summation*.[1]

The correlogram of the process (1) is, as is readily verified,

$$(3) \qquad \varrho_\nu = (a_0 a_\nu + a_1 a_{\nu+1} + \cdots)/(a_0^2 + a_1^2 + \cdots) \qquad \nu \geq 0.$$

We shall next consider two special cases of the process (1).

a. *The process of moving averages.*[2] The summation (1) is finite, giving

$$(4) \qquad \zeta_t = a_0 \varepsilon_t + a_1 \varepsilon_{t-1} + \cdots + a_h \varepsilon_{t-h} \qquad a_0 \neq 0, \ a_h \neq 0.$$

In this case the sums involved in formulae (2)–(3) are also finite. For the correlogram (3) we obtain $\varrho_\nu = 0$ for all $\nu > h$.

A simple illustration is provided by the process

$$(5) \qquad \zeta_t = \varepsilon_t + a_1 \varepsilon_{t-1} \qquad \text{with } a_1 = 0.44.$$

The correlogram of this process is given by $\varrho_1 = 0.37$ and $\varrho_2 = \varrho_3 = \cdots = 0$ [see Fig. 1, broken line].

11 – 525552 *H. Wold*

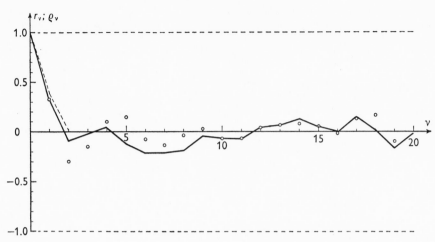

Fig. 10·2·1. Correlogram of the level of Lake Väner 1871—1930 (heavy line), correlogram of a fitted process of moving averages (broken line), and transformed correlogram of the rainfall in the drainage basin of Lake Väner (circles).[3]

For later reference we shall now state, without proofs, a few facts about the process of moving averages. To begin with, we have

THEOREM 1.[4] *Let* $V(z)$ *be the polynomial of order* h *obtained from*

$$(6) \qquad U(x) = 1 + \varrho_1 \cdot (x + x^{-1}) + \varrho_2 \cdot (x^2 + x^{-2}) + \cdots + \varrho_h \cdot (x^h + x^{-h})$$

by the substitution $x + x^{-1} = z$. *For* $\varrho_0 (=1)$, $\varrho_1, \ldots, \varrho_h$ *to be the correlogram of a process of moving averages (4), it is necessary and sufficient that the equation* $V(z) = 0$ *should have no real root of odd multiplicity in the interval* $-2 < z < 2$.

Next, let us consider a sequence $\varrho_1, \ldots, \varrho_h$ that fulfils the condition of Theorem 1. The parameters a_i in (4) will then in general not be uniquely determined. There will exist at most 2^h different sequences $a_0 (=1)$, $a_1, \ldots, a_h$ that produce the given correlogram ϱ_ν. One and only one of these sequences is such that all roots $z_1, \ldots, z_h$ of the equation

$$(7) \qquad z^h + a_1 z^{h-1} + \cdots + a_{h-1} z + a_h = 0$$

lie *on or within the periphery* of the unit circle, that is $|z_1| \leq 1, \ldots, |z_h| \leq 1$. Finally, if this sequence a_i is used in the definition (4) of the process, the variables ε_t can be obtained explicitly in terms of the $\zeta_t, \zeta_{t-1}, \ldots$ by a serial development analogous to (8) below, except that an infinite number of terms will be involved.

b. *The autoregressive process.*[5] As before, let $\{\varepsilon_t\}$ be a purely random process. If $b_1, \ldots, b_h$ are constants, the relations

$$(8) \qquad \zeta_t + b_1 \zeta_{t-1} + \cdots + b_h \zeta_{t-h} = \varepsilon_t \qquad\qquad -\infty < t < \infty$$

give, by formal inversion,

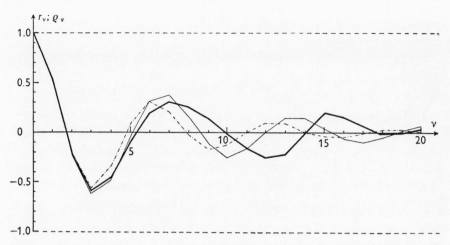

Fig. 10·2·2. Correlogram of Myrdal's consumer price index for Sweden 1840–1913 (heavy line), and two correlograms of fitted autoregressive processes (light lines).

$$(9) \qquad \zeta_t = \varepsilon_t + a_1 \varepsilon_{t-1} + a_2 \varepsilon_{t-2} + \cdots \qquad\qquad -\infty < t < \infty$$

where the constants $a_1, a_2, \ldots$ are recursively determined by

$$(10\,\text{a}) \qquad a_k + b_1 a_{k-1} + \cdots + b_{k-1} a_1 + b_k = 0 \qquad\qquad 0 < k \le h$$

$$(10\,\text{b}) \qquad a_k + b_1 a_{k-1} + \cdots + b_{h-1} a_{k-h+1} + b_h a_{k-h} = 0 \qquad\qquad k > h.$$

Provided the sum (9) is convergent, the variables ζ_t constitute a process $\{\zeta_t\}$ of moving summation. This is called the *autoregressive process*, also known as the *process of disturbed harmonics*.

THEOREM 2.[6] *A necessary and sufficient condition for the series* (9) *to be convergent is that all roots* z_i *of the equation*

$$(11) \qquad z^h + b_1 z^{h-1} + \cdots + b_{h-1} z + b_h = 0$$

should lie within the periphery of the unit circle; that is $|z_1| < 1, \ldots, |z_h| < 1$.

Now suppose that $b_1, \ldots, b_h$ fulfil the condition of Theorem 2, so that $\{\zeta_t\}$ is well-defined as a stationary process. Then

$$(12) \qquad \sigma_\zeta^2 = \varkappa \cdot \sigma_\varepsilon^2 \qquad \text{with } \varkappa = 1 + a_1^2 + a_2^2 + \cdots.$$

Substituting $t \pm \nu$ for t in (8), multiplying by (9), and equating the mathematical expectation of the two members, we obtain

$$(13\text{a}) \qquad \varrho_\nu + b_1 \varrho_{\nu-1} + \cdots + b_{h-1} \varrho_{\nu-h+1} + b_h \varrho_{\nu-h} = 0 \qquad\qquad \nu > 0$$

$$(13\text{b}) \qquad \varrho_\nu + b_1 \varrho_{\nu+1} + \cdots + b_{h-1} \varrho_{\nu+h-1} + b_h \varrho_{\nu+h} = a_\nu/\varkappa \qquad\qquad \nu \ge 0.$$

The correlogram ϱ_ν of the autoregressive process may be obtained in terms of the a_k, making use of formula (3). Alternatively, the correlogram may be obtained in terms of the b_k by first solving the system of $h-1$ linear equations provided by (13a) for $1 \leq \nu \leq h-1$, which gives $\varrho_1, \ldots, \varrho_{h-1}$, and then using (13a) recursively for $\nu \geq h$.

Fig. 2 (stippled line) shows the correlogram of the autoregressive process defined by

(14) $\zeta_t + a_1 \zeta_{t-1} + a_2 \zeta_{t-2} = \varepsilon_t$ with $a_1 = -0.88$, $a_2 = 0.68$.

3. The harmonic process.[1] – To define this type of process we consider an n-dimensional random variable $\eta = (\eta_1, \ldots, \eta_n)$ with dispersion determinant $\varLambda_n$. By (9·1·12) we have $\varLambda_n \geq 0$. Now suppose that the distribution of η is singular, i.e. that $\varLambda_n = 0$; say that $\varLambda_n$ is of rank $h < n$. According to a theorem of R. Frisch (1928), the η_i will then satisfy $n - h$ independent relations, say

(1) $c_{k1}(\eta_1 - m_1) + \cdots + c_{kn}(\eta_n - m_n) = 0$ $k = 1, \ldots, n-h$.

If we write $y = (y_1, \ldots, y_n)$ for the elementary events of the probability field $(\Omega_n, \mathfrak{F}, P)$ that defines η, relations (1) are equivalent to the statement that an event y will with probability 1 satisfy all the $n - h$ relations. In other words, almost all y will belong to the h-dimensional linear subspace of Ω_n determined by the relations (1).

The notion of singularity extends from Ω_n to the space Ω of a stochastic process. To see this, let $\{\eta_t\}$ be a stationary process (9·3·1) with dispersion matrix $\varLambda$ defined by (9·3·6), and suppose the distribution of $\eta_t, \eta_{t-1}, \ldots, \eta_{t-h}$ is singular of rank h. According to (1), these variables will then satisfy a relation of type

(2) $\eta_t - m_\eta + c_1(\eta_{t-1} - m_\eta) + \cdots + c_h(\eta_{t-h} - m_\eta) = 0$ $c_h \neq 0$

with $m_\eta = E\eta$. Now, thanks to the stationarity, further conclusions can be drawn. Firstly, the relation (2) is valid for all t. As is already done in (2), we may take the coefficient of $\eta_t - m_\eta$ to equal unity, and further we infer that $c_h \neq 0$. Next, multiplying (2) by $\eta_{t-\nu} - m_\eta$, the left-hand member and its mathematical expectation will be zero, giving

(3) $\varrho_\nu + c_1 \varrho_{\nu-1} + \cdots + c_h \varrho_{\nu-h} = 0$ $\nu = 0, \pm 1, \pm 2, \ldots$

Interpreting (3) as a linear difference equation for the correlogram ϱ_ν, the general solution of (3) gives a formula for ϱ_ν in terms of harmonics with polynomial and exponential coefficients [see Ex. 15]. Since the ϱ_ν are correlation coefficients, we have $|\varrho_\nu| \leq 1$ for all ν, and so it follows that the formula for ϱ_ν must reduce to a sum of pure harmonics, thus

(4) $\varrho_\nu = a_0 + \sum_{i=1}^{s} (a_i \cos \nu \lambda_i + b_i \sin \nu \lambda_i)$, $\nu = 0, \pm 1, \pm 2, \ldots$

where the λ_i, a_i, b_i are constants, with $0 < \lambda_i \leq \pi$. Now if we consider the characteristic equation of (3),

(5) $z^h + c_1 z^{h-1} + \cdots + c_{h-1} z + c_h = 0$,

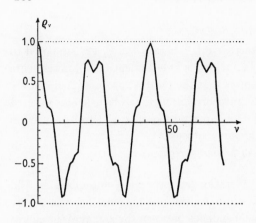

Fig. 10·3·1. Correlogram of a harmonic process with two components.

Fig. 10·4·1. Spectral functions (9·3·10) of four stationary processes.

the representation (4) implies that all roots z_i of (5) must be simple, and lie *on the periphery* of the unit circle, $|z_1| = \cdots = |z_h| = 1$. Finally, interpreting (2) in terms of the realizations $y = (\ldots, y_{t-1}, y_t, y_{t+1}, \ldots)$ of the process, we infer that almost all realizations y will satisfy (1) for all t. Hence the realizations will with probability 1 allow the representation

$$(6) \qquad y_t = \alpha_0 + \sum_{i=1}^{s} (\alpha_i \cos \lambda_i t + \beta_i \sin \lambda_i t), \qquad -\infty < t < \infty.$$

Here, the λ_i are the same angular frequencies as in (4), whereas the α_i and β_i are random variables, in general shifting from the one realization to the other. The realizations thus are built up by ordinary harmonics. Each harmonic component is periodic, and if we write

$$(7) \qquad \alpha \cos \lambda t + \beta \sin \lambda t = \gamma \cos (\lambda t + \varphi); \qquad \gamma = \sqrt{\alpha^2 + \beta^2}; \qquad \tan \varphi = \beta/\alpha$$

γ is its *amplitude* and φ its *phase*; its *period* is $p = 2\pi/\lambda$.

The stationary process $\{\eta_t\}$ thus defined is called the *harmonic process*. For illustration, we give in Fig. 1 the correlogram of a harmonic process with two components, the frequencies being $\lambda_1 = 3/10$ and $\lambda_2 = \pi/3$ [see also Ex. 19].

The Schuster periodogram (1898) is a classical device for the search for periodicities in an observed time-series.[2] If we write y_t^* for the given series, the periodogram analysis approximates y_t^* by a harmonic sum (6). The approximation yielded by the periodogram method will thus have the form of a realization of the harmonic process $\{\eta_t\}$ as defined above.

For an empirical time-series y_t^*, a representation like (6) will never be exact. If the deviations or residuals are regarded as random disturbances that are additively superimposed on the hypothetical harmonic, this assumption leads to a process $\{\eta_t^*\}$ defined by

(8) $$\eta_t^* = \eta_t + \zeta_t \qquad\qquad -\infty < t < \infty$$

where the η_t form a harmonic process $\{\eta_t\}$, whereas the ζ_t are supposed to form a suitable stationary process $\{\zeta_t\}$ which is independent of $\{\eta_t\}$ in the sense of (9·2·6). The traditional assumption is that the residual process $\{\zeta_t\}$ is purely random. To take into account the autocorrelation that often is encountered in observed residuals, it is sometimes adequate to assume $\{\zeta_t\}$ to be a process of moving averages or an autoregressive process.

Process (8) is called the *process of hidden periodicities*.

4. A comparative survey. – The stationary processes considered in Ch. 10·1–3 are of widely different structure. At the one extreme are the purely random processes $\{\varepsilon_t\}$, where the independence between the ε_t makes the course of the realizations completely random and irregular. At the other extreme are the harmonic processes, $\{\eta_t\}$, where the realizations are completely regular, with probability 1 allowing the functional representation (10·3·6). For the other processes considered, the realizations present traces both of randomness and regularity.

The situation is reflected in the correlogram. For the purely random process, the independence between the variables results in a correlogram $\varrho_\nu = 0$ for all $\nu > 0$. The harmonic process gives a correlogram ϱ_ν in the form of a harmonic sum (10·3·4). According to well-known properties of such sums, ϱ_ν oscillates in the entire range $0 \le \nu < \infty$ without damping [see Fig. 10·3·1]; specifically, however large ν_0 is taken there will exist a $\nu > \nu_0$ such that ϱ_ν approximates to 1 with any prescribed accuracy. The correlograms of the other processes of Ch. 10·2–3 may be regarded as intermediate between these two extremes. Thus for the process of moving summation (10·2·1) we have $\varrho_\nu \to 0$ as $\nu \to \infty$. For the moving average process (10·2·4), in particular, we have $\varrho_\nu = 0$ for all $\nu > h$. For the autoregressive process (10·2·8–9) we infer from (10·2·13 a) that the correlogram is a sum of harmonic terms with exponential or polynomial-exponential factors that tend to zero as $\nu \to \infty$. As to the process of hidden periodicities (10·3·8), let us write ϱ_ν^* and ϱ_ν for the correlograms of $\{\eta_t^*\}$ and its harmonic component $\{\eta_t\}$. If the residual process $\{\zeta_t\}$ is purely random, we have $\varrho_\nu^* = c \cdot \varrho_\nu$ for all $\nu > 0$, where c is a constant factor, $0 < c < 1$.

Fig. 1 shows the spectral functions (9·3·10) that correspond to four correlograms considered in the preceding section. The extremes are here the straight line $W(\lambda) = \lambda$ given by the purely random process, and the step-function given by the harmonic process. For the harmonic process, the discontinuity points λ_i of $W(\lambda)$ indicate the frequencies of the harmonics (10·3·4) and (10·3·6), while the saltus of $W(\lambda)$ at $\lambda = \lambda_i$ equals the squared amplitude $a_i^2 + b_i^2$ of a harmonic in (10·3·4). The spectral functions $W(\lambda)$ of the moving average process (broken curve), and the autoregressive process (stippled curve) are continuous.

It is important to realize the similarity as well as the fundamental difference between the process of hidden periodicities (10·3·8) and the autoregressive process (10·2·8). Both have the harmonic process (10·3·6) as a limiting case, as seen from (10·3·8) if we make the residual $\{\zeta_t\}$ vanish in the limit, and from (10·2·8) if we make $\{\varepsilon_t\}$ vanish and at the same time let the roots of (10·2·11) tend to h different points z_i on the periphery of the unit circle.[1]

The difference lies in the effect of the random element. In the process (10·3·8), on the one hand, the development of the random component $\{\zeta_t\}$ does not at all affect the harmonic component $\{\eta_t\}$, the two components being by hypothesis independent of each other. This type of approach is adequate for a great many terrestrial and cosmic phenomena. It applies, for example, to tidal variations. The lunar and solar effects are then described by the periodic terms that constitute η_t, whereas the residual ζ_t covers the effect of storms, earthquakes, and other random factors that do not influence the trend of the tides. — In the autoregressive process (10·2·8), on the other hand, the random element ε_t does affect the course of the entire process. According to the illustration given by Yule (1927) in the classical paper where the model was first introduced, ζ_t will describe the movement of a pendulum kept in motion by a stream of random shocks ε_t. The left-hand member of (10·2·8) determines the swings of the pendulum when there are no shocks. According to Theorem 10·2·2 these natural swings must be damped, lest the course of the process be divergent.[2] When exposed to shocks, the pendulum will tend to move in accordance with the natural swings, but these swings will be continually disturbed, changing gradually in amplitude and phase. (Hence the alternative term, the *process of disturbed harmonics*.) As to the applications, this type of process has been successful in many cases where the model (10·3·8) with its rigid periodicity has failed. Yule applied a process of type (10·2·8) to sunspot data, adding the important remark that "disturbance can only be excluded if either (1) the variable is quite unaffected by external circumstance, or (2) we are dealing with a forced vibration and the external circumstances producing this forced vibration are themselves undisturbed." — The autoregressive scheme has in Ch. 3·2 been referred to as fundamental for the theory of recursive systems (2·7·1), a topic which will be dealt with in Ch. 12·7.

Turning finally to the ergodicity of the processes of Ch. 10·1–3, we have

THEOREM 1. *The process of moving summation (10·2·1) is ergodic.*

Hence, in particular, the purely random process (10·1·1), the process of moving averages (10·2·4), and the autoregressive process (10·2·8) are ergodic. On the other side, the harmonic process (10·3·6) and the process of hidden periodicities (10·3·8) will in general not be ergodic [cf Ex. 31].

Briefly indicating the proof of Theorem 1, we note first that if a process $\{\xi_t\}$ is ergodic the process $\{\zeta_t\}$ defined by a functional transform of type (9'2'7) will also be ergodic, since any transform of $\{\zeta_t\}$ will constitute a transform of $\{\xi_t\}$. Now the process of moving summation (10'2'1) is a functional transform of the purely random process $\{\varepsilon_t\}$, and so it remains to show that $\{\varepsilon_t\}$ is ergodic.

To see this, let us first consider transforms (9'2'7) that involve a finite number of variables, say $\zeta = \zeta_t = \zeta(\xi_t, \ldots, \xi_{t+n})$, where n is fixed. Now if $\{\xi_t\}$ is purely random, the sequence $\ldots, \zeta_{t-n}, \zeta_t, \zeta_{t+n}, \zeta_{t+2n}, \ldots$ will likewise constitute a purely random process, say $\{\zeta^{(t)}\}$. Thus by the law of large numbers [Ch. 10'1] the phase average of $\{\zeta^{(t)}\}$ will equal the expectation $E\zeta^{(t)} = E\zeta$. The same holds true for the process $\{\zeta^{(t+k)}\}$ obtained from $\{\zeta^{(t)}\}$ by replacing t by $t+k$ throughout ($1 < k < n$). Since $E\zeta^{(t)} = E\zeta^{(t+k)}$ the phase averages of the processes $\{\zeta^{(t+k)}\}$ will likewise coincide, and equal $E\zeta$. Observing that a phase average of $\{\zeta_t\}$ is the arithmetical average of phase averages of the processes $\{\zeta^{(t+k)}\}$ with $k = 1, \ldots, n$, it follows that the phase average of $\{\zeta_t\}$ equals $E\zeta$. Since n is arbitrary *the proof that the purely random process is ergodic may now be completed by a well-known argument of approximation.

Theorem 1 reveals a deep-going difference between the processes of moving summation on the one hand, the harmonic process on the other. It will be noted that ergodicity is just one of several important properties that the processes of moving summation share with the purely random process. For one thing, the central limit theorem and the other theorems mentioned in Ch. 10'1 (i)–(iv) remain valid if $\{\varepsilon_t\}$ is a process of moving summation.[3] The situation is similar as regards linear forecasting or prediction, a topic which we are going to consider in Ch. 12, making use of the regression methods there developed.

Chapter 11.

STRUCTURAL PROBLEMS IN TIME-SERIES

ANALYSIS

1. Hypothesis testing. – The years around 1927 marked a new epoch in the analysis of stationary time-series. Earlier, the study of stationary series was dominated by the search for periodicities, with the Schuster periodogram (1898) for the principal method, and with the purely random variation as the only counterhypothesis against a strictly periodic variation. For a long time it had been recognized, of course, that the idea of rigid periodicity was of limited scope, especially in economic and social applications, and that there was need for an approach in which the idea of periodicity was relaxed so as to allow for gradual changes in amplitude and phase. A development in this direction

was initiated by Yule (1921, 1926, 1927). In Russia, theoretical investigations of related topics — notably the "sinusoidal limit theorem" by Slutsky
(1927) and Romanovsky (1932) — foreshadowed the general theory of stochastic
processes founded by Kolmogorov (1933) and Khintchine (1933). The stationary process, the definition and groundwork of which are due to Khintchine
(1934), was employed by the author (1938) for a unified treatment of several
approaches in time-series analysis which had earlier been uncoordinated,
among them the periodogram analysis and Yule's approaches.[1]

Statistical inference (in the general sense of using observational data for
drawing conclusions about the phenomena that generate the data) takes in
time-series analysis the form of investigating the structure of the stochastic
processes of which the observed series are regarded as realizations. For the
analysis of stationary time-series, theoretical schemes of widely different structure are provided by the stationary stochastic process, as we know from the
survey of special cases in Ch. 10. Here as always in statistical inference there
are three types of problem, (a) the specification of hypotheses, (b) the testing
of hypotheses, and (c) the estimation of parameters. With regard to the treatment of these problems we may distinguish three stages or phases in the
analysis of stationary time-series.

The first phase includes the empirical applications by Schuster (1898) of
periodogram analysis, by Yule (1927) of the autoregressive scheme, and by
the author (1938) of the two processes of moving summation. The theoretical
scheme adopted as a basis for the analysis is fitted to the observed data by
the simple device of identifying the unknown parameters with the corresponding expressions obtained from the observations. The device is similar to
the large-sample method in classical statistics, i.e. the method of estimating
theoretical moments and functions of moments by corresponding empirical
expressions. In the classical case, the rationale of the large-sample method
is established by a well-known theorem [for a rigorous proof, see Cramér
(1945, Ch. 28·4)]. In the analysis of stationary time-series, the rationale of
the device in question is embodied in Birkhoff-Khintchine's ergodic theorem
[Ch. 9·4] and simple corollaries thereof [Theorems 9·4·1 and 10·4·1]. For a
process of moving averages, in particular, it follows that the empirical correlogram forms a consistent estimate of the theoretical correlogram, and further
we have seen that a single realization will suffice to reveal the entire structure
of the process. In the scheme of hidden periodicities, on the other hand, a
single observed series can be used for the prediction of the future development
of the series, but in general it does not contain information on the entire
structure of the generating process.

In the second phase, the typical problem is to establish the distribution
of a parameter estimate under specific assumptions about the generating

process. The earliest test of this type is perhaps the Abbe-Helmert criterion of randomness (1863), which is based on the first coefficient r_1 in the empirical correlogram.[2] Further contributions in this direction are due to J. von Neumann (1941), R. L. Anderson (1942) and others. Under this heading we may also include the approach of U. Grenander (1950), who for a stationary process with continuous time-parameter has constructed an estimate of the mean with certain optimal properties.

In the third phase, the inference is not restricted to a single parameter, but refers to the entire structure of the generating process. A classic contribution of this type is R. A. Fisher's test (1929) for the largest peak in a periodogram, the counterhypothesis being that the observed series belongs to a purely random process. When it comes to the processes of moving summation, the obvious basis for a structural analysis is the empirical correlogram. What makes the hypothesis testing difficult is that the test should take the entire correlogram into consideration, not only a single autocorrelation coefficient. The first method in this direction is M. H. Quenouille's test (1947) for the autoregressive process, a test based on an arbitrary number of autocorrelation coefficients. For the process of moving averages, a related test was devised by the author (1949). Quite recently, a new line of approach has been opened up by P. Whittle (1951, 1952). Making use of the methods of spectral theory of linear transformations, Whittle has succeeded in constructing correlogram tests which are free from certain shortcomings of the earlier methods. Whittle's tests are constructed on a least-squares basis, and they are of optimal efficiency as large-sample methods. They lead to a uniform treatment of the processes of moving summation, and in the rapid progress of Whittle's work results of still wider scope are in sight.

The rest of this chapter is devoted to a brief account of Whittle's approach.[3] By way of introduction, we shall now sum up those properties of the correlogram which make it a useful and desirable test quantity.

(i) In the case of a time-series generated by a process of moving summation (10·2·1), the structure of the process is largely determined by the theoretical correlogram, of which the empirical correlogram is a consistent estimate [see Theorems 10·2·1–2 above]. The general scope of the process (10·2·1) is clear from the author's theorem on predictive decomposition [Theorem 12·6·1].

(ii) For such a series the empirical autocorrelation coefficients have a joint distribution which according to a theorem by M. Bartlett (1946) is to a first approximation independent of the distribution function of the disturbance variable ε_t, or residual [cf Ex. 21]. The advantage of Bartlett's theorem is obvious in view of the paucity of the information generally available on the residual.

(iii) The correlogram is the most informative statistic not involving functions of the observations of higher than second order [P. Whittle (1951)]. Indeed, if (10·2·1) is a Gaussian process, it may be seen that the likelihood of the series considered is asymptotically a function *only* of the autocovariances, so that there is scarcely any advantage to be gained by using any other statistic. In other words, the most powerful test for discriminating between two Gaussian hypotheses is asymptotically a correlogram test. Maximum likelihood tests deduced for Gaussian hypotheses will be useful also for non-Gaussian hypotheses, since they are the tests that would be obtained on a least-squares criterion.

2. Hypothesis discrimination a priori.[1] – Let us write $x_1, \ldots, x_n$ for the given time-series, or in vector notation

$$\boldsymbol{x} = (x_1, \ldots, x_n) = \begin{bmatrix} x_1 \\ \vdots \\ x_n \end{bmatrix} \qquad \boldsymbol{x}' = [x_1, \ldots, x_n].$$

We shall regard $\boldsymbol{x}$ as belonging to a realization of a stationary process $\{\xi_t\}$ of type (10·2·1). The dispersion matrix of $\{\xi_t\}$ will be denoted $\boldsymbol{\Lambda}$.

We shall in this section consider the case where we wish to distinguish between two fully specified models, say

$$(1) \qquad \xi_t = \varepsilon_t + a_1^{(1)} \varepsilon_{t-1} + a_2^{(1)} \varepsilon_{t-2} + \cdots; \qquad \xi_t = \varepsilon_t + a_1^{(2)} \varepsilon_{t-1} + a_2^{(2)} \varepsilon_{t-2} + \cdots.$$

We shall assume that the residual variables ε_t are distributed normally with zero mean, so that the two models $\{\xi_t\}$ are Gaussian processes. In practice we must of course estimate the mean, and the variables will only by way of approximation have a normal distribution, but for a series of moderate length these deviations are not serious.

Under these assumptions, the likelihood of the sample series $x_1, \ldots, x_n$ is completely determined by its dispersion matrix $\boldsymbol{\Lambda}$. We shall write

$$(2) \qquad\qquad \boldsymbol{\Lambda} = \varkappa_j \cdot \boldsymbol{V}_j \qquad\qquad j = 1, 2$$

the subscript j referring to the two hypotheses, and with the scale factors $\varkappa$ defined by

$$\varkappa_1 = [1 + (a_1^{(1)})^2 + (a_2^{(1)})^2 + \cdots] \sigma_\varepsilon^2; \qquad \varkappa_2 = [1 + (a_1^{(2)})^2 + (a_2^{(2)})^2 + \cdots] \sigma_\varepsilon^2.$$

By classical test theory the best test-function for discriminating between the two hypotheses is the ratio[2]

$$(3) \qquad\qquad \lambda = \frac{\boldsymbol{x}' \boldsymbol{V}_1^{-1} \boldsymbol{x}}{\boldsymbol{x}' \boldsymbol{V}_2^{-1} \boldsymbol{x}}.$$

We note that λ is independent of $\varkappa_1$ and $\varkappa_2$, and consequently also of σ_ε^2. The greater the ratio λ, the less probable is the first hypothesis with respect to the second, and vice versa.

The λ-test is the ratio between two quadratic forms of order n. The evaluation of such forms being no easy matter, the procedure is greatly simplified if the following lemma is used.

THEOREM 1. *If the power series*

$$(4) \qquad \Lambda(z) = \sum_{\nu=-\infty}^{\infty} \gamma_\nu z^\nu \qquad with \ \ \gamma_\nu = \sigma_\xi^2 \cdot \varrho_\nu = E\left(\xi_t\,\xi_{t+\nu}\right)$$

converges for $|z| = 1$, *then*

$$(5) \qquad \boldsymbol{\Lambda} \sim \Lambda(\boldsymbol{W}) \qquad with \ \ \boldsymbol{W} = \boldsymbol{W}_n = \begin{bmatrix} 0 & 1 & 0 & \cdots & 0 \\ 0 & 0 & 1 & \cdots & 0 \\ \cdot & \cdot & \cdot & \cdots & \cdot \\ 0 & 0 & 0 & \cdots & 1 \\ 1 & 0 & 0 & \cdots & 0 \end{bmatrix}$$

in the sense that we have

$$\lim_{n \to \infty} \frac{\boldsymbol{x}' \Lambda(\boldsymbol{W}_n)\,\boldsymbol{x}}{\boldsymbol{x}' \boldsymbol{\Lambda}\,\boldsymbol{x}} = 1$$

for almost all realizations $\boldsymbol{x}$.

We see that $\Lambda(e^{i\lambda}) = W'(\lambda)$, where $W(\lambda)$ is the spectral function (9·3·10). Thus (5) forms a spectral representation of $\boldsymbol{\Lambda}$ by way of a matrix $\Lambda(\boldsymbol{W})$ which is defined as a power series in the auxiliary matrix $\boldsymbol{W}$.

As a fairly direct result of Theorem 1 we infer that a quadratic form of the type $\boldsymbol{x}' \boldsymbol{V}^{-1} \boldsymbol{x}$ is asymptotically a linear function of the autocovariances. In fact, we have

THEOREM 2. *If the sequences* b_ν *and* $C_\nu(-\infty < \nu < \infty)$ *are defined by*

$$[\Lambda(z)]^{-1} = \sum_{\nu=-\infty}^{\infty} b_\nu z^\nu, \qquad C_\nu = \sum_{t=1}^{n-\nu} x_t\,x_{t+\nu} \sim \boldsymbol{x}' \boldsymbol{W}^\nu \boldsymbol{x}, \qquad with \ \ b_\nu = b_{-\nu} \ and \ C_\nu = C_{-\nu},$$

then

$$\boldsymbol{x}' \boldsymbol{\Lambda}^{-1} \boldsymbol{x} \sim \sum_{\nu=-\infty}^{\infty} b_\nu\,C_\nu.$$

Applying Theorem 2 to the ratio (3), we see that a test quantity of asymptotically equal power is given by

$$(6) \qquad \lambda^* = \frac{\sum b_\nu^{(1)}\,C_\nu}{\sum b_\nu^{(2)}\,C_\nu} \qquad with \ \ [\Lambda_j(z)]^{-1} = \sum_{\nu=-\infty}^{\infty} b_\nu^{(j)} z^\nu; \qquad j = 1, 2.$$

That is, the test which discriminates between the two hypotheses with greatest power is asymptotically a correlogram test. Furthermore, since $b_\nu^{(j)} \to 0$ as $\nu \to \pm\infty$, we see that it is the earlier autocorrelation coefficients which are given the greatest weighting, an indication of the fact that it is just these that carry the bulk of the discriminatory information. From the practical point of view, the sums in the numerator and denominator of λ^* may be terminated at a certain finite ν.

Illustration 1. Suppose that the two hypotheses refer respectively to an autoregressive scheme and a moving average, both of second order:

$$\xi_t + b_1\,\xi_{t-1} + b_2\,\xi_{t-2} = \varepsilon_t; \qquad\qquad \xi_t = \varepsilon_t + a_1\,\varepsilon_{t-1} + a_2\,\varepsilon_{t-2}.$$

Then we obtain the spectral functions

(7) $$\Lambda_1(z) = (1 + b_1 z + b_2 z^2)^{-1} (1 + b_1 z^{-1} + b_2 z^{-2})^{-1}$$

(8) $$\Lambda_2(z) = (1 + a_1 z + a_2 z^2)(1 + a_1 z^{-1} + a_2 z^{-2})$$

so that

$$(\Lambda_1(z))^{-1} = 1 + b_1^2 + b_2^2 + b_1(1 + b_2)(z + z^{-1}) + b_2(z^2 + z^{-2})$$

$$(\Lambda_2(z))^{-1} = \frac{1}{(p-q)(1-pq)} \sum_{\nu=-\infty}^{\infty} \left(\frac{p^{|\nu|+1}}{1-p^2} - \frac{q^{|\nu|+1}}{1-q^2} \right) z^\nu$$

where p and $q\,(\neq p)$ are the roots of

$$1 + a_1 z + a_2 z^2 = 0$$

or their reciprocals, p and q being chosen so as to fall within the unit circle [cf Theorem 10·2·1 and Ch. 11·3, Illustration 3].[3] Thus, we can take as test function

$$\lambda^* = (1 + b_1^2 + b_2^2 + 2 b_1 (1 + b_2) r_1 + 2 b_2 r_2) : \sum_{-s}^{s} \left(\frac{p^{|\nu|+1}}{1-p^2} - \frac{q^{|\nu|+1}}{1-q^2} \right) r_\nu$$

where $r_\nu = C_\nu / C_0$ is the observed correlogram, and s is a number ensuring that

$$\sum_{s+1}^{\infty} \left(\frac{p^{\nu+1}}{1-p^2} - \frac{q^{\nu+1}}{1-q^2} \right) < \delta$$

where δ is a predetermined small quantity. We see that the optimum test function, λ^*, is simply a ratio of linear functions of the autocorrelation coefficients.

To complete the test, the question of the distribution of λ^* must be settled. The exact distribution function can in general be obtained only by long and tedious numerical methods, but the following result, derived from Theorems 1–2, enables us to form a good approximation to it.

THEOREM 3. *If* $\Gamma(z)$ *is a function of z having a valid expansion on* $|z| = 1$,

$$\Gamma(z) = \sum_{\nu=-\infty}^{\infty} g_\nu z^\nu$$

such that $g_\nu = g_{-\nu}$, *then the cumulants of the linear function of the covariances*

$$\zeta = x' \Gamma(W) x$$

are asymptotically given by

$$k_s = \frac{2^{s-1}(s-1)!\,n}{2\pi i} \int_{|z|=1} [\Gamma(z)\,\Lambda(z)]^s \frac{dz}{z} \qquad s = 1, 2, \ldots$$

Applying this theorem to the special case

$$\Gamma(z) = [\Lambda_1(z)]^{-1} - \lambda_0^* [\Lambda_2(z)]^{-1}$$

we find

(9) $$k_s \approx \frac{2^{s-1}(s-1)!\,n}{2\pi i} \int_{|z|=1} \left[1 - \lambda_0^* \frac{\Lambda_1(z)}{\Lambda_2(z)} \right]^s \frac{dz}{z}$$

if $\varLambda_1(z)$ corresponds to the null hypothesis, so that $\varLambda(z) = \varLambda_1(z)$. These are the cumulants of the variate

$$\zeta = x' \left[[\varLambda_1(W)]^{-1} - \lambda_0^* [\varLambda_2(W)]^{-1} \right] x$$

whose distribution is related to that of λ^* since

(10) $\qquad\qquad\qquad \zeta \geq 0 \qquad$ is the same as $\qquad \lambda^* \geq \lambda_0^*$

so that the two events (10) have the same probability, $P(\zeta \geq 0)$.

Using (9), we have the Gram-Charlier expansion of ζ's frequency function, which is, in the Edgeworth-Cramér form,[4]

$$(11) \qquad \varphi(\zeta) = \left[\exp\left(-\frac{k_3}{3!} \left(\frac{\partial}{\partial \zeta}\right)^3 + \frac{k_4}{4!} \left(\frac{\partial}{\partial \zeta}\right)^4 - \cdots \right) \right] \cdot \left[\frac{1}{\sqrt{2\pi k_2}} e^{-\frac{(\zeta - k_1)^2}{2k_2}} \right]$$

and with the help of this, $P(\zeta \geq 0)$ may be evaluated to the required degree of accuracy.

Illustration 2. Let us consider the evaluation of the frequency function for λ^* of the previous illustration. If we take the moving average hypothesis as null hypothesis, then

$$k_s = \frac{2^{s-1}(s-1)! \, n}{2\pi i} \int_{|z|=1} \left[\frac{\varLambda_2(z)}{\varLambda_1(z)} - \lambda_0^* \right]^s \frac{dz}{z} =$$

$$= \frac{2^{s-1}(s-1)! \, n}{2\pi i} \int_{|z|=1} \left[(1 + a_1 z + a_2 z^2)(1 + a_1 z^{-1} + a_2 z^{-2}) \cdot \right.$$

$$\left. \cdot (1 + b_1 z + b_2 z^2)(1 + b_1 z^{-1} + b_2 z^{-2}) - \lambda_0^* \right]^s \frac{dz}{z} .$$

If we write the bracket in the integrand as

$$c_0 + c_1 [z + z^{-1}] + c_2 [z^2 + z^{-2}] + c_3 [z^3 + z^{-3}] + c_4 [z^4 + z^{-4}]$$

then

$$k_1 = n \, c_0 \qquad\qquad k_2 = 2n [c_0^2 + 2c_1^2 + 2c_2^2 + 2c_3^2 + 2c_4^2],$$

and in general, if we write the coefficient of $z^{-\nu}$ as $c_{-\nu}$,

$$k_s = 2^{s-1}(s-1)! \, n \sum_{\nu_1} \sum_{\nu_2} \cdots \sum_{\nu_s} c_{\nu_1} c_{\nu_2} \cdots c_{\nu_s} \quad \text{with} \quad \sum_i \nu_i = 0.$$

The cumulant k_s then gives a term in the expansion (11) of order $n^{-\frac{s}{2}+1}$.

3. Discrimination a posteriori.

– While there are perhaps very special cases where the hypotheses to be tested may be supposed fully specified, as in the previous section, in the vast majority of cases only the *kind* of hypothesis is specified. For example, we may wish to see whether a given series can be better represented by a moving average or an autoregressive model, but at the outset we do not concern ourselves over the actual values taken by the parameters involved. One could perhaps express this situation by saying that one and the same body of observational material must serve both as estimation and testing material.

We shall see that this problem, although so much more general than that of the previous section, has a solution which is almost parallel. For, suppose that the likelihood of the sample on the two alternative hypotheses is

$$f(x; \alpha_1, \alpha_2 \ldots \alpha_h) \qquad\qquad g(x; \beta_1, \beta_2 \ldots \beta_k)$$

where $\alpha_1, \alpha_2 \ldots \alpha_h$; $\beta_1, \beta_2 \ldots \beta_k$ are the parameters involved in the two hypotheses, and are of unspecified value. Then it may be proved that the best test function for distinguishing between these two composite hypotheses is[1]

$$(1) \qquad\qquad \max f(x, \alpha) / \max g(x, \beta)$$

where $\max f(x, \alpha)$ is the maximum value of $f(x; \alpha_1 \ldots \alpha_h)$ for the sample in question when the parameters α are free to vary, and similarly for $\max g(x, \beta)$.

Now, in the case of a stationary Gaussian process of the type hitherto considered, the parameters may be chosen so that $\max f(x, \alpha)$ takes a particularly elegant form. If $\varLambda(z)$ is the spectral function deduced for the hypothesis corresponding to $f(x, \alpha)$, we shall write

$$\varLambda(z) = A \cdot M(z),$$

where A is a normalizing scale factor defined by the relation

$$(2) \qquad\qquad \frac{1}{2\pi i} \int\limits_{|z|=1} \log \varLambda(z) \frac{dz}{z} = \log A.$$

In (2) we recognize a fundamental formula by Kolmogorov (1941), showing that A is the prediction variance of the process $\{\xi_t\}$ considered [cf Ch. 12·5–6]. Subject to certain conditions on the hypotheses (11·2·1), A will thus equal the variance of the residual ε_t.

It may now be shown that

$$(3) \qquad\qquad \max f(x, \alpha) = (2\pi e \widehat{A})^{-\frac{n}{2}}$$

where $\widehat{A}$ is the maximum likelihood estimate of A, given by

$$(4) \qquad\qquad \widehat{A} = \min \frac{x'[M(W)]^{-1}x}{n}$$

the expression on the right being the minimum of the quadratic form in question w.r.t. those parameters which are still free when A is fixed. It will be noted that $\widehat{A}$ may be interpreted as forming a least-squares estimate of the prediction variance A.

We infer from (1) and (3) that the optimum statistic for discriminating between the two hypotheses is

$$(5) \qquad\qquad \lambda = \widehat{A}_1 / \widehat{A}_2$$

where $\hat{A}_1$, $\hat{A}_2$ are the $\hat{A}$ statistics corresponding to the two hypotheses.

The parallel between (11·2·3) and (5) is evident if we pay regard to (4). The similarity goes further, however. From the fact that $\hat{A}$ is a maximum likelihood statistic, it may be shown that it has approximately the same distribution as that of the linear function of the covariances

$$A^* = \frac{x'\,[M^*\,(W)]^{-1}\,x}{n}$$

where $M^*(W)$ is the value of $M(W)$ obtained in (4) when all the covariances $x'\,W^\nu x$ have their expectation values, the expectations being formed on the basis of the null hypothesis. Thus λ of (5) is asymptotically distributed as a rational function of the autocovariances, and we may use Theorem 11·2·3 to evaluate the frequency function of $A_1^* - \lambda_0\,A_2^* \sim \hat{A}_1 - \lambda_0\,\hat{A}_2$.

Illustration 3. Let us follow up illustrations 1–2 of the previous section, and this time assume the values of a_1, a_2, b_1, b_2 to be unknown. If $\Lambda_1(z)$ and $\Lambda_2(z)$ as given by (11·2·7–8) are substituted in (2), we find that $A_1 = A_2 = 1$ if only the roots of

(6) $$z^2 + a_1 z + a_2 = 0 \quad \text{and} \quad z^2 + b_1 z + b_2 = 0$$

lie within the unit circle. This is so, since

$$\int\limits_{|z|=1} \log\,(z - q)\,(z^{-1} - q)\,\frac{dz}{z} = 0 \qquad \text{if } |q| < 1.$$

For the autoregressive scheme, the roots of the indicial equation (6) lie always inside the unit circle, while this may be achieved for the moving average scheme in all cases except that in which there is a root on the periphery of the circle. Disregarding this exceptional case, we can set $M_1(z) = \Lambda_1(z)$ and $M_2(z) = \Lambda_2(z)$.

Applying formula (4), we find

$$\hat{A}_1 = \begin{vmatrix} C_0 & C_1 & C_2 \\ C_1 & C_0 & C_1 \\ C_2 & C_1 & C_0 \end{vmatrix} : \begin{vmatrix} C_0 & C_1 \\ C_1 & C_0 \end{vmatrix}$$

and

$$\hat{A}_2 = \frac{1}{(p-q)\,(1-pq)} \sum_{-\infty}^{\infty} \left(\frac{p^{|\nu|+1}}{1-p^2} - \frac{q^{|\nu|+1}}{1-q^2} \right) C_\nu$$

where p and q are determined by

(7) $$\frac{\partial \hat{A}_2}{\partial p} = 0 \qquad \frac{\partial \hat{A}_2}{\partial q} = 0.$$

To solve (7) in practice, we choose ϱ_1, ϱ_2 tentatively so as to approximate the empirical autocorrelation coefficients r_1, r_2, and determine the corresponding values of a_1, a_2 and $\hat{A}_2$. Repeating the calculation of $\hat{A}_2$ for a few neighbouring values of a_1, a_2, the minimum of $\hat{A}_2$ is then located by approximating $\hat{A}_2$ by a quadratic expression in a_1, a_2.

Now that the statistics $\hat{A}_1$ and $\hat{A}_2$ have been obtained, there remains the question of their distribution. If the null hypothesis is that of a second order moving average scheme, let this scheme be

$$x_t = \varepsilon_t + c_1\,\varepsilon_{t-1} + c_2\,\varepsilon_{t-2}$$

so that the hypothetical spectral function is

$$\Lambda_0(z) = (1 + c_1 z + c_2 z^2)\,(1 + c_1 z^{-1} + c_2 z^{-2}).$$

This generates autocovariances proportional to $(1 + c_1^2 + c_2^2,\ c_1(1 + c_2),\ c_2, 0, 0 \ldots)$. For such covariances, we obtain the following maximum likelihood estimates,

$$a_1 = c_1 \qquad\qquad a_2 = c_2$$

whereas b_1, b_2 are estimated by the equations

$$c_1\,(1 + c_2) + (1 + c_1^2 + c_2^2)\,b_1 + c_1\,(1 + c_2)\,b_2 = 0$$

$$c_2 + c_1\,(1 + c_2)\,b_1 + (1 + c_1^2 + c_2^2)\,b_2 = 0.$$

We shall as above write $M_1^*(z)$, $M_2^*(z)$ for the normalized spectral function obtained when these values of a_1, a_2, b_1, b_2 have been substituted. Then the sth cumulant of $\hat{A}_1 - \lambda_0\,\hat{A}_2$ is asymptotically given by

$$k_s = \frac{2^{s-1}(s-1)!\,n}{2\pi i} \int\limits_{|z|=1} \left[\frac{M_2^*(z)}{M_1^*(z)} - \lambda_0 \right]^s \frac{dz}{z}.$$

The calculations from now on are precisely the same as in illustration 2 of Ch. 11·2.

Of course, the significance points obtained in this manner for $\hat{A}_1/\hat{A}_2$ are functions of the parameters c_i of the hypothetical process. Although no parameters appear in the actual test function, they are necessarily found in its distribution. In practice, the soundest procedure would seem to be to form the maximum likelihood estimates of the parameters c_i, and then form a judgement of the extreme values that would be expected. Then the significance points of $\hat{A}_1/\hat{A}_2$ can be evaluated for these extreme values of the c_i.

The only approximation in this method is in the limit form adopted for the cumulants, and examination of special cases would seem to indicate that this is not a bad approximation. However, one wonders just how much distribution functions calculated on the basis of normally distributed variates are in error when the variates are in actual fact not normally distributed. It is clear that there is an approximation here, but it is also clear that it is a much better one than that of previous correlogram tests, which supposed the *autocorrelation coefficients* to be normally distributed.

4. Tests for goodness of fit.[1] – It has been seen in previous sections that the asymptotically most powerful test function for discriminating between two Gaussian hypotheses H_0, H_1 is $\lambda = \hat{A}_0/\hat{A}_1$, where $\hat{A}_0$ and $\hat{A}_1$ are the corresponding least-squares estimates of the prediction variance, A. Even when the hypotheses are no longer Gaussian, λ has still certain optimum properties with which, however, we shall not concern ourselves here.

Suppose that H_0 is a very general hypothesis, so that all hypotheses considered are simply special cases of H_0. For instance, a hypothesis H_0 of general scope is that the given series is generated by a process which is purely nondeterministic in the sense of predictive decomposition [Theorem 12·6·1]. It is clear that λ gives a measure of the *goodness of fit* of hypothesis H_1, when we restrict our consideration to those hypotheses which are special cases of H_0. We have in this case $0 \le \lambda \le 1$. A value of λ near zero indicates bad fit, while perfect fit corresponds to $\lambda = 1$.

Let us suppose, then, that H_0 is the hypothesis of a purely nondeterministic series. We shall construct the corresponding estimate of the prediction variance, $\hat{A}_0$, in the following manner.

As already indicated, a purely nondeterministic series may be represented as a moving summation (10·2·1). This is only one of a whole group of possible representations, and an autoregressive representation is valid to any degree of approximation, in symbols

(1) $$\xi_t + b_1 \xi_{t-1} + b_2 \xi_{t-2} + \cdots = \varepsilon_t.$$

Now, suppose we continue representation (1) only as far as order k, so that the least-squares estimate of the prediction variance becomes

(2) $$\hat{A}_0 = \begin{vmatrix} C_0 & C_1 & \cdots & C_k \\ C_1 & C_0 & \cdots & C_{k-1} \\ \cdots & \cdots & \cdots & \cdots \\ C_k & C_{k-1} & \cdots & C_0 \end{vmatrix} : \begin{vmatrix} C_0 & C_1 & \cdots & C_{k-1} \\ C_1 & C_0 & \cdots & C_{k-2} \\ \cdots & \cdots & \cdots & \cdots \\ C_{k-1} & C_{k-2} & \cdots & C_0 \end{vmatrix}.$$

As k becomes larger (yet that k must be of lower order of magnitude than the number of observations, $k < < n$), the representation becomes more exact, and we can derive from (2) an unbiased estimate of the true prediction variance. That is, for k sufficiently large (in practice most usually between 10 and 15), formula (2) provides a sufficient approximation to $\hat{A}_0$. The estimate $\hat{A}_1$ is, of course, given by formula (11·3·4).

Having settled the question of the construction of λ, we have now to consider its distribution. This is very simply derived, thanks to

THEOREM 1.[2] *Given a true hypothesis, let A^*, $\hat{A}$ be the least-squares estimates of A when h parameters are respectively known and unknown. Then $n(A^* - \hat{A})/A$ is asymptotically distributed as χ^2 with h degrees of freedom.*

It has long been known that results of this nature hold for independent variates, but here we see that they hold for correlated variates also, at least for those we have considered. We shall merely note that the result is arrived at by an application of Theorem 11·2·3 and equation (11·3·2).

We know then, from the partition theorem of χ^2, that

$$\frac{n}{A}[(A^* - \hat{A}_0) - (A^* - \hat{A}_1)] = \frac{n}{A}[\hat{A}_1 - \hat{A}_0]$$

is asymptotically distributed as χ^2 with $k - h$ degrees of freedom. Estimating A by $n\hat{A}_0/(n-k)$, and neglecting "studentisation", it follows that

$$(3) \qquad\qquad \Psi^2 = (n-k)\frac{\hat{A}_1 - \hat{A}_0}{\hat{A}_0} = (n-k)\frac{1-\lambda}{\lambda}$$

is asymptotically distributed as χ^2 with $k - h$ degrees of freedom. This gives us, in effect, our λ distribution.

Illustrations. The following is a brief summary of results obtained when applying the above method to the data of Figs. 10˙2˙1–2.

The level of Lake Väner 1871–1930 has a correlogram that invites us to try a moving average (10˙2˙4) of first order. The parameter involved is readily estimated by the use of the device (11˙3˙4), which has led to the process (10˙2˙5). The test (4) gives $\Psi^2 = 7.11$ with 9 degrees of freedom. The probability that Ψ^2 should be exceeded is $P \sim 0.70$, so the fit is good. An attractive feature of model (10˙2˙5) is that the generating series $\{\varepsilon_t\}$ may be interpreted as rainfall. The small circles in Fig. 10˙2˙1 are the correlogram of an empirical series obtained as a moving average of the rainfall in the drainage area of Lake Väner. On the other hand, an autoregressive model (10˙2˙8) is likewise attractive from theoretical viewpoints. While an autoregression of first order is not satisfactory, a model of order 2 is found to be better, with $P \sim 0.52$. However, the fit is not perfect, and there is evidence of disagreement farther out in the correlogram.

Myrdal's index series 1840—1913 suggests an autoregressive process, as would also be reasonable from the viewpoint of economic theory [Ch. 3˙2]. Trying a process of second order, the device (11˙3˙4) leads to the process (10˙2˙14). Applying the test (4), we obtain $\Psi^2 = 10.83$ (7) and $P \sim 0.14$, which is is no more than a moderate fit. Introducing a_3 as a third parameter the fit is not significantly better. An autoregression with parameters a_1, a_2, a_4 is definitely better, with $\Psi^2 = 7.58$ (6) and $P \sim 0.37$ [the corresponding correlogram is the thin full-drawn line in Fig. 10˙2˙2]. Again there is evidence of disagreement farther out in the correlogram, which could possibly be explained by the inclusion of greater lags.

One fact is evident from the foregoing, that the theory of fit testing is both simpler and less approximate than that of discriminatory testing. This is a fortunate circumstance, for often we do not need to resort to a discriminatory test to decide which of a group of hypotheses is best. Briefly, if we have no reason to prefer any of the hypotheses to the others, then the statistical analysis is our only basis of judgement, and it seems reasonable to accept that hypothesis which gives best fit by the criterion just derived (i.e. that whose Ψ^2 statistic is least significant). Only when we have some prior reason for discriminating between the hypotheses is an explicit discriminatory test necessary or appropriate.

In fitting a theoretical correlogram it often occurs that two or more different hypotheses turn out to be acceptable when testing the goodness of fit. This is a situation which has parallels in other tests, but which to the author's knowledge has not been systematically investigated in statistical literature. By way of a provisional rule of thumb it would seem reasonable (a) to regard any hypothesis as acceptable if P lies between, say, 25% and 75%, (b) to reject or be suspicious against the hypothesis if P is below 15%, say, (c) to suspect overfitting if P is above 85%, and (d) to leave the choice between two or more hypotheses open if the P-values obtained lie between 25% and 75%, in which case a decision cannot be made until further observations become available. [See also Ch. 15·2 (v).]

In conclusion, it may be mentioned that a λ statistic with asymptotic frequency function (3) may be derived for much more general hypotheses than those considered here. Thus, H_0 may admit deterministic components in the process, or even admit certain types of non-stationarity, without invalidating the results. Of course, $\hat{A}_0$ must be suitably modified in these cases .

EXERCISES FOR PART III.[1]

1 (Wold 1943—44). Given an arbitrary function $U(q_1, \dots, q_n)$, write $\Delta_k = \Delta_k [U]$ for any difference of U of first order in k dimensions; thus recursively

$$\Delta_k = \Delta_1 [\Delta_{k-1}], \quad \text{with} \quad \Delta_1 = U(q_1, \dots, q_i + a, \dots, q_n) - U(q_1, \dots, q_n),$$

and with Δ_2 given by Ex. II, 23. Considering the following set of conditions,

(a) Preference function: $\Delta_1 \geq 0$

(b) Gossen preference function: $\Delta_1 \geq 0; \quad \Delta_k = 0$ for $k = 2, \dots, n$

(c) Distribution function: $\Delta_k \geq 0$ for $k = 1, \dots, n; \quad U(+\infty, \dots, +\infty) = 1,$

verify that the two first conditions are necessary and sufficient for $U(q_1, \dots, q_n)$ to form (a) a preference function, (b) an additive index-function of a Gossen map.

Condition (c) is necessary for U to form a probability distribution function in n dimensions. Thus if we restrict ourselves to nonnegative values of the variables, the level map of a continuous distribution function allows the interpretation of an indifference map, but not always conversely, and the level map can never be a Gossen map. In the case of two variables, the level curves of a distribution function are always convex towards the origin.

2. Suppose ξ_1, ξ_2, ξ_3 are three random variables such that their joint distribution function is normal, with the three expectations equal to zero, $E(\xi_i) = 0$, the three variances equal to unity, $E(\xi_i^2) = 1$, and the three covariances equal to one-half, $E(\xi_i \xi_k) = \frac{1}{2}$. Show that the inequalities (9·1·12) are satisfied, which ensures that the distribution is well-defined, and that $\Delta_3 > 0$, which according to (9·1·13) ensures that the distribution is nonsingular.

3. With ξ_1, ξ_2, ξ_3 defined by the preceding exercise, form $\zeta_1 = \xi_1, \zeta_2 = \xi_2 + \xi_3, \zeta_3 = \xi_1 + \xi_2 + \xi_3$ and calculate the dispersion matrix Λ_3 of the variables $\zeta_1, \zeta_2, \zeta_3$. Show that $\Lambda_3 = 0$, which by (9$\cdot$1$\cdot$13) implies that the distribution of the ζ_i is singular.

4 (Frisch, 1928). If the variables $\xi_i (i = 1, \ldots, n)$ have the dispersion matrix Λ, the variables

$$\eta_i = \sum_{k=1}^{n} c_{ik} \xi_k \qquad (i = 1, \ldots, m)$$

have the dispersion matrix $C \Lambda C'$.

5. A square matrix $A = [a_{ik}]$ is called *triangular* if $a_{ik} = 0$ for $k > i$. Show that, if Λ is the dispersion matrix of a nonsingular distribution, Λ allows a unique representation of the type $\Lambda = AA'$, where A is triangular with all $a_{ii} > 0$. This is known as *Jacobi's parameter representation* of a positive definite matrix.

6 (Khintchine, 1934). If a Gaussian process is stationary, it is uniquely defined by its expectation m, its variance σ^2, and its correlogram ϱ_ν, in symbols

$$E\,\xi_t = m; \qquad E\,(\xi_t - m)^2 = \sigma^2; \qquad E\,(\xi_t - m)\,(\xi_{t \pm \nu} - m) = \sigma^2 \cdot \varrho_\nu; \qquad \nu = 1, 2, \ldots$$

Given an infinite matrix Λ of type (9$\cdot$3$\cdot$6), show that (9$\cdot$3$\cdot$7) is a necessary and sufficient condition for Λ to be the dispersion matrix of a stochastic process.

7. Letting x_t be a logistic curve, $x_t = (a + b \cdot e^{\gamma(t - t_0)})/(1 + e^{\gamma(t - t_0)})$, show that the phase average $M x$ will not exist as a limiting value in the sense of (9$\cdot$4$\cdot$2).

8. Considering the averages α_t instead of the sums Σ_t in (10$\cdot$1$\cdot$4), illustrate the behaviour of α_t by a graph that corresponds to Fig. 10$\cdot$1$\cdot$1.

Further indicate how the theorems in Ch. 10$\cdot$1 (i)–(iii) are modified if we drop the assumption that the process $\{\varepsilon_t\}$ has zero mean, say that the ε_t have mean m and variance σ^2. Similarly, indicate how the definitions (10$\cdot$2$\cdot$1–2) are affected.

9. Show that there exist four, and only four, moving averages (10$\cdot$2$\cdot$4) of order $h = 3$ with $a_0 = 1$ and with correlogram $\varrho_1 = -42/85; \varrho_2 = 4/17; \varrho_3 = -8/85$, viz.[1]

$$\zeta_t = \varepsilon_t - \frac{1}{2}\varepsilon_{t-1} + \frac{1}{4}\varepsilon_{t-2} - \frac{1}{8}\varepsilon_{t-3} \qquad\qquad \zeta_t = \varepsilon_t - 2\,\varepsilon_{t-1} + 4\,\varepsilon_{t-2} - 8\,\varepsilon_{t-3}$$

$$\zeta_t = \varepsilon_t - \frac{1}{2}\varepsilon_{t-1} + 4\,\varepsilon_{t-2} - 2\,\varepsilon_{t-3} \qquad\qquad \zeta_t = \varepsilon_t - 2\,\varepsilon_{t-1} + \frac{1}{4}\varepsilon_{t-2} - \frac{1}{2}\varepsilon_{t-3}.$$

In accordance with the condition attached to equation (10$\cdot$2$\cdot$7), verify that the first of these relations gives a development of ε_t in terms of $\zeta_t, \zeta_{t-1}, \zeta_{t-2}, \ldots$

10. Show that if and only if $-\frac{1}{2} \le r \le \frac{1}{2}$ there will exist a process of moving averages with correlogram $\varrho_\nu = 0$ for all $\nu > 0$ except $\nu = k$, and with $\varrho_k = r$.

Hint: Make use of formulae (9$\cdot$3$\cdot$9–10).

11. In order that ϱ_1, ϱ_2 and $\varrho_3 = \varrho_4 = \cdots = 0$ should be the correlogram of a process of moving averages it is necessary and sufficient that the point (ϱ_1, ϱ_2) should lie in the region composed by (a) the ellipse E with equation $2\varrho_1^2 + 16(\varrho_2 - 1/4)^2 = 1$, and (b) the region between E and the two lines that pass through the point $(\varrho_1 = 0, \varrho_2 = -\frac{1}{2})$ and touch E at $(\varrho_1 = \pm 2/3, \varrho_2 = 1/6)$, respectively.

Hint: Make use of Theorem 10$\cdot$2$\cdot$1.

12.[1] Letting $\{\varepsilon_t\}$ be a purely random process, the relations

$$\zeta_t = \frac{1}{2}\varepsilon_t - \frac{3}{4}\varepsilon_{t-1} - \frac{3}{8}\varepsilon_{t-2} - \frac{3}{16}\varepsilon_{t-3} - \cdots$$

$$\zeta_t = \frac{1}{2}\varepsilon_t + \frac{3}{4}\varepsilon_{t-1} - \frac{3}{8}\varepsilon_{t-2} + \frac{3}{16}\varepsilon_{t-3} - \cdots$$

define two processes of moving summation (10˙2˙1). Show that both processes have the same correlogram as $\{\varepsilon_t\}$, that is $\varrho_1 = \varrho_2 = \cdots = 0$. Similarly, show that the process

$$\zeta_t = \frac{1}{4}\varepsilon_t + \frac{1}{8}\varepsilon_{t-1} - \frac{15}{16}\varepsilon_{t-2} - \frac{15}{32}\varepsilon_{t-3} - \frac{15}{64}\varepsilon_{t-4} - \cdots$$

has the same correlogram as the moving average process $\{\zeta_t\} = \{\varepsilon_t + \frac{1}{2}\varepsilon_{t-1}\}$.

13. A stochastic process $\{\xi_t\}$ is called a *Markov process* if

$$E(\xi_t | \xi_{t-1}, \xi_{t-2}, \ldots, \xi_{t-n}) = E(\xi_t | \xi_{t-1}) \qquad \text{for all } n = 2, 3, \ldots$$

The autoregressive process (10˙2˙8) is a Markov process if and only if $h = 1$. Further show that for such a process the correlogram ϱ_ν and the coefficients a_ν of the representation (10˙2˙9) are given by

$$\varrho_\nu = (-b_1)^\nu \qquad\qquad a_\nu = (-b_1)^\nu \qquad\qquad \nu = 0, 1, 2, \ldots$$

14 (Wold, 1938). Considering an autoregressive process $\{\zeta_t\}$ of second order, $h = 2$, suppose that the roots of (10˙2˙11) are conjugate complex, say

$$z_1 = A + iB \qquad\qquad z_2 = A - iB.$$

Show that the correlogram of $\{\zeta_t\}$ is a damped harmonic, viz.

$$\varrho_\nu = C^\nu \cos \nu \lambda + \frac{A}{B}\frac{1-C^2}{1+C^2} \cdot C^\nu \sin \nu \lambda, \quad \text{with } C = +\sqrt{A^2 + B^2}, \quad \cos \lambda = A/C, \quad (0 < \lambda < \pi).$$

Similarly, the coefficients in the representation (10˙2˙9) are given by

$$a_\nu = C^\nu \cdot \cos \nu \lambda + \frac{A}{B} \cdot C^\nu \cdot \sin \nu \lambda \qquad\qquad \nu = 0, 1, 2, \ldots$$

15. Given a linear difference equation

$$x_t + b_1 x_{t-1} + \cdots + b_h x_{t-h} = 0$$

and an arbitrary set of initial values $x_{t-1} = c_1, \ldots, x_{t-h} = c_h$, the series $x_t, x_{t+1}, x_{t+2}, \cdots$ can be obtained by recursive deductions. Show that the resulting series will form the general solution of the equation.

In explicit form, the general solution is given by[1]

$$x_t = \sum_{k=1}^{i} H_{m_k-1}^{(1)}(t) \cdot p_k^t + \sum_{k=1}^{j} \left[H_{n_k-1}^{(2)}(t) \cos \lambda_k t + H_{n_k-1}^{(3)}(t) \sin \lambda_k t \right] \cdot q_k^t$$

where i, j and p_k, m_k and n_k are given by the factorization into real products

$$z^h + b_1 z^{h-1} + \cdots + b_{h-1} z + b_h = \prod_{k=1}^{i} (z - p_k)^{m_k} \prod_{k=1}^{j} (z^2 - 2 s_k \cdot z + q_k^2)^{n_k},$$

the angular frequencies λ_k are given by

$$\cos \lambda_k = s_k / q_k$$

and $H_r^{(s)}$ denotes a polynomial of order r with arbitrary coefficients.

16 (Wold, 1938). Considering the representation (10˙2˙9) of an autoregressive process, (10˙2˙10 b) forms a difference equation satisfied by the a_k for $k > h$. Show that the a_k satisfy no linear difference equation of order $< h$.

Hint: Use (10˙2˙10 a) to calculate fictitious coefficients b_0, b_{-1}, ..., b_{-h} and show that $b_0 = 1$, $b_{-1} = \cdots = b_{-h} = 0$.

17 (Wold, 1938). Use the result of the preceding exercise to verify Theorem 10˙2˙2. Further show that, if $\{\varepsilon_t\}$ is any stationary process, the condition laid down in the theorem is sufficient in order that $\{\zeta_t\}$ should be a well-defined stationary process.

18 (Wold, 1938[1]). Given a purely random process $\{\varepsilon_t\}$, show that the nonlinear relation

$$\xi_t = \varepsilon_t + (\xi_{t-1})^2$$

will define a stationary process $\{\xi_t\}$, provided ε_t is confined to the range $-\frac{1}{4} \le \varepsilon_t \le \frac{1}{4}$, that is provided Prob $[|\varepsilon_t| \le \frac{1}{4}] = 1$.

19. The discontinuous spectral function shown in Fig. 10˙4˙1 is given by

$$W(\lambda) = 0 \text{ for } 0 < \lambda < 0.3; \qquad W(\lambda) = 0.8\,\pi \text{ for } 0.3 < \lambda < \pi/3; \qquad W(\lambda) = \pi \text{ for } \lambda > \pi/3.$$

Fig. 10˙3˙1 shows the corresponding correlogram as defined by (9˙3˙9),

$$\varrho_\nu = 0.8 \cos 0.3\,\nu + 0.2 \cos \pi\nu/3 \qquad \nu = 0, \pm 1, \pm 2, \ldots$$

Letting a matrix $\Lambda = [\lambda_{ik}]$ of type (9˙3˙6) be defined by $\lambda_{ik} = \sigma^2 \cdot \varrho_{|i-k|}$, show that (9˙3˙7) is satisfied, which ensures that Λ is the dispersion matrix of a stationary process. Further show that the correlogram satisfies the relations

$$\varrho_\nu - (0.6 + 2\,\pi/3)\,\varrho_{\nu-1} + (2 + 0.4\,\pi)\,\varrho_{\nu-2} - (0.6 + 2\,\pi/3)\,\varrho_{\nu-3} + \varrho_{\nu-4} = 0; \quad \nu = 0, \pm 1, \pm 2, \ldots$$

Thus Λ is of finite rank (in this case of rank 4), which according to Ch. 10˙3 implies that a process with Λ for dispersion matrix is a harmonic process.

20. Let H_s be the hypothesis that a given time-series $y_1, \ldots, y_n$ belongs to a process $\{\eta_t^*\} = \{\eta_t + \varepsilon_t\}$ of type (10˙3˙8) such that $\{\varepsilon_t\}$ is purely random and $\{\eta_t\}$ is a harmonic process with realizations (10˙3˙6), where $\alpha_0 = 0$ and the frequencies $\lambda_1, \ldots, \lambda_s$ have specified values with $0 < \lambda_i < \pi$. Further let a_i, b_i be the estimates of α_i, β_i obtained by periodogram analysis, thus

(1)
$$a_i = \frac{2}{n} \sum_{t=1}^{n} y_t \cos \lambda_i t \qquad b_i = \frac{2}{n} \sum_{t=1}^{n} y_t \sin \lambda_i t \qquad i = 1, \ldots, s$$

and let $C(\lambda_i)$ be the periodogram ordinate with abscissa λ_i, thus

$$C(\lambda_i) = \frac{n}{4} (a_i^2 + b_i^2).$$

a. On the hypothesis that the given series $y_1, \ldots, y_n$ belongs to a purely random process, $n\,C(\lambda_i)$ is approximately distributed as χ^2 with n degrees of freedom.

b (Whittle[1]). Forming $A = \sum_{t=1}^{n} y_t^2;$ $B_s = \sum_{t=1}^{n} \left[y_t - \sum_{i=1}^{s} (a_i \cos \lambda_i t + b_i \sin \lambda_i t) \right]^2$

and $F_s = \dfrac{n - 2s}{2s} \cdot \dfrac{A - B_s}{B_s}$ $F_{sk} = \dfrac{n - 2(s+k)}{2k} \cdot \dfrac{B_s - B_{s+k}}{B_{s+k}},$

F_s provides a test of H_s on the null hypothesis H_0 that the s harmonic components are absent, F_s being approximately distributed as Fisher's F statistic with $(2s, n-2s)$ degrees of freedom; more generally, letting H_s be the null hypothesis, show that F_{sk} is asymptotically distributed as Fisher's $F(2n, n-2s-2k)$.

c (Wiener, 1930). The empirical periodogram and correlogram of a stationary time-series are related by the asymptotical formula

$$C^2(\lambda) \sim s_y^2 \cdot \sum_{-n/2}^{n/2} r_k \cos k\lambda.$$

Hence for a process of moving summation the expectation of the periodogram ordinate is asymptotically proportional to the spectral density $W'(\lambda)$. As shown by Bartlett (1946), a truncated sum $\sum_{-a}^{a} r_k \cos k\lambda$ formed by the use of the empirical correlogram gives a good approximation to $W'(\lambda)$, provided λ is not too small.

21 (Bartlett, 1946). Let $\{\xi_t\}$ be the stationary process defined by

$$\xi_t = \cdots + a_{-1}\varepsilon_{t-1} + a_0\varepsilon_t + a_1\varepsilon_{t+1} + \cdots \qquad \text{with } \sum_{\nu=-\infty}^{\infty} a_\nu^2 < \infty$$

where $\{\varepsilon_t\}$ is a purely random process. Considering a realization (9·2·1) of $\{\xi_t\}$, let r_k be the sample correlogram (9·4·8). Then the theoretical correlogram ϱ_k of $\{\xi_t\}$ is given by a formula similar to (10·2·3), and for n large we have the asymptotic relations

$$E\, r_k \sim \varrho_k \qquad \text{and} \qquad \text{cov}\,(r_k, r_{k+s}) \sim \frac{1}{n} \sum_{\nu=-\infty}^{\infty} (\varrho_\nu \varrho_{\nu-s} + \varrho_{\nu-k+1}\varrho_{\nu+k} + 2\varrho_k \varrho_{k+s}\varrho_\nu^2 - $$
$$-2\varrho_k \varrho_\nu \varrho_{\nu-k-s} - 2\varrho_{k+s}\varrho_\nu \varrho_{\nu-k}).$$

22 (Quenouille, 1949). If $x_1, \ldots, x_h$ is an autoregressive series of order h, a consistent estimate of parameter b_h is provided by the partial correlation coefficient of x_t and x_{t+h}, with $x_{t+1}, \ldots, x_{t+h-1}$ eliminated.

If the series is Gaussian, the autocorrelation coefficients $r_1, \ldots, r_h$ are asymptotically sufficient for estimating the parameters $b_1, \ldots, b_h$.

23 (Whittle[1]). It was suggested by Yule (1927) that the fit of an autoregressive scheme of order h should be tested by the use of the multiple autocorrelation coefficients R_k,

$$1 - R_k^2 = (1 - r_1^2)(1 - r_{2 \cdot 1}^2) \cdots \cdot (1 - r_{k \cdot 12 \ldots k-1}^2).$$

Forming $\Psi^2 = (n - h - p)(R_{h+p}^2 - R_h^2) : (1 - R_{h+p}^2)$, show that Ψ^2 is asymptotically distributed as χ^2 with p degrees of freedom.

24 (Whittle, 1951). Given a time-series x_t with observed correlogram r_k, suppose that we wish to fit a moving average of first order, say $x_t = \varepsilon_t + a\varepsilon_{t-1}$. Verify that the maximum likelihood method developed in Ch. 11·2 gives the following implicit relation for estimating a,

$$a - 2a^2 r_1 + 2a^3 r_2 - 2a^4 r_3 + \cdots = (1 - a^2)(r_1 - 2a r_2 + 3a^2 r_3 - 4a^3 r_4 + \cdots).$$

Further show that if we drop the assumption that the x_t are normally distributed, the method may be interpreted as a least-squares approach.

25 (Whittle, 1951). The power of any likelihood ratio test λ of type (11˙2˙3) is proportional to the expectation of λ, taken on the null hypothesis over the critical region ω, and the proportion factor equals the significance level $1 - a$, in symbols

$$\text{Power} = \int\limits_{\lambda_\omega}^{\infty} \lambda\,\varphi_0(\lambda)\,d\lambda \qquad\qquad 1 - a = \int\limits_{\lambda_\omega}^{\infty} \varphi_0(\lambda)\,d\lambda.$$

Proof:[1] Writing $f_0(x)$, $f_1(x)$ for the two likelihood functions,

$$\text{Power} = \int\limits_{\omega} f_1(x)\,dx = \int\limits_{\omega} \lambda f_0(x)\,dx = \int\limits_{\lambda_\omega}^{\infty} \lambda\,\varphi_0(\lambda)\,d\lambda.$$

26 (Doob, 1949[1]). Let $\{\zeta_t\}$ be the hybrid between an autoregressive and a moving-average process that is defined by (10˙2˙8), making $\{\varepsilon_t\}$ a moving average (10˙2˙4) of arbitrary order k. Show that the spectral function (11˙2˙4) of $\{\zeta_t\}$ is

$$\Lambda(z) = \frac{(a_0 z^k + a_1 z^{k-1} + \cdots + a_k)\,(a_0 z^{-k} + a_1 z^{-k+1} + \cdots + a_k)}{(z^h + b_1 z^{h-1} + \cdots + b_h)\,(z^{-h} + b_1 z^{-h+1} + \cdots + b_h)}.$$

It will be observed that Whittle's test theory [Ch. 11˙2–4] applies to any such process, provided that $\Lambda(z)$ has no zero on the periphery of the unit circle.

27. Let $\ldots, \varepsilon_t, \varepsilon_{t+1}, \ldots,$ and ζ be independent variables with zero expectation and unit variance. Making

(1) $\xi_t = a \cdot \zeta + \varepsilon_t$ $-\infty < t < \infty$

show that the process $\{\xi_t\}$ is stationary with correlogram $\varrho_1 = \varrho_2 = \cdots = a^2/(1 + a^2)$. Further show that $\{\xi_t\}$ is not ergodic.

28. Let S be any statistic based on deviates $x_t - \bar{x}$ from the sample mean. If F is the distribution of S on the assumption that the x_t belong to a purely random Gaussian process, show that S has the same distribution F if the x_t belong to a stationary Gaussian process $\{\xi_t\}$ with correlogram $\varrho_1 = \varrho_2 = \cdots = a^2/(1 + a^2)$.

Hint: Process (1) of Ex. 27 having the same correlogram, we infer from the uniqueness theorem of the predictive decomposition [see Ch. 12˙6 (i)] that the given data allow this representation (1), with $a \cdot \zeta$ for deterministic and ε_t for nondeterministic component.[1]

29. Given two independent stationary processes $\{\eta_t'\}$ and $\{\eta_t''\}$ with zero expectations, unit variances and correlograms ϱ_ν', ϱ_ν'', let η_t be the sequence of random variables that with probability p equals $\{\eta_t'\}$ and with probability $1 - p$ equals $\{\eta_t''\}$. Show that $\{\eta_t\}$ is a well-defined stationary process with correlogram $\varrho_\nu = p\varrho_\nu' + (1 - p)\varrho_\nu''$.

Interpret the construction of $\{\eta_t\}$ as a functional transform (9˙2˙7) of a vector process.

30. Let $\{\eta_t'\}$, $\{\eta_t''\}$ be two harmonic processes (10˙3˙6) with realizations given by

$$y_t' = a' \cos \lambda' t + \beta' \sin \lambda' t \qquad\qquad y_t'' = a'' \cos \lambda'' t + \beta'' \sin \lambda'' t$$

respectively, and let $\{\eta_t\}$ be a mixed process in the sense of the preceding exercise. Show that $\{\eta_t\}$ is purely deterministic, an exact prediction of $\{\eta_t\}$ being provided by a recursive formula (12˙5˙11) of order 4. Further show that the phase prediction of $\{\eta_t\}$ can be performed by two alternative formulae of simpler structure.

31. Let two realizations $y' = (\ldots, y_t', y_{t+1}', \ldots)$, $y'' = (\ldots, y_t'', y_{t+1}'', \ldots)$ be defined by

$$y_t' = (-1)^t \qquad\qquad y_t'' = (-1)^{t+1} \qquad\qquad -\infty < t < \infty$$

and let $\{\eta_t\}$ be a stochastic process with realizations $y = (\ldots, y_t, y_{t+1}, \ldots)$ such that $y = y'$ with probability $1/2$ and $y = y''$ with probability $1/2$. Show that the process $\{\eta_t\}$ is stationary, harmonic, and ergodic.

Supposing that $y = y'$, $y = y''$, $y = y''' = (\ldots, 0, 0, \ldots)$ with probabilities $1/3$, show that $\{\eta_t\}$ is stationary and harmonic, but not ergodic.

32. Given an evolutive time-series $x_1, \ldots, x_{n+1}$, let us consider two alternative hypotheses for a trend involved in the series, viz.

(A) $x_t = a + \beta \cdot t + \varepsilon_t$;   (B) $x_t = a + \varepsilon_1 + \varepsilon_2 + \cdots + \varepsilon_t$; $(t = 1, \ldots, n+1)$

where in both cases $E(\varepsilon_t) = 0$. A test criterion λ for discriminating between the two hypotheses is obtained if we form

$$y_t = x_{t+1} - x_t; \qquad \bar{y} = \frac{1}{n} \Sigma y_t; \qquad s^2 = \frac{1}{n} \Sigma (y_t - \bar{y})^2; \qquad \lambda = \bar{y}/s; \qquad (t = 1, \ldots, n).$$

a. On the assumption that the ε_t belong to a purely random process, the distribution of λ is asymptotically normal for n large, with expectations and standard deviations differing between the two hypotheses, viz.

(A) $E(\lambda) \sim \beta$, $\sigma(\lambda) \sim \sigma_\varepsilon \sqrt{2} / \sqrt{n}$;   (B) $E(\lambda) \sim 0$, $\sigma(\lambda) \sim \sigma_\varepsilon / \sqrt{n}$.

b. More generally, assuming that the ε_t form a process of moving summation, the distribution of λ is asymptotically normal, with

(A) $E(\lambda) \sim \beta$;   (B) $E(\lambda) \sim 0$;

whereas the standard deviation may in both cases be obtained from the large sample formula

(A–B) $\sigma(\lambda) \sim \dfrac{s}{\sqrt{n}} \left(1 + 2\dfrac{n-1}{n} r_1 + 2\dfrac{n-2}{n} r_2 + 2\dfrac{n-3}{n} r_3 + \cdots \right)$,

where $r_1, r_2, \ldots$ is the observed correlogram of the series y_t.

33 (Wold, 1949 a). Considering model $(1\cdot 4\cdot 1)$, suppose that the demand function has a negative and the supply function a positive slope. Show that if γ is fixed and sufficiently small, p_t will converge to the Cournot equilibrium as $t \to \infty$.

34. Carry out a replication of the time-series experiment illustrated in Fig. $1\cdot 4\cdot 2$. Interpret the resulting sequence $d_t, s_t, p_t (t = 1, 2, \ldots)$ as the realization of a vector process.

Hint: Form the disturbances $z_t^{(i)}$ by the use of the author's tables of random normal deviates (1948 c), making their expectation 0 and their standard deviation 0.15.

35. Assuming $E \xi^2$ to be finite, establish $(9\cdot 4\cdot 3)$ as a necessary and sufficient condition for $M x = E \xi$.

PART IV

Theory and methods of regression analysis

Chapter 12.

LEAST-SQUARES REGRESSION AS A LINEAR APPROXIMATION

1. The principle of least squares. – From the general viewpoint of mathematical method, regression analysis is a special application of linear approximation according to the principle of least squares. To develop this order of ideas we shall in this introductory section review the simple set of abstract notions that gives the appropriate basis for the formal theory of linear least-squares approximation.[1] In the rest of the chapter we shall then mainly be concerned with those aspects of regression thus belonging to the theory of least squares in general.

First we state two fundamental definitions.

A. A set of elements $f, g, h, \ldots$ is said to form a *linear space*, say R, if (a) for any f and any real constant a the scalar product $a \cdot f$ is an element in R, (b) for any two f, g the sum $f + g$ is an element in R, and (c) the operations (a)–(b) follow the rules of ordinary algebra. Specifically, R contains a null element, say Θ, such that $a \cdot \Theta = \Theta$ and $f + \Theta = f$.

B. Considering any two elements f, g in R, the real quantity (f, g) is called an *inner product* if we have

$$(af, g) = a(f, g); \qquad (f_1 + f_2, g) = (f_1, g) + (f_2, g); \qquad (g, f) = (f, g);$$

$$(f, f) \neq 0 \quad \text{for} \quad f \neq \Theta, \qquad (f, f) = 0 \quad \text{for} \quad f = \Theta.$$

Following the customary notation, the null element Θ will be denoted by 0.

Given a linear space R for which an inner product (f, g) is defined, R is made metric by defining the *distance* between any two of its elements. The distance between f and g, denoted $\|f - g\|$, is defined by

$$\|f - g\| = +(f - g, f - g)^{1/2}.$$

The distance between f and the null element, $\|f\| = (f, f)^{1/2}$, is called the *norm* of f. As is readily verified, we have *Schwartz' inequality* and the *triangle inequality*, in symbols

$$|(f, g)| \leq \|f\| \cdot \|g\| \qquad\qquad \|f - g\| \leq \|f\| + \|g\|.$$

As is sufficient for our purpose we have assumed that (f, g) is real. If we allow (f, g) to be complex-valued with $(g, f) = \overline{(f, g)}$, the $f, g, \ldots$ are elements in what is known as *Hilbert space*.

Let f and $f_1, \ldots f_h$ be fixed elements in R. Forming

$$(1) \qquad\qquad f^* = b_1 f_1 + \cdots + b_h f_h,$$

where $b_1, \ldots, b_h$ are constants, we shall approximate f by an element f^* such that the distance between f and f^* is the shortest possible. Writing

$$(2) \qquad\qquad f = f^* + z \qquad\qquad z = f - f^*$$

where z is called the *remainder* or the *residual* of the approximation, we should accordingly make

$$(3) \qquad\qquad \|z\| \qquad \text{a minimum.}$$

To determine the coefficients $b_1, \ldots, b_h$ we develop $\|z\|^2$,

$$\|z\|^2 = \|f - f^*\|^2 = (f, f) + \sum_{i=1}^{h} \sum_{k=1}^{h} (f_i, f_k) \cdot b_i b_k - 2 \sum_{i=1}^{h} (f, f_i) \cdot b_i,$$

and make the derivatives with respect to $b_1, \ldots, b_h$ equal to zero, obtaining

$$(4) \qquad \begin{cases} (f_1, f_1) \cdot b_1 + \cdots + (f_1, f_h) \cdot b_h = (f, f_1) \\ \cdot\ \cdot\ \cdot\ \cdot\ \cdot\ \cdot\ \cdot\ \cdot\ \cdot\ \cdot\ \cdot\ \cdot\ \cdot\ \cdot \\ (f_h, f_1) \cdot b_1 + \cdots + (f_h, f_h) \cdot b_h = (f, f_h). \end{cases}$$

This is known as the system of *normal equations* for determining the coefficients b_i of the approximating element f^*. Writing $\mathbf{\Lambda}_h$ for the coefficient matrix of (4), and Λ_h for its determinant,

$$(5) \qquad \mathbf{\Lambda}_h = \begin{bmatrix} (f_1, f_1) \cdots (f_1, f_h) \\ \cdot\ \cdot\ \cdot\ \cdot\ \cdot\ \cdot\ \cdot \\ (f_h, f_1) \cdots (f_h, f_h) \end{bmatrix}; \qquad \Lambda_h = \begin{vmatrix} (f_1, f_1) \cdots (f_1, f_h) \\ \cdot\ \cdot\ \cdot\ \cdot\ \cdot\ \cdot\ \cdot \\ (f_h, f_1) \cdots (f_h, f_h) \end{vmatrix},$$

let Λ_h^{ik} denote the cofactors of Λ_h. Without proof, we state the fundamental[2]

THEOREM 1. *The determinant Λ_h is nonnegative, $\Lambda_h \geq 0$. The condition $\Lambda_h > 0$ is necessary and sufficient in order that the normal equations* (4) *should uniquely determine all coefficients b_i of the approximating element f^*. If $\Lambda_h > 0$, the approximation f^* and its coefficients $b_i (i = 1, \ldots, h)$ are given by*

$$(6) \qquad f^* = \begin{vmatrix} 0 & (f, f_1) & \cdots & (f, f_h) \\ -f_1 & (f_1, f_1) & \cdots & (f_1, f_h) \\ \cdot & \cdot\ \cdot\ \cdot\ \cdot\ \cdot\ \cdot\ \cdot\ \cdot \\ -f_h & (f_h, f_1) & \cdots & (f_h, f_h) \end{vmatrix} : \Lambda_h, \qquad b_i = \sum_{k=1}^{h} (f, f_k) \cdot \frac{\Lambda_h^{ik}}{\Lambda_h}$$

and the residual and its squared norm by

$$z = f - b_1 f_1 - \cdots - b_h f_h, \qquad \|z\|^2 = (f, f) - b_1 \cdot (f, f_1) - \cdots - b_h \cdot (f, f_h)$$

or, in determinants,

$$(7) \quad z = \begin{vmatrix} f & (f, f_1) & \cdots & (f, f_h) \\ f_1 & (f_1, f_1) & \cdots & (f_1, f_h) \\ \cdot & \cdot & \cdots & \cdot \\ f_h & (f_h, f_1) & \cdots & (f_h, f_h) \end{vmatrix} : \Lambda_h, \quad \|z\|^2 = \begin{vmatrix} (f, f) & (f, f_1) & \cdots & (f, f_h) \\ (f_1, f) & (f_1, f_1) & \cdots & (f_1, f_h) \\ \cdot & \cdot & \cdots & \cdot \\ (f_h, f) & (f_h, f_1) & \cdots & (f_h, f_h) \end{vmatrix} : \Lambda_h.$$

If we consider all elements of type (1) with $-\infty < b_i < \infty$, these form a subspace of R known as the *linear manifold* spanned upon $f_1, \ldots, f_h$. The element f^* given by (6) is called the *projection* of f on this subspace. If $(f, g) = 0$, the elements f and g are called *orthogonal*. As seen from (7 a), we have

THEOREM 2. *The residual z is orthogonal to every $f_1, \ldots, f_h$; in symbols,*

$$(8) \qquad\qquad\qquad (z, f_i) = 0 \qquad\qquad\qquad i = 1, \ldots, h.$$

The case $\Lambda_h = 0$ being excluded in Theorem 1, we note that the condition $\Lambda_h = 0$, known as *Gram's criterion*, is necessary and sufficient for $f_1, \ldots, f_h$ to be linearly related, i.e. for the existence of a relation

$$(9) \qquad\qquad b_1 f_1 + \cdots + b_h f_h = 0 \qquad \text{with at least one } b_i \neq 0.$$

THEOREM 3. *Suppose f allows the representation*

$$f = \beta_1 f_1 + \cdots + \beta_h f_h + z^*$$

where z^* is an element that (a) is of small norm, and (b) is nearly orthogonal to $f_1, \ldots, f_h$, say

$$\|z^*\| \leq \varepsilon, \qquad |(z^*, f_i)| \leq \varepsilon \cdot \|z^*\| \cdot \|f_i\| \qquad i = 1, \ldots, h.$$

Further suppose $\Lambda_h > 0$, and let

$$f = b_1 f_1 + \cdots + b_h f_h + z$$

be the least-squares representation of f in accordance with Theorem 1. Then

$$(10) \qquad\qquad\qquad |b_i - \beta_i| \leq c \cdot \varepsilon^2 \qquad\qquad\qquad i = 1, \ldots, h.$$

In fact,

$$b_i = \sum_{k=1}^{h} (f, f_k) \frac{\Lambda_h^{ik}}{\Lambda_h} = \sum_{k=1}^{h} (\beta_1 f_1 + \cdots + \beta_h f_h + z^*, f_k) \cdot \frac{\Lambda_h^{ik}}{\Lambda_h} =$$

$$= \beta_i + \sum_{k=1}^{h} (z^*, f_k) \frac{\Lambda_h^{ik}}{\Lambda_h} = \beta_i + c \cdot \varepsilon^2,$$

where c does not depend upon z^*.

2. Regression analysis in statistics and probability theory. – In regression analysis we must distinguish between the empirical concepts that refer to the statistical observations, and the corresponding theoretical concepts that refer to a hypothetical probability distribution. From a formal viewpoint, empirical regression as well as theoretical regression are special applications of the method of linear approximation developed in the previous section. In both cases, the elements f, g, ... of our space R have to be specified as variables for which the inner product (f, g) is defined as a *product moment*. We shall carry out this specification in detail, beginning with the statistical aspect.

Let us consider n observations, each of which comprises $h+1$ measurements, say

$$x_1^{(0)}, x_1^{(1)}, \ldots, x_1^{(h)}; \quad x_2^{(0)}, x_2^{(1)}, \ldots, x_2^{(h)}; \quad \ldots; \quad x_n^{(0)}, x_n^{(1)}, \ldots, x_n^{(h)}.$$

We shall regard each component of the n observations as a vector $x^{(i)}$,

(1) $$x^{(i)} = [x_1^{(i)}, x_2^{(i)}, \ldots, x_n^{(i)}] \qquad i = 0, 1, \ldots h$$

so that addition and scalar multiplication are defined by

$$x^{(i)} + x^{(k)} = [x_1^{(i)} + x_1^{(k)}, \ldots, x_n^{(i)} + x_n^{(k)}] \qquad a\,x^{(i)} = [a\,x_1^{(i)}, \ldots, a\,x_n^{(i)}].$$

Now let $(x^{(i)}, x^{(k)})$ be defined as the product moment of $x^{(i)}$ and $x^{(k)}$,

(2) $$(x^{(i)}, x^{(k)}) = \frac{1}{n} \sum_{\nu=1}^{n} x_\nu^{(i)} \cdot x_\nu^{(k)} \qquad i, k = 0, 1, \ldots, h.$$

Then $x^{(0)}, x^{(1)}, \ldots, x^{(h)}$ may be interpreted as elements in a linear space R such as dealt with in the previous section.

Being now in a position to apply the approximation method (12·1·1–8), we shall approximate $x^{(0)}$ in terms of $x^{(1)}, \ldots, x^{(h)}$, thus

$$x^{(0)} = b_1 x^{(1)} + \cdots + b_h x^{(h)} + z$$

or, explicitly,

(3) $$x_\nu^{(0)} = b_1 x_\nu^{(1)} + \cdots + b_h x_\nu^{(h)} + z_\nu \qquad \nu = 1, \ldots, n.$$

Writing s_z^2 for the residual variance, we see that the minimum condition (12·1·3) may in the present case be written

(4) $$\|z\|^2 = s_z^2 = \frac{1}{n} \sum_{\nu=1}^{n} (x_\nu^{(0)} - b_1 x_\nu^{(1)} - \cdots - b_h x_\nu^{(h)})^2 \qquad \text{a minimum.}$$

Here we recognize the traditional minimum condition of statistical regression analysis as based on the principle of least squares [cf. (1·5·2)]. In agreement with this interpretation it is seen that on insertion of (2) the general formulae (12·1·4–8) become the familiar formulae of statistical regression analysis.[1]

A few well-known facts about linear regression (3):

(i) In the special case when $h = 1$ and $x^{(1)} = [1, \ldots, 1]$, the representation (3) reduces to

$$x_\nu^{(0)} = \bar{x}_0 + z_\nu \quad \text{with} \quad \bar{x}_0 = \frac{1}{n} \sum_{\nu=1}^{n} x_\nu^{(0)}; \qquad \|z\|^2 = \frac{1}{n} \sum_{\nu=1}^{n} (x_\nu^{(0)} - \bar{x}_0)^2.$$

In words, the average $\bar{x}_0$ gives the constant element $[\bar{x}_0, \ldots, \bar{x}_0]$ that in the sense of (12·1·3) and (4) forms the best approximation to $x^{(0)} = [x_1^{(0)}, \ldots, x_n^{(0)}]$.

(ii) Let the constant $x^{(h+1)} = [1, \ldots, 1]$ be introduced in (1) as a specified element. The resulting approximation of type (3), say

(5) $$x_\nu^{(0)} = b_0 + b_1 x_\nu^{(1)} + \cdots + b_h x_\nu^{(h)} + z_\nu \qquad \nu = 1, \ldots, n,$$

is known as the *regression of* $x^{(0)}$ *on* $x^{(1)}, \ldots, x^{(h)}$, and the b_i are the *regression coefficients*. Making use of the terms introduced in Ch. 2·2, $x^{(0)}$ is the *regressand* and $x^{(1)}, \ldots, x^{(h)}$ are the *regressors*.

It is a familiar fact that we obtain

(6) $$x_\nu^{(0)} - \bar{x}_0 = b_1 (x_\nu^{(1)} - \bar{x}_1) + \cdots + b_h (x_\nu^{(h)} - \bar{x}_h) + z_\nu \qquad \nu = 1, \ldots, n$$

if regression (5) is formed with the regressors taken as deviations from their averages, i.e., the coefficients $b_1, \ldots, b_h$ will be the same in (5) and (6),[2] and

$$b_0 = \bar{x}_0 - b_1 \bar{x}_1 - \cdots - b_h \bar{x}_h, \quad \text{with} \quad \bar{x}_i = \frac{1}{n} \sum_{\nu=1}^{n} x_\nu^{(i)}.$$

Writing

(7) $$l_{ik} = \frac{1}{n} \sum_{\nu=1}^{n} (x_\nu^{(i)} - \bar{x}_i)(x_\nu^{(k)} - \bar{x}_k), \qquad i, k = 0, 1, \ldots, h$$

we see that (6) is obtained from Theorem 12·1·1 by making $\mathbf{\Lambda}_h = [l_{ik}]$ with $i, k = 1, \ldots, h$.

Applying (12·1·8) to (5) we infer firstly that $\Sigma 1 \cdot z_\nu = 0$, so that the residuals z_ν of (5) and (6) have zero mean, and secondly that they are unc - related with each of the regressors $x^{(1)}, \ldots, x^{(h)}$, in symbols

(8) $$\frac{1}{n} \cdot \sum_{\nu=1}^{n} z_\nu = 0; \qquad \frac{1}{n} \cdot \sum_{\nu=1}^{n} (x_\nu^{(i)} - \bar{x}_i) z_\nu = \frac{1}{n} \cdot \sum_{\nu=1}^{n} x_\nu^{(i)} z_\nu = 0 \qquad (i = 1, \ldots, h).$$

(iii) Regression analysis (1)–(8) applies when every $x^{(i)}$ is an infinite time-series. We may distinguish between the cases where the $x^{(i)}$ are infinite in both directions, as in (9·4·1), or only in one, as in (12·5·10). In any case, we have to assume that the following phase averages of type (9·4·2) exist,

(9) $$\bar{x}_i = \lim \frac{1}{t_2 - t_1 + 1} \sum_{t=t_1}^{t_2} x_t^{(i)}; \qquad (x^{(i)}, x^{(k)}) = \lim \frac{1}{t_2 - t_1 + 1} \sum_{t=t_1}^{t_2} x_t^{(i)} \cdot x_t^{(k)}$$

where $i, k = 0, \ldots, h$ and where the limit signs require either $t_1 \to -\infty, t_2 \to \infty$ independently of each other, or only $t_1 \to -\infty$. Formulae (1)–(8) remain the same, with ν running over the infinite range in question. It will be observed that if $x^{(i)} = x^{(k)}$, this will in the finite case imply that $x_\nu^{(i)} = x_\nu^{(k)}$ for $\nu = 1, \ldots, n$, but in the case of infinite series we can assert nothing more than

$$\|x^{(i)} - x^{(k)}\|^2 = \lim \frac{1}{t_2 - t_1 + 1} \sum_{t=t_1}^{t_2} (x_t^{(i)} - x_t^{(k)})^2 = 0.$$

For example, the relation $x^{(l)} = 0$ implies, respectively,

$$x_1^{(l)} = \cdots = x_n^{(l)} = 0, \qquad \text{and} \quad \|x^{(l)}\|^2 = \lim \frac{1}{t_2 - t_1 + 1} \sum_{t=t_1}^{t_2} (x_t^{(l)})^2 = 0.$$

Turning now to the theory of probability, let

$$(10) \qquad\qquad \xi_0, \, \xi_1, \, \ldots, \, \xi_h$$

be $h + 1$ random variables with distribution function $F(u_0, u_1, \ldots, u_h)$. Further let $a \cdot \xi_i$ and $\xi_i + \xi_k$ be random variables defined by the usual formulae in probability theory [cf. (9·1·8)], and let (ξ_i, ξ_k) be the product moment of ξ_i and ξ_k, in symbols

$$(11) \qquad (\xi_i, \xi_k) = E(\xi_i \cdot \xi_k) = \int\limits_{u_i=-\infty}^{\infty} \int\limits_{u_k=-\infty}^{\infty} u_i \, u_k \, d_{u_i u_k}^2 F(u_0, u_1, \ldots, u_h).$$

Then (10) may be interpreted as elements of a real, linear, metric space R. The linear approximation (12·1·1–8) now gives us the regression formulae of probability theory.[3] Specifically, if we introduce ξ_{h+1} as an $(h + 1)$:st regressor such that $\xi_{h+1} = 1$ with probability 1, independently of the variables (10), the representation (12·1·2) gives

$$(12) \qquad \xi_0 = b_0 + b_1 \xi_1 + \cdots + b_h \xi_h + \zeta, \qquad \xi_0^* = b_0 + b_1 \xi_1 + \cdots + b_h \xi_h$$

with coefficients $b_0, \ldots, b_h$ satisfying the least-squares condition

$$(13) \qquad \|\zeta\|^2 = \sigma_\zeta^2 = E(\xi_0 - b_0 - b_1 \xi_1 - \cdots - b_h \xi_h)^2 \qquad \text{a minimum,}$$

where σ_ζ^2 denotes the residual variance.

Again we have the same dualism as in (5)–(6), regression (12 a) being the same as

$$(14) \qquad \xi_0 - E \xi_0 = b_1(\xi_1 - E \xi_1) + \cdots + b_h(\xi_h - E \xi_h) + \zeta.$$

Here, as before, Theorem 12·1·1 applies directly, the moments

$$(15) \qquad \lambda_{ik} = E(\xi_i - E \xi_i)(\xi_k - E \xi_k) \qquad\qquad i, k = 0, 1, \ldots, h$$

defining the matrix $\Lambda_h = [\lambda_{ik}]$, $(i, k = 1, \ldots, h)$. The residual variable ζ of (12) and (14) has zero expectation, and is uncorrelated with the regressors $\xi_1, \ldots, \xi_h$; thus

$$(16) \qquad\qquad E \zeta = 0 \qquad\qquad E(\xi_i \cdot \zeta) = 0 \qquad\qquad i = 1, \ldots, h.$$

As regards the case $\Lambda_h = 0$, excluded in Theorem 12·1·1, we see that in regressions (3) and (12) this is the degenerate case when the joint distribution of the regressors is singular in the sense of (9·1·13).

3. The introduction of more regressors. – We are now in a position to verify statements (i)–(iii) in Ch. 2·3. These have been formulated without specifying whether the regression is taken in the sense of statistics or of probability theory. Actually, they hold good for both types of regression. The statements will now be proved for linear least-squares approximation in the general case $(12\cdot1\cdot2)$, so that regressions $(12\cdot2\cdot3)$ and $(12\cdot2\cdot12)$ will be included as special cases.

Let the residual in $(12\cdot1\cdot2)$ be denoted z_h, and let z_{h+1} be the residual obtained if an $(h+1)$:st element f_{h+1} is introduced in $(12\cdot1\cdot1)$. As an immediate consequence of the least-squares principle $(12\cdot1\cdot3)$ we obtain the fundamental

THEOREM 1.

$$\|f\| \geq \|z_h\| \geq \|z_{h+1}\| \geq 0.$$

The following elementary theorem covers statement (i) in Ch. $2\cdot3$; moreover, D–E deal with multicollinearity in the sense of Ch. $2\cdot6$.

THEOREM 2. *On the assumptions of Theorem $12\cdot1\cdot1$, let $b_1^*, \ldots, b_{h+1}^*$ be the coefficients of the least-squares approximation $(12\cdot1\cdot2)$ obtained on the introduction of f_{h+1}.*

First, suppose $\Lambda_h > 0$ and $\Lambda_{h+1} > 0$.

A. *In order that $b_{h+1}^* = 0$ it is necessary and sufficient that f_{h+1} is orthogonal to $f, f_1, \ldots, f_h$. If $b_{h+1}^* = 0$, then $b_i^* = b_i$ $(i = 1, \ldots, h)$.*

B. *In order that $b_i^* = b_i$ $(i = 1, \ldots, h)$ it is necessary and sufficient that f_{h+1} is orthogonal to $f_1, \ldots, f_h$.*

C. *In order that $b_1^* = b_1$ it is necessary and sufficient that f_{h+1} is orthogonal to the residual obtained when approximating f_1 in terms of $f_2, \ldots, f_h$. An equivalent condition is that f_1 is orthogonal to the residual obtained when approximating f_{h+1} in terms of $f_2, \ldots, f_h$.*

Next, suppose that $\Lambda_h > 0$ and $\Lambda_{h+1} = 0$.

D. *Then f_{h+1} is linear in $f_1, \ldots, f_h$; say $f_{h+1} = c_{i_1} f_{i_1} + \cdots + c_{i_m} f_{i_m}$. Here the indices $i_1, \ldots, i_m$ and the coefficients c_{i_k} are uniquely determined. The coefficients $b_{i_1}^*, \ldots, b_{i_m}^*$ and b_{h+1}^* are indeterminate, whereas all other b_i^* are uniquely determined.*

Finally, suppose $\Lambda_h = 0$.

E. *Then $\Lambda_{h+1} = 0$; hence the sequence $\Lambda_1, \Lambda_2, \ldots$ contains a first element Λ_a such that $\Lambda_a > 0$, $\Lambda_{a+1} = 0$, which brings us back to case D.*

Commencing with B, suppose the condition is fulfilled. Then on introduction of f_{h+1} the $h+1$ normal equations are seen to be formed by the h relations $(12\cdot1\cdot4)$ and the relation $(f_{h+1}, f_{h+1}) \cdot b_{h+1}^* = (f, f_{h+1})$. This clearly implies $b_i = b_i^*$ $(i = 1, \ldots, h)$. Conversely, if $b_i = b_i^*$ for all $i = 1, \ldots, h$ simultaneously, the first h relations must coincide in the two systems of normal equations, which gives $(f_i, f_{h+1}) = 0$ for $i = 1, \ldots, h$. Statement A is proved by a similar argument.

As regards the first part of C, we see that if f_1 in (12·1·1) is replaced by $f_1 + c_{12} f_2 + \cdots + c_{1h} f_h$, where the c_{1i} are arbitrary, then b_1 in (12·1·6) remains unchanged. Hence it involves no loss of generality to replace f_1 by the residual in the approximation of f_1 in terms of $f_2, \ldots, f_h$, say z'. On this substitution, the first equation in (12·1·4) reduces to $(z', z') \cdot b_1 = (f, z')$, since z' by (12·1·8) is orthogonal to $f_2, \ldots, f_h$. Now on introduction of f_{h+1}, the first normal equation gives $(z', z') \cdot b_1^* + (z', f_{h+1}) \cdot b_{h+1}^* = (f, z')$. Thus to obtain $b_1^* = b_1$, it is necessary and sufficient that *either* $b_{h+1}^* = 0$ *or* $(z', f_{h+1}) = 0$. By A, however, $b_{h+1}^* = 0$ implies $(z', f_{h+1}) = 0$. This completes the proof of the first part of C. For the second part, the proof is analogous.

To verify D it is sufficient to reflect that after the introduction of f_{h+1} the distance between f and f^* remains the same if f^* is replaced by $f^* + \lambda (f_{h+1} - c_{i_1} f_{i_1} - \cdots - c_{i_m} f_{i_m})$, where λ is arbitrary. Finally, we obtain E as a corollary to Gram's criterion; in fact, we can have $\Lambda_{h+1} > 0$ only if $\Lambda_h > 0$.

As an immediate corollary to Theorem 2, A and D, we note

THEOREM 3.[1] *Suppose $\Lambda_h > 0$. In order that*

$$\| z_h \| = \| z_{h+1} \|$$

it is necessary and sufficient that f_{h+1} is either orthogonal to $f, f_1, \ldots, f_h$ or identically linear in $f_1, \ldots, f_h$.

Making use of the same notations as in Theorems 2–3, we have the following theorem, which is equivalent to statement (ii) in Ch. 2·3.

THEOREM 4.[2] *Suppose f is not linear in $f_1, \ldots, f_h$. Let b be an arbitrary constant. Then there exists an element f_{h+1} with unit norm, and not identically linear in $f_1, \ldots, f_h$, such that*

$$b_1^* = b.$$

To see this, we make

$$f_{h+1} = p (q \cdot f_1 + z_h + g)$$

where p, q are parameters to be specified later, and g is an element that is orthogonal to $f, f_1, \ldots, f_h$. Then z_{h+1} can be written

$$z_{h+1} = \psi + (1 - p \cdot b_{h+1}^*) \cdot z_h - p \cdot b_{h+1}^* \cdot g$$

where

$$\psi = (b_1 - b_1^* - pq \cdot b_{h+1}^*) \cdot f_1 + (b_2 - b_2^*) \cdot f_2 + \cdots + (b_h - b_h^*) \cdot f_h.$$

According to the orthogonality properties (12·1·8) of the least-squares residuals z_h and z_{h+1}, we have

(1) $\quad \| z_{h+1} \|^2 = \| \psi \|^2 + (1 - p b_{h+1}^*)^2 \cdot \| z_h \|^2 + (p b_{h+1}^*)^2 \cdot \| g \|^2, \quad$ say $\| z_{h+1} \|^2 = \| \psi \|^2 + s^2.$

Being least-squares coefficients, the $b_1^*, \ldots, b_{h+1}^*$ make $\| z_{h+1} \|$ a minimum. Further we note that, for any given b_{h+1}^*, we obtain $\| \psi \| = 0$ if $b_1^*, \ldots, b_h^*$ are determined by

(2) $\quad b_1^* = b_1 - pq \cdot b_{h+1}^*, \qquad b_2^* = b_2, \qquad \ldots, \qquad b_h^* = b_h.$

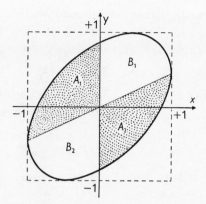

Fig. 12·3·1. Illustration of Theorem 12·3·5.

It follows that b^*_{h+1} must minimize s^2 in (1), which gives

$$b^*_{h+1} = \|z_h\|^2 / p \left(\|z_h\|^2 + \|g\|^2\right).$$

Inserting this value in (2), we obtain $b^*_1, \ldots, b^*_h$. Now if we make $q = (b_1 - b) / p\, b^*_{h+1}$, we obtain $b^*_1 = b$. Since p cancels in the denominator of q, we may finally dispose of p so as to make $\|f_{h+1}\| = 1$.

Coming finally to statement (iii) in Ch. 2·3, this refers to the question of whether the introduction of more approximating elements $f_{h+1}, f_{h+2}, \ldots$ has a systematic tendency to increase or diminish a least-squares coeffcient, say b_1. The following theorem shows that there is a certain quantitative symmetry between the two possibilities $b_1 > b^*_1$ and $b_1 < b^*_1$.

Without proof, we state

THEOREM 5.[3] *On the introduction of* f_{h+1}, *the following inner products enter as coefficients in the normal equations* (12·1·4),

(3) $(f, f_{h+1}), (f_1, f_{h+1}), \ldots, (f_h, f_{h+1}).$

Interpreting (3) *as a point* P *in* $(h+1)$-*dimensional Euclidean space* Ω_{h+1}, *the* $h(h+1)/2$ *inner products of* $f, f_1, \ldots, f_h$ *determine an ellipsoid* E *in* Ω_{h+1}, *such that* P *will lie in* E *for any element* f_{h+1}. *Let* A *and* B *be the two parts of* E *for which we have, respectively,*

$$b^*_1 > b_1 \quad or \quad b^*_1 < b_1,$$

according as P *lies in* A *or* B. *Then* A *and* B *are of equal volume, each being formed by two quarters of* E.

Illustration. Fig. 1 refers to the case $h = 1$ with $\varrho = (f, f_1) > 0$. The ellipsoid E here reduces to the ellipse with equation $x^2 + y^2 - 2\varrho x y = 1 - \varrho^2$. We have $b^*_1 > b_1$ or $b^*_1 < b_1$ according as the point $x = (f, f_2)$, $y = (f_1, f_2)$ belongs to A or B, which regions are seen to be of equal area.

4. Regression as graduation of conditional expectation. – Considering the random variables (12·2·10), let us form the conditional distribution of ξ_0 for given values of $\xi_1, \ldots, \xi_h$. Let us write ξ_0' for the conditional variable, and

(1) $$\xi_0' = E_0 + \zeta_0 \quad \text{with} \quad E_0 = E(\xi_0 \,|\, \xi_1, \ldots, \xi_h).$$

Thus E_0 is the conditional expectation of ξ_0, sometimes called the 'true regression' of ξ_0 on $\xi_1, \ldots, \xi_h$. The variable ζ_0 is a residual, and in immediate consequence of (9·1·10) we have

(2) $$E'(\zeta_0) = 0 \qquad E(\xi_i \cdot \zeta_0) = 0 \qquad i = 1, \ldots, h$$

where expectation E' is formed w.r.t. the conditional distribution of ξ_0, thus with $\xi_1, \ldots, \xi_h$ fixed, while E refers to the joint distribution of $\xi_0, \xi_1, \ldots, \xi_h$.

The conditional expectation E_0 forms a well-defined random variable in the sense of (9·1·10). The linear regression (12·2·12) may be interpreted as a least-squares graduation of E_0, an important fact that we state as

THEOREM 1.[1] *If we form the regression* (12·2·12) *on the basis of the variables* (12·2·10), *with* ξ_0 *replaced by its conditional expectation* $E(\xi_0 \,|\, \xi_1, \ldots, \xi_h)$, *the regression coefficients* $b_0, b_1, \ldots, b_h$ *will remain the same.*

For the proof we need only verify that the inner products $(\xi_0, 1) = E\,\xi_0$ and $(\xi_0, \xi_i) = E(\xi_0 \cdot \xi_i)$ are not affected by the substitution in question. Now if we make use of (9·1·10), we obtain

$$(E_0, 1) = E[E_0] = E[E(\xi_0 \,|\, \xi_1, \ldots, \xi_h)] = E\,\xi_0.$$

Similarly, which completes the proof of Theorem 1,

$$(E_0, \xi_i) = E[\xi_i \cdot E(\xi_0 \,|\, \xi_1, \ldots, \xi_h)] = E[E(\xi_0 \cdot \xi_i \,|\, \xi_1, \ldots, \xi_h)] = E(\xi_0 \cdot \xi_i).$$

In ξ_0^* and E_0 as defined by (12·2·12) and (1) we have two approximate expressions for ξ_0. The analogy between the two approximations shows itself in (12·2·16) and (2), and is further brought out by Theorem 1. The difference between the two approximations is clear from the residual expectations (12·2·16a) and (2a). In words, E_0 gives an unbiased estimate of ξ_0 in the sense that its residual ζ_0 has zero expectation for any fixed values of $\xi_1, \ldots, \xi_h$, whereas ξ_0^* is unbiased only if we form the expectation of its residual ζ as an average over the joint probability distribution of $\xi_1, \ldots, \xi_h$. This fact implies the familiar inequality

(3) $$E\,\zeta_0^2 \le E\,\zeta^2.$$

In words, the two expectations are residual variances, and the accuracy of the approximation reached by E_0 is at least as high as that reached by ξ_0^*.

We have $E\,\zeta_0^2 = E\,\zeta^2$ if, and only if, $\xi_0^* = E_0$ with probability 1, that is if ξ_0^* and E_0 coincide for almost all $\xi_1, \ldots, \xi_h$. In such case, the regression of ξ_0 on $\xi_1, \ldots, \xi_h$ is called linear, or, as we shall say, *strictly linear*. A sufficient condition for the regression to be strictly linear is, as is well known, that the joint distribution of $\xi_0, \xi_1, \ldots, \xi_h$ is a normal (Gauss-Laplace) distribution.

To distinguish the least-squares regression ξ_0^* from the 'true regression' E_0, we shall call ξ_0^* the *moment regression* of ξ_0 on $\xi_1, \ldots, \xi_h$. The moment regression will accordingly coincide with the 'true regression' if and only if E_0 is linear in $\xi_1, \ldots, \xi_h$.

5. Regression and prediction.[1] – We shall now apply moment regression (12·2·12) to variables ξ_t that belong to a stochastic process (9·2·5). For a start we consider the regression

$$(1) \qquad \xi_{t+k} = b_0 + b_1 \xi_{t-1} + \cdots + b_h \xi_{t-h} + \zeta.$$

In (1) we have a formula for the *prediction* of the future variable ξ_{t+k} in terms of the past variables

$$(2) \qquad \xi_{t-1}, \xi_{t-2}, \ldots, \xi_{t-h}$$

of the process. The regression residual ζ in (1) is the *prediction error*. In (1), the b_i and ζ will in general depend on t, k and h.

In prediction it is important to distinguish between the space aspect and the phase aspect of the analysis [Ch. 9·4]. Until further notice we are considering the space aspect. The prediction (1) thus refers to the universe of realizations (9·4·1) of the process considered. For t and k fixed, (1) gives us for each realization x a prediction of x_{t+k} with prediction error z_{t+k}. Forming the mean of the prediction error as a space average over the universe we obtain $E\zeta$, which is zero. The linear prediction (1) is optimal in the sense that any other set of fixed coefficients b_i would give a higher variance $E(\zeta^2)$.

Now let $h \to \infty$, so that the prediction (1) takes into account more and more of the past development (2) of the process. Making use of Gram-Schmidt's orthogonal development, it can be shown that the regressional prediction of ξ_{t+k} will tend to a well-defined limit, say Pred ξ_{t+k}, in symbols

$$(3) \quad \text{Pred } \xi_{t+k} = \lim_{h \to \infty} (b_0 + b_1 \xi_{t-1} + \cdots + b_h \xi_{t-h}); \quad \xi_{t+k} = \text{Pred } \xi_{t+k} + \zeta_{tk}.$$

Here ζ_{tk} is the limiting prediction error. The variance of ζ_{tk}, called the *prediction variance*, will be denoted Var pred ξ_{t+k}. We have

$$(4) \qquad \text{Var pred } \xi_{t+k} = E(\xi_{t+k} - \text{Pred } \xi_{t+k})^2 = \lim_{h \to \infty} E(\zeta^2) \geq 0,$$

where the expectations are formed w.r.t. the joint probability distribution of $\xi_{t+k}, \xi_{t-1}, \xi_{t-2}, \ldots$. We note that the limit in (4) is reached from above, for according to Theorem 12·3·1 the variance of ζ will decrease or remain constant as h is allowed to increase.

For the prediction we may alternatively make use of the conditional expectation (12·4·1). This gives

(5) $$\xi_{t+k} = E\left(\xi_{t+k} \mid \xi_{t-1}, \ldots, \xi_{t-h}\right) + \zeta_0.$$

According to (12·4·3), the prediction formula (5) is more efficient than (1) in the sense that the variance of ζ_0 is smaller than or possibly equal to the variance of ζ. The two prediction formulae will coincide if and only if the regression (1) is strictly linear; if this is so for all h, we have

(6) $$\mathrm{Pred}\ \xi_{t+k} = E\left(\xi_{t+k} \mid \xi_{t-1}, \xi_{t-2}, \ldots\right).$$

The above analysis is purely formal inasmuch as we have not at all entered upon the problems encountered in practice when it comes to calculating the regressional prediction (1) and performing the limit passage $h \to \infty$. The formulae should accordingly be regarded as a theoretical framework, serving to indicate what at best can be reached by the use of prediction formulae of type (1)–(5).

The prediction formulae (1)–(5) will now be applied to the stationary processes of Ch. 10·1–2, and as will serve our purpose we shall then drop the assumption that the processes have zero expectation. As an immediate consequence of the stationarity we note, to begin with, that the coefficients b_i of (1) are independent of t.

For the purely random process $\{\varepsilon_t\}$ with expectation m_ε we have

(7) $$\mathrm{Pred}\ \varepsilon_{t+k} = m_\varepsilon \qquad \mathrm{Var\ pred}\ \varepsilon_{t+k} = \sigma_\varepsilon^2.$$

In words, a complete knowledge of the past development $\varepsilon_{t-1}, \varepsilon_{t-2}, \ldots$ of the process does not enable us to make a better forecast than the unconditional expectation m_ε, a trivial forecast that leaves us with a prediction variance equal to the unconditional variance σ_ε^2.

Considering a process $\{\xi_t\}$ of moving summation (10·2·1), we obtain

(8 a) $$\mathrm{Pred}\ \xi_{t+k} = (a_0 + \cdots + a_k)\, m_\varepsilon + a_{k+1}\, \varepsilon_{t-1} + a_{k+2}\, \varepsilon_{t-2} + \cdots$$
(8 b) $$\mathrm{Var\ pred}\ \xi_{t+k} = (a_0^2 + \cdots + a_k^2)\, \sigma_\varepsilon^2.$$

Formula (8 b) shows that the efficiency of the forecast varies with the range of the prediction, the forecast becoming gradually less efficient for increasing k. It will be noted that $\mathrm{Var\ pred}\ \xi_{t+k} = \sigma_\xi^2$ as $k \to \infty$. Thus for large prediction ranges the situation is the same as for the purely random process, only a trivial forecast being possible.

In the case of finite moving summations (10·2·4), formula (8 b) shows that $\mathrm{Var\ pred}\ \xi_{t+k}$ attains the limiting value σ_ξ^2 for $k = h + 1$. In other words, the process of moving averages allows non-trivial forecasts only over time spans that are $\leq h$.

For the autoregressive process (10·2·8), the prediction formulae (8) remain the same, except that the coefficients a_i are specified by the system (10·2·10). For this process, formula (8 a) is seen to be equivalent to the following recursive formulae, where the b_i are the same as in (10·2·10),

(9) $\begin{cases} \text{Pred } \xi_t = m_\xi - b_1(\xi_{t-1} - m_\xi) - \cdots - b_h(\xi_{t-h} - m_\xi), \\ \text{Pred } \xi_{t+1} = m_\xi - b_1(\text{Pred } \xi_t - m_\xi) - b_2(\xi_{t-1} - m_\xi) - \cdots - b_h(\xi_{t-h+1} - m_\xi), \end{cases}$

and so on for $t+2$, $t+3$, $\ldots$

Let us now turn to the phase aspect of prediction. We are thus concerned with a fixed realization x of the process considered. Making use of the regression method of Ch. 12·2 (iii), we predict x_{t+k} in terms of $x_{t-1}, \ldots, x_{t-h}$. Keeping k and h fixed, and allowing t to vary, the prediction error z_{t+k} will have zero for phase average, $M z_{t+k} = 0$, and its phase variance $M(z_{t+k}^2)$ will be a minimum. Making $h \to \infty$ we obtain the limiting prediction and its variance, denoted Pred x_{t+k} and Var pred x_{t+k}, and we have

$$\text{Var pred } x_{t+k} = \lim_{h \to \infty} M(z_{t+k}^2) \geq 0.$$

In general, space prediction will differ from phase prediction, and they will coincide if and only if the process is ergodic. Knowing from Theorem 10·4·1 that the processes dealt with in (3)–(9) are ergodic, it follows that these formulae remain the same for phase prediction. In particular, the ergodicity implies that the coefficients a_i, b_i will be the same for all realizations x, and that

$$\text{Var pred } x_{t+k} = \text{Var pred } \xi_{t+k}.$$

Following up the interpretation in terms of phase averages, we may in (7) take m_ε to be the average of the past values of the given realization, say e_{t-1}, e_{t-2}, $\ldots$, that is a phase average formed as in (9·4·2) by making $t_1 \to -\infty$. For a process of moving summation $\{\xi_t\}$, with a given realization

(10) $$x_{t-1}, x_{t-2}, \ldots,$$

the situation is more complicated, for in (8 a) both a_1, a_2, $\ldots$ and e_{t-1}, e_{t-2}, $\ldots$ will have to be deduced from the given values (10). Now if $\{\xi_t\}$ is an autoregressive process (10·2·8), a single realization (10) will give us, in terms of phase averages, the correlogram $\varrho_1, \varrho_2, \ldots$ of the process $\{\xi_t\}$. By (10·2·13 a), the ϱ_ν determine $b_1, \ldots, b_h$; inserting in (10·2·10) we then obtain $a_1, a_2, \ldots$, and finally (10·2·8) gives e_{t-1}, e_{t-2}, $\ldots$ If on the other hand $\{\xi_t\}$ is a process of moving averages (10·2·4), let us consider the special case when the condition attached to (10·2·7) is fulfilled. Again the sequence (10) gives the correlogram $\varrho_1, \ldots, \varrho_h$. Via the polynomial (10·2·6) we then obtain the $a_1, \ldots, a_h$ of (10·2·4), and finally an inversion similar to (10·2·8) will give us e_{t-1}, e_{t-2}, $\ldots$

Coming to the processes of Ch. 10·3, the harmonic process $\{\eta_t\}$ will allow an exact forecast. Considering the space aspect of prediction, (10·3·2) and (10·3·5) give the recursive forecasts

(11) $\begin{cases} \text{Pred } \eta_t = \alpha_0 - c_1(\eta_{t-1} - \alpha_0) - \cdots - c_h(\eta_{t-h} - \alpha_0) \\ \text{Pred } \eta_{t+1} = \alpha_0 - c_1(\text{Pred } \eta_t - \alpha_0) - c_2(\eta_{t-1} - \alpha_0) - \cdots - c_h(\eta_{t-h+1} - \alpha_0) \end{cases}$

and so on for $t+2$, $t+3$, $\ldots$ with

(12) $$\text{Var pred } \eta_{t+k} = 0 \qquad\qquad k = 0, 1, 2, \ldots$$

Considering the process of hidden periodicities (10·3·8), suppose that the residual is purely random, or $\{\zeta_t\} = \{\varepsilon_t\}$. Then

(13) $\qquad$ Pred $\eta_{t+k}^* =$ Pred η_{t+k}; $\qquad$ Var pred $\eta_{t+k}^* = \sigma_\varepsilon^2$.

It will be observed that the coefficients c_i in (11) are constants. Thus if we consider the phase aspect of prediction, (11) applies as well to the realizations y of the process. The process not being ergodic, we note that the individual realizations y may allow simpler, though mutually different, prediction formulae (cf Ex. III, 30). As regards α_0 we note that in phase prediction we have $\alpha_0 = M y$, and that space prediction may deal with α_0 as a harmonic (10·3·7) with zero frequency and infinite period. In order to apply (13) in practice, the harmonic $y_{t-1}, y_{t-2}, \ldots$ must be separated from $y_{t-1}^*, y_{t-2}^*, \ldots$, which can be done by periodogram analysis [cf Ex. III, 20].

6. Predictive decomposition of the stationary process. – The purely random process and the harmonic process stand out as two extremes of the stationary process. This was obvious from the viewpoints adopted in Ch. 10·4, and on comparing the prediction formulae in Ch. 12·5 the conclusion is confirmed. Summing up, the purely random process is completely *nondeterministic* in the sense that on the basis of the past development of the process we can obtain no better forecast than the unconditional expectation, whereas the harmonic process is completely *deterministic* in the sense that we can obtain an exact forecast over any future time span, the term e x a c t meaning that the variance of the prediction error is zero. The other processes dealt with in Ch. 10 fall between these extremes.

The stationary processes considered in Ch. 10 being of widely different structure, it is natural to ask oneself whether there exist still other types. As will be shown presently, the answer is in the negative as far as properties of linear prediction are concerned. To make this assertion mathematically rigorous we need as a prerequisite the following definition, by which the notion of a linear form (12·1·1) extends to an infinite number of elements $f_1, f_2, \ldots$

Suppose f allows the representation

$$f = b_{h1} f_1 + b_{h2} f_2 + \cdots + b_{hh} f_h + z_h$$

with $\|z_h\| \to 0$ as $h \to \infty$; then f is said to be *linear* in $f_1, f_2, \ldots$ Specifically, if for a stochastic process $\{\xi_t\}$ every variable ξ_t is linear in $\xi_{t-1}, \xi_{t-2}, \ldots$ we shall say that the process is *deterministic*. Thus prepared, we have

THEOREM 1.[1] *Given a stationary process* $\{\xi_t\}$ *with discrete time-parameter* t, *suppose* $\{\xi_t\}$ *is not deterministic. Then* $\{\xi_t\}$ *allows the decomposition*

(1) $\qquad \xi_t = \eta_t + \zeta_t \ \ with \ \ \zeta_t = a_0 \varepsilon_t + a_1 \varepsilon_{t-1} + a_2 \varepsilon_{t-2} + \cdots$

where the components $\varepsilon_t, \eta_t, \zeta_t$ ($t = 0, \pm 1, \pm 2, \ldots$) *constitute stationary random processes with the following properties:*

A. *Each of the variables* $\varepsilon_t, \eta_t, \zeta_t$ *is linear in* $\xi_t, \xi_{t-1}, \xi_{t-2}, \ldots$.

B. *The process* $\{\eta_t\}$ *is deterministic.*

C. *The variables* ε_t *have zero mean,* $E(\varepsilon_t) = 0$; *unit variance,* $E(\varepsilon_t^2) = 1$; *and are mutually uncorrelated,* $E(\varepsilon_s \cdot \varepsilon_t) = 0$ *for* $s \neq t$.

D. *The process* $\{\eta_t\}$ *is uncorrelated with the processes* $\{\varepsilon_t\}$ *and* $\{\zeta_t\}$, *in symbols* $E(\eta_s \cdot \varepsilon_t) = E(\eta_s \cdot \zeta_t) = 0$ *for* $s = t$ *as well as* $s \neq t$.

E. *We have* $a_0 > 0$, *and* $a_0^2 + a_1^2 + a_2^2 + \cdots < \infty$.

Briefly indicating the proof, we may without loss of generality assume $E(\varepsilon) = E(\zeta) = 0$, since B is not invalidated if a constant is added in $\{\eta_t\}$. Our first step is to represent ξ_t in terms of $\xi_{t-1}, \ldots, \xi_{t-h}$ by a linear regression relation, say

$$(2) \qquad \xi_t + b_1^{(h)} \xi_{t-1} + \cdots + b_h^{(h)} \xi_{t-h} + b_0^{(h)} = \varepsilon_t^{(h)},$$

where $\varepsilon_t^{(h)}$ is the regression residual. The limit passage $h \to \infty$ gives the process $\{\varepsilon_t\}$, if necessary after multiplication by a constant so as to obtain $\sigma_\varepsilon = 1$. The conclusion A is now immediate. Further, by the correlation properties (12·2·16) of regression residuals, we infer $E(\xi_{t-k} \cdot \varepsilon_t) = 0$ for $k > 0$. This gives $E(\varepsilon_s \cdot \varepsilon_t) = 0$, which completes the proof of C. Next E follows immediately. The second step is to form the regression of ξ_t on $\varepsilon_t^{(h)}, \ldots, \varepsilon_{t-k}^{(h)}$, say

$$(3) \qquad \xi_t = a_{0k}^{(h)} \cdot \varepsilon_t^{(h)} + \cdots + a_{kk}^{(h)} \cdot \varepsilon_{t-k}^{(h)} + \eta_{tk}^{(h)}$$

where $\eta_{tk}^{(h)}$ is the regression residual. Making first $h \to \infty$ and then $k \to \infty$, this leads to the representation (1). Again making use of the properties of regression residuals, we obtain D. Inserting (3) in (2) it is then not difficult to verify B, which completes the proof of Theorem 1.

Let us examine the decomposition (1) from the viewpoint of prediction. Thanks to the correlation properties B–D, it is easy to apply the linear prediction method of Ch. 12·5 in terms of space averages. It is seen that for the component $\{\zeta_t\}$ this leads to the same prediction formula (12·5·8) as for the process of moving summation. It will be observed, however, that in the process of moving summation (10·2·1) we have assumed the variables ε_t to be independent, but in the component ζ_t of (1) the ε_t are only uncorrelated. As a consequence the two predictions are subject to the same difference as between the conditional expectation (12·4·1) and the moment regression (12·2·12). Thus, when applied to the process of moving summation (10·2·1), the prediction error of (12·5·8 a) will have zero expectation for any fixed values of $\varepsilon_{t-1}, \varepsilon_{t-2}, \ldots$ When applied to the component ζ_t of our decomposition (1) we can in general assert that the prediction error will be of zero expectation only when formed w.r.t. the joint distribution of $\varepsilon_{t-1}, \varepsilon_{t-2}, \ldots$.

According to Theorem 1 B the component $\{\eta_t\}$ of (1) allows a linear forecast that is exact, i.e. a forecast with prediction variance zero. The prediction formula is of the same type as the recursive formula (12·5·11) obtained for the harmonic process, with the qualification that the finite linear form in the right-hand member of (12·5·11) may be replaced by a limit expression with $h \to \infty$. Just as with (12·5·11), the same limit formula gives an exact phase prediction for the realizations of the component process.

Theorem 1 will be called the theorem of *predictive decomposition*, to stress that the two components of (1) have been separated from the viewpoint of prediction. The process $\{\eta_t\}$ is called the *singular* or *deterministic* component of the given process $\{\xi_t\}$, and $\{\zeta_t\}$ the *regular* or *nondeterministic* component.[2] We have seen that the processes considered in Ch. 10 are simple type cases of the general representation (1).[3]

A. Kolmogorov (1941), making use of the powerful methods of spectral analysis, has generalized and deepened the theorem on predictive decomposition. Among his many brilliant results we note:

(i) The representation (1) is unique in the sense that $\{\xi_t\}$ allows no other decomposition of type (1) with components that have the properties A–E.

(ii) General criteria are given for the decomposition (1) in terms of the spectral function $W(\lambda)$ of the process [see (9·3·10)]. In particular, Kolmogorov gives formula (11·3·2) for the variance of the residual process $\{\varepsilon_t\}$ in the representation (1). As a corollary, he obtains a necessary and sufficient condition for $\{\xi_t\}$ to be completely deterministic, i.e. for the component $\{\zeta_t\}$ to be absent. This case occurs not only if $W(\lambda)$ is a step-function, but more generally if the integral

$$(4) \qquad \int_0^\pi \big| \log W'(\lambda) \big| \, d\lambda \quad \text{is infinite.}$$

(iii) Kolmogorov extends the notion of stationarity to a sequence f_t of abstract elements in Hilbert space [Ch. 12·1], the definition being that the inner product (f_t, f_{t+v}) is independent of t, and develops his theory on this basis. Accordingly, his analysis bears the same relation to the above Theorem 1 as the general theory of least-squares approximation in Ch. 12·1 to the regression applications in Ch. 12·2.

7. The resolving power of recursive systems. – The stochastic processes considered in Chs. 10–11 and 12·5–6 are one-dimensional, but it is clear that much of the theory allows a straightforward extension to systems of time-series and vector processes. In view of the abundance of possible variations and combinations, it is also clear that the main difficulty does not lie in developing formulae of great generality, but rather in picking out those processes for further study that merit interest from the viewpoint of the applications. In Ch. 3·2 we have given a number of references to the literature on the subject. We are now in a position to support the statement in Ch. 3·2 on the scope of recursive systems (2·7·1). We have

THEOREM 1.[1] *Given a set of q time-series, say*

(1) $$x_t^{(1)}, \ldots, x_t^{(q)} \qquad\qquad -\infty < t < \infty$$

suppose their averages and second-order moments are well-defined in the sense of (9·4·2), say

(2) $$M x_t^{(i)} = \bar{x}_i \qquad M (x_t^{(i)} - \bar{x}_i)(x_{t+v}^{(k)} - \bar{x}_k) = l_{ik}(v),$$

where $i, k = 1, \ldots, q$; $v = 0, \pm 1, \pm 2, \ldots$ Let $\delta > 0$ and the integer $p\,(0 \le p < q)$ be arbitrarily given. Further let $z_t^{(i)}$ be defined for $i = p+1, p+2, \ldots, q$ by

(3) $$x_t^{(i)} = b_i + \sum_{j=1}^{i-1} b_{ij}^{(0)} x_t^{(j)} + \sum_{j=1}^{q} b_{ij}^{(1)} x_{t-1}^{(j)} + \cdots + \sum_{j=1}^{q} b_{ij}^{(h)} x_{t-h}^{(j)} + z_t^{(i)}.$$

Then the maximal lag h and the constants $b_{ij}^{(k)}$ can be so chosen that the $z_t^{(i)}$ will satisfy

(4) $$M z_t^{(i)} = 0 \qquad M (z_t^{(i)} \cdot x_{t-a}^{(j)}) = 0 \qquad\qquad i = p+1, \ldots, q$$

where $j = 1, \ldots, q$; $a = 0, 1, \ldots, h$ for $j = 1, \ldots, i-1$; $a = 1, \ldots, h$ for $j = i, \ldots, q$; and

(5) $$-\delta < M (z_t^{(i)} \cdot x_{t-a}^{(j)}) < \delta \qquad -\delta < M (z_t^{(i)} \cdot z_{t-b}^{(k)}) < \delta, \qquad i = p+1, \ldots, q$$

where $j = 1, \ldots, q$; $k = p+1, \ldots, q$; $a = h+1, h+2, \ldots$; further $b = 0, \pm 1, \pm 2, \ldots$ for $i \ne k$ and $b = \pm 1, \pm 2, \ldots$ for $i = k$.

A few comments:

(i) In Theorem 1 the $x_t^{(1)}, \ldots, x_t^{(p)}$ correspond to the exogenous variables $x_t^{(i)}$ of system (2·7·1), and $x_t^{(p+1)}, \ldots, x_t^{(q)}$ to the endogenous variables $y_t^{(i)}$. The $z_t^{(i)}$ of Theorem 1 correspond to the disturbances $z_t^{(i)}$ of (2·7·1); on the other hand, comparing (4) with (12·2·8), we see that each of the relations (3) may be interpreted as a least-squares regression with $z_t^{(i)}$ for residual.

In other words, for any set of time-series with well-defined moments (2), Theorem 1 secures a recursive representation of type (2·7·1), and the relations involved will have the properties of least-squares regressions. Moreover, thanks to (5) we may arrange the relations so that the disturbances $z_t^{(i)}$ will to any prescribed accuracy have the noncorrelation properties sometimes assumed in the applications of recursive systems.

(ii) To indicate the proof of Theorem 1, let x be an arbitrary sequence (9·4·1) such that the phase average $\bar{x} = M x$ and the autocovariances $l(v)$ are well-defined. If the sequence

(6) $$\ldots, X_{t-1}, X_t, X_{t+1}, \ldots$$

is defined in accordance with (9·2·8), we have

THEOREM 2.[2] *Letting inner products be defined by $(X_t, X_{t+v}) = l(v)$, the elements X_t of (6) form an abstract space R in the sense of Ch. 12·1, and the sequence (6) is stationary in the sense of Ch. 12·6 (iii).*

We see that Ch. 12·2 (iii) may be interpreted as an application of this simple lemma. Theorem 2 now enables us to apply Kolmogorov's general theory of stationary sequences [Ch. 12·6 (iii)] to the sequence (6). In particular, we obtain for X_t a decomposition of type (12·6·1), say

$$(7) \qquad\qquad x_t = z_t + y_t \qquad\qquad t = 0, \pm 1, \pm 2, \ldots$$

which obeys all assertions of Theorem 12·6·1 and Ch. 12·6, (i)–(ii), only that the expectations E must be replaced by corresponding phase averages M.

Theorem 1 is closely related to (7), being an extension of the first step (12·6·2) in the proof of Theorem 12·6·1. Observing that Theorem 2 is valid in the multivariate case, it is not difficult to see that (12·6·2) extends so as to give Theorem 1.

(iii) Writing S for the recursive system (3), we note that the representation S has a parallel for systems of the simple type (2·7·3), say S'. The representation S' may be established by the same arguments as S. Both S and S' giving us a model for causal analysis, we see that in S' the causal dependences between the endogenous variables are always directed forward in time, whereas S allows the chain of causation to include dependences between endogenous variables at the same time period. Hence S is more general than S' as a causal model. Further we note, as pointed out in Ch. 2·7, that model S cannot be extended in the direction of the structural system (2·7·2) without losing the possibility of a causal interpretation.

We have seen that model S is more general than S' from the viewpoint of causal analysis, and it is further clear that S will in general have smaller disturbances than model S'. From the viewpoint of prediction, on the other hand, models S and S' are of equal scope, for if the development of all endogenous variables is known up to period t, the two models give the same prediction variance for any future period $t + k$.

(iv) As shown by V. Zasuhin (1941), Theorem 12·6·1 as well as Kolmogorov's results referred to in Ch. 12·6 (i)–(iii) extend to stationary vector processes. Thanks to Theorem 2 we may in this way generalize (7) so as to obtain a predictive decomposition for a *system* of time-series. This decomposition will be unique in the sense of Kolmogorov's theorem. For the representations S and S', on the other hand, there is no similar uniqueness theorem. Thus in (3) it will in general be possible to obtain the same set of residuals $z_t^{(i)}$ for different sets of coefficients $b_{ij}^{(k)}$. Further we note that there are several recursive representations of type S and S', for the enumeration order of the variables considered is arbitrary, and we have a free choice as regards p, the number of exogenous variables.

Chapter 13.

SAMPLING ASPECTS OF REGRESSION ANALYSIS

1. Regression coefficients as sampling estimates. – In Ch. 12 we have stressed the formal analogy between the empirical regression (12·2·5) and the theoretical regression (12·2·12). As regards the theoretical regression we have in Ch. 12·4 distinguished between

A. Strictly linear regression, in which case the approximation given by (12·2·12) coincides with the conditional expectation (12·4·1 b).

B. Moment regression, in which case (12·2·12) forms a linear graduation of the conditional expectation.

Least-squares regression will now be examined from the viewpoint of sampling theory. That is, the theoretical regression (12·2·12) will be regarded as a given hypothesis, and the empirical regression (12·2·5) as an estimate of the hypothetical regression. We see that A and B will then play the part of alternative specifications of the hypothetical regression. In regression theory we may distinguish between two corresponding lines of development. The basic hypotheses of the two approaches will be referred to as the *Gauss-Fisher* and the *Galton-Yule* specifications. The two approaches are complementary and partly overlapping, neither being more general than the other.

2. Large-sample properties of regression coefficients.[1] – We shall write the empirical regression in the form (12·2·6), replacing $x^{(0)}$ by y, or

(1) $$y_\nu = b_0 + b_1(x_\nu^{(1)} - \bar{x}_1) + \cdots + b_h(x_\nu^{(h)} - \bar{x}_h) + z_\nu \qquad \nu = 1, \ldots, n$$

(2) with $$b_0 = \bar{y} = \frac{1}{n}\sum_{\nu=1}^{n} y_\nu \qquad b_i = \frac{1}{L}\sum_{k=1}^{h} L^{ik} l_{0k} \qquad i = 1, \ldots, h.$$

Here L is the determinant of the dispersion matrix $L = [l_{ik}]$; $i, k = 1, \ldots, h$, and L^{ik} its cofactors; the l_{ik} are defined by (12·2·7).

In classical sampling theory, the hypotheses behind an empirical regression (1)–(2) are specified as follows.

A. *Gauss-Fisher specification.*[2] Given any observed values $x_\nu^{(1)}, \ldots, x_\nu^{(h)}$ ($\nu = 1, \ldots, n$) of the h regressors, the observed values $y_1, \ldots, y_n$ of the regressand are sample values of n random variables $\eta_1, \ldots, \eta_n$ that allow the representation

(3) $$\eta_\nu = \beta_0 + \beta_1 (x_\nu^{(1)} - \bar{x}_1) + \cdots + \beta_h (x_\nu^{(h)} - \bar{x}_h) + \zeta_\nu \qquad \nu = 1, \ldots, n$$

where the β_i are constants, the $\bar{x}_i$ are the observed means of the regressors, and the residuals ζ_ν are random variables which (a) are independent of the regressor observations $x_\nu^{(1)}, \ldots, x_\nu^{(h)} (\nu = 1, \ldots, n)$ in the sense that the joint probability distribution of $\zeta_1, \ldots, \zeta_n$ involves none of the $x_\nu^{(i)}$ as a parameter, (b) are mutually independent in the sense of probability theory, and (c) have the same distribution with zero mean and finite variance.

B. *Galton-Yule specification*.[3] The empirical data $y_\nu, x_\nu^{(1)}, \ldots, x_\nu^{(h)} (\nu = 1, \ldots, n)$ are observations of $n (h + 1)$ random variables $\eta_\nu, \xi_\nu^{(1)}, \ldots, \xi_\nu^{(h)} (\nu = 1, \ldots, n)$ such that (a) the $(h + 1)$-dimensional variables $\xi_\nu = (\eta_\nu, \xi_\nu^{(1)}, \ldots, \xi_\nu^{(h)})$, n in number, are mutually independent, and (b) all ξ_ν have the same $(h + 1)$-dimensional distribution with finite variances. The theoretical regression is the moment regression (12·2·12 b), which we write in the form (12·2·14),

(4) $$\eta_\nu = \beta_0 + \beta_1 (\xi_\nu^{(1)} - m_1) + \cdots + \beta_h (\xi_\nu^{(h)} - m_h) + \zeta_\nu \qquad \nu = 1, \ldots, n$$

with $\beta_0 = E (\eta_\nu)$, so that all $E (\zeta_\nu) = 0$.

According to classical regression theory, (1) may serve as an estimate of the theoretical regression, under either one of Hypotheses A or B. More precisely, the b_i are random variables that possess the following four large-sample properties.

Asymptotically for n large:

a. The b_i are unbiased estimates of the theoretical coefficients β_i,

(5) $$E b_i \sim \beta_i \qquad\qquad i = 0, 1, \ldots, h.$$

On Hypothesis A, formula (5) holds good as an exact relation for any n.

b. The b_i are consistent estimates of the β_i. On Hypothesis A, the standard errors are given by

(6) $$d (b_0) \sim s_z / \sqrt{n - 1}, \qquad d (b_i) \sim s_z \sqrt{L^{ii} / (n - h - 1) L} \qquad i = 1, \ldots, h.$$

On Hypothesis B, the standard errors are still of order $1 / \sqrt{n}$, but formulae (6) will not be valid unless further conditions are satisfied.

c. The observed residual variance s_z^2 is a consistent estimate of the residual variance of the theoretical regression,

(7) $$E (s_z^2) \sim \sigma_\zeta^2 \qquad d (s_z^2) \sim c / \sqrt{n}. \qquad (c = \text{const.})$$

d. The standardized variables

(8) $$\lambda_i = \frac{b_i - \beta_i}{d (b_i)} \qquad\qquad i = 0, 1, \ldots, h$$

will under general conditions of regularity tend to be distributed according to the normal (Gauss-Laplace) distribution.

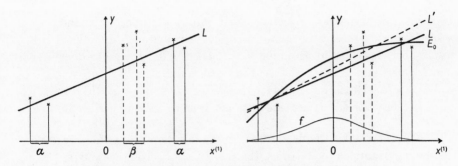

Fig. 13·2·1. Least-squares regression and the possible influence of
the regressor distribution.

a. Strictly linear regression.   b. Moment regression.

For the proofs of Theorems a–d, reference is made to H. Cramér (1945),
and to the more general theorems of Ch. 13·4–5 [see also Ex. 13].

Considering the scope of Hypotheses A–B, we see that A assumes the theoretical regression to be strictly linear, whereas B allows the conditional expectation of η_ν to be curvilinear, with (4) for linear graduation. In this respect,
accordingly, Hypothesis B is more general than A. The price of this advantage is (a) that B refers to a specified distribution of the regressors, the
graduation (4) in general being affected by a change in this distribution, and
(b) that the asymptotical formulae (6) will in general not be valid. The distinction between Hypotheses A and B thus brings in relief the fundamental advantage of functional transformations that make the theoretical regression
strictly linear [see Ch. 1·5 (i)].

The situation is illustrated in Fig. 1, which refers to the case of one regressor. There
is a first set α of four observations and a second set β of three observations. Line L
is the theoretical regression. With strictly linear regression, L is not affected if the set
α is enlarged by the set β. The increase makes a change in the distribution of the
regressor x, and in the case of moment regression, on the other hand, this change
makes the regression shift from L to L'. Moment regression must therefore be defined
on the basis of a specified frequency distribution of the regressor, e.g. the distribution f.
For regression relations that invite an interpretation in terms of moment regression,
see Figs. 1·2·2 and 1·3·1b.

We see that Hypothesis A is more general than B as regards the nature
of the regressors, whereas B is more general than A as regards the nature of
the regression relation. The Gauss-Fisher specification A thus applies whether
or not the regressors are subject to an a priori distribution; in particular it
applies in the case of experimental data where the regressors are under controlled variation. The Galton-Yule specification B is suited for applications
where the regressors are not controlled. The regressor distribution may here

be random or purposively selected, but if purposively selected it must follow a specified pattern, say an equally weighted distribution.[4] Hypothesis B has usually been specified by assuming the variables to follow a multi-dimensional normal distribution. In such case the regression is strictly linear, and B becomes a special case of A, a fact that helps to explain why the distinction in scope between the approaches has not been stressed in earlier literature.

3. Theoria combinationis. – According to this theory, one of Gauss' fundamental contributions to statistics, the coefficients b_i of a least-squares regression (13·2·1) will under certain conditions have the property of being themselves optimal in the sense of least-squares approximation. After the detailed discussion in Ch. 2·8 it is sufficient for our purpose to state the Gauss-Markov theorem and its proof.

THEOREM 1. *On the Gauss-Fisher specification, the least-squares regression coefficients have the smallest variance among all unbiased linear estimates of the theoretical regression coefficients.*

Following A. C. Aitken (1935), we give the proof in matrix form, as is convenient since the regressors are fixed variables. Thus let (13·2·3) be written

(1) $$\boldsymbol{\eta} = \boldsymbol{X\beta} + \boldsymbol{\zeta}$$

where we have assumed $\beta_0 = E(\eta_\nu) = 0$, which involves no loss of generality, and where $\boldsymbol{X} = [x_i^{(k)} - \bar{x}_k]$ is the $n \times h$ matrix of the regressor observations, measured from their means. The ζ_ν have zero expectation, so that $E\,\boldsymbol{\zeta} = 0$, and are independent with equal variances, so that their dispersion matrix is

$$\boldsymbol{V}(\boldsymbol{\zeta}) = \sigma_\zeta^2 \cdot \boldsymbol{I} \qquad (\boldsymbol{I} \text{ is the unit matrix}).$$

The coefficients b_i of the least-squares regression (13·2·1) are linear in the y_ν,

(2) $$\boldsymbol{b} = \boldsymbol{By} \qquad \text{with } \boldsymbol{B} = (\boldsymbol{X'X})^{-1} \cdot \boldsymbol{X'}$$

We verify that the b_i are unbiased, $E\,\boldsymbol{b} = \boldsymbol{BX\beta} = \boldsymbol{\beta}$, and note that their dispersion matrix is

$$\boldsymbol{V}(\boldsymbol{b}) = E(\boldsymbol{b} - \boldsymbol{\beta})(\boldsymbol{b} - \boldsymbol{\beta})' = \boldsymbol{B}\,E(\boldsymbol{\zeta\,\zeta'})\,\boldsymbol{B}' = \sigma_\zeta^2 \cdot \boldsymbol{BB}' = \sigma_\zeta^2 \cdot (\boldsymbol{X'X})^{-1}.$$

Now let $\boldsymbol{b}^* = \boldsymbol{Cy}$ be any linear unbiased estimate of $\boldsymbol{\beta}$, so that

$$E\,\boldsymbol{b}^* = \boldsymbol{CX\beta} = \boldsymbol{\beta}, \qquad \text{which implies } \boldsymbol{CX} = \boldsymbol{I}.$$

For the dispersion matrix of $\boldsymbol{b}^*$ we then obtain $\boldsymbol{V}(\boldsymbol{b}^*) = \sigma_\zeta^2\,\boldsymbol{CC'}$. This may be split up as a sum of two matrices,[1]

$$\boldsymbol{V}(\boldsymbol{b}^*) = \sigma_\zeta^2\big((\boldsymbol{X'X})^{-1} + \big((\boldsymbol{X'X})^{-1}\boldsymbol{X'} - \boldsymbol{C}\big)\big(\boldsymbol{X}(\boldsymbol{X'X})^{-1} - \boldsymbol{C'}\big)\big) = \boldsymbol{V}_1 + \boldsymbol{V}_2.$$

Observing that $\boldsymbol{V}_1$ and $\boldsymbol{V}_2$ are positive definite, and that $\boldsymbol{V}_1$ does not involve the unknown C, we infer that each of $b_1^*, \ldots, b_h^*$ will be of minimum variance if we can make $V_2 = 0$. This completes the proof, since $V_2 = 0$ gives

$$C = (X' X)^{-1} X' = B.$$

Theoria combinationis has been generalized by Aitken (1935), his assumptions permitting the disturbances ζ_ν to be interdependent, say with dispersion matrix

(3) $$Z = E[\zeta \zeta'].$$

We restate Aitken's result as

THEOREM 2. *On the Gauss-Fisher specification as generalized by (3), the unbiased linear estimates of the theoretical regression coefficients that are of minimum variance are given by*

(4) $$b^* = C y \qquad \text{with } C = (X' Z^{-1} X)^{-1} X' Z^{-1}$$

and the dispersion matrix of the estimates is

$$V(b^*) = C Z^{-1} C' = (X' Z^{-1} X)^{-1}.$$

For a proof[2] we consider a representation $\zeta = A \epsilon$ such that $\varepsilon_1, \ldots, \varepsilon_n$ are uncorrelated with unit variance, so that $\epsilon = A^{-1} \zeta$ with $E(\epsilon \epsilon') = I$ and $Z = E(\zeta \zeta') = A A'$ with $Z^{-1} = (A^{-1})' A^{-1}$. Then (1) gives

$$A^{-1} \eta = A^{-1} X \beta + A^{-1} \zeta \quad \text{or} \quad \eta^* = A^{-1} X \eta + \epsilon \quad \text{with} \quad \eta^* = A^{-1} \eta.$$

This brings us back to Theorem 1, since any linear form in the η_ν^* is linear in the η_ν, and conversely. Hence $b^* = C y = B y^* = B A^{-1} y$, where B will be given by (2) if we substitute $A^{-1} X$ for X, which gives

$$C = B A^{-1} = (X' (A^{-1})' A^{-1} X)^{-1} \cdot X' (A^{-1})' A^{-1} = (X' Z^{-1} X)^{-1} X' Z^{-1}.$$

We see that the Aitken estimates b_i^* are more complicated than the least-squares estimates b_i. A more serious disadvantage, however, is that the b_i^* involve the autocovariances of the disturbances, so that these must be known a priori or estimated from the empirical data.

4. Regression analysis of time-series data.[1] – It is a familiar fact that the classical hypotheses A–B of Ch. 13˙2 are not appropriate in the case of time-series, owing to the after-effects and autocorrelations that are such a striking feature in most time-series data. In Theorem 13˙3˙2 we have seen Aitken's treatment of the problem of regression estimation that here arises, his approach being to minimize the variance of the estimating regression coefficients. We are now going to examine the situation from the viewpoint of the traditional approach of least-squares regression, which is to minimize the variance of the regression residuals. Our primary purpose is to establish the general theorem behind formulae (2·5·2), viz. that the least-squares regression is unbiased and consistent under conditions much more general than the classical hypotheses.

We shall mainly consider the case of strictly linear regression. Using the same notation as in Ch. 13·2, except that we shall take t instead of ν for running index, we write the theoretical regression

$$(1) \qquad \eta_t = \beta_0 + \beta_1 (x_t^{(1)} - \bar{x}_1) + \cdots + \beta_h (x_t^{(h)} - \bar{x}_h) + \zeta_t \qquad t = 1, \ldots, n.$$

The extended hypothesis is in three parts, denoted $A_1^* - A_3^*$. The salient point is A_3^*, for if we make $a_1 = a_2 = \cdots = 0$ in (2), the set $A_1^* - A_3^*$ will essentially be the same as A of Ch. 13·2. Further we note that A_1^* is introduced for the sake of convenience, allowing us to express the results in terms of limiting moments, as $n \to \infty$.[2]

A_1^*. The regressor series $x_t^{(1)}, \ldots, x_t^{(h)}$ $(t = 1, \ldots, n)$ are stationary to the second order; i.e. their means $\bar{x}_i$, their variances s_i^2 and covariances l_{ik}, and their lagged product moments $l_{ik}(\nu)$ exist as phase averages in the sense of the definition

$$l_{ik}(\nu) = \lim_{n \to \infty} \frac{1}{n - \nu} \sum_{t=1}^{n-\nu} (x_t^{(i)} - \bar{x}_i)(x_{t+\nu}^{(k)} - \bar{x}_k) \qquad \begin{cases} i, k = 1, \ldots, h \\ \nu = 0, \pm 1, \pm 2, \ldots \end{cases}$$

where $l_{ik}(\nu) = l_{ki}(-\nu)$ and $l_{ik}(0) = l_{ik}$.

A_2^*. The regressand series $y_1, \ldots, y_n$ belongs to a realization of a stochastic process $\{\eta_t\}$ that allows the representation (1), where the residuals $\zeta_1, \ldots, \zeta_n$ belong to a process $\{\zeta_t\}$ which (a) is independent of the regressor observations $x_t^{(1)}, \ldots, x_t^{(h)}$ $(t = 1, \ldots, n)$, (b) is stationary, and (c) has zero mean, $E(\zeta_t) = 0$.

A_3^*. The residuals ζ_t of the theoretical regression (1) allow the representation

$$(2) \qquad \zeta_t = \varepsilon_t + a_1 \varepsilon_{t-1} + a_2 \varepsilon_{t-2} + \cdots \qquad \text{with} \qquad \sum_{i=1}^{\infty} a_i^2 < \infty \qquad \text{and}$$

$$(3) \qquad E(\varepsilon_t) = 0 \qquad E(\varepsilon_t \cdot \varepsilon_{t+\nu}) = 0 \qquad (\nu = \pm 1, \pm 2, \ldots).$$

Otherwise expressed, assumption (2) requires that in the predictive decomposition (12·6·1) of the residual process $\{\zeta_t\}$ the deterministic component should be absent.

Our theorem will involve the variance σ_ε^2 and the autocorrelation coefficients ϱ_ν of the residuals ζ_t,

$$(4) \qquad \sigma_\zeta^2 = (1 + a_1^2 + a_2^2 + \cdots) \cdot \sigma_\varepsilon^2; \qquad \varrho_\nu = (a_\nu + a_1 a_{\nu+1} + a_2 a_{\nu+2} + \cdots) \cdot \sigma_\varepsilon^2 / \sigma_\zeta^2.$$

Further we shall make use of the matrix $\boldsymbol{L} = [l_{ik}]$, $(i, k = 1, \ldots, h)$, the adjugate $\boldsymbol{L}^* = [L^{ik}]$ of $\boldsymbol{L}$, and the matrix $\boldsymbol{C} = [c_{ik}]$ defined by

$$(5) \qquad c_{ik} = l_{ik} + \varrho_1 [l_{ik}(1) + l_{ik}(-1)] + \varrho_2 [l_{ik}(2) + l_{ik}(-2)] + \cdots; \quad i, k = 1, \ldots, h.$$

The symbol $o(q)$, finally, denotes a quantity such that $o(q)/q \to 0$ as $n \to \infty$.

THEOREM 1. *If we adopt Hypotheses $A_1^* - A_3^*$ for the theoretical regression (1), the empirical regression (13·2·1) will for n large have the following asymptotical properties.*

A. *The regression coefficients b_i are unbiased,*

(6) $$E(b_i) = \beta_i \qquad\qquad i = 0, 1, \ldots, h.$$

B. *The b_i are consistent, and their standard errors are given by*

(7) $$d(b_0) \sim \frac{s_z}{\sqrt{n-1}}\sqrt{1 + 2\varrho_1 + 2\varrho_2 + \cdots}\,; \quad d(b_i) \sim \frac{s_z}{L}\sqrt{\frac{d_{ii}}{n-h-1}}\,; \quad i = 1, \ldots, h$$

where the d_{ii} are the diagonal elements of the matrix

(8) $$[d_{ik}] = \boldsymbol{L}^* \cdot \boldsymbol{C} \cdot \boldsymbol{L}^*.$$

C. *The covariances of the b_i are*

(9) $$\operatorname{cov}(b_0, b_i) \sim o(1/n), \quad \operatorname{cov}(b_i, b_k) \sim \frac{s_z^2}{L^2} \cdot \frac{d_{ik}}{n}\,; \quad i, k = 1, \ldots, h.$$

D. *The observed variance of the residuals provides a consistent estimate for its hypothetical value*

(10) $$E(s_z^2) \sim \sigma_\zeta^2, \qquad d(s_z^2) \sim o(1).$$

The well-known proof of (13·2·5) extends without difficulty to the present case. Thus with b_0 defined as in (13·2·2) we obtain, making use of (1) and Hypothesis A_3^*,

$$E b_0 = \frac{1}{n}\sum_{t=1}^{n} E\,\eta_t = \beta_0 + \frac{1}{n}\sum_{t=1}^{n}\left(\sum_{i=1}^{h}\beta_i\,(x_t^{(i)} - \bar{x}_i) + E\,\zeta_t\right) = \beta_0 + E\,\zeta_t = \beta_0.$$

Similarly, considering b_1, we obtain the following expression for $E b_1$

$$\frac{1}{L}\sum_{k=1}^{h} L^{1k}\,E(l_{0k}) = \frac{1}{L}\sum_{k=1}^{h} L^{1k}\left[\beta_1\,l_{1k} + \cdots + \beta_h\,l_{hk} + (x_t^{(k)} - \bar{x}_k)\,E\left(\zeta_t - \frac{1}{n}\sum_t \zeta_t\right)\right]$$

where all terms except the first vanish, giving $E b_1 = \beta_1$. Proceeding to (7)–(9), it is sufficient to carry through the deductions for $\operatorname{cov}(b_1, b_2)$. Without loss of generality, we make $\bar{x}_i = 0$ for $i = 1, \ldots, h$. We obtain

$$\operatorname{cov}(b_1, b_2) = E(b_1 - \beta_1)(b_2 - \beta_2) =$$

$$= \frac{1}{L^2} E\left[\left(\frac{1}{n}\sum_k L^{1k}\sum_t\left(\beta_1 x_t^{(1)} + \cdots + \beta_h x_t^{(h)} + \zeta_t - \frac{1}{n}\sum_t \zeta_t\right)x_t^{(k)} - \beta_1\cdot L\right)\cdot\right.$$

$$\left.\cdot\left(\frac{1}{n}\sum_k L^{2k}\sum_t\left(\beta_1 x_t^{(1)} + \cdots + \beta_h x_t^{(h)} + \zeta_t - \frac{1}{n}\sum_t \zeta_t\right)x_t^{(k)} - \beta_2\cdot L\right)\right]$$

$$= \frac{1}{n^2 L^2} E\left[\sum_k L^{1k}\sum_t\left(\zeta_t - \frac{1}{n}\sum_t \zeta_t\right)x_t^{(k)}\right]\left[\sum_k L^{2k}\sum_t\left(\zeta_t - \frac{1}{n}\sum_t \zeta_t\right)x_t^{(k)}\right].$$

Thus far, our arguments have been the same as in the familiar proof of (13·2·5–6). In the next step we shall make use of Hypothesis A_3^*. Inferring by the ergodic theorem $10\cdot4\cdot1$ that $E(\Sigma\,\zeta_t/n)\to0$ as $n\to\infty$, we may omit $\Sigma\,\zeta_t/n$, which gives

$$\operatorname{cov}(b_1,\,b_2)\sim\frac{1}{n^2L^2}\,E\,(\sum_k L^{1k}\sum_t\zeta_t\,x_t^{(k)})\,(\sum_k L^{2k}\sum_t\zeta_t\,x_t^{(k)}).$$

On insertion of (2) we rearrange the terms as follows,

(11) $$\sum_{t=1}^{n}\zeta_t\,x_t^{(k)}\sim\sum_{t=1}^{n}(x_t^{(k)}+a_1\,x_{t+1}^{(k)}+a_2\,x_{t+2}^{(k)}+\cdots)\cdot\varepsilon_t\,,$$

a simple device which is the salient point of the proof. Paying regard to (5), we obtain

$$\operatorname{cov}(b_1,\,b_2)\sim\frac{\sigma_\varepsilon^2}{n\cdot L^2}\sum_i\sum_k L^{1i}\,L^{2k}\frac{1}{n}\sum_t(x_t^{(i)}+a_1\,x_{t+1}^{(i)}+\cdots)\,(x_t^{(k)}+a_1\,x_{t+1}^{(k)}+\cdots)$$

$$=\frac{\sigma_\zeta^2}{n\cdot L^2}\sum_i\sum_k L^{1i}\,L^{2k}\cdot c_{ik}+o\,(1/n)$$

in agreement with formulae (8)–(9), as was to be verified.

To prove (10), finally, we need only reflect that according to (7) the $b_0, b_1, \ldots, b_h$ deviate from their expectations $\beta_0, \beta_1, \ldots, \beta_h$ by amounts that are of order $1/\sqrt{n}$.

As an immediate corollary of Theorem 1 we obtain

THEOREM 2. *On the assumptions of Theorem 1, the autocorrelation coefficients of the observed residuals are asymptotically unbiased and consistent estimates of the hypothetical coefficients ϱ_k. Their standard errors are of order $1/\sqrt{n}$.*

A few remarks:

(i) Making use of matrix symbols, the proof of Theorems 1–2 may be reduced so as to be almost immediate.[3] Thus if we write $E(\boldsymbol{\zeta}\,\boldsymbol{\zeta}')=\boldsymbol{Z}=[z_{ik}]$ for the dispersion matrix of the disturbances ζ_t, we have $z_{ik}=\sigma_\zeta^2\cdot\varrho_{|i-k|}$, and the dispersion matrix of the b_i is given by

$$V(b)=BZB'=(X'X)^{-1}\cdot X'ZX\cdot(X'X)^{-1}$$

which on development reduces to (9).

(ii) In the case $h=1$, i.e. when $x^{(1)}$ is the only regressor, (7) gives

(12) $$d(b_1)\sim\frac{s_z}{s_1}\cdot\frac{\sqrt{1+2\,\varrho_1\,r_1^{(1)}+2\,\varrho_2\,r_2^{(1)}+\cdots}}{\sqrt{n-2}}$$

where s_1 and s_z are the observed standard deviations of the regressor $x^{(1)}$ and the residual z, respectively, both based on the n observations, and $r_1^{(1)}, r_2^{(1)}, \ldots$ is the observed correlogram of $x^{(1)}$.

It will be noted that the automoments involved in (5) and (12) are observed values for the regressors $x_t^{(i)}$, but hypothetical values for the residuals z_t. The hypothetical values have been introduced in order to avoid questions of convergence for sums like (5). As regards the problem met with here of fitting a hypothetical model (2) to the observed residuals z_t, reference is made to the methods of Ch. 11·2–4.

(iii) The general formula (7) will often yield a greater standard error for the regression coefficients than the classical formula, but the converse may also occur. The following two corollaries of Theorem 1 show that the classical formulae (13·2·6) are of a wider scope than indicated by the Gauss-Fisher specification.

COROLLARY 1.[4] *If the residuals ζ_t are non-autocorrelated, i.e. if $a_1 = a_2 = \cdots = 0$, formula (7) for the standard error $d(b_i)$ shrinks to the classical formula (13·2·6), and similarly for the covariances (9),*

$$\text{cov}(b_i, b_k) \sim \frac{s_z^2}{n-h-1} \cdot \frac{L_{ik}}{L} \qquad i, k = 1, \ldots, h.$$

COROLLARY 2. *If all lagged correlations between the explanatory series $x^{(1)}, \ldots, x^{(h)}$ are zero, (7) shrinks to the classical formula (13·2·6), and similarly for the covariances (9).*

(iv) Hypothesis A_3^* and the lag rearrangement (11) is a combined device that may be used also in other situations where it is desirable to account for autocorrelation in the residuals; for example, factor analysis as applied to time-series data, analysis of variance as applied for comparison of mean values of different time-series, and so on.

(v) Turning to the Galton-Yule specification (13·2·4), we note that this allows a similar extension. Thus we may assume that the variables ξ_t constitute a $(h+1)$-dimensional process $\{\eta_t, \xi_t^{(1)}, \ldots, \xi_t^{(h)}\}$ which is *stationary*; then if we form the moment regression (13·2·4) this will define a disturbance process $\{\zeta_t\}$ which is stationary; without aiming at the greatest possible generality we assume that $\{\zeta_t\}$ is *ergodic*. As in Ch. 13·2 we may then assert that the empirical regression (13·2·1) will for n large provide an estimate of the moment regression that is asymptotically unbiased and consistent; similarly, the residual variance is an unbiased and consistent estimate. Formulae (7)–(9) for the standard errors and covariances, however, will in general not be valid for moment regression; we see that the situation is in this respect analogous to the classical formulae (13·2·6).

5. The asymptotically normal distribution of regression coefficients. – For a broad category of sampling functions, which includes the least-squares regression coefficients as a special case, it follows from the central limit theorem and its extensions that the distribution will, for large samples, but otherwise under very general conditions, be asymptotically normal.[1] This fundamental fact is the theoretical basis for the traditional device of employing the normal distribution for large-sample significance tests. We shall make extensive use of this device in the subsequent empirical studies. In this section we shall give a few references to the relevant versions of the central limit theorem. However, it would carry us outside the scope of this volume to enter in detail upon the theorems in question.

Let us first consider the situation from the viewpoint of the classical assumptions of independence [Ch. 13·2]. On the Galton-Yule specification B, the regression coefficients (13·2·2) are functions of the sampling moments $\bar{y}$, $\bar{x}_i$, l_{ik} of the theoretical variables η, $\xi^{(1)}$, ..., $\xi^{(h)}$. Here we can directly apply the general theorem that, under certain conditions that are fulfilled in the present case, any function of sampling moments will have a distribution that in large samples is asymptotically normal.

On the Gauss-Fisher specification A the situation is the same for b_0, whereas the coefficients b_i are linear forms in the independent residuals ζ_ν. We infer that if the ζ_ν follow the normal distribution, which is the traditional assumption, the regression coefficients will be normally distributed. However, their distribution will be asymptotically normal under much more general conditions. A sufficient condition may be obtained from the central limit theorem in the version given by Lyapunov (1901). The condition is, roughly speaking, that the coefficients in the linear form that constitutes b_i should not vary too much in magnitude.

Illustration. With $h = 1$ in (13·2·1) let the variable $x_t^{(1)}$ be time t. Writing (13·2·1) as

$$y_t = b_0 + b_1 t + z_t \qquad\qquad t = 0, \pm 1, \ldots, \pm T$$

formulae (13·2·2) then reduce to

$$b_0 = \frac{1}{2T+1} \Sigma z_t \qquad b_1 = \beta_1 + \frac{\Sigma t z_t}{\Sigma t^2},$$

all sums running over t from $-T$ to $+T$. Let us write

$$t z_t = x_t, \qquad \Sigma t z_t = x_{-T} + \cdots + x_T, \qquad \sigma^2 = \Sigma E(x_t^2), \qquad \varkappa^3 = \Sigma E(|x_t|^3).$$

Now suppose that $E(|z_t|^3)$ is finite. Then, as is easily verified,

$$\varkappa/\sigma = o(T^{4/3})/o(T^{3/2}) = o(T^{-1/6}) \to 0 \text{ as } T \to \infty.$$

Thus, by Lyapunov's criterion,[2] the central limit theorem applies to b_1, the conclusion being that the statement of Ch. 13·2d extends to this case.

Coming finally to the schemes considered in Ch. 13·4, we require here some generalization of the central limit theorem to interdependent variables, a type of extension first given by S. Bernstein (1927). Specifically, it is known that the central limit theorem remains valid if there is interdependence between any two variables in the sequence considered, on condition that if the distance between the two variables in the sequence is allowed to increase the degree of interdependence should tend to zero, and not too slowly. Now on hypotheses $A_1^* - A_3^*$ the residuals ζ_t will often satisfy this condition, their structure being given by formula (13·4·2). For a direct application of Bernstein's theorem to the regression coefficients b_i we must assume that the variables ε_t of (13·4·2) are independent, not merely uncorrelated. And as before we must assume that, in the linear forms of the ζ_t that constitute the b_i, the coefficients do not differ too much in order of magnitude. The situation is accordingly much the same as under the classical assumptions of Ch. 13·2 already dealt with.

Chapter 14.

THE ANALYSIS OF FAMILY BUDGET DATA

1. The numerical procedure. – In Ch. 1 we saw in broad outline how demand elasticities are deduced by regression analysis. We shall now show in detail how the method works when applied to family budget data. By way of a numerical illustration this first section gives the scheme of calculation. In the following sections we shall discuss a few questions specific to the treatment of family budget data.

Let us calculate the income elasticity of food, say for workers' and low grade employees' families in 1913. The published records group the families in 4 subgroups according to size, as measured in consumer units [Ch. 14·5]. We calculate first the food elasticity for each of the subgroups. Referring to the subgroup of 2.3–2.9 consumer units, Table 1 shows how the calculations proceed from the records of primary data up to the insertion in the regression formula. In the records every subgroup is broken down into 4 income classes according to yearly income per consumer unit. Rows 1–3 of Table 1 are taken directly from the records. For each income class these give (1) the number of households in the sample, (2) the average number of consumer units per household, (3) the average income per consumer unit. The records further show the expenditure per consumer unit for a large number of specified budget items. By summation over the food items (including liquor and tobacco) we obtain row 4, which gives the average food expenditure per consumer unit.

TABLE 14·1·1.[1] *Family budget data for workers and low grade employees, 1913, family size 2.3–2.9 consumer units.*

Scheme of calculations	Yearly income per consumer unit			
	Below 600	600–750	750–1050	1050 or more
1 n_ν = Number of households	136	179	111	22
2 c_ν = Consumer units per household	2.60	2.57	2.50	2.48
3 x_ν = Income per consumer unit	543.1	681.3	861.9	1232.8
4 y_ν = Food expenditure per consumer unit	291.8	331.6	374.4	407.1
5 $u_\nu = n_\nu c_\nu$ = Total number of cons. units .	353.6	460.0	277.5	54.6
6 $Y_\nu = \log y_\nu$	2.4651	2.5206	2.5733	2.6097
7 $X_\nu - m_x$	−.1051	−.0067	.0955	.2509
8 $u_\nu \cdot (X_\nu - m_x)$	−37.2	−3.1	26.5	13.7

The material is now ready for the calculation of the food elasticity of the subgroup under analysis. Assuming that the demand function has constant elasticity, say E, and thus is of type (1·1·1b), we are led to apply the linear logarithmic regression (1·5·6b). This gives

$$(1) \qquad E = \frac{\Sigma u_\nu (X_\nu - m_x) Y_\nu}{\Sigma u_\nu (X_\nu - m_x)^2} \qquad \text{with } m_x = \frac{\Sigma u_\nu \log x_\nu}{\Sigma u_\nu},$$

where all summations run over the four income classes. Inserting from rows 7–8 of Table 1, we obtain $E = 4.68/9.90 = 0.47$ as an estimate of the income elasticity of food, in families of 2.3–2.9 consumer units.

The four groups of the material cover, respectively, 1.8, 1.9–2.2, 2.3–2.9 and 3.0 or more consumer units. The calculation of the income elasticity for food is now repeated for each of the four size groups. This gives in the present case

$$(2) \qquad E^{(1)} = 0.44 \qquad E^{(2)} = 0.44 \qquad E^{(3)} = 0.47 \qquad E^{(4)} = 0.45.$$

Finally, an income elasticity for food is calculated for the aggregate of all four groups. This aggregate elasticity, say E, is calculated as a weighted average of the elasticities (2)

$$(3) \qquad E = \frac{k^{(1)} E^{(1)} + k^{(2)} E^{(2)} + k^{(3)} E^{(3)} + k^{(4)} E^{(4)}}{k^{(1)} + k^{(2)} + k^{(3)} + k^{(4)}}.$$

For the weights $k^{(i)}$ we shall use two alternative formulae,

$$(4) \qquad k^{(i)} = \Sigma u_\nu^{(i)} y_\nu^{(i)}, \qquad k^{(i)} = \Sigma u_\nu^{(i)} (X_\nu^{(i)} - m_i)^2.$$

Reference is made to Ch. 14·6 for a discussion of the choice of weights. As a rule the two alternatives give nearly the same results. In the present case both methods give $E = 0.45$.

2. A check against regression bias.[1] – In Table 14·1·1 the family budget data dealt with are grouped according to family income. The grouping causes a substantial reduction in the computational work. Sheppard's correction should be applied, if necessary; in other respects the grouping of a regressor has no systematic influence on the resulting elasticities. In the analysis of family budget data reported in Part V we have accordingly worked exclusively on grouped data.

The 1913 records give the budget data in grouped form as well as specified for each household. A fraction of these data has been used in Fig. 1·2·1a to illustrate that the grouping does not influence the regression analysis.

The sample used in Fig. 1·2·1a has been selected so as to be homogeneous; it covers 50 workers' and low grade employees' families in Gothenburg of size 2.2–2.6 consumption units. In Table 1 the same sample has been employed for testing the choice of regression for the purpose of demand analysis.[1] The expenditures are specified in 11 groups (much the same as in Table 1·6·1, but there are now two categories of food). For each item, four different regression lines have been calculated from the 50 observations, viz. (a) the least-squares regression of expenditure on income, (b) the 'diagonal' regression,[2] (c) the orthogonal regression, (d) the least-squares regression of income on expenditure. The four regressions obtained for food (B) are shown in Fig. 1·2·1b. If we interpret the four lines as alternative estimates of the demand function, the lowest elasticity is given by the regression of expenditure on income [line L]. This is the type of regression used in the present work. The other lines give much higher elasticities; the highest estimate is given by the regression of income on expenditure [line L'''], whereas the diagonal [L'] and the orthogonal [L''] regressions give intermediate values. Table 1 shows the income elasticities thus obtained for all of the 11 items.

Coming now to the check or test, this consists in the comparison of two methods for calculating the income elasticities for total expenditure. The results are shown in rows 11–12. The first method [row 11] is to calculate the total-expenditure elasticity in the same way as for each of the 11 items; the calculation thus refers to a scatter diagram of the same type as in Fig. 1·2·1b, and with expenditures obtained by summing over the 11 items. The second method [row 12] is to make use of formula (6·4·2), calculating the total-expenditure elasticity as a weighted average of the 11 elasticities for the sub-items. In principle, the two methods should lead to the same elasticity. We see that the two values coincide for method (a), while there is a large deviation for all the other methods. We conclude that methods (b)–(d) are biased, giving too high elasticities, whereas no such bias is present in the traditional method (a).

TABLE 14·2·1. *Income elasticity of all expenditures as a weighted average of the elasticities of separate budget items.*

Budget item	Expenditure per consumer unit	Income elast. based on regression				Correlation income-expenditure
		Expend. upon income	Diagonal	Orthogonal	Income upon expend.	
1 a Food, group A (plain)	182.8	.26	.70	.42	1.86	.38
1 b » » B (finer)	175.3	.71	1.16	1.28	1.90	.61
2 Housing	108.7	.64	1.27	1.60	2.54	.50
3 Fuel, cleaning............	43.7	.43	1.11	1.29	2.83	.39
4 Furniture	25.4	2.07	4.22	8.24	8.61	.49
5 Clothing	97.8	1.31	2.35	3.71	4.20	.56
6 Hygiene, medical care	15.2	1.70	3.79	7.98	8.45	.45
7 Education, etc............	33.8	1.41	2.27	3.26	3.66	.62
8 Professional unions	30.6	1.51	4.14	10.77	11.34	.37
9 Taxes	33.7	1.96	3.13	4.69	4.98	.63
10 Other expenditures	23.8	2.93	4.52	6.77	6.97	.65
11 Total expenditure	770.8	.88	.92	.92	.97	.95
12 Weighted average	770.8	.90	1.72	2.57	3.42	—

We see that if the scatter in Fig. 1·2·1b showed a perfect correlation, so that all observations were situated on a straight line, the four regressions would coincide. The last column of Table 1 shows that the correlation is almost perfect for total expenditure, but far from perfect for the 11 sub-items. This is only natural, the situation being that the expenditure has a tendency to greater individual variation for the sub-items than for the total expenditure. Clearly it is this tendency that gives rise to the bias in the 'elasticities' derived from the regressions (b)–(d). [See also Ex. 23.]

For total expenditure the scatter shows an almost perfect correlation, as seen from the value 0.95 given in the last column, and in accordance herewith the four regressions, or at least the first three, are nearly equal. If we consider Frisch-Haavelmo's method of correcting the diagonal elasticity by a constant reduction factor [cf Ch. 2·2 (i); the factor they have employed is 0.7], it follows that this device is not satisfactory, for the corrected elasticities remain self-contradictory in the same way as the uncorrected values.

A similar test may be devised for the regression analysis of market statistics. For example, suppose the data of Fig. 1·3·1 are specified for each of the cooperative stores. Since the price movement is the same for all stores, we may alternatively calculate the price elasticity as a weighted average of the elasticity for each individual store. Comparing with the elasticity obtained from the pooled data, methods (b)–(d) will then display the same bias and self-contradiction as in Table 1, for by the law of large numbers the pooled data have a tendency towards a smoother variation in the quantities sold. On the other hand, if we consider the least-squares regression of quantity on price, i.e. the traditional method for the deduction of price elasticity from market statistics, this will again be free of bias.

3. Quantity versus expenditure as regressand. – What is recorded in family budget data is usually the *expenditures* on the specified items of the budget. In some cases, however, supplementary information is given about the *quantities* purchased of the various items. The question then arises whether we had better use the expenditure or the quantities for the empirical deduction of demand elasticities. This is one case of many where alternative variants of method are available for demand analysis. Several questions of this type have already been dealt with; e.g., whether we should work with linear or curvilinear regression, or whether aggregate data should be analysed by multiple regression or by splitting up the material and then pooling the results by the use of a weighted average. In this and subsequent sections we shall take up a number of method variants for consideration. The main viewpoints adopted in the discussion will be the following: (a) the material available for the alternative methods, (b) general relations between the variant elasticities, (c) differences in the interpretation and application of the elasticity variants.

To obtain quantity data it is necessary that the budget item does not display too great a variation in quality and variety. Thus in family budget data it is difficult to measure quantities for clothing and housing, and it may be regarded as impossible for items such as recreation, intellectual purposes, taxes, gifts, etc. In the Swedish data under consideration, expenditures are recorded for all budget items, whereas supplementary information on quantities is given for sub-items of food, liquor, fuel, and light. The measurement of aggregate quantities is a problem in itself. In Ch. 5˙6 we have seen three formulae that may be used for different purposes. For instance, food aggregates can be formed with reference to calories, vitamin contents, etc., for the special purpose of nourishment studies [cf Ch. 17˙7].

According to the type of data referred to, we shall speak of *quantity* and *expenditure elasticities*. It may be argued that the quantity elasticity will in general be smaller than the expenditure elasticity, in symbols $E_\mu q < E_\mu x$. We note three tendencies in this direction. (a) As soon as a commodity is available in different varieties, it stands to reason that an increase of income or a reduction of prices will induce the consumers to shift towards more expensive qualities, with the result that demand variations will be smaller if measured by quantities than by expenditures. (b) The phenomenon of price discrimination has a similar effect. (c) For vegetables, fish and other commodity groups that display a seasonal variation, the consumer's response to the price cycle will be less marked, the higher his income. As a consequence, income differences between consumers will be reflected less markedly in the yearly demand as measured by quantities than by expenditures. We see that this argument applies to price movements in general, not only to seasonal changes.[1]

The tendencies (a)–(b) can be brought out in formal relations if we regard price as a function of income. As is readily verified, this gives

$$(1) \qquad x\,(\mu,\,p) = p\,(\mu) \cdot q\,(\mu,\,p); \qquad E_\mu x = E_\mu q + \frac{E_\mu p}{1 + E_\mu p} \,.$$

Both $E_\mu q$ and $E_\mu x$ will then be somewhat underestimated by the elasticities given by the family budget data, say $E_\mu^* q$ and $E_\mu^* x$; in fact, we obtain

$$(2) \qquad E_\mu^* q = E_\mu q - e_p\, q \cdot E_\mu p; \qquad E_\mu^* x = E_\mu x - e_p\, x \cdot E_\mu p.$$

With regard to Swedish conditions, the above arguments would lead us to expect that the two elasticity variants are nearly equal for milk, butter and eggs, and that quantity elasticities are somewhat smaller than expenditure elasticities for cheese, vegetables, fish and meat. On the whole, these conclusions are confirmed by the empirical calculations reported in Part V.

As regards the interpretation of quantity and expenditure elasticities, we see that the two variants answer somewhat different questions. Both serve as a measure for the dependence of demand upon income changes. The expenditure measures the demand from the viewpoint of purchasing power; it would therefore seem that for the purpose of economic analysis it is the expenditure elasticity that is the more relevant, and in particular for applications concerned with the consumers' propensity to consume. The quantity elasticity refers rather to the physical satisfaction of demand; this variant accordingly comes to the foreground in questions about the nourishment level, the standard of living, and so on.

4. Income versus total expenditure as regressor. – In family budget statistics, the expenditure data come directly from the household records compiled for the purpose, whereas the family income is a piece of supplementary information, either secured in connexion with the expenditure data or obtained from tax records or other sources. Since it is often difficult to obtain accurate and reliable income figures, the sampling surveys of family budgets are sometimes carried out without recording the family income. The question accordingly arises whether it is essential for demand analysis to use the income as regressor when forming the least-squares regression, or whether the income may be replaced by total expenditure as obtained from the household records. The two variants will in this section be referred to as demand elasticities w.r.t. *income* and *expenditure*, respectively.

If we regard total expenditure as a function of income, say $x = x(\mu)$, the two elasticity variants stand in the relation

(1) $$E_\mu q = E_\mu x \cdot E_x q$$

or in words: for any commodity, the demand elasticity w.r.t. income equals the demand elasticity w.r.t. expenditure, multiplied by the income elasticity of total expenditure. Formula (1) is an immediate corollary of the rule for differentiating a function of a function [cf Ex. II, 11].

It is an empirical fact that for the income classes under consideration total expenditure is approximately proportional to income. In the higher of these income classes a somewhat larger proportion of income is reserved for savings. It follows that elasticity w.r.t. income is approximately equal to elasticity w.r.t. expenditure, with some tendency to be smaller. We shall not endeavour, however, to make numerical estimates of the difference between the two variants. This and the closely related question of the income elasticity of savings are not purely static problems, and dynamic analysis falls outside of the program of the present work.

Since they are nearly equal, there is not a great deal to choose between the two elasticity variants in practice. If nonetheless we wish to pursue the distinction between the two elasticities, they should not be regarded as competitive but rather as complementary. They answer different questions, and which variant should be employed depends upon whether we are concerned with the effect of changes in income or in total expenditure. Both elasticities have a place in demand analysis. It would seem, however, that from the viewpoint of the applications it is the income elasticity that is of primary relevance, problems referring to total expenditure entering secondarily via assumptions concerning the propensity to consume.

5. The age scale of consumption.[1] – When making use of family budget data for the estimation of income elasticities, the simple idea behind the method is to compare the consumption habits in family groups that differ as regards income level but are similar in other respects. One of the difficulties encountered when applying this method in practice is to make allowance for size and age structure of the families. We note that biased elasticities may be expected if these factors are not taken into account. In fact, it is known that the consumption habits are influenced by the number of children in the family and their age distribution, and it is also an empirical fact that income and family size usually are intercorrelated. Under such circumstances the presence of bias may be concluded from Theorem 12·3·2B. Further we note that, since the factors in question are not purely quantitative, the bias cannot be removed by introducing them as regressors by way of a multiple regression analysis. As briefly described in Chs. 1·2 and 14·1 we have therefore

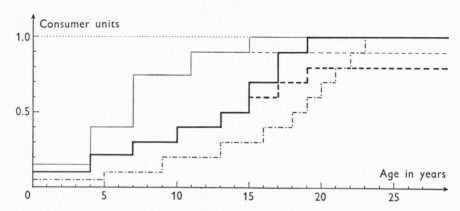

Fig. 14·5·1.[2] The German-Austrian scale for consumer units (heavy lines), the American scale (full-drawn thin lines), and a tentative scale for housing expenditures in 1913 (stippled line).

adopted an indirect method. This consists in deducing the income elasticity as a weighted average of the elasticities calculated separately for subgroups of the entire sample of families. Family size and age distribution are here allowed for in two ways. On the one hand the division into subgroups is made according to family type. In the regression analysis of each subgroup, on the other hand, income and expenditure per consumer unit are evaluated for each family by applying a fixed scale of consumption as a function of age. Owing to the division into subgroups the method is not sensitive to the choice of scale within the subgroup. In other words, the evaluation of consumer units within each subgroup does not have much effect on the average elasticity finally obtained.

Table 1 and Fig. 1 show three different consumption scales. Among the applications of such scales we note the setting of consumption norms that are adequate from the viewpoint of calorie intake, health protection, and so on. The standard-setting aspect of consumption scales, however, is of secondary interest in the present application. What is required for our purpose is a scale that gives a realistic picture of just how consumption actually varies as a function of age in the material under analysis.

It stands to reason that the age distribution of consumption is different for different budget items. We note that for any item the actual consumption scale can be roughly estimated by the following method of trial and error. On the one hand we calculate the income elasticity as a weighted average by the method described; as already mentioned, the choice of consumption scale will here have little or no influence on the resulting elasticity. On the other hand we calculate the income elasticity directly, without splitting up the data into subgroups, but applying instead a tentative scale for the evalua-

TABLE 14·5·1.[3] *Consumer units according to (a) the German-Austrian scale, and (b) the American scale.*

Age in years	0–3	4–6	7–9	10	11–12	13–14	15–16	17–18	19 or more
(a) Men	.1	.2	.3	.4	.4	.5	.7	.9	1.0
Women	.1	.2	.3	.4	.4	.5	.6	.7	.8
(b) Men	.15	.4	.75	.75	.9	.9	1.0	1.0	1.0
Women	.15	.4	.75	.75	.9	.9	.9	.9	.9

tion of consumer units. The second elasticity being more sensitive to the proper choice of scale, a comparison between the two elasticity estimates will reveal whether or not the scale adopted is realistic. More precisely, if income and family size are negatively correlated, as they are in most of the Swedish data, it is easy to verify the following rule of thumb:

If the scale adopted gives too much weight to the children's consumption, small elasticities will be overestimated by direct pooling, and large elasticities will be underestimated, and conversely if the scale gives too little weight to the children's consumption.

Hence if the two elasticities differ, we may infer in which direction the scale should be corrected. Recalculating the second elasticity estimate by the corrected scale, and proceeding in this way by trial and error, the method leads to a rough estimate of the consumption scale for the budget item considered.

Table 2 reports some experiments made using the above method on the basis of the data for 1913. Let us first consider the results obtained for total expenditure [row 1]. The data being split up in four family types, cols. 2–5 show that the income elasticity for total expenditure is nearly equal for the four types. Col. 6 gives 0.892 for weighted average of the four elasticities; this is the elasticity for the entire material as estimated by the first method. In cols. 7–9 the same elasticity has been estimated by the second method, making use of the three alternative consumption scales of Fig. 1. On comparison with col. 6 we conclude that too much weight is given to children's consumption by the American and the German-Austrian scales, whereas the tentative third scale gives them too little weight. Apparently there is not much to choose between the German-Austrian and the tentative scale. For final result we take it that the age distribution of total expenditure is approximately given by the German-Austrian scale.

In the regression analysis behind cols. 7–9 an evaluation as per consumer unit is made for the regressand-expenditure variable as well as for the regressor-income variable. It lies in the logic of the method that for each variable

TABLE 14·5·2.[4] *Income elasticities calculated by the use of different consumption scales. Family budget data, 1913.*

Budget item	Consumer units per household				Weighted average	All households		
	1.8	1.9–2.2	2.3–2.9	3.0 or more		German-Austrian scale	American scale	Special scales
(1)	(2)	(3)	(4)	(5)	(6)	(7)	(8)	(9)
1 Total expenditure.	.86	.91	.89	.89	.892	.909	.924	.886
2 Food, stimulants..	.44	.44	.47	.45	.45	.49	—	—
3 Clothing	1.12	1.21	1.14	1.16	1.17	1.02	1.21	—
4 Housing	.70	.76	.73	.81	.76	.95	—	.75
5 Milk	.25	.39	.52	.58	.48	.50	—	—
6 Butter..........	.35	.66	.74	.74	.69	.71	—	—
7 Cheese..........	.50	.30	.54	.21	.37	.43	—	—
8 Eggs	.47	.84	.85	1.01	.86	.99	—	—
9 Meat and pork ...	.26	.37	.55	.51	.46	.59	—	—

the evaluation should be made by a realistic scale, and so the two scales will in general have to be different. Further it is clear that when the method is applied to total expenditure we should, as is done in row 1, use the same scale for regressand and regressor. It will be observed that the scale thus established for total expenditure, for these data the German-Austrian scale, should be used throughout for the regressor-income when the method is applied to the separate budget items.

Proceeding to the results given in rows 2–4 of Table 2, these refer to three of the main items of the family budget [cf Table 1·6·2]. We see that the German-Austrian scale is fairly realistic for the aggregate item of nourishment, only that children's consumption is somewhat exaggerated. For clothing, the German-Austrian scale gives too little weight to the children. Applying instead the American scale to clothing expenditure, the elasticity obtained (1.21) is in close agreement with col. 6, and so we conclude that the American scale gives a good fit to the age distribution of clothing expenditure. For housing, finally, it appears that the German-Austrian scale gives far too much weight to the children. Trying here the special scale shown in Fig. 1, this turns out to be approximately correct, to judge from the elasticity shown in col. 9.

Finally, rows 5–9 show the results obtained for a few of the main food items. We see that the German-Austrian scale is nearly realistic for milk, butter and cheese, whereas it overestimates the children's consumption of eggs, meat and pork.

6. Weighted elasticity averages. – The formulae[1]

$$(1) \qquad k^{(i)} = \sum_\nu u_\nu^{(i)} \cdot y_\nu^{(i)} \qquad\qquad k^{(i)} = \sum_\nu u_\nu^{(i)} (X_\nu^{(i)} - m_i)^2$$

were given in (14·1·4) as two alternative sets of weights for the calculation of income elasticity as a weighted average of elasticities referring to subgroups of the material under analysis. It need hardly be indicated that the formulae extend to any number of subgroups, and that the classification can be made according to more than one attribute, say family type, social class, geographical district, and so on. The two methods will in practice give nearly the same results, provided the subgroups are not too different as regards demand structure and sample size. For illustration, reference is made to Table 1.

Formula (1a) is a direct application of (6·4·2). The weights $k^{(i)}$ are here the total expenditures of the ith subgroup for the commodity considered. We note that if the calculation refers to quantity elasticity [Ch. 14·3] the weights will instead be given by formula (6·4·1). It will further be observed that we are not bound to pool the subgroups in the same proportions as they appear in the sample of family budget data. Thus, if the sample is selected in such a manner that the subgroups are not proportional to the subgroups in the population universe, we may form an elasticity estimate for the population by making $u_\nu^{(i)} = n_\nu^{(i)} \cdot c_\nu^{(i)}$, with population figures for $n_\nu^{(i)}$, the number of households. [Cf also Table 16·2·1.]

Turning to the rationale of the weights (1b), suppose that each estimate $E^{(i)}$ of a subgroup elasticity is a random variable with expectation E_i and variance σ_i^2. Then the aggregate elasticity (6·4·2) will have the expectation

$$m(E) = k_1 E_1 + \cdots + k_s E_s \qquad \text{where } k_i = k^{(i)} / (k^{(1)} + \cdots + k^{(s)}),$$

with the $k^{(i)}$ given by (1a). Forming now an estimate of type

$$E^* = \alpha_1 E^{(1)} + \cdots + \alpha_s E^{(s)} \qquad \text{with } \alpha_1 + \cdots + \alpha_s = 1,$$

we propose to determine $\alpha_1, \ldots, \alpha_s$ by the condition that the variance of $E^* - m(E)$, say V, should be a minimum. In passing we note that if the $E^{(i)}$ are exact estimates, so that $\sigma_i = 0$, the optimal weights will be given by (1a), for on making $\alpha_i = k_i$ $(i = 1, \ldots, s)$ we obtain $V = 0$.

Now suppose that within each subgroup the regression of expenditure upon income is logarithmically linear for the commodity considered, and that the relation is of type (13·2·3), say

$$Y_\nu^{(i)} = \beta_0 + E_i \cdot (X_\nu^{(i)} - m_i) + z_\nu^{(i)} \qquad\qquad i = 1, \ldots, s.$$

Suppose further that the subgroup elasticities are equal, $E_1 = \cdots = E_s$, and that the residuals $z_\nu^{(i)}$ have the same distribution in all of the subgroups. It is easy to see that this leads to $\sigma_i^2 \sim \text{const.}/k^{(i)}$ with $k^{(i)}$ given by (1b), and that

TABLE 14·6·1.[2] *Income elasticities, calculated (a) as a weighted average of elasticities for different family types, and (b) by direct pooling of the data for all family types. Family budget data; item groups as in Table 1·6·1.*

Item group	Workers and low grade employees							Middle-class	
	1913		1923	1933				1923	1933
	Average, by formula		Direct pooling	Direct pooling	Average, by formula		Direct pooling	Direct pooling	Direct pooling
	(1 a)	(1 b)			(1 a)	(1 b)			
I	.45	.45	.49	.51	.53	.51	.50	.46	.44
II	.76	.75	.95	1.20	1.28	1.30	1.25	.81	.79
III	.74	.70	.89	.93	.67	.65	.84	.82	.86
IV	1.85	1.85	2.04	1.82	1.41	1.38	1.70	1.28	.94
V	1.17	1.17	1.02	.96	.96	.94	.77	.61	.93
VI	1.31	1.42	1.39	1.48	1.09	1.12	1.22	.84	.91
VII	1.70	1.62	1.57	1.50	1.88	1.85	1.23	.69	.81
VIII	1.44	1.33	1.37	1.44	1.24	1.22	1.29	1.44	1.26
IX	5.20	5.08	3.93	2.72	1.73	1.58	2.44	2.35	1.94
X	1.82	1.79	1.85	1.87	1.83	1.83	1.84	1.57	1.46
I–X	.89	.89	.91	.96	.97	.97	.95	.92	.91

V will be a minimum if $\alpha_i = \text{const.}/\sigma_i^2 \sim \text{const.}\ k^{(i)}$ $(i=1, \ldots, s)$. Hence the optimal weights of (14·1·3) will in this case be given by (1b). We see that the resulting aggregate elasticity may be written

$$(2) \qquad E = \frac{\sum_\nu u_\nu^{(1)} (X_\nu^{(1)} - m_1) \cdot Y_\nu^{(1)} + \cdots + \sum_\nu u_\nu^{(s)} (X_\nu^{(s)} - m_s) \cdot Y_\nu^{(s)}}{\sum_\nu u_\nu^{(1)} (X_\nu^{(1)} - m_1)^2 + \cdots + \sum_\nu u_\nu^{(s)} (X_\nu^{(s)} - m_s)^2} .$$

It will be observed that the average elasticity estimate (2) can be interpreted as an immediate application of a familiar device in the analysis of covariance.[3] Further we note that formula (2) allows a simple geometric interpretation. The ith subgroup giving a scatter diagram for $(X_\nu^{(i)}, Y_\nu^{(i)})$, let the scatters thus obtained for $i=1, \ldots, s$ be superimposed in such a manner that their centres of gravity coincide, i.e. so that the X-coordinate will have the same mean in each scatter, and similarly for the Y-coordinate. For the pooled scatter, the regression coefficient will then be given by (2).

The above discussion gives an idea of the problems that arise if we wish to allow for differences between the subgroup elasticities on the one hand and differences between their confidence intervals on the other. In practice, both of these features are in the picture simultaneously. It is not our purpose, however, to pursue the matter further. In view of the general experience that the aggregate elasticity will be nearly the same for the two weightings considered, it would seem that there is not much to be gained by a more elaborate treatment.

For comparison with the weighted averages, Table 1 gives elasticities obtained by direct pooling of the data, making use of the method described in Ch. 14·5. In pooling the data for all families, the age distribution has here been evaluated in accordance with the German-Austrian scale. Since the published tables of the 1923 and 1933 data are partly based on the American scale, these were transformed by the German-Austrian scale before the pooling.

7. Dynamic aspects of demand as a function of income. – In our demand analysis we have thus far adopted a strictly static approach, the basic hypothesis being that demand is a well-defined function of income, prices, and other influencing factors. We shall now briefly discuss certain dynamic features of the demand pattern. For one thing we shall examine the consumers' demand pattern from the viewpoint of short-term versus long-term reactions to changes in income. Further we shall consider the question of whether any systematic difference may be expected between income elasticities that refer, respectively, to family budget data on the one hand and market statistics on the other.

A priori, it may be argued that after a change in his income, say by 10 %, it will take some time before the consumer has accustomed himself to the new situation. For example, on purchasing things that earlier were not within reach, he may find that some of them had been over-estimated, the consequence being that the immediate expansion of his budget will be somewhat modified in the long run. Specifically, the family budget is composed of things that vary greatly in durability, and it may well be that the short-term expansion has a tendency to concentrate on commodities for immediate consumption. In the sense indicated we may accordingly distinguish between *short-term* and *long-term* elasticities. The empirical analysis in Part V has for its purpose the determination of the long-term elasticity of demand. From the viewpoint of the practical applications of demand analysis, it is clearly the long-term elasticities that are of primary importance. Further we note that in confining ourselves to the study of long-term elasticity this aim is in perfect agreement with our general programme of making a static approach.

For the large majority of consumers, the income level is fairly stable. Hence, if we consider a group of families that is covered by our family budget data, the changes in income that occur in the course of time are on the whole small and infrequent as compared with the existing income differences between the families in the group. We may accordingly conclude that the families have usually adapted themselves to the income level at which they have been recorded, so that the budget data primarily reflect the demand pattern in the sense of long run reactions to income changes. In other words, the income elasticities derived from family budget data can most immediately be interpreted as long-term elasticities.[1] This view has been stressed in the introductory treatment in Ch. 1·2.

In their highly interesting studies on savings, J. Duesenberry (1949) and F. Modigliani (1949) have made use of a dynamic approach along the general lines of Keynes' analysis of the propensity to consume.[2] To explain the actual course of savings as shown by the statistical data — both family budget material and time-series data are employed — savings are assumed to display a certain persistency or hysteresis, in the sense that the consumer has a tendency to maintain his total expenditure on the same level as that which he has previously reached. Specifying Keynes' general argument, Duesenberry and Modigliani base their analysis on the assumption that consumption (=income minus savings) is a function, not only of yearly income, but also of the highest income reached in some previous year. It need hardly be stressed that the persistency in question is not confined to the propensity to consume, and hence to the consumers' savings habits, but may be a general feature of economic demand. As a general phenomenon, the tendency may be called *Keynes' persistency effect*.

It stands to reason that the consumer group cannot in the long run spend more money than it earns. Thus, if income falls, the consumers must in the long run adapt themselves to the lower level. Hence, and this conclusion is entirely in line with Keynes' theory, the persistency effect is in principle a short-term phenomenon. Since we are here interested primarily in the long run aspects of the demand structure, it would therefore fall outside the scope of the present volume to enter upon an analysis along the Duesenberry-Modigliani lines.

A feature in the Duesenberry-Modigliani approach that has attracted much attention is that changes in demand are not symmetric w.r.t. upward and downward changes in income. In fact, their hypothesis implies that consumption expands if income rises, but does not contract in the same measure if income falls. This feature has sometimes been described by saying that we are here concerned with an *irreversible* demand function. In passing we note that this terminology is not very fortunate, for if we speak of demand as a function, this should eo ipso be reversible in the functional sense [cf (2·2·3–4)]. It would be more in conformity with current terminology to say that changes in demand are in this approach dealt with as an irreversible *process*.

It may be argued that the change in demand induced by a rise in income will in certain cases be irreversible even in the long run, since the change may result in a permanent change of the consumer habits. If we wish to maintain the notion of demand function, this phenomenon may be regarded as a *shift* in the demand function in question. Such shifts, when they occur, may obviously be of importance from the viewpoint of applications.

Finally we turn to the question of whether the income elasticities obtained from family budget data present any systematic difference from income

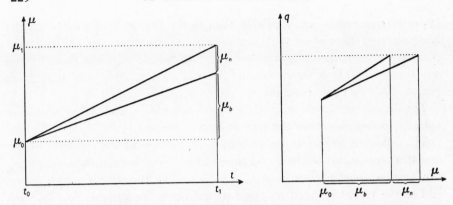

Fig. 14·7·1. Income elasticities; market statistics v. family budget data.

elasticities that refer to the time-series data of market statistics. Since family budget elasticities, according to a previous remark in this section, should be regarded as long-term elasticities, the question at issue may be specified so as to refer to the long-term elasticities of market statistics. It would seem that this is a question where a purely theoretical discussion is not likely to be very convincing. It may be argued a priori that the two types of long-term elasticity should on the whole display no substantial difference, but it is also easy to point out tendencies to systematic deviation. The scope and validity of such theoretical arguments can only be tested empirically, preferably by making forecasts and observing whether or not they are successful. The conclusions arrived at in the general remarks ventured below should therefore be regarded as tentative.

For one thing, a long-term shift in demand of the type just mentioned may give rise to differences between family budget and market statistics elasticities. For example, if the families in one of the higher income classes of the budget data suffered a general decrease in their income, it may perhaps occur that they would adopt a demand pattern different from that inferred from the budget data, since their earlier experience would be different from that of the families in the lower income classes. It may well be that such deviations are of importance, but in any case we may conclude that the deviations will be of different sign for different budget items. This is a typical case where only empirical investigations can give more precise information. We note that for the demand curves shown in Fig. 1·2·2 deviations of this type seem to be present for food, but not for housing.

Another source of discrepancy is the continual introduction of novel commodities into the market.[3] The family budget data refer to a short period, where the choice of commodities and services may be regarded as fixed, whereas the market statistics cover a longer period, at the end of which more types of commodity are available than in the beginning. To follow up the argument, let us assume that the average income rises during the period covered by the market statistics [see Fig. 1 a]. Some part of the rising income will then be spent on novel commodities and services introduced during the period. Hence we may conclude:

The income elasticities of family budget data on the whole tend to be smaller than the income elasticities that refer to market statistics.

The following simple argument may give a rough idea of the size of the deviation. Let (t_0, t_1) be the period covered by the market statistics. Supposing the average income rises from μ_0 to μ_1, let μ_n be the amount which at the end of the period is spent on novel commodities. We write $\mu_b = \mu_1 - \mu_0 - \mu_n$. The income range of the market statistics being (μ_0, μ_1), this would roughly correspond to an income range $(\mu_0, \mu_0 + \mu_b)$ in family budget data at period t_0 [cf Fig. 1 b]. Thus if we consider a commodity that does not belong to the novelties, and if we write E and E^* for its income elasticities as referring to budget data and market statistics, respectively, our argument gives

$$dq = E \, d\mu = E^* \, d\mu^* \qquad d\mu^* = \frac{\mu_b}{\mu_b + \mu_n} \cdot d\mu.$$

Hence the approximate relationship

$$E \sim \frac{\mu_b}{\mu_b + \mu_n} E^*.$$

Chapter 15.

THE ANALYSIS OF MARKET STATISTICS

1. The numerical procedure. – The present chapter is a parallel to the preceding one. Having in Ch. 14 dealt with the specific problems of demand analysis encountered in the treatment of family budget data, we shall now turn to the problems that arise in the analysis of market statistics.

The numerical illustration given in this first section covers (i) the calculation of elasticities by the ordinary method of least-squares regression, and (ii) the device of conditional regression analysis. The general method (i) has been developed in (12·2·1–7). A brief outline has been given in Chs. 1·3 and 2·6; for graphic illustration, see Fig. 1·3·1.

The present illustration refers to the total demand for butter and margarine in Sweden. The data employed are shown in Table 1. Col. 1 gives the yearly consumption in kilograms per capita. Col. 2 gives the yearly price of butter

TABLE 15·1·1. *The calculation of elasticities from market statistics. Butter and margarine, 1921–39.*

t	d_t	p'_t	$\mathfrak{P}$	p_t	$x_t^{(0)}$	$x_t^{(1)}$	$x_t^{(0)}x_t^{(1)}$	$(x_t^{(1)})^2$	μ'_t	$x_t^{(2)}$	d_t^*
Year	(1)	(2)	(3)	(4)	(5)	(6)	(7)	(8)	(9)	(10)	(11)
1921	12.16	4.62	241	1.92	−14.58	11.77	−171.6	138.5	909	−11.32	12.08
22	12.63	3.29	195	1.68	−12.93	6.19	− 80.0	38.3	732	−11.51	13.14
23	13.46	3.12	177	1.76	−10.17	8.10	− 82.4	65.6	719	− 8.09	13.39
24	14.12	3.03	174	1.74	− 8.09	7.56	− 61.2	57.2	743	− 5.94	13.91
1925	14.94	2.94	176	1.67	− 5.64	5.87	− 33.1	34.5	756	− 5.69	14.34
26	15.34	2.61	172	1.51	− 4.49	1.56	− 7.0	2.4	772	− 3.76	15.75
27	15.65	2.52	171	1.47	− 3.62	.33	− 1.2	.1	786	− 2.75	16.28
28	17.04	2.46	171	1.44	.07	− .74	− .1	.5	798	− 2.09	16.71
29	17.62	2.31	169	1.37	1.53	−2.87	− 4.4	8.2	842	.78	17.99
1930	18.04	2.13	164	1.30	2.55	−5.15	− 13.1	26.5	860	2.98	19.22
31	18.44	1.99	159	1.25	3.48	−6.63	− 23.1	44.0	816	2.03	19.42
32	18.85	1.88	156	1.21	4.46	−8.36	− 37.3	69.9	753	− .64	19.20
33	18.77	1.94	153	1.27	4.27	−6.19	− 26.4	38.3	726	− 1.36	18.38
34	19.11	2.16	154	1.40	5.05	−1.75	− 8.8	3.1	782	1.56	17.87
1935	19.91	2.09	156	1.34	6.83	−3.78	− 25.8	14.3	858	5.05	19.37
36	20.38	2.06	158	1.30	7.87	−4.98	− 39.2	24.8	907	6.94	20.25
37	20.44	2.30	162	1.42	7.97	−1.33	− 10.6	1.8	994	9.79	19.92
38	20.20	2.42	166	1.46	7.46	− .15	− 1.1	.0	1 062	11.64	20.08
39	20.44	2.53	171	1.48	7.97	.55	4.4	.3	1 114	12.39	20.07
Totals	—	—	—	—	− .01	.00	−622.0	568.3	—	.01	—

and margarine, calculated as weighted average of retail prices. Col. 9 gives the national income per capita. For further information on the data employed, reference is made to Ch. 17·1.

(i) We shall assume that the demand function is of type (1·1·3), i. e. that the price and income elasticities are constant, say e and E. The elasticities will be calculated on the basis of two alternative hypotheses, viz.

$$(1) \qquad d_t = c \cdot p_t^{-e} \qquad\qquad d_t = c \cdot p_t^{-e} \cdot \mu_t^{E}.$$

Here $p_t = p'_t/\mathfrak{P}_t$ is real price, i.e. nominal price p'_t divided by a consumer price index $\mathfrak{P}_t$. Similarly, $\mu_t = \mu'_t/\mathfrak{P}_t$ is real income. We introduce logarithmic variables, so that relations (1) become linear. Forming the deviations from the averages, and multiplying all variables by 100 so as to avoid decimal zeros, we write

$$x_t^{(0)} = 100 \, (\log d_t - a_0); \quad x_t^{(1)} = 100 \, (\log p_t - a_1); \quad x_t^{(2)} = 100 \, (\log \mu_t - a_2)$$

with
$$a_0 = \frac{1}{n} \Sigma \log d_t; \qquad a_1 = \frac{1}{n} \Sigma \log p_t; \qquad a_2 = \frac{1}{n} \Sigma \log \mu_t.$$

Relations (1) then become

(2) $\qquad x_t^{(0)} = - e\,x_t^{(1)} \qquad\qquad x_t^{(0)} = - e\,x_t^{(1)} + E\,x_t^{(2)}.$

For the corresponding least-squares regressions we write

(3) $\qquad x_t^{(0)} = - e\,x_t^{(1)} + z_t \qquad x_t^{(0)} = - e\,x_t^{(1)} + E\,x_t^{(2)} + z_t$

so that e and E in (3) are estimates of e and E in (1)–(2).

Let us first consider (1a). In accordance with (12·2·1-7) we obtain the estimate

(4) $\qquad\qquad e = - l_{01}/l_{11} = 622.0/568.3 = 1.09.$

The calculations can be followed in Table 1, the successive deduction of cols. 4–8 being obvious from the above. Proceeding, let d_t^* be the estimate of demand given by the parameters thus obtained. We may then calculate

(5) $\quad z_t = x_t^{(0)} + e\,x_t^{(1)}; \quad z_t' = \dfrac{1}{100}z_t; \quad \log d_t^* = \log d_t - z_t'; \quad z_t^* = d_t - d_t^*$

which gives first $\log d_t^*$ and then d_t^*.

In (5) we have written z_t^* and z_t', respectively, for the residual deviations from the quantities and their logarithms. Next we calculate the variance of the residuals z_t in (3), obtaining

$$s^2(z_t) = l_{00} + e\,l_{01} = 16.29; \quad \text{hence } \gamma = s(z_t)/\sqrt{l_{00}} = s(z_t')/s\,(\log d_t) = 0.559.$$

Here and in the following the observed variance of a variable y is denoted $s^2(y)$.

We see that hypothesis (1a) leaves $\gamma = 56\%$ of the standard deviation of $\log d_t$ unexplained. The quotient γ will be called the *residual ratio*. Working out d_t^* and z_t^*, we find that the residual ratio for d_t is slightly higher, or

$$\gamma = \left[\frac{1}{n}\cdot \Sigma\,(z_t^*)^2\right]^{1/2} / s\,(d_t) = 62\%.$$

Proceeding to hypothesis (1 b), the income variables μ_t and $x_t^{(2)}$ are given in cols. 9–10 of Table 1. The least-squares estimates of elasticities e and E are given by two normal equations, in accordance with (1·5·3) and (12·1·4). We obtain

(6) $\quad \begin{cases} - l_{11}\,e + l_{12}\,E = l_{01} \\ - l_{21}\,e + l_{22}\,E = l_{02} \end{cases} \qquad \begin{cases} 568.3\,e + 435.2\,E = 622.0 \\ 435.2\,e + 896.6\,E = 870.8. \end{cases}$

Hence $e = 0.56$; $E = 0.70$. The calculation of residuals z_t and estimates d_t^* proceeds by formulae similar to (5). For the residual variance we obtain

$$s^2(z_t) = l_{00} + e\,l_{10} - E\,l_{20} = 1.665, \quad \text{giving } \gamma = s(z_t)/\sqrt{l_{00}} = 0.179,$$

which shows that hypothesis (1b) leaves only 18 % of the standard deviation of $\log d_t$ unexplained.

The results under (i) are summed up in Table 2a, where H_0 indicates the null hypothesis adopted.

(ii) For the data under analysis, there is a considerable correlation between price and income, $r(x_t^{(1)}, x_t^{(2)}) = -0.61$. The simultaneous estimation of price and income elasticity will accordingly be disturbed by a tendency to multicollinearity in the sense of Ch. 2·6. To examine the situation we apply the method of conditional regression. This being a flexible device, which in practice will have to be adapted in accordance with the a priori information, we shall here illustrate two frequent cases.

a. According to the empirical results in our analysis of family budget data, the income elasticity of agricultural products is something like 0.3 or 0.4. It would therefore seem appropriate to carry out the conditional analysis on the a priori assumption that income elasticity is not far from 0.4. Denoting the hypothetical value by E_0, we shall try alternative hypotheses, say $E_0 = 0.40$ or $E_0 = 0.50$. Given E_0, we see that we are brought back to the case of one explanatory variable, the regression (3 b) being replaced by

$$(7) \qquad x_t^* = -e\, x_t^{(1)} + z_t \quad \text{with} \quad x_t^* = x_t^{(0)} - E_0\, x_t^{(2)}$$

for regressand. Further we see that the conditional estimate for price elasticity e is obtained from the first equation in (6 a) on replacing E by E_0, which gives

$$(8) \qquad e = -\frac{l_{01}}{l_{11}} + \frac{l_{12}}{l_{11}} E_0 = 1.09 - 0.766\, E_0.$$

The estimates e obtained for the E_0-values 0.25, 0.40, 0.50, 0.55 are given in Table 2 b.

Forming the residual variance, a simple deduction gives

$$(9) \qquad s^2(z_t) = \frac{1}{n} \sum_t (x_t^{(0)} - E_0\, x_t^{(2)})^2 + \frac{e}{n} \sum_t (x_t^{(0)} - E_0\, x_t^{(2)})\, x_t^{(1)}$$
$$= l_{00} + E_0^2\, l_{22} - 2\, E_0\, l_{20} + e\, l_{10} - e\, E_0\, l_{12}.$$

We see that the variance $s^2(z_t)$ and the residual ratio $\gamma = s(z_t)/s(x_t^{(0)})$ will depend upon E_0. The ratios γ obtained are given in Table 2 b.

Since butter and margarine belong to our necessities, we should according to Ch. 6·5 expect $E < e$. On comparing the alternative results in Table 2 b, the estimates $E_0 = 0.55$, $e = 0.67$ appear to be rather plausible. These estimates give the residual ratio $\gamma = 22\,\%$, which is only slightly above the minimum value $\gamma = 18\,\%$.

b. The a priori inequality $E < e$ will now be employed for a conditional regression analysis. Writing

$$(10) \qquad E = \lambda \cdot e,$$

TABLE 15·1·2. *Butter and margarine demand. Elasticity estimates obtained by ordinary and conditional regression; corresponding residual ratios and standard errors.*

a. Ordinary regression.   b. Fixed income elasticity E.   c. Fixed ratio $\lambda = E/e$.

H_0	Elasticities		Ratio γ, %	H_0	Elasticities		Ratio γ, %	H_0	λ	Elasticities		Ratio γ, %
	e	E			e	E				e	$E = \lambda e$	
A	1.09	—	56	A	.90	.25	39	A	1.0	.64	.64	19
B	.56	.70	18	B	.78	.40	30	B	.9	.68	.61	20
				C	.71	.50	24	C	.8	.72	.57	21
				D	.67	.55	22	D	.7	.76	.53	23

Standard errors

A_0 ±.18   —
A_m ±.36   —   Standard errors   Standard errors
B_0 ±.076; ±.060 C_0 ±.076 — B_0 ±.033 ±.030
B_m ±.098; ±.079 C_m ±.098 — B_m ±.043 ±.039
B_a ±.083; ±.069 C_a ±.112 — B_a ±.039 ±.035

we let λ be fixed in advance by way of alternative assumptions, say $\lambda = 1.0$ or $\lambda = 0.8$. Introducing (10) in the regression (3 b), we obtain

$$(11) \quad x_t^{(0)} = -e(x_t^{(1)} - \lambda x_t^{(2)}) + z_t, \quad \text{or} \quad x_t^{(0)} = -e x_t^{**} + z_t \text{ with } x_t^{**} = x_t^{(1)} - \lambda x_t^{(2)},$$

showing that we are again brought back to the case of one regressor.

Table 2c gives the conditional estimates obtained by fixing λ alternatively as 1.0, 0.9, 0.8 and 0.7. We see that the analysis gives a rather clear indication in favour of the estimates $E \sim 0.6$, $e \sim 0.7$. For one thing, it seems likely a priori that λ should be about 0.8 or 0.9. Further we note that the resulting value for the residual ratio lies very near the minimum, or $\gamma = 20\%$. It may finally be remarked that the estimates do not differ much from those obtained by the previous device [see Table 2b], but nevertheless there seems to be an improvement. Table 1, col. 11, gives the 'theoretical' values d_t^* of demand as obtained from the regression (11) with $\lambda = 0.9$, that is the values given by (1b) for $E = 0.61$, $e = 0.68$.

It needs no comment that the variants a–b apply with any number of regressors, and that their number is in both cases reduced by 1.

2. The standard error of empirical elasticities. – Following up the illustration in the previous section, we shall now estimate the standard errors of the elasticities arrived at.

(i) Let us first consider the estimate (15·1·4) of the price elasticity, or $e = 1.09$. According to the classical formula (13·2·6) the standard error of e is

$$(1) \qquad d(e) = s(z_t)/s(x_t^{(1)})\sqrt{n-2} = 0.179.$$

According to the autocorrelative formula (13·4·7) the standard error is obtained by multiplying (1) by the correction factor

(2) $$f = \sqrt{1 + 2\,r_1^{(1)}\,\varrho_1 + 2\,r_2^{(1)}\,\varrho_2 + \cdots}$$

where $r_1^{(1)}$, $r_2^{(1)}$, ... is the observed correlogram of the price variable $x_t^{(1)}$, and ϱ_1, ϱ_2, ... is the theoretical correlogram of the regression residuals z_t. The observed correlogram of the residuals z_t, which is shown in Fig. 1a (heavy broken line), gives evidence of a considerable autocorrelation. This feature is in itself an unfavourable indication of the significance of the regression relation considered, for if the relation is to be regarded as giving a satisfactory explanation of the variation in the demand, we should require that the residuals should be rather irregular [Ch. 2·3]. Let us nevertheless for the purpose of illustration continue the evaluation of the standard error. We see that a rather close fit to the observed correlogram of the residuals is obtained by the linearly decreasing correlogram $\varrho_\nu = (6 - \nu)/6$ with $\nu = 1, \ldots, 6$ (the thin broken line in Fig. 1a); the corresponding process is a moving average (10·2·4) of order 5 with $a_0 = a_1 = \cdots = a_5 = 1$. Making use of these values for ϱ_ν, the correction factor (2) becomes $f = 2.04$, which gives a standard error as large as $d(e) = 0.36$. The two estimates obtained for $d(e)$ are given in the lower part of Table 15·1·2 a.

(ii) Next let us consider the estimates $e = 0.56$, $E = 0.70$ given by (15·1·6). To apply the classical formula (13·2·6) for the standard errors, we form the matrix L with determinant L,

$$L = \begin{bmatrix} l_{11} & l_{12} \\ l_{21} & l_{22} \end{bmatrix} = \frac{1}{19} \cdot \begin{bmatrix} 568.3 & -435.2 \\ -435.2 & 896.6 \end{bmatrix}; \qquad L = \frac{1}{19^2} \cdot 320\,139,$$

we require the adjugate matrix L^* with elements L^{ik} given by

$$L^{11} = l_{22} = 896.6/19; \quad L^{22} = l_{11} = 568.3/19; \quad L^{12} = L^{21} = -l_{12} = 435.2/19,$$

and the standard deviation of the residuals z_t, or $s(z_t) = 1.31$. The resulting standard errors are

(3) $\qquad d(e) = s(z)\sqrt{L^{11}/16\,L} = 0.076; \qquad d(E) = s(z)\sqrt{L^{22}/16\,L} = 0.060.$

To apply the autocorrelative formula (13·4·7) we further form the empirical correlogram r_ν of the residuals z_t. This being shown in Fig. 1a [heavy unbroken line], we have finally to fit a theoretical correlogram ϱ_ν. We have considered two alternative hypotheses.

The first is that the residual series is a process of moving averages of first order with $\varrho_1 = 0.47$ and $\varrho_2 = \varrho_3 = \cdots = 0$ [the dotted line in Fig. 1a]. Forming the elements c_{ik} in accordance with (13·4·5) we obtain

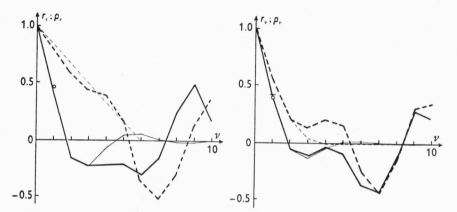

Fig. 15·2·1. Residual correlograms. Butter and margarine 1921–39.
a. Ordinary regression analysis.   b. Conditional regression analysis.

(4) $\begin{cases} c_{11} = 29.91 + 2\,(0.47)\,(24.38) = 52.8; \quad c_{22} = 47.20 + 2\,(0.47)\,(40.21) = 85.0, \\ c_{12} = c_{21} = -\,22.91 + (0.47)\,(-\,23.23 - 18.85) = -\,42.7. \end{cases}$

Next we calculate

$$L^{*}\,C = \frac{1}{19} \cdot \begin{bmatrix} 897 & 435 \\ 435 & 568 \end{bmatrix} \begin{bmatrix} 52.8 & -42.7 \\ -42.7 & 85.0 \end{bmatrix} = \frac{10^{2}}{19} \cdot \begin{bmatrix} 288 & -13 \\ -13 & 297 \end{bmatrix}$$

and[1]

$$L^{*}\,C L^{*} = [d_{ik}] = \frac{10^{2}}{19^{2}} \cdot \begin{bmatrix} 288 & -13 \\ -13 & 297 \end{bmatrix} \begin{bmatrix} 897 & 435 \\ 435 & 568 \end{bmatrix} = \frac{10^{6}}{19^{2}} \cdot \begin{bmatrix} 25.8 & -11.8 \\ -11.8 & 16.3 \end{bmatrix}.$$

Hence the standard errors

(5) $\qquad d\,(e) = \dfrac{s\,(z)}{L} \cdot \sqrt{d_{11}/16} = 0.098; \qquad d\,(E) = \dfrac{s\,(z)}{L} \cdot \sqrt{d_{22}/16} = 0.079.$

For our alternative hypothesis we have used an autoregressive process of second order, with parameters determined by the method of least squares. This gives the initial coefficients $\varrho_1 = r_1$ and $\varrho_2 = r_2$; the resulting correlogram is shown in Fig. 1a [thin unbroken line]. The calculations then proceed as in (4)–(5), except that the elements c_{ik} will be given by infinite, but rapidly convergent series. The resulting standard errors are

(6) $\qquad\qquad\qquad d\,(e) = 0.083 \qquad\quad d\,(E) = 0.069.$

Table 15·1·2 a sums up the alternative results (3), (5)–(6). We see that the autocorrelative formula has in this case only led to a moderate increase in the standard errors.

(iii) It is apparent from the two above illustrations how the numerical calculation of standard errors is performed with an arbitrary number of regressors. Having thus far considered the case of ordinary regression analysis, we further see that the same methods apply to elasticities obtained by the two devices of conditional regression analysis that were illustrated in Ch. 15·1 (ii).

To illustrate the calculation of standard errors of conditional estimates, we shall first consider the approach (15·1·7), say the elasticities $E_0 = 0.50$, $e = 0.71$. Having fixed $E_0 = 0.50$ a priori, the standard error of e is calculated on the basis of the regression (15·1·7). The correlogram of the residual z_t is the heavy broken line in Fig. 1b. Fitting a moving average of first order with $\varrho_1 = 0.42$, the standard error will be given by formulae of type (1)-(2). The classical and the autocorrelative formulae give, respectively,

(7) $\qquad d(e) = 0.076$ and $d(e) = 0.098$ with $f = 1.30$.

Similarly, fitting a second order autoregression with $\varrho_1 = r_1 = 0.55$ and $\varrho_2 = r_2 = 0.20$ we obtain

(8) $\qquad\qquad d(e) = 0.112$ with $f = 1.49$.

Next let us consider the approach (15·1·10–11), say the elasticities $e = 0.68$, $E = 0.61$ obtained by fixing $\lambda = 0.9$. To calculate the standard error of e we use the regression (15·1·11). The residual correlogram is the heavy unbroken line in Fig. 1b. Again we have fitted a first order moving average, obtaining $\varrho_1 = 0.40$, and a second order autoregression with $\varrho_1 = r_1 = 0.39$ and $\varrho_2 = r_2 = -0.06$. The standard errors given by the classical formula and the two specifications of the autocorrelative formula are, respectively,

(9) $\qquad d(e) = 0.033 \qquad d(e) = 0.043 \qquad d(e) = 0.039$.

Since $E = \lambda \cdot e$, where λ is known a priori, we are in the present case in a position to supply E with a standard error, viz. by the simple formula

(10) $\qquad\qquad d(E) = \lambda \cdot d(e).$

Making use of the alternative estimates (9), this gives

$\qquad d(E) = 0.030 \qquad d(E) = 0.039 \qquad d(E) = 0.035$.

The standard errors obtained for the conditional elasticities are shown in Table 15·1·2 b–c. On the whole, the standard errors are small, especially in the approach working with a fixed λ.

The decrease in the standard error is equivalent to a decrease in the multi-collinearity and to an increase in the determinacy of the elasticity estimates. This is the main advantage of the conditional regression analysis. By way of conclusion we stress the fact that the results of a conditional regression stand and fall with the hypotheses adopted. As regards the variants b–c here considered it would seem that both are useful in practice. In view of the general scope of Theorem 6·5·1 it would seem that the device of working with a fixed λ is often preferable to the approach where $E = E_0$ is fixed.

(iv) In calculating standard errors by the use of the autocorrelative formula we have made use of a theoretical correlogram fitted to the observed correlogram of the residuals. For a refined analysis the goodness of fit may be tested by the method due to P. Whittle that has been described in Ch. 11·4. We shall now give an illustration showing how Whittle's method works when applied to one of the correlograms in Fig. 1.

Considering the case (15·1·6), the moving average with $\varrho_1 = 0.47$ as well as the second order autoregression has been fitted by the method of least squares [see Ch. 11·3]. In each of these hypotheses, the residual series z_t is regarded as a moving summation (10·2·1) of a purely random element, say ε_t, and each hypothesis leads to an estimate of the variance $\sigma^2(\varepsilon_t)$. The moving average of first order gives

$$s^2(\varepsilon_t) = 0.7353 \, s^2(z_t),$$

whereas the autoregression of second order gives

$$s^2(\varepsilon_t) = 0.7330 \, s^2(z_t).$$

To apply Whittle's test we make use of (11·4·3) to form an approximation to the 'true' value of $\sigma^2(\varepsilon_t)$, that is, true on the hypothesis that z_t is any process of type (10·2·1). Making $k = 7$, we obtain

$$\hat{A}_0 = 0.5972 \, s^2(z_t) \sim \sigma^2(\varepsilon_t).$$

We are now in a position to form the test ratio (11·4·3) for each of the two correlograms fitted. The moving average gives

$$\Psi^2 = 2.78 \qquad \text{with 6 degrees of freedom, and } P = 83.3\%$$

and for the second order autoregression we obtain

$$\Psi^2 = 2.73 \qquad \text{with 5 degrees of freedom, and } P = 74.0\%.$$

For comparison we have finally calculated the ratio Ψ^2 on the hypothesis that the regression residual is purely random; this gives

$$\Psi^2 = 8.09 \qquad \text{with 7 degrees of freedom, and } P = 32.9\%.$$

On the null hypothesis that the hypothesis tested is true, P has a rectangular distribution over the interval $(0; 1)$. Hence the test suggests that the regression residual belongs to a process of moving summation. It is also seen that both the first order moving average and the second order autoregression have given satisfactory P-values.

(v) The autocorrelative formula (13·4·7) being a new device which has been systematically used in the calculations to be reported in Part V, we can appropriately make two or three remarks on the experience thus far collected

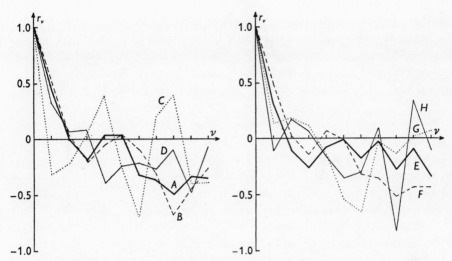

Fig. 15·2·2. Residual correlograms obtained in the analysis of market statistics.
Yearly data 1921–39.

A: Total food expenditure.   E: Agricultural food products.
B: Vegetable foods.   F: Agricultural vegetable foods.
C: Animal foods.   G: Agricultural animal foods.
D: Sugar and syrup.   H: Pork.

in its application. For illustration, Fig. 2 brings together some typical correlograms of residuals from our regression analysis of market statistics.

The first point that should be noted is perhaps that the more the regression explains of the variation in the regressand, the less pronounced, as a rule, is the autocorrelation in the regression residual. A typical instance is seen in Fig. 1: when taking the price variable for single regressor, the residual ratio γ is fairly high, and the residual correlogram shows a substantial autocorrelation, with the first four or five coefficients well above zero; when income is introduced for second explanatory variable, the ratio γ drops sharply, and the residual correlogram becomes more damped and irregular.

Secondly, even if a regression relation gives a satisfactory explanation of the regressand, there will as a rule be some autocorrelation present in the regression residual. When working on time-series consisting of about 20 observations it often happens that the hypothesis of a purely random residual is admissible, Whittle's test giving $P = 25\%$ or more. It is quite frequent, however, that the P-values obtained lie below 15 %, and although an isolated P-value of 10 % is not sufficient for rejection, the hypothesis of purely random variation can scarcely be retained if such P-values are encountered again and again.

Thirdly, as regards the residual correlograms obtained when working with time-series not longer than about 20 observations, most if not all of them could very well be fitted by quite simple correlograms. In at least 50 % of the cases it was possible to use a first order moving average with ϱ_1 about 0.4 or 0.5. In some cases an autoregression of low order was better. As compared with the classical formula, such correlograms were usually found to give a moderate increase of the standard-error, often between 5 % and 25 %.

3. The question of trend removal. – When applying regression analysis to market statistics for the purpose of making estimates of price elasticities, the question arises whether or not the variables dealt with should be cleared of their trends before the regression analysis is commenced. As is well known, there are arguments both for and against trend removal. We shall in this section review the situation, and begin with the arguments favouring the direct use of the recorded variables without previous removal of their trend.

To begin with the traditional argument against trend removal, the trend is obtained by introducing the time variable as regressor, but since time in itself does not constitute a cause variable, the trend cannot provide a causal explanation of the phenomenon under analysis.[1]

Next, suppose there is a trend in price, in income, or in any variable used as a regressor in order to explain the demand variations. Such trends should then influence the demand-regressand in accordance with the hypothetical relationship between regressand and regressors. Hence, if the trends were removed before the analysis, this would be to throw away some of the statistical information that is available on the relationship studied. If there is a substantial trend in the price variable, this is clearly a strong argument in favour of not removing the trend.[2]

For price elasticities we may distinguish between short- and long-term elasticities in the same way as was done in Ch. 14·7 for income elasticities. Just as with income elasticities we may argue that there will in general be some difference between price elasticities taken in the short-term and the long-term sense, and again we may conclude that it is the long-term elasticity that is of primary interest in practical applications.[3] Incidentally, the deduction of short-term elasticity is complicated by the fact that the consumers' first reactions to price changes are often capricious, sometimes being highly exaggerated, in other cases almost absent. Such irregularities are, as everybody knows, partly due to the advertising and propaganda that usually accompany even minor price changes, factors which blur the effect of a price change and no doubt have their share in the common misconception that price changes have a negligible effect on demand. Thus, to study the short-term effect of price changes it would be necessary to make allowance for advertising and similar factors.

According to the definition of a trend, this is the long run variation of the variable considered, whereas the trend deviations are short-term fluctuations. Hence, if we work on trend-free data, the resulting elasticities should be regarded rather as short-term elasticities. As regards the elasticities based on data with trends included, these appear to be something intermediate between short- and long-term elasticities. A strict estimation of long-term elasticities would require that we disregard the short-term fluctuations in the variables under analysis, thus working only with the trends, and in some cases it would further be appropriate to introduce a lag in the price trend to allow for a period of adjustment in demand. Anyhow, we see that, since our primary interest is in the long-term elasticity, it is in point of principle not desirable to remove the trends before estimating the price elasticity.

The salient point in the above arguments is that trends in price and other cause variables will produce a trend in the demand. We note that if a trend is present in the demand this will often dominate the short-term fluctuations. Summing up our arguments against trend removal we may thus conclude that a primary object of demand analysis is to obtain an explanation of the demand trend in terms of the trends in prices, income, and other explanatory variables.

Turning now to the arguments in favour of trend removal, the main point is, as stressed by Yule (1926), that trends may give rise to spurious correlation and spurious regression. In consumer demand, specifically, trends may arise from changes in taste, changes in the distribution of incomes, and so on. According to the above discussion the trends in themselves are not dangerous; on the contrary. The difficulty is that if a trend is present in demand it may be due to other factors than those specified as regressors. Thus, when working with the trend-affected variables the regression gives us a tentative explanation of the variations in demand, inclusive of the trend variation, and the question is whether or not the regressors include all of the relevant factors. In point of principle this is the type of situation that is always present in the choice of regressors. The difficulty, however, is greater when it comes to an explanation of the trend. This will usually have the form of a smooth curve, so that only a few degrees of freedom will be available for judging and testing the significance of the resulting elasticities, and for the same reason there is a greater risk of multicollinearity.

Summing up, we have seen that for practical as well as theoretical reasons it is desirable to work with the time-series data without removing their trends. Sometimes they have to be removed, but this should be regarded as a last resort, to be tried only if the causal explanation of trends in demand meets with unsurmountable difficulties. As far as the empirical studies in Part V are concerned, the time-series under analysis have on the whole shown a regular behaviour, and no serious doubts have arisen in the interpretation of trends.

Finally we note that a number of regression methods have been suggested that are based on the same general idea as the trend method. Such are, for example, the method of link relatives, the method of trend ratios, and the method of working with first differences of the observed series. For obvious theoretical reasons, as is also confirmed by experience, these methods give regression coefficients that are nearly the same as those obtained by removing the trends.[4] Just as for the trend method we may accordingly conclude that these methods, if applied in demand analysis, will give us short-term elasticities, and that in principle they have the character of emergency measures that may be used as a last resort if the regressand is affected by trend factors other than those of the regressors.

4. Nominal versus real prices and incomes. – This issue having been dealt with in some detail in Chs. 6·6 and 8·3, we shall here add just one or two concluding remarks.

The essential point in the present issue is that inflationary and deflationary trends are to be interpreted as changes in the monetary unit, so that when working with real values we may regard the monetary unit as approximately constant during the period covered by the market statistics under analysis.[1] We note that the passage from nominal to real values is a device that is logically consistent with the definition of a demand function, for the nominal prices and incomes that refer to one and the same time point will be divided by the same index number, and we know from Theorem 4·5·2 that demand functions are homogeneous of order zero, so that the division leaves the demand functions unaltered. It will further be noted that the reference to Theorem 4·5·2 is legitimate if — as in the present work — we confine ourselves to a static approach. If on the other hand we consider a dynamic demand problem, say to what extent the savings habits are influenced by anticipations of inflationary and deflationary trends, it is not sufficient to work with real prices and incomes, and among the explanatory variables we must further include income changes, lagged incomes, etc.

In the preceding comment, the distinction between real and nominal values has been considered from the viewpoint of the statistical deduction of demand elasticities. A proposition like Theorem 6·6·1, on the other hand, deals with the two variants from the viewpoint of their application. For estimating the quantitative effect of given changes in prices and income on demand we see that it does not matter whether we work with real or nominal elasticities, provided of course that the variant employed corresponds to the given price and income variables. As regards the applications we may further note that, if the commodity considered forms only a small fraction of the total budget, Theorem 6·6·1 shows that the difference between the real and nominal elasticity will be small or negligible.

5. Aggregate commodities. Parallel versus isolated price changes. – In Chs. 5·6 and 6·4 we have considered some theoretical aspects of the demand for aggregate commodities and their constituents. Turning now to some related questions of empirical demand analysis, we shall examine two lines of approach, taking into consideration on the one hand the aggregate demand, on the other hand the demand for one of the substitute constituents.[1]

(i) Let the total demand for the aggregate commodity considered be measured by any of formulae (5·6·1–3), say q^*, and let the price of the aggregate be measured by a suitable price index, say p^*. Then q^* and p^* are in this approach dealt with as the quantity and price data in an ordinary demand analysis [Ch. 15·1]. For example, considering the aggregate demand of butter and margarine, formulae

$$(1) \qquad p^* = \frac{q_1 p_1 + q_2 p_2}{q_1 + q_2} \qquad q^* = c \cdot (p^*)^{-e} \cdot \mu^E$$

show (a) a price index for the aggregate demand, and (b) a demand function with constant price elasticity e and constant income elasticity E.

(ii) In this approach we consider a specific commodity, assuming its demand to be a function of (a) the price of the commodity, (b) the price of one or more other commodities or substitutes, (c) income, and, if necessary, other explanatory variables. For example, considering butter demand, we may assume

$$(2) \qquad q_1 = c \cdot (p_1)^{-e_{11}} \cdot (p_2)^{-e_{12}} \cdot \mu^{E_1}.$$

Here e_{11} is the price elasticity of butter, e_{12} is the cross elasticity of butter w.r.t. margarine price, and E_1 is the income elasticity of butter. Since a rise in the price of margarine will in general cause a rise in butter demand, we have $e_{12} < 0$.

Formula (2) can be rewritten as follows,

$$(3) \qquad q_1 = c \cdot (p_1)^{-e_{11}^*} \cdot \left(\frac{p_2}{p_1}\right)^{-e_{12}} \cdot \mu^{E_1}, \qquad \text{with } e_{11}^* = e_{11} + e_{12}.$$

Comparing (2) and (3), we note

e_{11} is the price elasticity of butter, subject to the condition that margarine price is held constant,

e_{11}^* is the price elasticity of butter, subject to the condition that the price ratio p_2/p_1 of margarine and butter is held constant,

e_{12} is the cross elasticity of butter w.r.t. margarine price, subject to the condition that butter price is held constant. Alternatively, according to (3), we may interpret e_{12} as the elasticity of butter w.r.t. the price ratio of margarine and butter.

In other words, e_{11} is the price elasticity of butter, on condition that there is an *isolated price change in butter*, not in margarine, whereas e_{11}^* is the price elasticity of butter, on condition that there is a *proportional change in the price of margarine and butter*. Knowing that $e_{12} < 0$, we infer from (3b)

$$(4) \qquad\qquad e_{11}^* < e_{11}.$$

In empirical demand analysis, we may work with any of formulae (2) or (3). The difference lies in the choice of explanatory variables; thus in (3) one of the regressors will be the price ratio p_2/p_1. It will be observed that the theoretical identity between approaches (2) and (3) will hold good only approximately when it comes to the empirical analysis. Specifically, there will in general be some discrepancy between the two estimates obtained for e_{12}.

It may occur that the market statistics show that the price changes of margarine and butter have on the whole been proportional during the period covered by the data. Approach (2) will then be disturbed by a multicollinearity in the sense of Ch. 2·6; otherwise expressed, the data do not contain sufficient information for the estimation of both the elasticities e_{11} and e_{12}. In such case we may instead make use of approach (3), taking the price ratio p_2/p_1 to be constant, and keeping in mind in the applications that the resulting price elasticity of butter, e_{11}^*, is subject to the condition that margarine price changes in proportion to the butter price.

Finally, if we compare approaches (i) and (ii) we see that (ii) extracts more information from the material than (i). In practice, approach (i) may serve to give a broad outline of the demand structure. Approach (ii) gives more detailed results, but requires more detailed and better data, and can therefore be used only if such are available. We see that in principle it is possible to subject each constituent of the aggregate to an analysis in accordance with approach (ii). It need hardly be added that the demand functions arrived at will not add up exactly so as to give an aggregate demand function of type (1). Nevertheless there will in general be an approximate agreement between the results obtained in the two approaches (i) – (ii).

EXERCISES FOR PART IV.[1]

1. Let L be the least-squares regression line in a scatter diagram of three observations, e.g. the three circles in Fig. 1·2·1. Show that if the middle observation lies on the one side of L the two other observations lie on the opposite side.

2. Show that the least-squares regression of y on x is independent of the measuring units of x and y; that is, if L and L_a are the regressions before and after a change in the units, L_a coincides with the line obtained by subjecting L to the same change in the units.

3. Let x and y be the horizontal and vertical axes in a scatter diagram like the crosses in Fig. 1'2'1b. Writing L' and L'', respectively, for the *diagonal* and the *orthogonal* regressions of y on x, these are, in symbols easily understood,

(L') $y - m_y = b' \ (x - m_x)$ with $b' = \pm \sigma_y / \sigma_x$;

(L'') $y - m_y = b'' \ (x - m_x)$ with $b'' = \tan v$,   where $\tan 2v = \dfrac{2 \sigma_x \sigma_y r_{xy}}{\sigma_x^2 - \sigma_y^2}$;

which definitions are subject to the qualification that L' and L'' should be intermediate between the regressions of y upon x and of x upon y.

Show that L' but not L'' is independent of the measuring units of x and y.

Further show that the two regressions coincide if, and only if, $\sigma_x = \sigma_y$.

4. Adopting Yule's notation for regression coefficients, let

$$b_{01}, \quad b_{01 \cdot 2}, \quad b_{01 \cdot 23}, \quad \ldots, \quad b_{01 \cdot 23 \ldots n}, \ldots$$

be the coefficient of x_1 in the regression of x_0 upon a set of regressors $x_1, x_2, \ldots$ which is successively extended. For graphical illustration we attach a plane set of vectors v_n to the end-point of a horizontal base line, making v_n of slope $b_{01 \cdot 23 \ldots n}$ and of length $R_{0 \cdot 12 \ldots n}$. Interpret Theorems 12'3'1–5 in terms of such a graph.[1]

5. When forming the regression (12'2'5) it is often convenient to work with variables reduced by suitable constants, say $x_v^{(t)} - a_i$ instead of $x_v^{(t)}$ $(i = 0, 1, \ldots, h)$. Show that this substitution does not affect the coefficients $b_1, \ldots, b_h$.

6. Given a representation (12'1'1) with $h + k$ approximating elements,

$$f = b_1 f_1 + \cdots + b_h f_h + b_{h+1} f_{h+1} + \cdots + b_{h+k} f_{h+k} + z,$$

we form a similar representation

(1) $f = b_1^* f_1^* + \cdots + b_h^* f_h^* + z^*$

by taking the f_i^* to be the least-squares residuals obtained when representing the f_i in terms of $f_{h+1}, \ldots, f_{h+k}$, say

$$f_i = b_{i1} f_{h+1} + \cdots + b_{ik} f_{h+k} + f_i^* \qquad\qquad i = 1, \ldots, h.$$

Then establish

$$b_1^* = b_1, \quad \ldots, \quad b_h^* = b_h.$$

Moreover, letting f^* be defined in the same way as the f_i^*, show that it has no influence on the b_i^* whether (1) is formed with f or f^* to the left.

Special case (Frisch and Waugh, 1933): In time-series regression we obtain the same regression coefficients when working on data from which linear trends have been removed as when we keep the trends and include time t in the set of regressors.

7. Given the regression relations

$$x_0 = a_0 + a_1 x_1 + \cdots + a_h x_h + z \qquad x_1 = b_0 + b_1 y_1 + \cdots + b_k y_k + u = x_1^* + u,$$

suppose u is uncorrelated with x_0 and $x_2, \ldots, x_h$. Show that if we substitute x_1^* for x_1 in the first regression, we shall obtain the regression of x_0 upon $x_1^*, x_2, \ldots, x_h$, possibly with a different residual.

Special case: The predictive relation (12'5'9 b). As seen from this example, the substitution will in general increase the residual variance.

8. Considering an autoregressive process $\{\xi_t\}$, verify that the prediction formulae (12'5'8–9) are equivalent, with probability 1.

9. Let $\qquad x_1 = a_0 + a_2 x_2 + \cdots + a_h x_h = x_1^* + z,$

$$y = b_0 + b_1 x_1 + b_2 x_2 + \cdots + b_h x_h + z^* \quad \text{and} \quad y = c_0 + c_2 x_2 + \cdots + c_h x_h + z^{**}$$

be three least-squares regressions. If $x_2, \ldots, x_h$ are known, the three regressions give two predictions for y, viz.

$$y^* = b_0 + b_1 x_1^* + b_2 x_2 + \cdots + b_h x_h \quad \text{and} \quad y^{**} = c_0 + c_2 x_2 + \cdots + c_h x_h.$$

Show that the two predictions are equivalent, so that $y^* = y^{**}$ with probability 1. Generalizing to the case of $m \, (< h)$ substitutional regressions with

$$x_i = a_{i0} + a_{i,\, m+1} x_{m+1} + \cdots + a_{ih} x_h \qquad (i = 1, \ldots, m),$$

use the result to verify the final statement in Ch. 2'7 (i), viz. that systems (2'7'1) and (2'7'3) are equivalent for the purpose of prediction.

10. Forming the regression of $x^{(0)}$ upon $x^{(1)}, \ldots, x^{(h)}$, suppose $x^{(0)}$ is not linear in $x^{(1)}, \ldots, x^{(h)}$, whereas we assume multicollinearity in the sense of Ch. 2'6, so that one or more linear relations are exactly satisfied by $x^{(1)}, \ldots, x^{(h)}$. According to Theorem 12'3'2 D at least one of the regression coefficients will then be indeterminate. Making use of the classical formula (13'2'6) for standard errors, or alternatively the more general formula (13'4'7), show that for every indeterminate coefficient the standard error is infinite.[1]

11 (Wold; 1940, 1950). Forming a regression $y = b_0 + b_1 x^{(1)} + \ldots + b_h x^{(h)} + b_{h+1} x^{(h+1)} + z$, let us apply conditional regression by fixing b_{h+1} a priori, say $b_{h+1} = b^*$. Then (a) the conditional least-squares estimates $b_0, b_1, \ldots, b_h$ will be given by an ordinary system of normal equations (12'1'4), provided we work with $y^* = y - b^* x^{(h+1)}$ instead of y, and (b) on the null hypothesis that b^* equals its theoretical value, say β_{h+1}, the resulting $b_0, b_1, \ldots, b_h$ will have the properties of ordinary least-squares estimates, so that under general conditions they will be approximately unbiased, consistent, and normally distributed; specifically, Theorems 13'2 a–d and 13'4'1–2 will apply if we replace y by y^*.

Special case: The conditional regression (15'1'7).

12 (J. Durbin[1]). Let $\eta_\nu = \beta_0 + \beta_1 x_\nu^{(1)} + \beta_2 x_\nu^{(2)} + \zeta_\nu$ be a theoretical regression in accordance with the Gauss-Fisher specification (13'2'3). Adopting Yule's notation for empirical regression coefficients, show that $\beta_2 > d\,(b_{02\cdot1})$ is, for large samples, a necessary and sufficient condition in order that $d\,(b_{01\cdot2}) < d(b_{01})$.

This suggests the rule of thumb that, if the estimate $b_{02\cdot1}$ of β_2 is smaller than its standard error, we had better drop $x^{(2)}$ as an explanatory variable when estimating β_1. It will be noted that this rule rests on the classical assumption of independent observations.

13. Considering two random variables x, y with $\mu_{ik} = E(x - m_x)^i \, (y - m_y)^k$ for central moments of their joint probability distribution, let b be the least-squares regression coefficient of y upon x in a sample of n independent pairs of observation $x_i, y_i \, (i = 1, \ldots, n)$. Show that, asymptotically for n large, b is normally distributed with mean and variance

$$E\,(b) \cong \beta = \frac{\mu_{11}}{\mu_{20}} \qquad d^2\,(b) \cong \frac{1}{n} \left(\frac{\mu_{22}}{\mu_{20}^2} - \frac{2\,\mu_{11}\mu_{31}}{\mu_{20}^3} + \frac{\mu_{11}^2\mu_{40}}{\mu_{20}^4} \right).$$

Hint: Make use of the central limit theorem for functions of moments [see H. Cramér (1945, Ch. 27'7–8)].

14 (Wold, 1950). Let $y_t = a + bx_t + z_t$ be the regression of y upon x, formed on the basis of a sample x_t, y_t $(t = 1, \ldots, n)$ of the random variables ξ_t, η_t $(t = 1, \ldots, n)$. Suppose that we have

$$\eta_t = \alpha + \beta \xi_t + \zeta_t \quad \text{with} \quad \xi_t = \varepsilon_1 + \varepsilon_2 + \cdots + \varepsilon_t$$

where $\varepsilon_1, \ldots, \varepsilon_n$ and $\zeta_1, \ldots, \zeta_n$ are independent normal variables with expectation zero and standard deviation σ_ε and σ_ζ, respectively. Verify the relations

$$E(a) = \alpha; \quad E(b) \simeq \beta; \quad d(a) \simeq c_1/\sqrt{n}; \quad d(b) \simeq c_2/n; \quad (c_1, c_2 \text{ are constants}).$$

We see that, as usual, a and b are unbiased and consistent estimates of α and β. The standard error of b, however, is not of the usual order $c/\sqrt{n}$, which is due to the fact that the regressor ξ_t forms an evolutive process.

15. The following theorems A–C illustrate the rationale of randomization in controlled experiment. The two first theorems refer to the case of strictly linear regression, whereas linearity is not assumed in the third. Verify the theorems, and generalize to the case of several controlled variables, say $x^{(1)}, \ldots, x^{(h)}$.

Suppose y is a function of one controlled variable x and a number of disturbance factors $\varepsilon^{(1)}, \ldots, \varepsilon^{(s)}$. The $\varepsilon^{(i)}$ may or may not be observable, but they have a well-defined probability distribution, say $P^{(\varepsilon)}$. Performing n observations x_i, y_i $(i = 1, \ldots, n)$, suppose the experiment is randomized to the effect that, if we write $\varepsilon_i = (\varepsilon_i^{(1)}, \ldots, \varepsilon_i^{(s)})$ for the disturbance factors of the ith observation, then (a) all ε_i have the same distribution $P^{(\varepsilon)}$, and (b) $\varepsilon_1, \ldots, \varepsilon_n$ are independent in the sense of (9'1'9). Let

$$y = a + bx + z \quad \text{with} \quad a = y; \quad b = r\frac{s_y}{s_x}$$

be the regression of y upon x as formed on the basis of the n observations.

A. Further suppose that y allows the representation

(1) $$y = \alpha + \beta x + \zeta(\varepsilon^{(1)}, \ldots, \varepsilon^{(s)})$$

and let $E^{(\varepsilon)}$ denote expectations formed w.r.t. the distribution $P^{(\varepsilon)}$. Then

(2) $$E^{(\varepsilon)}(b) = \beta; \quad d(b) = \frac{\sigma_\zeta}{s_x} \cdot \frac{1}{\sqrt{n}} \quad \text{with} \quad \sigma_\zeta^2 = E^{(\varepsilon)}(\zeta^2) - (E^{(\varepsilon)}\zeta)^2$$

showing that b is an unbiased and consistent estimate of β.

In (1), we note, it involves no loss of generality to assume $E^{(\varepsilon)}(\zeta) = 0$, which gives

(3) $$E(a) = \alpha \qquad d(a) = \sigma_\zeta/\sqrt{n}.$$

B. More generally, suppose that y allows the representation (1), with a disturbance $\zeta(x, \varepsilon^{(1)}, \ldots, \varepsilon^{(s)})$ which depends upon x, but still satisfies

(4) $$E^{(\varepsilon)}(\zeta) = 0 \qquad \text{for all } x.$$

Further suppose the observations x are arranged according to a specified distribution, say $P^{(x)}$, for example an equally weighted distribution. Then (2)–(3) remain valid, asymptotically for large samples, provided all expectations $E^{(\varepsilon)}$ are replaced by expectations $E^{(x, \varepsilon)}$ formed w.r.t. the joint distribution of $x, \varepsilon^{(1)}, \ldots, \varepsilon^{(s)}$, where x is independent of the disturbance factors $\varepsilon^{(i)}$.

C. Still more generally, let x and the $\varepsilon^{(l)}$ be subject to the assumptions under B, and suppose y is an arbitrary function, say

(5) $$y = \eta\,(x,\,\varepsilon^{(1)},\,\ldots,\,\varepsilon^{(s)}) = E^{(\varepsilon)}\,(\eta\,|\,x) + \zeta\,(x,\,\varepsilon^{(1)},\,\ldots,\,\varepsilon^{(s)}),$$

where $E^{(\varepsilon)}(\eta\,|\,x)$ is the conditional expectation of η for fixed x. Then, for large samples, b is an unbiased estimate of the moment regression coefficient, in symbols

(6) $$y = \beta\,x + \zeta^*\,(x,\,\varepsilon^{(1)},\,\ldots,\,\varepsilon^{(s)}); \quad \beta = \frac{E^{(x,\,\varepsilon)}\,(x\,y) - E^{(x)}\,(x)\cdot E^{(x,\,\varepsilon)}\,(y)}{E^{(x)}\,(x^2) - [E^{(x)}\,(x)]^2}; \quad E^{(x,\,\varepsilon)}\,(b) = \beta.$$

Moreover, the standard error of b is of order $1/\sqrt{n}$, so that b is also a consistent estimate.

In (5), we note, the residual ζ will satisfy (4). In (6), on the other hand, we can in general assert nothing more than

$$E^{(x,\,\varepsilon)}\,(\zeta^*) = 0.$$

16. Forming an empirical regression by making use of the traditional method and, alternatively, the method of Aitken, let the standard deviation of the residuals in the resulting regressions be denoted s and s^*. In the notation of Ch. 13·3 we have

$$s = \left[\frac{1}{n}\,(y - Xb)'\,(y - Xb)\right]^{1/2}; \quad s^* = \left[\frac{1}{n}\,(y - Xb^*)'\,(y - Xb^*)\right]^{1/2} \text{ and } s \le s^*.$$

17. Let $f_1,\,\ldots,\,f_n$ and f be $n+1$ elements in Hilbert space, and suppose we wish to approximate the f_i by a linear expression in f, say $f_i = a + b\,f + z_i$ $(i = 1,\,\ldots,\,n)$, making $S = \Sigma\,\|z_i\|^2$ a minimum.

Establish a parallel to the Gauss-Markov theorem 13·3·1. Generalize for a linear form in several elements $f,\,g,\,\ldots$, and by forming S as a weighted sum of squared norms.

18. The linear regression (12·2·5) extends to the case when the observations are complex numbers. The principle of least squares then requires that $\Sigma\,|z_\nu|^2$ be a minimum, where $|z_\nu|$ is the modulus of the residual z_ν. Show that the regression coefficients will be determined by the following system of normal equations.

$$b_1 \Sigma\,x_\nu^{(1)}\,\bar{x}_\nu^{(i)} + \cdots + b_h \Sigma\,x_\nu^{(h)}\,\bar{x}_\nu^{(i)} = \Sigma\,x_\nu^{(0)}\,\bar{x}_\nu^{(i)} \qquad (i = 1,\,\ldots,\,h)$$

where $\bar{x}$ stands for the complex conjugate of x.

More generally, show how (12·1·4) should be modified if the elements in (12·1·1) have complex inner products with $(f,\,g) = \overline{(f,\,g)}$. Interpret the resulting approximation as an orthogonal projection in (complex) Hilbert space.

19 (Elfving, 1952). Suppose that y allows the representation

(1) $$y = \alpha + \beta\,x + z,$$

where z is a disturbance variable independent of x. Further suppose the disturbances z_i of different observations $(x_i,\,y_i)$ are independent. Wishing to estimate β by a least-squares regression coefficient b formed on the basis of n observations $(x_i,\,y_i)$, suppose we are in a position to allocate $x_1,\,\ldots,\,x_n$ freely among k potential observations, say $x^{(1)} < x^{(2)} < \cdots < x^{(k)}$. Show that the standard error $d\,(b)$ of b will be the smallest possible if we allocate the observations x_i so as to make half of them equal $x^{(1)}$, half equal $x^{(k)}$.

Illustration. In Buffon's famous needle experiment for the 'statistical' determination π, let (1) be the equation of the needle, taking the x-axis to be parallel to the tiles, so that β is the slope of the needle against the tiles. To estimate β as accurately as possible, we should allocate the observations to the ends of the needle, making the same number of observations at each end (for the purpose of this illustration, we assume that there are errors of observation in y, but not in x).

20. To fit any of Törnqvist's demand functions (1'1'5) to a set of data μ_ν, d_ν according to the principle of least squares, we may proceed as follows. (a) Fixing a tentative value for parameter β, the principle of least squares gives us a linear system of normal equations for determining the other parameter or parameters; for the resulting parameters we calculate the residuals z_ν and their square sum. (b) Repeating the calculation for other values of β, let $S(\beta)$ be the curve obtained when plotting the residual square sum against β. (c) Find by interpolation or graphic construction the value of β, say β_0, for which $S(\beta)$ is a minimum, and find by interpolation or by a new system of normal equations the corresponding values of the other parameters, say α_0 or α_0, γ_0.

The table below shows the food expenditure in the 50 Gothenburg families of Fig. 1'2'1:

ν	1	2	3	4	5	6
μ_ν	579	665	711	754	851	1043
d_ν	300	341	351	369	377	411

Make use of the above method to fit (1'1'5 a), and show that the resulting least-squares estimates are
$$\alpha_0 = 705 \qquad \beta_0 = 730.$$

21 (Törnqvist, 1941). An alternative to the method of the preceding exercise is to weight the residuals when forming their square sum, minimizing not $\Sigma\, z_\nu^2$ but instead $\Sigma\, [(\mu_\nu + \beta)\, z_\nu]^2$. The weighting brings a considerable reduction in the computations, and if the Törnqvist function gives at all a reasonable fit, the weighting has no appreciable effect on the parameter estimates.

Show that the weighting leads to a linear system of normal equations for the simultaneous estimation of all parameters. As applied to the data of the previous exercise, this device gives

for formula (1'1'5 a): $\alpha_0 = 667$; $\beta_0 = 647$;

for formula (1'1'5 b): $\alpha_0 = 481$; $\beta_0 = -276$; $\gamma_0 = 391$.

22 (Törnqvist, 1941). Verify the following identity for broken linear forms:

(1) $\qquad$ If $\quad y = \dfrac{A\,x + B}{C\,x + D} \quad$ then $\quad \dfrac{y - y_0}{y - y_1} : \dfrac{y_2 - y_0}{y_2 - y_1} = \dfrac{x - x_0}{x - x_1} : \dfrac{x_2 - x_0}{x_2 - x_1}$

where y_i is the value of y for $x = x_i$ $(i = 0, 1, 2)$.

The familiar identity (1) gives a short-cut method for estimating Törnqvist's functions, or alternatively for obtaining the tentative value of parameter β required in the method of Ex. 20. Thus if we take three equidistant incomes μ_0, μ_1, μ_2 and calculate the corresponding demand values d_0, d_1, d_2 by graphic graduation or some other approximation, (1) gives us the function of type (1'1'5 b) that passes through the three points (μ_0, d_0), (μ_1, d_1), (μ_2, d_2), or in explicit form

(2) $\qquad d = \dfrac{(\lambda\, d_1 - 2\, d_0)\, \mu - d_1\, \mu_0 + 2\, d_0\, \mu_1}{(\lambda - 2)\, \mu - \lambda\, \mu_0 + 2\, \mu_1} \quad$ with $\quad \lambda = \dfrac{d_2 - d_0}{d_2 - d_1}$.

For function (1'1'5 a) the same device applies if we make $\mu_0 = d_0 = 0$; the resulting parameters are

$$\alpha = \frac{d_1 \, d_2}{2 \, d_1 - d_2} \qquad \beta = \frac{2 \, \mu_1 \, (d_2 - d_1)}{2 \, d_1 - d_2} .$$

For function (1`1`5 c), finally, the same method can be used if we work with the variables $x = \mu$, $y = d/\mu$.

Illustration. To fit function (1`1`5 a) to the data of Ex. 20, we make $\mu_0 = 0$; $\mu_1 = 550$; $\mu_2 = 1100$ and obtain $d_0 = 0$; $d_1 \sim 295$; $d_2 \sim 420$, which gives the estimates

$$\alpha = 729 \qquad \beta = 809.$$

23 (Wold, 1940). Show that the theoretical relations (6`4`1–2) between income elasticities of aggregate and separate commodities will be approximately satisfied by the empirical elasticities obtained from family budget data, provided the elasticities are deduced by the least-squares regression of expenditure (or quantity) on income.

Establish a similar theorem for the relation (7`2`5) between price elasticities referring to individual and market demand.

Hint: The regression formula for empirical income elasticities is

$$(1) \qquad E_\mu x = \frac{\Sigma \log x^{(i)}/x^* \cdot \log \mu^{(i)}/\mu^*}{\Sigma \, (\log x^{(i)}/x^*)^2} , \qquad \text{where} \quad \mu^* = \left(\prod_{i=1}^{s} \mu^{(i)} \right)^{1/s} \quad \text{and} \quad x^* = \left(\prod_{i=1}^{s} x^{(i)} \right)^{1/s}$$

are the geometric averages of individual incomes and expenditures. Writing $\bar{x}$ for the arithmetic average of expenditures, and using subscripts to denote the m sub-items,

$$(2) \qquad \log \frac{x_\nu^{(i)}}{x_\nu^*} \simeq \frac{x_\nu^{(i)} - \bar{x}_\nu}{\bar{x}_\nu}; \qquad \bar{x}_1 \log \frac{x_1^{(i)}}{x_1^*} + \cdots + \bar{x}_m \log \frac{x_m^{(i)}}{x_m^*} \simeq \bar{x} \log \frac{x^{(i)}}{x^*}, \qquad (i = 1, \ldots, s).$$

Making use of (2 b) it is easy to see that (6`4`2) will be approximately satisfied if the elasticities involved are estimated by the use of (1a).

24 (Wold, 1940). In the rule of thumb given in Ch. 14`5 the point of demarcation between elasticities over- and underestimated is unit elasticity in the case when the same scale of consumption is used for regressor and regressand, whereas the demarcation will be at some other point if the two scales differ.

25. Given a set of n time-series $x_t^{(1)}, \ldots, x_t^{(n)}$, formula (12`7`3) provides a recursive representation of m ($\leqq n$) series. Show that the total number of such representations is

$$n! \left(1 + \frac{1}{1!} + \frac{1}{2!} + \cdots + \frac{1}{(n-1)!} \right) \simeq n! \, e.$$

Further show that the number of causally different representations is $n!$. This fact brings out in full relief the necessity of having a sound theoretical basis for the model when a recursive system (2`7`1) is applied to empirical data.

26. Let a q-dimensional stochastic process $\{x_t^{(1)}, \ldots, x_t^{(q)}\}$ be defined by a linear recursive system (12`7`3) with $p = 0$, so that all $x_t^{(i)}$ are endogenous variables. Further let $\left| b_{ik}(\lambda) \right|$ be the determinant defined by

$$b_{ik}(\lambda) = b_{ik}^* + b_{ik}^{(1)} \lambda + b_{ik}^{(2)} \lambda^2 + \cdots + b_{ik}^{(h)} \lambda^h \qquad (i, \, k = 1, \ldots, h)$$

where $b_{ik}^* = b_{ik}^{(0)}$ for $k < i$, $b_{ii}^* = -1$ and $b_{ik}^* = 0$ for $k > i$. Suppose the disturbance process $\{z_t^{(1)}, \ldots, z_t^{(q)}\}$ is stationary and nondeterministic. Then for $\{x_t^{(1)}, \ldots, x_t^{(q)}\}$ to be stationary it is necessary and sufficient that all roots of the equation $\left| b_{ik}(\lambda) \right| = 0$ should lie within the periphery of the unit circle.

Hint: See Mann and Wald (1943) for a related theorem on structural systems (2`7`3). Special case: Setting $h = 1$ we obtain Theorem 10`2`2.

27. Given a linear recursive system, suppose that in each relation the residual is uncorrelated with all explanatory variables of the same relation. Assuming the parameters to be unspecified, we may then distinguish two cases, say (A) and (B), according as for an arbitrary period t all residuals $z_t^{(1)}$, $z_t^{(2)}$, ... are or are not necessarily uncorrelated.

Verify that the following systems are of the type indicated,

$$\text{(A)} \quad \begin{cases} y_t^{(1)} = \alpha x_t + z_t^{(1)} \\ y_t^{(2)} = \beta y_t^{(1)} + \gamma x_t + z_t^{(2)} \end{cases} \qquad \text{(B)} \quad \begin{cases} y_t^{(1)} = \alpha x_t + z_t^{(1)} \\ y_t^{(2)} = \beta y_t^{(1)} + z_t^{(2)}. \end{cases}$$

More generally, show that the recursive system belongs to category (A) if, in every relation but the last one, the effect variable and all explanatory variables are included among the explanatory variables of a later relation.

28. Considering system (B) of the preceding exercise, suppose the disturbances $z_t^{(1)}$, $z_t^{(2)}$ are (a) intercorrelated, say with correlation coefficient ϱ, and (b) uncorrelated with the exogenous variable x_t. Show that $y_t^{(1)}$ and $z_t^{(2)}$ will be intercorrelated, with coefficient

(1) $\qquad \qquad \lambda \cdot \varrho \quad$ where $\quad \lambda = \sigma(z_t^{(1)}) / \sigma(y_t^{(1)})$.

The correlation (1) implies that the least-squares estimate of β will be biased. Assuming that ϱ and λ are small of the first order, show that the bias will be small of the *third* order. This being a stronger statement than the proximity theorem [cf Ch. 2·3], finally show that the argument extends to any recursive system of category (B).

29. For a relation K in a structural system of the linear type (2·7·2) to be identifiable, the criterion of Koopmans (1949) states as necessary and sufficient that a relation with the same properties as K cannot be obtained as a linear combination of other relations in the system. According to this criterion, a linear recursive system is always identifiable.[1]

Hint: Make use of the case distinction (A)–(B) of Ex. 27.

30. This and the two remaining exercises deal with supplementary and more or less obvious variations of the recursive approach.

a. Given a linear recursive model (R), suppose that yearly statistical data are available, but that the period of the model is shorter, say a quarter of a year. A rough estimate of the model is obtained if we interpolate quarterly data from the yearly data, and take the resulting quarterly data as a basis for estimating the parameters of (R) by the use of least-squares regression.

Devise a sampling experiment to investigate the accuracy of this approximate method.

b (Bentzel and Wold, 1946). Let the recursive model considered be modified by introducing approximate interpolations of type

$$x_{t+1/4} = \tfrac{3}{4} x_t + \tfrac{1}{4} x_{t+1}; \qquad x_{t+1/2} = \tfrac{1}{2} x_t + \tfrac{1}{2} x_{t+1}; \qquad x_{t+3/4} = \tfrac{1}{4} x_t + \tfrac{3}{4} x_{t+1}.$$

Show that this formal device transforms model (R) into a structural model (S). After the transformation, it will be noted, the model does not allow an immediate causal interpretation.

31. Suppose that $y_t^{(1)}$, $y_t^{(2)}$ are related by a bilateral causal interdependence, and that both variables depend on a lagged explanatory variable, say x_{t-1}. We may then represent $y_t^{(1)}, y_t^{(2)}$ by way of a joint conditional distribution, with x_{t-1} for conditional variable. Assuming normal distribution, the conditional distribution has 7 parameters. In fact, writing

(1) $\qquad E(y_t^{(i)} \mid x_{t-1}) = \alpha_i + \beta_i x_{t-1}; \quad y_t^{(i)} = \alpha_i + \beta_i x_{t-1} + z_t^{(i)} \qquad (i = 1, 2)$

the parameters are

$$\alpha_1, \ \alpha_2, \ \beta_1, \ \beta_2, \ \mu_{11}, \ \mu_{12}, \ \mu_{22} \quad \text{with} \quad \mu_{ik} = E\left(z_t^{(i)} \cdot z_t^{(k)} \mid x_{t-1}\right).$$

Considering the following points A–C, show that the arguments extend to multilateral interdependence between any number of variables $y_t^{(1)}, y_t^{(2)}, \ldots$.

A. Show that the method of least-squares regression gives unbiased estimates of α_1, α_2, β_1, β_2 and that the variances and the covariance of the regression residuals provide unbiased estimates of μ_{11}, μ_{22} and μ_{12}.

B. We see that system (1b) leads to an extension of regression analysis to the simultaneous treatment of two or more regressands. The difference from the case of a single regression relation is that the estimation of the conditional dispersion matrix $[\mu_{ik}]$ enters as an essential part of the analysis. The approach (1b) may accordingly be referred to as *simultaneous regression analysis* or, alternatively, *matrix regression*.

The idea of matrix regression is clearly of general scope, applicable not only in time-series analysis. If we consider a controlled experiment where there are several effect variables, each measuring a particular aspect of the phenomenon under analysis, e.g. the weight and the dry content in a plant experiment, the effect variables may be treated by matrix regression.[1]

C. Let us compare the approach of matrix regression with the approach of structural systems (2·7·2–3). We see that the reduced form (2·7·3) is formally the same as a system of simultaneous regressions. Given x_{t-1}, the system (1b) and the corresponding reduced form are accordingly equivalent for the purpose of estimating $y_t^{(1)}$ and $y_t^{(2)}$.

Suppose we know x_{t-1} and one of the variables $y_t^{(1)}, y_t^{(2)}$. The other variable may then be estimated by the use of a linear regression,

(2)   either $y_t^{(1)} = \overset{*}{\alpha}_1 + \overset{*}{\beta}_1 x_{t-1} + \overset{*}{\gamma}_1 y_t^{(2)} + z_t'$ or $y_t^{(2)} = \overset{*}{\alpha}_2 + \overset{*}{\beta}_2 x_{t-1} + \overset{*}{\gamma}_2 y_t^{(1)} + z_t''$.

This, however, is not a system of simultaneous regressions in the sense of A–B. We note that the system (2) is formally of the structural type (2·7·2). Further we note that, if $\overset{*}{\gamma}_1 \neq 0$ and $\overset{*}{\gamma}_2 \neq 0$ the system (2) will not allow a causal interpretation.

32, a. On constructing a linear recursive system, suppose two endogenous variables, say $y_t^{(i)}$ and $y_t^{(i+1)}$, lead to very complicated causal relationships. We may then make the short-cut of treating them as jointly dependent, by the device of matrix regression. Show that this short-cut will in no way disturb the application of least-squares regression to the recursive relations of the system.

b. A similar case is present if $y_t^{(i)}$ and $y_t^{(i+1)}$ are regarded as being in equilibrium. Introducing

(1) $y_t^{(i)} \sim y_t^{(i+1)}$ or $y_t^{(i)} - y_t^{i+1} = z_t$

where z_t is an 'error in the equation' [cf Ch. 2·4] we obtain a mixed system of recursive and equilibrium relations, and again we conclude that the recursive part of the system can be treated by least-squares regression.

c. An alternative device for dealing with (1) is to introduce $S = \underset{t}{\Sigma}(y_t^{(i)} - y_t^{(i+1)})^2$ as a side condition in the regression analysis of the recursive relations. Fixing $S = S_0$, it turns out that the regression estimates will in general depend upon S_0. (The limiting case $S_0 = 0$ corresponds to the method adopted by L. Klein (1950) in his applications of structural systems, the difference being that Klein uses maximum-likelihood estimates instead of least-squares analysis.)

PART V

By L. JURÉEN and H. WOLD

Empirical findings

Chapter 16.

INCOME ELASTICITIES OBTAINED FROM FAMILY BUDGET DATA

1. Introductory. – As explained in the Preface and in Ch. 1·6, the empirical findings here recorded were compiled from a series of investigations by the authors into the demand structure in Sweden. Since these studies were carried out at the request of government agencies primarily for purposes of food rationing and agricultural policy, they have centered on food demand. The Swedish data available for demand analysis — family budget data and market statistics — have been systematically sifted in the course of these investigations. Having employed hundreds of statistical series we cannot, in the space available, give more than a selection of the results obtained. The exposition will stress the practical applications of demand analysis, paying particular attention to the aggregate demand within the main social strata for the principal groups of food items. At the same time it will be stressed how theory and empirical results support each other and combine to give a reliable picture of the demand structure.

The present chapter deals with family budget data, Ch. 17 with market statistics. In Ch. 18 the empirical findings are employed for two experiments in demand prediction. Reference is made to the original investigations for a more detailed exposition and for further results. Most of Ch. 16 and part of Ch. 17 are derived from Wold (1940), part of Ch. 16 and most of Ch. 17 from Juréen (1952). Ch.18 is entirely based on works by Juréen (1949, 1950).

2. The statistical data. – Three major family budget surveys have been carried out in Sweden, viz. in the years 1913, 1923 and 1933. The surveys were conducted by the Social Welfare Board, a government agency. The 1913 investigation covered the consumption habits among industrial workers and low grade employees. The data for 1923 and 1933 further include a number of middle class families. Moreover, around 1933, the Board made special surveys of the consumption habits among farm workers (including forestry workers) and small farmers. In all of these surveys the households kept detailed accounts of their incomes and expenditures for a period of approximately one year. Table 1·6·1 gives the number of families that submitted complete accounts.

The Social Welfare Board has also made a number of less extensive investigations. During World War II, surveys were made of consumption habits in different social classes, with the budget period limited to 2 or 4 weeks. After the war, the surveys were made on an interview instead of account basis, although accounts have been kept of food expenditures during a short period (1 or 2 weeks). None of these was designed to give data suitable for the deduction of demand elasticities.

In budget surveys based on accounts kept during a whole year, only those families and households can be included which are willing to take the trouble to do detailed bookkeeping. For obvious reasons, such families cannot be allocated and selected by the standard methods of sampling. In order to give some idea of the limitations of the samples obtained, we shall briefly describe the procedure followed in the Swedish survey of 1913. In the main, the 1923 and 1933 surveys followed the same design.

People were induced to participate in the budget survey by advertisements and articles in local newspapers all over the country. Remuneration was granted for completely finished accounts, and additional prizes were awarded for the most carefully kept accounts. When the campaign had lasted for some time, a total of 2 325 accounting books were distributed in 39 communities. The survey had been planned for family households, and primarily for those consisting of man and wife and non-adult children. The great majority of households were selected from towns and villages. The main purpose was to survey consumption habits and the cost of living in workers' families, but the sample was extended to include employees of low grade in public or private service. The survey was thus limited to certain social groups or classes. On the other hand, it was decided not to fix any upper or lower limits for the yearly income. In short, the intention was to obtain a sample that in certain respects represented the cost of living in urban districts. In view of the method of selection, however, neither this nor the later surveys can be regarded as samples with a perfect stratification. In this connection it should be added that the individual families were selected, not by the survey centre, but by the local agencies and authorities.

When the accounts were collected at the end of the budget year, it emerged that over 700 accounts were not finished or had never even been started. In the preparatory examination of the data it was further found necessary to exclude more than 250 of the accounts. The statistical material of the survey consisted finally of 1 355 accounts distributed over 36 towns and villages. This makes a response of 58%, which is a high percentage in view of the large amount of work involved in the keeping of detailed accounts. From the point of view of representativeness, however, the planning of the survey and the response percentage must be regarded as less satisfactory (this remark also applies to the 1923 and 1933 surveys). It may further be imagined that the device of putting a premium on accounts that are well kept may result in a biased selection of families as well as a systematic colouring of the figures. Moreover, the low percentage of response indicates that the sample does not reach a high degree of representativeness even from a geographical viewpoint.

3. Comparison between budget data and market statistics. – In the light of the critical remarks of the previous section, it is an important question whether the families that were willing to keep current accounts of their incomes and expenditures had approximately the same consumption habits as the great majority of other families, or whether their habits were perhaps markedly different. Before giving the demand elasticity figures that have been estimated from the family budget data, we shall try to answer this question, at least in part. This can be done by using the family budget data to estimate the national totals of food consumption, and comparing them with estimates based on production and other market statistics (an account of the market statistics data will be given in Ch. 17). Table 1 shows such a comparison.

Remembering what has been said, one can hardly expect the family budget data to yield very close estimates of the actual figures for the national totals of consumed quantities. Besides, in judging the validity of the figures we have not only to consider whether the families surveyed give a correct picture of the consumption habits in the various strata, but we also must remember that we cannot determine with complete exactness the weights that should be attached to the average quantities when summing the various strata, a source of error that might well result in considerable deviation, since there are large differences in consumption habits of different social classes. The national totals were estimated on the basis of family budget data for (a) industrial workers, (b) low grade employees, (c) farm and forestry workers and small farmers. The average consumption within the three strata was weighted in the proportions 65 : 10 : 25, in accordance with Swedish population statistics for the period under consideration. The middle class families were disregarded when estimating the national totals, since the survey had defined these households in such a manner that their number cannot be determined from the population statistics. In any case, however, their number is very small in comparison with that of the three other strata.

TABLE 16·3·1.[1] *National totals of food consumption, main items, estimated from* (i) *family budget data, and* (ii) *market statistics.*

Food item	Consumption, 10^6 kg	
	Family budget data 1933/34	Market statistics 1934
Milk and cream....................	1 400.0	1 479.0
Butter and margarine	109.8	102.2
Butter........................	62.4	59.4
Margarine	47.4	42.8
Cheese	30.8	31.3
Eggs............................	67.0	45.0
Meat	237.0	242.7
Beef.........................	51.5	46.8
Veal..........................	25.6	33.3
Mutton, lamb..................	3.4	3.1
Pork..........................	100.3	89.7
Processed meat	56.2^a	69.8
Fish	83.1	82.4
Salt herring	22.1	25.3
Other fish.....................	61.0	57.1
Flour, grain and bread	650.1	649.5
Wheat flour	258.0	257.7
Rye flour	174.0	134.6
Other flour and grain	65.7	78.4
Dry bread, rye	41.4	38.8
Plain bread....................	111.0	$140.0^{\beta\,\gamma}$
Sugar...........................	201.0	225.0
Potatoes	684.0	780.0^{β}
Other root vegetables.............	40.0	$60.0^{\beta\,\gamma}$
Peas and beans	10.2	13.0
Other vegetables	33.0	$60.0^{\beta\,\gamma}$
Fruits and berries, Swedish	125.0	$150.0^{\beta\,\gamma}$
Coffee	28.0^{δ}	37.7

^{a} The figure is too low, owing to complete quantity data not having been reported for farm workers and small farmers. $^\beta$ Not reduced for marketing spoilage. $^\gamma$ Estimates with considerable error margins. $^\delta$ See the text.

As can be seen from Table 1, the two series of estimates are fairly concordant for most of the food items, in spite of the sources of error indicated above. Except for potatoes, the market statistics for which have been revised in the light of the family budget data, the two series of estimates are independent, inasmuch as they are based on entirely different sources of information. Thus, notwithstanding the limited size of the samples, the subjective element in the selection, and the possibility that the accounts were subjected to some 'make up' in the course of the continuous recording, it would seem that the family budget data of the Social Welfare Board give a reasonably accurate picture of the average food-consumption habits in the strata covered by the surveys. To judge from the deviations present in Table 1, however, we may perhaps conclude that the families contributing to the survey lived on a somewhat higher standard than other families. For foodstuffs of animal origin, for instance, the consumption is somewhat higher than the market statistics would have led us to believe, in spite of the fact that the market totals include the consumption in restaurants and other premises, while the family budget data do not. For vegetable foods, on the other hand, the market totals give as a rule somewhat higher values.

As just mentioned, the national totals were estimated from the budget data without regard to the unspecified food quantities under the budget item "meals at restaurants, etc." This incompleteness of the estimate explains, among other things, the low figures for coffee consumption in the budget data.

We may conclude from the comparison in Table 1 that the family budget data, in spite of their shortcomings, constitute statistical material that should be, by and large, quite as useful for the purpose of demand analysis as the time-series data of market statistics. The rest of this chapter is devoted to an account of the income elasticities derived from the Swedish budget data. For the documentation of the data employed, reference is made to the published records and reports of the budget surveys, which are very detailed and give summaries and table explanations in French [Refs. 22–25].

A few basic features of the family budget data were reviewed in Ch. 1·6. For the different social strata, Table 1·6·1 gives the average expenditure for ten main groups of budget items, in per cent of the family income. The first requirement for a calculation of income elasticities from such data is a classification of the families according to income. In the published data an income classification is given for industrial workers, employees, and middle-class families, viz. according to income per consumer unit [Ch. 14·5]. The illustration given in Fig. 1·2·2 shows that there were four income classes in the 1913 survey, three in the 1923 and 1933 surveys. For farm workers and small farmers (1933) the classification according to income was obtained from unpublished data placed at our disposal by the Social Welfare Board.

4. Income elasticities estimated from differences between social strata.
As seen from Table 1·6·1, food is the main item in the family budget. There are substantial differences, however, between the social strata. In 1933 the farm workers spent more than half their income on food (including stimulants), whereas the corresponding figure is less than a quarter for middle-class families. On the other hand, if we reckon in absolute figures the

17 – 525552 H. Wold

TABLE 16·4·1.[1] *Food consumption in different social strata. Budget data, 1933.*

	Social strata	Average income per household	Food expenditure		Logarithmic data	
			Average per household	Per cent of income	Income	Food expenditure
1a	Farm and forestry workers.	1 704	862	50.6	−.3248	−.1741
1b	Small farmers	1 952	833	42.7		
2	Industrial workers and low grade employees	4 079	1 382	33.9	.0237	.0380
3	Middle-class families	7 725	1 732	22.4	.3011	.1361

food expenditure is greatest among middle-class families. The aggregate figures for 1933 are given in Table 1.

Having arranged the social strata in ascending order of income, we see that there is an almost regular increase in food expenditure, whereas the food percentage is decreasing. We note in passing that the main reason why farm workers (including forestry workers) have somewhat higher absolute expenditures for food than the small farmers is that a smaller fraction of the workers' earnings takes the form of agricultural products, and such earnings in kind are as a rule evaluated at lower prices than products actually purchased.

Table 1 can be used to give a tentative estimate of the income elasticity of the demand for food. In fact, let us for a moment disregard the influence that the social position and the social milieu may have on the demand habits. Regarding the average income per household and the average food expenditure as coordinates of a demand function, we may then calculate demand elasticities in the usual way. The two last columns of Table 1 give the corresponding logarithms, with reduction to zero mean. For the sake of simplicity we have here pooled the data for farm workers and small farmers (unweighted averages; 1 828 and 848 crowns for income and expenditure, respectively).

Making use of strata 1 and 2, we obtain $E = 0.61$ for the income elasticity of food. Strata 2 and 3 give $E = 0.35$. An average elasticity is obtained if we make use of strata 1 and 3; the resulting figure is $E = 0.50$. Alternatively, we can use regression analysis to form an average elasticity by taking the three strata into consideration simultaneously [Ch. 14·1]. Again, we obtain $E = 0.50$.

We repeat that these income elasticities of the demand for food are but rough and tentative estimates. Yet the results are of interest, for one thing because they are based on the entire budget material for 1933, and further because they display a general feature of great importance: if we disregard the possible influence of social factors, the demand for food has an income elasticity that presents a clear tendency to decrease as income increases. Such tendencies must always be kept in mind when dealing with demand elasticities that are estimated on the hypothesis of constancy, and this remark applies in particular to the 'constant' elasticities reported in the next section. Constant elasticities should in general be interpreted as average values, and in principle they will be valid only for the range of incomes covered by the data employed. Constant elasticities should, accordingly, not be given without indicating the range to which they refer, and it is necessary in any case to indicate the average income level in the sample.

The question is, however, whether the decrease in the income elasticity is mainly due to the rising income, or whether the tendency is to a considerable degree due to the influence of social factors on consumer habits, independently of income. We note that the geometric mean of the average income levels of strata 1 and 3 is 3 652 crowns, an amount which is only slightly smaller than the average income of stratum 2. Further we note from Table 14·6·1 that in stratum 2 the income elasticity of food, according to three variant methods of estimation, is $E = 0.53, 0.51$, or 0.50. We see that this is in excellent agreement with the income elasticity $E = 0.50$ estimated on the basis of the data given in Table 1 for strata 1 and 3. It would seem that the concordance is not accidental. The close agreement suggests the conclusion that the income level is the factor of primary importance behind the differences in the income elasticity for food, and that the social factors have only a small or negligible influence on this elasticity. The empirical results that will be recorded later in this chapter support on the whole this tentative conclusion.

5. Empirical results. Constant income elasticities. – In this section we shall record the main results obtained from using the family budget data for the estimation of demand functions of type (1·1·1b), i.e. functions with constant income elasticities. The analysis refers to the following aspects of the demand structure: (a) aggregate income elasticities, with expenditures classified in ten item groups, (b) specific income elasticities for food and stimulants, (c) differences in the demand structure among the social strata, (d) variations of the demand structure with time. The numerical results are given in Tables 1–4 of the present section and in the previous Tables 1·6·2, 14·5·2 and 14·6·1. The method employed has been explained in Chs. 1·2, 1·5 and 14·1, and its rationale has been discussed in Chs. 2·1–4 and 14·2–7.

The budget data for 1913 and 1933 have been published in such a manner that income elasticities can be calculated for families of different sizes. Tables 1·6·2, 14·6·1 and the present Table 1 show the results obtained when calculating the income elasticity of expenditures as specified on ten aggregate items. The item groups are as follows. I: Food and stimulants. II: Housing. III:

TABLE 16·5·1.[1] *Income elasticities for different family types among workers and low grade employees. Family budget data, 1933.*

Item group (see the text)	Families without children	Families with children, the eldest in age									Average elasticity by formula (14·6·1 a–b)	
		below 7 years		7–15 years			15 years or more				
		1 child	2–3 ch.	1 child	2–3 ch.	4 or more	1 child	2–3 ch.	4 or more	(a)	(b)
I	.56	.45	.37	.66	.48	.44	.29	.59	.74	.53	.51
II	1.28	1.33	1.48	1.39	1.32	1.86	1.98	.90	.57	1.28	1.30
III	.55	.59	.71	.54	.67	1.08	.48	.66	1.05	.67	.65
IV	1.53	1.31	.82	2.40	.99	2.44	2.05	1.08	1.28	1.41	1.38
V	1.22	.73	.84	.80	.99	1.45	.59	.92	1.55	.96	.94
VI	1.46	1.04	1.52	.84	1.09	1.40	.43	1.32	.93	1.09	1.12
VII	1.60	1.81	1.42	1.68	1.86	2.74	1.29	2.34	2.13	1.88	1.85
VIII	1.17	.93	1.23	.96	1.35	1.32	1.08	1.61	1.42	1.24	1.22
IX	3.77	2.36	1.66	.	2.28	5.63	.	1.73	.	1.73	1.58
X	1.50	1.90	3.06	1.75	1.87	1.96	2.08	1.60	.57	1.83	1.83
I–X	1.05	.92	.94	.96	.98	1.16	.89	.98	1.03	.97	.97
Average	1.08	.93	.99	1.02	.98	1.18	.95	1.01	1.01	1.01	.98
Sample size	51	130	54	122	236	30	36	115	50	824	824

Fuel, light, cleaning, laundry. IV: Furniture. V: Clothing (including shoes). VI: Hygiene. VII: Expenditures for intellectual purposes, travel, recreation. VIII: Taxes, insurance, subscriptions to professional unions. IX: Servants and domestic help. X: Other expenditures, including support of relatives, gifts, interest on loans, telephone, correspondence.

The main feature of the results obtained is the stable hierarchy that subsists between the item groups in their demand sensitivity. For aggregates I, III and V the demand is under-elastic, which indicates that these items are chiefly necessities, the consumption of which is relatively well satisfied even at low income levels. Item groups II, IV and VI have roughly normal elasticity, showing that the expenditures are here approximately proportional to the income. Item groups VII–X prove to be mainly luxuries, the demand being over-elastic, so that the satiation of consumption is relatively low at low income levels and rapidly increases at higher levels.

The elasticities in Table 1 are given without indicating the standard errors, and it is the same in our other tables based on family budget data. Referring to the discussion in Ch. 2·5, the main reason for the omission is that in a regression analysis of non-experimental data the standard errors carry little weight as significance indicators. For the income elasticities derived from family budget data, as a matter of fact, the standard errors as calculated by the classical formula are small, especially for the elasticities obtained as weighted averages for different family types. To supply the elasticities with standard errors might therefore give a false impression of accuracy. In judging the reliability of the results, the criterion of main relevance lies in the regularity and consistency that may be established by comparing the elasticity estimates obtained for different budget items, different social strata, different periods, and so on.

Since the data are subdivided with respect to family size, the average elasticities for all families given in Table 1 are free from the bias that could result from differences in the age distribution. It is interesting, for several reasons, to make a comparison with the elasticities obtained by the alternative device given in Ch. 14·5, that of a direct pooling of the data. Results of this type are presented in Tables 14·5·2 and 14·6·1.

Commencing with the income elasticity of all expenditures, i.e. items I–X, in workers' and employees' families, the two methods give for 1913 the elasticities 0.89 and 0.91. As pointed out in Ch. 14·5 the deviation may be due to a bias in the consumption scale employed, i.e. the German-Austrian scale, the conclusion being that this scale slightly overvalues the children's actual share in the family budget. The values 0.97 and 0.95 obtained for 1933 suggest that a change has taken place. Thus we may infer that the children's share in the demand has increased and become greater than indicated by the German-Austrian scale. The difference between the two estimates is not large, however, and so it would seem that for 1933 we can still use the German-Austrian scale for calculating the income per consumer unit.

Turning to the separate item groups, let us consider the demand for food in 1933. Table 14·6·1 gives the income elasticities 0.53 (or 0.51) and 0.50, showing that the bias due to the age distribution is almost absent. The German-Austrian scale is, therefore, realistic for food if this item is taken as a whole. As compared with 1913 the figures suggest that the children's share in the food consumption has increased somewhat. For housing expenditure in 1933 the two methods give almost equal elasticities, viz. 1.28 and 1.25. The bias that was found for 1913 [see Ch. 14·5] has thus disappeared, showing that the German-Austrian scale in 1933 does not overvalue the relative importance of the children for housing demand.

Tables 1·6·2 and 14·6·1 show that the income elasticities for the ten item groups are, on the whole, remarkably stable. When comparing the results for 1913 and 1933, however, it must be kept in mind that the income level and the consumption habits were influenced by the economic depression at the beginning of the 'thirties. The real incomes, having risen rapidly after the post-war depression in the early 'twenties, culminated in 1929—30, and from that time until the end of 1933 there was a strongly marked decrease. According to the budget data the real value of the income per consumer unit was only slightly higher in 1933 than in 1913 (we shall return to this comparison later on in this section). This must be the main reason why several budget items, according to Table 1·6·2, have almost the same income elasticity in 1913 and 1933. This is so for budget items I, III, VIII and X in particular. An interesting feature, pointed out in Ch. 1·6, is the increase in the elasticity of housing expenditure (item II) in workers' and employees' families. The indication is that there was greater uniformity in housing standards at different income levels in 1913 than in 1933. The increase in the elasticity may be explained to some extent by structural changes in housing equipment, an important factor being the introduction of modern conveniences, such as central heating, hot running water, etc. For another thing, the Swedish prices of agricultural products were extremely low in the early 'thirties. Hence it may be argued that many families with relatively high incomes were willing to spend a larger part of their income than before in order to join the rush for so-called modern housing. As a matter of fact, budget data reveal a substantial change in the balance between the expenditures for food and housing, the figures in per cent of income being 45% and 12% for 1913, respectively, but 34% and 14% for 1933.

For the remaining items (IV, V, VI, VII and IX) Table 14·6·1 shows a falling trend in the income elasticities, indicating a tendency towards a softening of the differences between the demand satiation at different income levels.

Table 14·6·1 further gives elasticities for 1923 and, finally, for middle-class families. Owing to the incompleteness of the published data, the calculation of elasticities could here be performed only by direct pooling. It is possible that this introduces a bias on account of the differences in the age distribution of the consumers, but we note that a correction for this bias can be made in the treatment of the 1923 data for workers and employees, viz. by assuming that the correction required is the average of the bias found in the analysis of the 1913 and 1933 data. By applying this rough correction we have obtained the elasticities given in Table 1·6·2. We see that the corrected values for 1923 fall in quite naturally between the elasticities for 1913 and 1933 obtained by the more refined method of weighting the elasticities of different family types.

For middle-class families, Table 14·6·1 gives income elasticities that, with one or two exceptions, are lower than for workers and low grade employees. The demand for food has the lowest elasticity, and this is somewhat lower than for workers and employees. Housing expenditure for the middle class has an elasticity about as low as for workers and employees in 1913. Budget items with about the same income elasticity in the two social strata are no. III (fuel, light, cleaning, laundry) and no. VIII (taxes, insurance, subscriptions).

Part of the preceding comment refers to the trends revealed in the income elasticities. We note from Table 1·6·2 that the upward and downward trends balance so that the elasticities have an almost constant average, near unity.

By an argument used in Ch. 14·2 we see that this is a consequence of the fact that in the data under analysis the total expenditures are nearly equal to the income. Further we note that the trends do not, on the whole, affect the ranking order of the elasticities. In other words, as stressed at the beginning of this section, the ranking order reflects a hierarchy of the budget items in the demand structure, and the hierarchy is fairly stable. It is also interesting to examine the distribution of the elasticities. For workers and employees we see that the elasticities present nearly the same scatter in the three surveys, and there is only a small decrease in their dispersion. For middle class families, on the other hand, we find a tendency towards greater concentration of the elasticities, and for 1933 most of them lie in the interval 0.8–1.0.

Thus far in this section, the income elasticities have referred to aggregate items in the budget. We know from Ch. 6·4 that such aggregate elasticities are average values of the various sub-items. Turning now to the income elasticities of specified food items, we shall see that they present a large dispersion around the aggregate elasticity for food expenditure.

Table 2 shows the income elasticity for some twenty items of food and stimulants. The estimates have been obtained by the method of direct pooling that was used in Table 14·6·1. We have seen that this method gives correct results for food demand as a whole, but it is clear that a bias due to differences in the age distribution of the demand may be expected for separate food items. Thus, according to the rule of thumb in Ch. 14·5, the elasticities in Table 2 are somewhat too high for those items which are consumed mainly by the adults. Among such items we note meat, fish, eggs, and all of the stimulants.

Table 2 demonstrates great differences between the food items as regards the response of demand to changes in the income level. Among the highly sensitive items are liquors, tobacco and "eating out". For these items the elasticity is as a rule greater than unity, showing that the demand rises more rapidly than income. For food in general the elasticity is lower, the average being about 0.40 for workers and employees and about 0.33 for middle class families. Elasticities above the average have been obtained for fruits and berries, cream, butter, eggs, fish and meat, i.e. mainly for animal foods. Less sensitive than foods in general to income changes are, on the other hand, cheese, coffee, tea and chocolate, milk, sugar, and cereals. The consumption of these items has thus a more uniform distribution over the income scale. Flour, bread, margarine and skim milk have given negative elasticities. Here the consumption decreases as income rises, clearly because demand largely turns to foodstuffs that are more expensive relative to their nourishment value. So far as food is concerned, a rise in the income level is primarily reflected in increased consumption of animal foods and green vegetables, especially at the expense of the cereals.

Middle-class families have as a rule lower income elasticities than workers and employees. Thus here food consumption is even more equally distributed over the income scale. This is primarily due to the fact that the average income level is higher among middle-class families.

Table 2 also gives some information on trends in the food elasticities. When interpreting the figures we must keep in mind that 1933 lay at the bottom of an economic depression, whereas 1913 was a year of prosperity. Hence no marked upward trend in real incomes after 1913 is to be noted from the family budget data. For workers and low grade employees, in fact, the average income per consumer unit was 744 in 1913, 696 in 1923 and 808 in 1933, and for middle-class families the figures are 1 521 in 1923 and 1 530 in 1933. In view of the small changes in real income it is only natural that the aggregate elasticities for food demand have been almost constant; 0.40 for workers and employees and 0.32–0.33 for middle-class families. We note, however, that important changes have taken place. Thus for animal foods the elasticity has decreased, leading to a more uniform distribution of the consumption. The same tendency is present for expensive vegetables, notably fruits and berries; here it may be noted that the increase in relative weight in the budget, in combination with the high elasticities, has brought about an increase in the aggregate elasticity of vegetable foods. For workers and employees there is a rather sharp drop in the elasticities of stimulants between 1923 and 1933. Assuming that the figures give a true picture of developments, the interpretation is that families in the lower income classes have increased their demand for stimulants much more than families in higher income classes. If this is a general feature, it means that the consumption of stimulants in the lower social strata tends to lie above the average in periods of economic depression.

Table 2 allows us to compare quantity and expenditure elasticities for a number of food items [Ch. 14·3]. The two variants are practically equal for butter, margarine, cream and eggs. In other cases we find a more or less marked tendency for the quantity data to give the lower elasticity; this group includes milk, cheese and fish. These results are in agreement with the theoretical discussion in Ch. 14·3, which led to the conclusion that the difference between the two variants is small or negligible for standardized foods, whereas the quantity elasticity is smaller than the expenditure elasticity for foods that are marketed in different qualities and prices.

As regards the quantity elasticities, most of our calculations refer to aggregate items, with quantity totals defined by the formula (5·6·1) of direct summation. In some cases we have made an alternative calculation by the use of formula (5·6·2), making the weights w_i proportional to the average prices of the sub-items. We see that the weighted and the direct summation

TABLE 16·5·2.[2] *Income elasticities for main foodstuffs, with demand measured by (a) quantities, (b) expenditures. Family budget data.*

Food items	Workers and low grade employees						Middle-class families			
	1913		1923		1933		1923		1933	
	Quant.	Exp.	Quant.	Exp.	Quant.	Exp.	Quant.	Exp.	Quant.	Exp.
nimal foods	—	.52	—	.49	—	.39	—	.34	—	.27
ilk and cream	—	.52	.18	.34	.09	.27	.10	.14	−.04	.07
Milk	.41	.50	.10	.18	.01	.08	.10	.12	−.10	−.08
ordinary............	.65	.73	.20	.24	.03	.10	.11	.13	−.09	−.08
skimmed	−1.29	−1.20	−2.80	−2.62	−1.17	−1.17	−1.77	−2.19	−.68	−.62
Cream	—	.73	1.43	1.50	1.09	1.08	.08	.23	.54	.56
ıtter and margarine										
(1) weighted sum	.36	.39	.38	.41	.31	.34	.24	.24	.24	.26
(2) quantity total......	.27	—	.24	—	.16	—	.20	—	.16	—
Butter	.68	.71	.64	.67	.64	.67	.30	.31	.39	.42
Margarine	−.40	−.41	−.44	−.40	−.37	−.33	.00	−.02	−.21	−.20
heese	.36	.43	.19	.31	.16	.30	−.09	.06	.20	.34
ggs	.92	.99	.73	.79	.41	.51	.55	.53	.31	.37
eat and meat products.	—	.53	—	.60	—	.49	—	.43	—	.35
Meat, (1) weighted sum	.48	.59	.49	—	.25	—	.37	—	.08	—
(2) quantity total	.49	—	.50	—	.25	—	.37	—	.08	—
ish, (1) weighted sum ..	—	.65	.35	.63	—	.57	.68	.77	—	.48
(2) quantity total..	—	—	.31	—	—	—	.58	—	—	—
ther animal foods......	—	−.46	−.31	−.31	−.35	−.32	.83	.80	−.02	.04
egetable foods	—	.25	—	.27	—	.33	—	.32	—	.37
read	—	.11	—	.55	—	.50	—	.07	—	.24
plain bread	—	−.16	.06	—	−.01	—	−.24	—	−.09	—
biscuits, cakes	—	.78	—	—	—	—	—	—	—	—
lour	—	−.22	−.59	−.47	—	−.50	−.01	.00	—	−.36
rains	—	.21	−.13	−.03	−.04	.06	.29	.34	.00	.24
egetables, potatoes, etc.	—	.35	—	} .60	—	.46	—	} .63	—	.66
ruits and berries	—	1.20	—		—	.84	—		—	.70
ugar and syrup	—	.28	.17	.21	.01	.23	.28	.23	.08	.39
offee, tea, chocolate	—	.30	—	.35	—	.27	—	.17	—	.19
pices and other veg. foods	—	.78	—	.71	—	.46	—	.78	—	.50
nimal and veg. foods ...	—	.40	—	.40	—	.37	—	.33	—	.32
iquors.................	—	1.30	1.30	1.42	.95	1.08	1.02	1.18	.89	1.00
obacco	—	1.42	—	1.36	—	.94	—	1.10	—	1.02
estaurant consumption .	—	1.85	—	1.76	—	2.14	—	.83	—	1.48
ood and stimulants	—	.49	—	.51	—	.50	—	.46	—	.44

TABLE 16'5'3.[3] *Income elasticities for animal foodstu*

a. Industrial workers and low grade employees; data for 1913.

Food item; demand measured as (1) quantity totals (2) weighted summation of quantities (3) expenditures	Family type (number of consumer units)				All families, aggregate elasticity		
					by formula		direct pooling
	1.8	1.9–2.2	2.3–2.9	3.0–	14'6'1a	14'6'1b	
(1) Quantity totals							
1 Milk.........................	.13	.11	.24	.35	.23	.20	.23
2 Butter and margarine..........	.27	.41	.35	.25	.33	.34	.27
3 Butter.....................	.33	.63	.69	.77	.67	.64	.68
4 Margarine..................	.10	−.05	−.24	−.37	−.23	−.16	−.40
5 Cheese........................	.41	.38	.38	.18	.32	.34	.36
6 Eggs	.42	.72	.76	.96	.77	.75	.92
7 Fresh meat[a]	.18	.26	.47	.47	.39	.36	.49
8 Beef	.40	.29	.40	.37	.36	.35	.42
9 Veal	.17	.71	.84	.76	.72	.70	.84
10 Pork	−.21	−.07	.23	.43	.16	.11	.32
11 Canned meat...............	.17	.03	.08	.56	.22	.17	.19
12 Minced meat[β]	—	—	—	—	—	—	—
13 Sausage and other processed meat	—	—	—	—	—	—	—
(2) Weighted summation of quantities							
14 Milk	.18	.23	.41	.55	.38	.35	.41
15 Butter and margarine..........	.28	.47	.43	.37	.41	.41	.36
16 Fresh meat[a]	.16	.24	.46	.47	.38	.35	.48
(3) Expenditures							
17 Milk	.25	.39	.52	.58	.48	.46	.50
18 Butter and margarine..........	.31	.49	.46	.36	.42	.43	.39
19 Butter.....................	.35	.66	.74	.74	.69	.67	.71
20 Margarine..................	.08	−.07	−.25	−.35	−.23	−.17	−.41
21 Cheese........................	.50	.30	.54	.21	.37	.39	.43
22 Eggs	.47	.84	.85	1.01	.86	.83	.99
23 Fresh meat[a]	.26	.37	.55	.51	.46	.44	.59
24 Beef	.53	.39	.45	.36	.41	.42	.50
25 Veal	.35	.98	1.08	1.02	.97	.95	1.11
26 Pork	−.14	.05	.31	.45	.24	.20	.40
27 Canned meat[γ]	.27	.09	.19	.63	.30	.25	.27
28 Sausage and other processed meat	.73	.11	.23	.24	.23	.25	.18

[a] 1913: Beef, veal, mutton, lamb and pork. 1933: All kinds of meat and pork.
[β] Is not specified in the data for 1913.   [γ] 1933: Including processed food.

l margarine. Family budget data, 1913 and 1933.

b. Industrial workers and low grade employees; data for 1933.

Families without children	Families with children, the eldest in age							All families, aggregate elasticity		
	below 7 years		7–15 years			15 years or more			by formula		direct pooling
	1 child	2–3 ch.	1 child	2–3 ch.	4 or more	1 child	2–3 ch.	4 or more	14·6·1a	14·6·1b	

1	−.32	−.15	.08	−.22	−.10	.09	−.62	.10	.89	.01	−.09	−.01
2	.02	−.12	.19	.03	.18	−.04	.13	.45	.35	.16	.11	.16
3	.28	.08	1.39	.47	.27	1.51	.63	.22	−.21	.36	.36	.64
4	−.41	−.37	−1.00	−.57	.10	−.84	−.55	.71	.70	.00	−.15	−.37
5	.02	.36	.34	−.12	−.04	−.42	.08	.48	1.34	.23	.17	.16
6	.07	−.02	.04	.35	.36	.22	.13	.50	.83	.31	.26	.41
7	−.06	−.23	.08	.25	.05	.64	−.32	.19	.18	.08	.04	.25
8	−.61	.11	.90	.57	−.03	.11	.00	−.18	1.24	.20	.11	.08
9	.45	.40	.80	.44	.35	.71	−.42	.18	.48	.36	.37	.64
10	−.31	−.73	−.32	−.11	.10	.84	−.56	.28	−.44	−.09	−.16	.20
11	−.15	.54	1.28	.76	.04	−2.13	2.48	−.95	.13	.06	.19	.26
12	.49	−.20	−.44	.62	−.22	.92	.04	.30	.43	.10	.05	.06
13	.69	.30	−.63	.47	.49	−.01	.31	1.05	1.17	.53	.47	.31
14	−.27	−.14	.09	−.22	−.10	.14	−.61	.14	.82	.01	−.08	.01
15	.11	−.06	.54	.18	.20	.31	.30	.38	.21	.22	.19	.31
16	−.05	−.22	.07	.25	.05	.65	−.31	.19	.17	.08	.04	.25
17	.08	.16	.09	.04	.12	.42	−.29	.31	1.24	.25	.17	.08
18	.15	.02	.54	.24	.25	.46	.38	.30	.26	.25	.23	.34
19	.34	.16	1.38	.51	.33	1.65	.76	.27	−.14	.42	.42	.67
20	−.43	−.29	−.97	−.46	.12	−.67	−.56	.71	.73	.04	−.11	−.33
21	.28	.45	.18	.08	.13	−.29	.41	.68	1.50	.37	.32	.30
22	.28	.22	.22	.50	.57	.66	.18	.66	1.31	.53	.47	.51
23	.14	.07	.36	.38	.23	.52	.39	.35	.34	.28	.25	.43
24 25	} δ .36	.23	.61	.54	.21	.92	.49	.60	.69	.43	.39	.43ε
26	−.16	−.15	.06	.19	.27	−.01	.27	.15	−.06	.12	.08	—
27	.77	.38	.33	1.32	.69	.68	.77	.80	1.52	.79	.74	—
28	.42	.44	−.43	.81	.61	−.40	.13	1.51	1.08	.66	.59	—

δ All kinds of meat, except pork.

ε Beef, veal, mutton, lamb, pork and minced meat.

TABLE 16˙5˙4.[4] *Income elasticity for*

a. Farm and forestry workers.

Food items. Demand measured as (1) quantity totals (2) expenditures	Families without children	Families with 1–3 children, the eldest in age			Fam. with 4 or more ch., the eldest		All families, aggreg. elasticity by formula	
		below 7	7–15	15 or more	7–15	15 or more	(14˙6˙1a)	(14˙6˙1b)
(1) Quantity totals								
Milk and cream	.29	.38	.18	.47	.39	.88	.36	.43
Butter	1.15	.34	.82	1.05	1.87	.63	.81	.91
Cheese	.51	.98	.24	1.32	−.28	2.02	.67	.93
Eggs	1.96	.72	.78	.99	1.15	1.09	.91	1.16
Meat and meat products	.54	.82	.44	.01	1.25	.42	.59	.47
Meat, except pork ..	−.75	.80	1.10	.14	1.30	2.10	.96	.61
Pork	1.07	.84	.36	−.22	1.28	−.50	.47	.38
Fish	.27	.80	.34	.26	.16	1.21	.48	.52
Flour	−.36	.10	−.08	.15	.03	−.19	−.01	−.08
Grains, flakes	.07	−.25	−.15	.17	−.84	1.06	−.15	.12
Sugar	.68	.37	.53	.29	.28	.44	.42	.45
Potatoes............	.62	.16	.23	−.06	−.16	−.13	.08	.16
(2) Expenditures								
Animal foods	.50	.80	.74	.70	.99	.90	.79	.73
Cereals, vegetables....	.50	.39	.42	.37	.40	.63	.43	.46
Agricultural products .	.39	.60	.60	.54	.72	.69	.61	.56
Food, all kinds.......	.51	.63	.60	.55	.74	.78	.64	.61

have given practically the same results for meat and fish. For butter and margarine, on the other hand, the direct summation has led to smaller elasticities than the weighted summation.

Table 3 shows the results of the elasticity calculations for separate family types, the items dealt with being animal foods and margarine. The calculations refer to workers' and low grade employees' families in 1913 and 1933. These budget data can be used to calculate both expenditure and quantity elasticities. The quantity elasticities have been formed on the basis of direct as well as weighted summation, both variants being used for milk, meat, butter and margarine. For the sake of comparison we repeat in the last column the corresponding elasticities from Table 2.

If we compare the results for different family types, we see that the elasticities present a regular variation in 1913. In 1933 the variation is more irregular, naturally enough, since the detailed classification in family types has led to relatively small subgroups. In the calculation of average elasticities for the *main foods. Family budget data 1933.*

b. Small farmers.

Food items. Demand measured as (1) quantity totals (2) expenditures	Families without children	Families with 1–3 children, the eldest in age			Fam. with 4 or more ch., the eldest		All families, aggreg. elasticity by formula	
		below 7	7–15	15 or more	7–15	15 or more	(14·6·1a)	(14·6·1b)
(1) Quantity totals								
Milk and cream	.33	−.02	.32	.10	1.11	.53	.34	.35
Butter	.44	.35	.87	.30	−.20	.39	.46	.37
Cheese	−.24	−.54	.26	.48	−1.08	.	.	.
Eggs	−.23	.40	.12	.19	.68	−.27	.16	.13
Meat and meat products	−.01	1.49	.61	.37	.84	.59	.62	.51
Meat, except pork ..	1.09	1.99	1.78	.55	−1.00	−.15	.62	.79
Pork	−.53	1.72	.26	.30	1.72	.63	.60	.45
Fish	−.19	.53	−.12	.35	.77	−.69	.04	.14
Flour	−.54	.39	−.07	−.03	−.05	.53	.10	−.09
Grains, flakes	.98	−.56	.60	.83	2.05	1.91	.95	.91
Sugar	−.12	.24	.09	.28	.73	.30	.25	.20
Potatoes............	−.70	.03	−.33	.02	.61	.10	−.03	−.14
(2) Expenditures								
Animal foods	.34	.77	.65	.33	.63	.74	.57	.50
Cereals, vegetables....	−.01	.62	.40	.16	.53	.76	.42	.29
Agricultural products .	.20	.57	.49	.23	.59	.73	.46	.38
Food, all kinds.......	.19	.73	.55	.27	.61	.78	.52	.42

entire sample of families, however, the fluctuations are evened out, so that such elasticities on the whole may be regarded as reliable.

Among the expenditure elasticities, margarine shows an increase from 1913 to 1933. From having been negatively elastic the demand for margarine has become practically inelastic. Apart from the stable expenditure elasticities for meat and cheese, other elasticities are higher for 1913 than for 1933.

Weighted and unweighted summations have given nearly the same quantity elasticities for meat, but, as might be expected, we find for butter and margarine that unweighted summation gives a lower elasticity. In 1913 we note a similar difference for milk; the fact that the two variants are equal for 1933 is due to the decline in the consumption of skim milk.

As explained in Ch. 14·5, some rough information on the age distribution of the demand can be obtained by comparing the different estimates of the aggregate elasticity referring to all families in the sample. To judge from the last three columns in Table 3, the German-Austrian scale was in 1913 on the whole correct for the consumption of milk, butter and cheese, whereas the children's share in the demand was overrated for eggs and fresh meat. In 1933, the children's consumption had grown in relative importance for milk, cheese and eggs, with an opposite tendency for butter. For margarine, the scale seems to underrate the consumption in the low age groups, the explanation being that in families with many children it is quite common for bread to be baked at home.

In Table 1'6'3, col. 1, we have brought together, in rounded figures, some of the estimates shown in Tables 2–3. Based on the data for 1933 for industrial workers and low grade employees, the figures are expenditure elasticities. For flour, sugar and the aggregate item milk and cream we have given figures obtained by direct pooling; otherwise, they are weighted averages of the elasticities for different family types.

Table 4 gives food elasticities obtained for small farmers and farm and forestry workers. Based on data for 1933, the results may be compared with those in Table 3 for industrial workers and low grade employees. Table 4 specifies only the main food items, and the elasticities refer to quantities (unweighted summation, except for cream, which has been evaluated in milk by counting 1 litre of cream as 5 litres of milk). The lower part of the table gives expenditure elasticities for three aggregate items and for the whole of the food budget.

The table shows that among farm and forestry workers the food demand is much more sensitive to income changes than among small farmers, especially for such items as fish, butter and eggs. A higher elasticity has also been obtained for sugar. For other food items the differences are so small that no specific tendencies can be distinguished. Considering the expenditure elasticities obtained for aggregate food items, we note that the elasticity for animal food is higher among workers than among farmers, a feature that explains most of the difference between the two strata in the aggregate elasticity for all food expenditures.

Lastly, let us compare the results given in Tables 3 and 4 for farm and forestry workers (stratum 1a), small farmers (stratum 1b) and industrial workers and low grade employees (stratum 2). We see that the income elasticities in strata 1a and 1b are considerably higher for meat and for milk. Strata 1b and 2 have given almost the same elasticities for butter and sugar, whereas stratum 1a shows a higher elasticity for these foods. In the demand for eggs, stratum 2 has an intermediate position between strata 1a and 1b. Milk demand is practically unelastic in strata 1a and 1b, and negatively elastic in stratum 2 [cf also Table 2]. The aggregate income elasticity for all food expenditures is definitely higher in strata 1a and 1b than in stratum 2.

6. Variable income elasticities. – In Ch. 16·4 we arrived at the tentative conclusion that income elasticities decrease with increasing income. This conclusion is confirmed by the analysis in Ch. 16·5, food elasticities being on the whole somewhat lower in social strata with higher average income. A clear case in point is the expenditure elasticity of animal foods. These elasticities are restated in Table 1, which further gives the corresponding average income levels (the income figures are normalized so as to refer to a family of 3.3 consumer units, and they are given in the money value of 1913, the nominal income being divided by the consumer price index of the Social Welfare Board).

The dependence of elasticity upon income comes out clearly. In middle-class families, whose incomes are relatively high, the consumption of animal foodstuffs is least influenced by income differences. Industrial workers and low grade employees have considerably lower incomes, and the consumption is here more sensitive to variation in the income level. In social strata with still lower incomes, such as small farmers and farm workers, the elasticity is found to be highest.

However, income elasticity varies with the income not only *between* but also *within* the strata. For empirical demand functions, in fact, it is frequently noticeable that the higher the income, the lower the elasticity. Reference is made to Fig. 1·2·2 for an illuminating case. A constant elasticity of the type calculated in the previous section will in such cases exaggerate the sensitivity of demand for income variations at high income levels, whereas the opposite is true at low income levels. This and similar graphs invite us to apply demand functions with variable income elasticity. Törnqvist's functions (1·1·5) are attractive for the purpose, and we find that these are very useful for the analysis of the Swedish budget data for 1913, 1923, and 1933. For reasons of space we shall give only a few examples of the results obtained.

TABLE 16·6·1.[1] *Income elasticities of the expenditure for animal foodstuffs, according to Tables 16·5·2–4, and corresponding average levels of real income.*

Social strata	1913		1923		1933	
	Real income	Elastic-ity	Real income	Elastic-ity	Real income	Elastic-ity
Middle-class	—	—	5 019	.34	5 049	.27
Industrial workers, and low grade employees	2 455	.52	2 297	.49	2 666	.39
Small farmers	—	—	—	—	1 245	.50
Farm and forestry workers	—	—	—	—	1 087	.73

TABLE 16·6·2.[2] *Income elasticity at different income levels, estimated*

a. Total food expenditure   b. Butter and margarine (quantity totals)

Parameters α, β of (1·1·5 a) Income per consumer unit	All families; family size in consumer units				Industrial workers	Low grade employees	All families
	1.8	1.9–2.2	2.3–2.9	3.0–			
a. Food (excl. stimulants)							
1 α = d (∞)	527	499	532	458	577	507	520
2 β	514	433	492	377	600	475	489
3 500.............	.51	.46	.50	.43	.55	.49	.49
4 750.............	.41	.37	.40	.33	.44	.39	.39
5 1 000.............	.34	.30	.33	.27	.38	.32	.33
6 1 250.............	.29	.26	.28	.23	.32	.28	.28
7 1 500.............	.26	.22	.25	.20	.29	.24	.25
b. Butter and margarine							
1 α = d (∞)	31	35	33	27	31	27	28
2 β	428	600	435	225	346	256	279
3 500.............	.46	.55	.47	.31	.41	.34	.36
4 750.............	.36	.44	.37	.23	.32	.25	.27
5 1 000.............	.30	.38	.30	.18	.26	.20	.22
6 1 250.............	.26	.32	.26	.15	.22	.17	.18
7 1 500.............	.22	.29	.22	.13	.19	.13	.16

Table 2 is based on the budget data for 1913 (for this survey the published tables are best specified). The elasticities refer to three groups of food items. The detailed results given under heading (c) will be used in Ch. 18 for making a forecast of the demand for agricultural products on the assumption of a continued increase of the Swedish real national income.

Since the data employed contain only 4 income classes, and since Törnqvist's functions are highly flexible, it is no wonder that they have given a close fit. Hence we have refrained from including in Table 2 any comparison between fitted and observed values. What is important, however, is that concordant results have been obtained for different family types and for different food items. For most of the items and item groups in the food sector, a satisfactory fit has been obtained by using one of Törnqvist's demand functions (1·1·5a–b) for necessities and relative luxuries, whereas the function (1·1·5c) for luxuries could not be used so often.

For inferior commodities, i.e. items with a negative income elasticity, the demand function is more complicated. Let us examine the demand for flour, which is perhaps the most important of the inferior foods. We have seen that *by the use of Törnqvist's demand function ($1\cdot1\cdot5a$). Budget data, 1933.*

c. Expenditures for main agricultural products (including margarine)[a]

	Family size in consumer units													Workers	Employees	All families
	Workers				Employees				All families						
	1.8	1.9–2.2	2.3–2.9	3.0–	1.8	1.9–2.2	2.3–2.9	3.0–	1.8	1.9–2.2	2.3–2.9	3.0–			
1	451	428	507	458	372	399	387	343	389	379	436	385	460	377	407
2	588	498	701	586	447	438	381	328	403	363	519	420	585	383	457
3	.54	.50	.58	.54	.47	.47	.43	.40	.45	.42	.51	.46	.54	.43	.48
4	.44	.40	.48	.44	.37	.37	.34	.30	.35	.33	.41	.36	.44	.34	.38
5	.37	.33	.41	.37	.31	.30	.28	.25	.29	.27	.34	.30	.37	.28	.31
6	.32	.28	.36	.32	.26	.26	.23	.21	.24	.23	.29	.25	.32	.23	.28
7	.28	.25	.32	.28	.23	.23	.20	.18	.21	.19	.26	.22	.28	.20	.23
n	78	317	298	240	35	148	150	89	113	465	448	329	933	422	1355
μ	911	791	660	557	1087	935	810	650	965	837	710	582	673	815	717
x	274	260	246	221	262	268	262	225	271	263	251	223	246	255	249

n = Sample size; μ = income per consumer unit; x = expenditures for agricultural products, per consumer unit.

[a] The aggregate includes meat, milk and cream, butter, margarine and other edible fats, cheese, eggs, flour, grain, bread, peas and beans, potatoes, sugar and syrup.

the flour demand is practically inelastic in rural families. For industrial workers and low grade employees, on the other hand, we have found the elasticity –0.5, whereas the demand in middle class families again tends to be inelastic. We shall now investigate the flour demand at different income levels for one and the same social stratum. For industrial workers and low grade employees, the only stratum for which figures are available for all of the three surveys, the budget data have given the results shown in Table 3.

In Fig. 1 the flour quantities of Table 3 have been plotted against income. We see that the data for 1913 give us nearly the same trend for the two strata. A free-hand demand curve having been fitted to this trend, the following average elasticities are read off from the curve in the income intervals indicated.

Income interval.................... 550–700   700–900   900–1 200

Income elasticity of flour, 1913.... – 0.13   – 0.50   – 0.27

It will be noted that these figures compare fairly well with the results given in Table 16·5·2 for the 1913 survey.

TABLE 16·6·3.[3] *Income and flour consumption; workers and low grade employees. Family budget data for 1913, 1923 and 1933.*

Sample size; number of families	Average per consumer unit		Sample size; number of families	Average per consumer unit	
	Real income, Sw. cr. 1913	Flour consumption, kg		Real income, Sw. cr. 1913	Flour consumption, kg
a. Data for 1913			b. Data for 1923		
Workers			*Workers and low grade employees*		
314	514	77.9	201	560	121.5
316	678	77.8	332	719	106.1
263	867	68.9	272	878	90.6
40	1 188	60.9	198	1 045	81.3
			120	1 163	78.5
Low grade employees			69	1 420	67.6
67	530	84.0			
120	688	75.6			
151	880	67.5	c. Data for 1933		
84	1 252	62.3			
			Workers and low grade employees		
Workers and low grade employees			298	670	81.2
381	517	79.0	521	983	66.1
436	681	77.2	231	1 398	53.2
414	872	68.3			
124	1 233	61.9			

The data for 1923 in Table 3 and Fig. 1 have been fitted by the function

$$(1) \qquad Q(\mu) = 32.4 \frac{\mu + 1\,711}{\mu + 40}; \qquad E = \frac{40}{\mu + 40} - \frac{1\,711}{\mu + 1\,711}.$$

We see that this is a Törnqvist demand function of the type given in (5·5·4), with a negative sign for parameter β. The resulting elasticities are given below for three income levels.

Income level............................	600	1 000	1 400
Income elasticity for flour, 1923......	− 0.68	− 0.59	− 0.52

The data for 1933 not having more than three income classes, any detailed analysis of the demand function is out of the question. As seen from Fig. 1, a function with constant elasticity gives a satisfactory fit to the observed data. The resulting elasticity is –0.57, and the demand function is given by

$$Q(\mu) = 3\,370 \cdot \mu^{-0.57}.$$

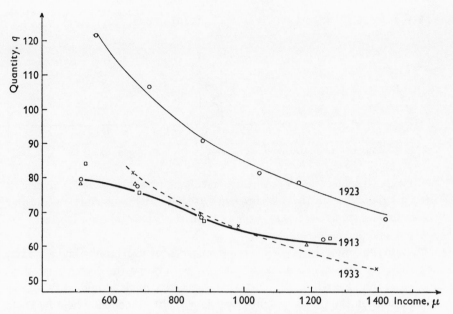

Fig. 16·6·1. Demand functions for flour. Budget data (money value of 1913).

Industrial workers, 1913: △   Low grade employees, 1913: □
Both strata, 1913 and 1923: ○   Both strata, 1933: ×

7. Conclusions. – When the variations in demand are described as a function of income and other explanatory variables, the question of the type of function to be chosen will depend upon the purpose of the analysis. If we wish to describe the observed variation in demand relating to moderate changes in income and prices, it will in practice be sufficient to use very simple functions. A first approximation to budget data can be obtained by a linear function (1·2·1),

$$(1) \qquad Q(\mu) = a + b\mu, \qquad \text{with income elasticity } E = \frac{b\mu}{Q(\mu)}.$$

With greater range in the income variation, a function (1·1·1b) with constant elasticity E usually gives a better fit, especially if demand is under-elastic. There will be no great difference in the results, however, since the constant E will be nearly the same as the elasticity (1b) that corresponds to the averages of income and quantities in the data under analysis. With still greater variation in income, the Törnqvist demand functions (1·1·5a–c) are often useful, being flexible and easy to handle.

If the purpose is to make an extrapolation of the estimated demand function beyond the income range covered by the given data, the choice of demand function is a matter of great importance. This remark applies, in particular, if the resulting demand functions are to be used for predicting

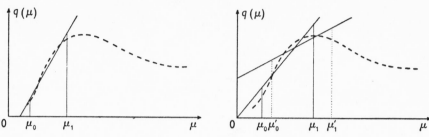

Fig. 16·7·1a–b. Demand variations over wide ranges of income.

the future demand development. Remembering that the national income in industrialized countries like Sweden has doubled in the course of two or three decades, it is clear that reliable forecasts can be obtained only if the demand function is a realistic one.

Considering from this viewpoint our analysis of the family budget data, it would seem that in a good many cases, but not always, the demand functions arrived at can be used for the purpose of forecasting demand under alternative assumptions on the future income development. Reference may here be made to Fig. 1. The broken curve describes roughly how the demand for cereals varied with increasing real income in Sweden in the years 1876–1939, a period during which the national income per capita has trebled. We may here distinguish five phases. At low income levels, phase I, demand is over-elastic, with income elasticity E falling from ∞ to 1. In the transitory phase II, the elasticity is normal, $E = 1$. At somewhat higher incomes, phase III, demand is under-elastic, and E falls from 1 to 0. In phase IV the demand is inelastic, $E = 0$; at still higher income levels, phase V, demand is so under-elastic as to have negative elasticity, and E falls from 0 to $-\infty$. In each of the five phases the curve may be fitted fairly well by the demand functions we have employed. In Fig. 1 we have graduated, using a linear function (1). We see that demand functions (1·1·1b) with constant elasticity would as a rule give a better fit in the various phases, and that still better results would be obtained by the use of Törnqvist's functions (1·1·5). Further, we see that none of the functions mentioned will be able to provide a close fit over more than two phases. The crucial feature is the hump of the curve, which requires more complicated functions for its proper description. It will be noted that we need not go beyond a broken polynomial of the second order to find functions of this type, say

$$(2) \qquad Q(\mu) = \frac{a\mu^2 + b\mu - c}{\mu^2 + \mu} \qquad a \geq 0, \ b > 0, \ c > 0.$$

It is not our purpose, however, to enter upon a statistical analysis on the basis of function (2).

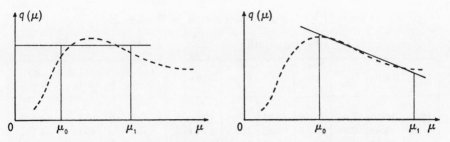

Fig. 16·7·1c–d. Demand variations over wide ranges of income.

Examining the empirical results of previous sections, the humped curve in Fig. 1 suggests itself as a general pattern for the variation of demand over wide ranges of income. This conclusion is further supported by the aggregate figures in Table 1·6·5. For animal foods and green vegetables, the Swedish data seem to indicate that the long run development of demand, as real income rises, is at present involved in a trend that may be described by phases I–III of the humped curve. For cereals and cheap vegetables, on the other hand, the long run development has now reached the phases IV–V, whereas the earlier trend, say up to World War I, was rather similar to the present situation for animal foods.

Chapter 17.

ELASTICITY CALCULATIONS BASED
ON MARKET STATISTICS

1. The statistical data. – Market statistics in the form of time series are the principal material for the estimation of price and cross elasticities, and such data can be used, moreover, for the estimation of income elasticities. As always in the application of regression methods, the data are subject to strict requirements as regards accuracy and reliability. On the whole, demand analysis works under less favourable conditions when dealing with market statistics than with family budget data. For one thing, the quantity data are usually subject to considerable errors, and they often consist of production statistics that will have to be corrected for stock changes, imports and exports, etc., in order to give a proper measure of demand, i.e. of the quantities actually purchased by the consumers during the period and in the market considered, corrections which in their turn are more or less approximate.

TABLE 17·1·1.[1] *Food consumption in Sweden, 1921–39.*

a. Kilograms per capita.   b. 10 000 calories per cap.

Year	Butter	Marga-rine	Meat, exc. pork	Pork	Flour	Sugar	Animal foods	Vegetable foods	All foods
1921	10.10	2.06	22.26	18.94	108.4	29.58	432	688	1 120
22	9.65	2.98	22.04	17.80	108.9	31.10	433	689	1 122
23	9.44	4.02	22.47	19.84	117.1	33.24	454	730	1 184
24	8.97	5.15	22.85	20.40	119.7	33.68	456	737	1 193
1925	8.44	6.50	23.37	18.50	111.7	37.09	459	715	1 174
26	8.48	6.86	22.34	19.01	106.0	36.79	462	694	1 156
27	8.50	7.15	22.65	21.76	104.3	37.81	482	690	1 172
28	8.53	8.51	24.18	21.26	106.8	39.82	495	706	1 201
29	8.39	9.23	25.14	19.73	105.8	42.02	497	706	1 203
1930	9.25	8.79	24.65	21.63	101.4	45.58	510	701	1 211
31	10.31	8.13	23.21	23.68	92.6	43.75	525	667	1 192
32	10.80	8.05	23.50	23.22	95.4	42.15	524	662	1 186
33	10.72	8.05	23.72	23.82	87.6	45.71	519	646	1 165
34	10.62	8.49	23.40	23.69	86.5	46.65	522	642	1 164
1935	11.07	8.84	23.55	21.74	86.0	49.04	522	649	1 171
36	11.42	8.96	23.62	21.30	85.3	49.92	528	645	1 173
37	11.07	9.37	24.61	23.24	86.2	50.81	531	651	1 182
38	10.93	9.27	25.33	21.60	84.2	50.18	526	640	1 166
39	11.03	9.41	24.81	22.78	85.8		538	685	1 223

For another thing, the prices, incomes and other explanatory variables must display fairly large variations if their effect is to be estimated in terms of demand elasticities, and in addition there is the risk that the analysis may be disturbed by relevant factors that have not been taken into account.

In the demand investigations under review, Wold (1940) worked mainly on statistics referring to local markets, whereas Juréen (1952) concentrated on national totals covering the consumption for the whole of Sweden. Since the two types of data are complementary, and a comparison of the results sheds light on their significance and reliability, both investigations have dealt with local as well as national data. The present exposition will in the main be confined to the analysis of national totals, but for comparison we shall also give results that refer to local markets. Our data are as a rule yearly series, but for milk and eggs we also used half-yearly and quarterly data.

Tables 1–2 show (a) national totals of quantities consumed, and (b) nominal prices for some of the main foodstuffs. These series constitute the market statistics of principal importance in the investigations under review. For a more complete documentation, including data for the local markets, reference

TABLE 17·1·2.[2] *Food prices in Sweden 1921–39. Nominal retail prices.*

a. Swedish crowns per kilogram.

b. Sw.cr. per 10 000 calories.

Year	Butter	Margarine	Meat, exc. pork	Pork	Flour	Sugar	Animal foods	Vegetable foods	All foods
1921	4.96	2.93	3.227	3.21	.580	1.70	7.27	2.28	4.20
22	3.75	1.78	2.406	2.50	.414	1.56	5.34	1.81	3.17
23	3.66	1.84	2.251	2.14	.361	1.07	4.89	1.55	2.83
24	3.74	1.78	2.188	1.97	.373	.96	4.84	1.60	2.84
1925	3.84	1.78	2.275	2.49	.409	.78	5.04	1.59	2.94
26	3.37	1.66	2.264	2.38	.387	.71	4.74	1.47	2.78
27	3.39	1.48	2.133	1.91	.401	.72	4.39	1.57	2.73
28	3.51	1.40	2.080	2.05	.393	.64	4.46	1.60	2.78
29	3.39	1.33	2.077	2.26	.369	.54	4.53	1.42	2.70
1930	2.84	1.38	2.081	2.10	.349	.45	4.30	1.25	2.54
31	2.55	1.29	1.988	1.47	.333	.42	3.85	1.26	2.40
32	2.35	1.25	1.802	1.41	.317	.47	3.62	1.23	2.29
33	2.44	1.27	1.638	1.42	.319	.47	3.56	1.14	2.22
34	2.76	1.41	1.718	1.36	.310	.46	3.69	1.14	2.28
1935	2.68	1.35	1.927	1.77	.334	.46	4.00	1.24	2.47
36	2.63	1.33	2.068	1.96	.345	.47	4.18	1.28	2.59
37	2.98	1.48	2.084	1.98	.366	.48	4.34	1.35	2.69
38	3.11	1.60	2.151	2.20	.385	.48	4.61	1.41	2.85
39	3.28	1.65	2.335	2.28	.384		4.83	1.42	2.92

is made to the original investigations. We shall now briefly comment upon our statistical data, commencing with the quantity series.

The local data are restricted in scope, most series referring to cooperative societies in Stockholm, the capital. Since most members of the societies are workers and low grade employees, we may expect that the elasticities based on these data lie somewhat higher than the average for the whole of the local market. Further, we note that there was a strong expansion of the cooperative movement in the inter-war period. To eliminate the resulting trend the quantity data have been evaluated in yearly purchases per member. This involves some approximation, since we know only the total number of members, not the number of customers in the cooperative milk shops, meat shops, etc. Supplementary local data have been employed for milk and meat. The data for milk have been obtained from dairy societies in the central part of Sweden, and for meat from the meat inspection agency in Stockholm.

For the quantity data for the whole of Sweden, our source is Juréen's detailed investigation (1952) of food production and consumption in Sweden. The statistical series are more heterogeneous for national totals than for local data. In principle, the national totals refer to the marketed quantities in the whole of Sweden, thus giving the purchases of all families in all social strata and in all parts of the country. For certain agricultural products the data further include the estimated consumption of natural produce within the rural population. For some foods, notably dairy products, margarine, and sugar, the series employed refer directly to the marketed quantities. For other products, such as meat, eggs, flour and bread, the quantity series have been obtained as total production + import − export. Correction has been made for more important changes in the stocks within the food industry and the wholesale market, but, for the stocks in the retail market, data are usually lacking for the inter-war period. For the products in question there are accordingly errors in the quantity data, but to judge from more complete figures available after 1939 the errors are not important. Of greater magnitude are the errors in the original figures for the consumption of natural produce. For this part of the consumption, however, the trends are fairly well known, so that corrections can be made; here the main sources are the family budget surveys of the Social Welfare Board and a number of special investigations reported in detail by Juréen (1952).

Price data are easy to obtain and relatively free from observational errors. Our basic price series are on the one hand the nominal prices of the Cooperative Union, on the other the national average prices published by the Social Welfare Board. For aggregate commodities, like butter and margarine, we have used average prices, weighted with the quantities consumed.

For the evaluation of real prices and incomes, the nominal figures have been reduced by the use of the consumer price index of the Social Welfare Board. The index series is reproduced in Table 15·1·1, col. 3.

Coming finally to the income factor, this requires particular attention, for one thing because the income development is of fundamental importance for the total demand for food, for another because several income series are available, all of which are more or less subject to the usual defects of income estimates. In the demand analysis referring to the Stockholm markets, we have used the yearly totals of individual incomes in the capital; this series is published by the Statistical Office of Stockholm. In our analysis of demand totals for the whole of Sweden we have taken for basic income series the national income figures published by the Central Bureau of Statistics; these data are compiled from the income taxation of all tax payers except registered Swedish companies and mutual banking societies. As an alternative income series we have used the yearly national index compiled by the Social Welfare Board for the wages of workers and employees.

Table 15·1·1, col. 9, shows the nominal income per capita as obtained from the income-taxation data of the Central Bureau of Statistics. Real income shows an average increase of 2.8% per year in the period 1921–39, which in a ten-year period makes 32%. In the period 1929–39 the yearly increase was almost the same, or 2.9%. Between 1932 and 1939 the increase was as large as 3.6% per year. These yearly rates of increase compare rather well with estimates based on the national production. For example, instead of 3.6% we obtain a somewhat lower figure, or 3.1%. For the inter-war period, as a matter of fact, the income totals as estimated from the national production and from the taxation totals have nearly parallel trends. If we consider the absolute figures, on the other hand, there is a substantial difference in level, but this is of no relevance for our purpose, since the demand analysis requires knowledge only of the relative income changes.

2. The demand for meat.[1] – The elasticity calculations reported in this section are based on the market statistics for the whole of Sweden during the inter-war period. We shall first deal with the separate demand for beef and for pork, which are the two main items (owing to the climate, pork belongs to the basic foodstuffs in Sweden). We shall then consider three aggregate items, viz. beef and pork, all kinds of meat except pork, and finally all kinds of meat. The figures in Table 1 indicate the relative importance of these items in the food budget.

TABLE 17·2·1. *Expenditure ratios for beef : pork and meat : pork.*

Beef	35	All kinds of meat except pork	53
Pork	65	Pork	47
	100		100

In Table 2 we have, at the left, the elasticities of beef demand calculated for different combinations of explanatory variables. At the right we have the corresponding elasticities for pork. We see that the income elasticity is about 0.3, both for beef and for pork, and we see also that these elasticities lie on the same level whether or not the prices are introduced as explanatory variables. Similarly, the price elasticity of pork and the cross elasticity of beef are rather stable, whereas the price elasticity of beef and the cross elasticity of pork are sensitive to the introduction of additional variables. The last row of the table shows the results obtained when all three variables are employed. These elasticities are our final estimates.

To examine whether the results are plausible we note, to begin with, that the analysis explains a fairly large part of the variation in the demand. For pork the residual ratio γ is as low as 26%, and here we find that the residuals are quite irregular, changing signs no less than 10 times. These features indicate that the main systematic factors have been taken into account, which

TABLE 17·2·2. *Separate demand elasticities for beef and pork. Market statistics 1921–39.*

Beef				Pork			
Demand elasticity w.r.t.			Ratio γ, in %	Demand elasticity w.r.t.			Ratio γ, in %
beef price	pork price	income		pork price	beef price	income	
e_{11}	e_{12}	E_1		e_{22}	e_{21}	E_2	
−.04	—	—	100	.41	—	—	69
—	−.09	—	97	—	.61	—	88
—	—	.28	62	—	—	.35	75
.34	−.22	—	94	.52	−.32	—	67
.00	—	.28	62	.40	—	.34	27
—	−.10	.29	55	—	.66	.36	55
.50	−.28	.30	43	.45	−.14	.33	26

Standard errors of the elasticities in the last row:

±.16   ±.07   ±.04   ±.06   ±.14   ±.04

speaks in favour of the validity of the estimates. The irregularity of the residuals is further of importance for the standard errors of the elasticity estimates. For beef as well as pork, the residual autocorrelation is small and irregular, suggesting a theoretical correlogram equalling zero. As a consequence, the classical formula (13·2·6b) gives the same standard errors as the autocorrelative formula (13·4·7b). As seen from the figures given in the lower part of Table 2, the elasticity estimates have rather small standard errors.

Finally we note that the cross elasticities arrived at can be tested by Hotelling-Juréen's relation (6·3·2), since the expenditures for beef and pork cover only a small fraction of the consumer budget. The proportions between the expenditures on beef and pork are known from Table 1. We obtain

(1) $$p_2 q_2 \cdot e_{21} / p_1 q_1 \cdot e_{12} = 65\,(0.14)/35\,(0.28) = 0.93.$$

The theoretical value being unity, we see that the cross elasticities are in close agreement with Hotelling-Juréen's relation. An alternative form of the same test is to use one cross elasticity to calculate the other; thus

(2) $e_{12} = -0.28$ gives $e_{21} = -0.15$, $e_{21} = -0.14$ gives $e_{12} = -0.26$,

showing a close agreement between the observed and the calculated values.

We have now examined the final estimates in Table 2 with regard to their standard errors and their accordance with a priori relationships. To judge from the results obtained, the elasticity estimates make a promising start in our analysis of the meat sector.

TABLE 17·2·3. *Separate and aggregate elasticities for meat and pork. Market statistics 1921–39.*

Food item	Demand elasticity with respect to				Ratio γ, in %
	price of meat except pork	price of pork	income	price of meat	
A Meat, except pork	.43	−.17	.24	—	45
B Pork	−.22	.47	.32	—	26
C_1 Meat, including pork....	—	—	—	.25	90
C_2 » » »	—	—	.27	—	58
C_3 » » »	—	—	.28	.28	33

Standard errors, by the classical formula:

A	±.12	±.05	±.03	—
B	±.14	±.06	±.03	—
C_1	—	—	—	±.12
C_2	—	—	±.04	—
C_3	—	—	±.02	±.04

Table 3 records similar elasticity calculations for (A) all kinds of meat, except pork, (B) pork, and (C) meat and pork. Considering the aggregate demand for meat and pork we note that the income and price elasticities obtained are equal, or about 0.3, and that the aggregate income elasticity, 0.28, is in agreement with the income elasticities obtained separately for pork (0.32), and for meat except pork (0.24).

The results in Tables 2–3 can be used to calculate price elasticities that refer to the situation when the two prices dealt with change in the same proportion. According to Theorem 6·4·3 such a price elasticity is the sum of the price and cross elasticities that refer to separate price changes. Table 4 shows the resulting estimates. For example, supposing the prices of beef and pork change in the same proportion, the price elasticity will be 0.22 for beef and 0.31 for pork. We see that the results in Table 4 are plausible from the viewpoint of the estimate previously obtained for the aggregate price elasticity of meat, which according to Table 3 is 0.28.

TABLE 17·2·4. *Price elasticities for different kinds of meat, calculated on the assumption of proportional changes in the prices.*

Beef and pork		All kinds of meat	
Beef	Pork	Meat except pork	Pork
.22	.31	.26	.25

TABLE 17·2·5. *Summary of elasticity estimates for meat, 1921–39.*

Category of meat	Price elasticity		Income elasticity
	Separate price changes	Proportional price changes	
Meat	—	.28	.28
Meat, all kinds except pork	.43	.26	.24
Beef..........................	.50	.22	.30
Pork (see the text)........... {	.45	.31	.33
	.47	.25	.32

In our comment on Tables 3–4 we have stressed the agreement between the elasticity estimates obtained. Such uniformity may be regarded as a check or test, and will therefore increase our confidence in the results. Further we may examine the estimates from the viewpoints adopted in our comment on Table 2. As regards the standard errors, these have been found to be no larger than for corresponding elasticities in Table 2. Similarly, the elasticities in Table 3 are in close agreement with Hotelling-Juréen's relation. In fact, if we calculate the ratio (1) for the (A) and (B), we obtain 1.15, or if the check is arranged as in (2),

$$e_{12} = -0.17 \text{ gives } e_{21} = -0.19 \qquad e_{21} = -0.22 \text{ gives } e_{12} = -0.20.$$

Concluding our analysis of meat demand, we remark that a final appraisal of our elasticity estimates cannot be made until we are in a position to compare them with our results for other foods. We have found, however, that the meat elasticities in themselves combine so as to make a plausible whole. The main results are summed up in Table 5. The two series given for pork are the estimates obtained when using, alternately, the beef price and the meat price as explanatory variable. The close agreement is an indication that the prices of meats other than beef and pork have had a negligible influence on pork demand.

In Table 1·6·3, cols. 2, 4 and 5, some of the results in Table 5 are given in rounded figures.

3. Butter and margarine.[1] – The increase in population and national income during the inter-war period opened the way for a considerable increase in the consumption of commodities with unsatiated demand, among them butter and margarine. Towards the end of World War I the Swedish margarine industry was practically at a standstill owing to lack of raw materials. The boom in the margarine industry during the 'twenties was strongly supported by the price development. The retail price of margarine thus fell by 25% in

TABLE 17·3·1. *Separate demand elasticities for butter and margarine. Market statistics 1921–39 and 1926–39.*

Period	Butter				Margarine			
	Demand elasticity w.r.t.			Ratio γ, in %	Demand elasticity w.r.t.			Ratio γ, in %
	butter price	margarine price	income		margarine price	butter price	income	
1921–1939	.70	—	—	74	2.67	—	—	71
	—	.05	—	100	—	1.74	—	90
	—	—	.39	82	—	—	2.13	58
	1.08	−.59	—	58	2.65	.03	—	71
	.54	—	.24	67	1.76	—	1.68	40
	—	−.18	.44	81	—	.47	2.00	57
{	.94	−.67	.30	43	2.18	−.81	1.80	36
{	±.15	±.14	±.09		±.46	±.49	±.27	
1926–1939	.79	—	—	77	−.02	—	—	100
	—	−.36	—	98	—	.00	—	100
	—	—	.66	76	—	—	.63	61
	1.04	−.88	—	60	−.03	.01	—	100
	.78	—	.65	38	.65	—	.81	44
	—	.24	.72	72	—	−.01	.63	61
{	.88	−.34	.55	34	.79	−.23	.85	39
{	±.15	±.23	±.12		±.21	±.14	±.11	

1922–29, while the butter price dropped only by 10%. Consumption per capita of margarine increased fourfold, whereas butter consumption rather showed a slight decrease.

These important changes in fat consumption can hardly be expected to be fully explained by the price and income development alone. As regards the increase in margarine consumption in Sweden, especially during the early 'twenties, it would seem that quality improvement and propaganda were equally important factors. Hence it may be feared that a demand analysis will be rather difficult, and in particular we cannot expect to arrive at very reliable results on the basis of market statistics for butter and margarine for the whole period 1921–39. If we choose a shorter period, on the other hand, there is the difficulty that the prices of butter and margarine have been largely parallel since 1933, when a margarine excise was introduced. In the analysis of market statistics for butter and margarine now to be reported we have made elasticity calculations both for the years 1921–39 and for the shorter period 1926–39. For the aggregate demand of butter and margarine we have, moreover, worked on data for the period 1930–38, which is approximately a complete trade cycle.

TABLE 17·3·2. *Price and income elasticity of*

a. Market statistics 1921–39.   b. Market statistics 1926–39.

Elasticity w.r.t.		Ratio γ, in %	Elasticity w.r.t.		Ratio γ, in %
price	income		price	income	
1.09	—	56	.40	—	95
—	.97	38	—	.64	56
.56	.70	18	.58	.69	35

Standard errors of the elasticities in the last row:

±.08	±.06	±.14	±.08
±.09	±.08	—	—

Table 1 shows the elasticities obtained when dealing with butter and margarine demand separately. We see that the two periods have given fairly concordant results for butter demand elasticity, whereas the margarine elasticities have turned out quite differently on reducing the period under consideration. The results seem to confirm that margarine consumption in the inter-war period has been systematically influenced by other factors besides those taken into account in our analysis, at least at the beginning of the period. Indeed, although it is reasonable that the demand elasticities decrease towards zero with time, it is highly doubtful whether the sharp trend in the elasticities in Table 1 is not partly spurious, being due to factors other than butter and margarine prices and income. The probable influence of such other factors may be brought out by testing the cross elasticities by the Hotelling-Juréen relation. According to the retail prices of the Social Welfare Board the relative expenditure on butter and margarine was 74 : 26 in the period 1921–39 and 71 : 29 in the period 1926–39. Making use of these figures and the cross elasticities given in Table 1 (the last row for each period), the ratio $p_2 q_2 \cdot e_{21}/p_1 q_1 \cdot e_{12}$ is found to equal 0.42 and 0.28 for the two periods. The theoretical value being unity, the deviations are quite substantial. It is true that the deviations are not significant in a statistical sense (the standard errors given in Table 1 are evaluated by the classical formula). However, whether the deviations are random or are due to relevant factors having been neglected, or to both of these circumstances, the negative result of the Hotelling-Juréen test shows that the cross elasticities obtained are not in agreement with the general hypotheses that underlie the analysis.

The development of margarine consumption during the inter-war period, and earlier as well, gives a clear example of the limitation of demand analysis as a basis for consumption forecasts. During this period the habits *the aggregate demand for butter and margarine.*

c. Market statistics 1930–38.

Ordinary regression analysis			Conditional regression analysis		
Elasticity w.r.t.		Ratio γ, in %	Price elasticity (fixed)	Income elasticity	Ratio γ, in %
price	income				
−.46	—	79	.4	.53	74
—	.35	62	.5	.58	79
.02	.34	62	.6	.63	85

Standard errors of the elasticities in the last row (classical formula):

±.30   ±.18   —   ±.14

of butter and margarine consumption have been influenced by price, income and other factors in a manner that escapes our quantitative analysis. In other words, the results recorded give no satisfactory basis for estimating the future trends in butter and margarine demand *separately*. Instead of going further into the problem of such an estimation, we shall restrict ourselves here to forecasts of the *total* demand for butter and margarine.

Table 2 shows the results of elasticity calculations for the aggregate butter and margarine demand. We see that the elasticities obtained with average price and income as explanatory variables are practically the same for the two periods 1921–39 and 1926–39. The residual ratio γ indicates that the analysis explains a large part of the variation in demand. The standard errors are fairly small, whether calculated by the classical [first row] or the autocorrelative formula [second row]. The price elasticities lie between 0.5 and 0.6. We note here an agreement with the price elasticities that Table 1 gives us on the assumption of *uniform* price changes; forming the sum of price and cross elasticities for the period 1926–39, Table 1 gives 0.54 for butter and 0.56 for margarine.

The income elasticity of the aggregate demand for butter and margarine is about 0.7, according to the calculations for periods 1921–39 and 1926–39. For the aggregate income elasticity we have thus a higher estimate than for the aggregate price elasticity. We note that this result is not in agreement with the rule of thumb of Ch. 6·5. Since it is not large, the difference might well be regarded as accidental; other possible explanations are the migration between rural and urban districts and the income levelling during the inter-war period. The situation was examined in some detail in Ch. 15·1–2. We have seen that there is a substantial correlation between price and income, and that the resulting partial indeterminacy of the price and income elasticities could be remedied by conditional regression analysis. The device of fixing the ratio $\lambda = E/e$ was found to give plausible results. Our final estimates are about 0.65 or 0.70 for the price elasticity e, and about 0.60 or 0.65 for the income elasticity E.

The results of the conditional regression seem to be plausible also in view of the strong recovery of fat consumption during the first years after World War I, a trend which tends to exaggerate the income elasticities relative to what would have been normal, say during the 'thirties. Now, if we consider the results actually obtained for the period 1930–38, we see that only about 40% of the demand variations can be explained by the price and income development. Further, we note a rather strong intercorrelation between price and income during this period. The circumstances thus being rather unfavourable for the analysis, we have made a trial with conditional regression analysis. To judge from the resulting estimates, the income elasticity was lower during the 'thirties than earlier in the inter-war period. For the numerical results, reference is made to the right-hand part of Table 2c. In accordance with the general formulae the conditional income elasticity E and the corresponding ratio γ are given by

$$E = 0.35 + 0.46\,e \qquad \gamma^2 = 0.391 + 0.041\,e + 0.832\,e^2$$

where e is the fixed price elasticity, which is assumed to be known a priori.

For the aggregate demand for butter and margarine in the period 1930–38, the price and income elasticities indicated by our analysis are nearly equal, both being about 0.5 or 0.6. Since the data are scarcely capable of giving clear-cut results, the estimates should be regarded as less reliable than those obtained for meat [Ch. 17·2]. We note that the estimates are somewhat higher than those found by Wold (1940), his figures being 0.4 or 0.5 for the aggregate price elasticity of butter and margarine and 0.2 or 0.3 for the aggregate income elasticity. Since Wold's estimate of the income elasticity is based on family budget data, it is not directly comparable, and according to the general argument of Ch. 14·7 it should be lower than the present estimate.

As before, we have in Table 1·6·3 given some of the main results in rounded figures.

4. Other animal products.[1] – In this section we shall briefly report the results obtained for milk, cheese and eggs.

a. *Milk.* The data dealt with here refer to consumer milk, including cream (evaluated in milk). The results obtained are shown in Table 1. We see that the price and income changes explain 50% of the demand variation in the period 1926–39, but only 24% in the period 1921–39. The standard errors of the elasticity estimates are high, for the double reason that the price changes are relatively small and that there is intercorrelation between price and

TABLE 17·4·1. *Price and income elasticities for consumer milk and cream. Market statistics 1921–39 and 1926–39.*

1921–39			1926–39			Conditional regression, 1926–39		
Price elasticity	Income elasticity	Ratio γ, %	Price elasticity	Income elasticity	Ratio γ, %	Fixed price elasticity	Income elasticity	Ratio γ, %
.31	—	77	.49	—	51	.2	−.10	57
—	−.06	90	—	−.17	63	.4	−.03	52
.28	−.02	76	.62	.05	50	.6	.04	51

income. The situation is a typical case where conditional regression analysis is called for. For the conditional income elasticity we obtain for the period 1926–39

$$E = -0.17 + 0.35\,e$$

where e is the fixed value of the price elasticity. As seen in Table 1, the hypothetical value e may vary over a rather wide range without having any considerable effect, either on the income elasticity E or on the residual ratio γ.

Corresponding calculations have been made for consumer milk, excluding cream consumption. The results derived from the parallel sets of data have been summed up in Table 1·6·3. According to this analysis, milk demand has been almost inelastic to income changes during the inter-war period. This is in fairly good agreement with the results of Wold (1940), who gives 0.2 or 0.3 for the price elasticity and about 0.2 for the income elasticity. Knowing that market statistics in general tend to give higher income elasticities than family budget data [Ch. 14·7], we note that there is ir. the present case an opposite tendency due to the rural-urban migration, the farmers having a higher per capita consumption of milk than the urban population. On the other hand we may expect in market statistics a slight tendency to overrate the income elasticity of milk because of the decreasing fertility rate during most of the inter-war period. The argument here is not so much that children consume more milk than adults, but rather that there is evidence that milk consumption habits among adults differ, depending upon whether there are many children in the family.

b. *Cheese.* Our quantity data for cheese are to some extent biased, the increase in cheese production being exaggerated because data on the farmers' home curdling are lacking, and such direct marketing has been on the decrease during the inter-war period. As a consequence, the income elasticity will be somewhat overestimated. Calculating the price and income elasticities in the same manner as we did previously, we obtain $e = 0.18$ and $E = 1.33$

for the period 1921–39, and $e = 0.17$ and $E = 1.22$ for the period 1926–39. The high figures obtained for the income elasticity are due to the strong trend in the consumed quantities, a trend which may be partly explained by the neglect of home curdling just mentioned, but which in the main is a real fact. Now, the more a real trend may be explained by factors other than the increase in income, the smaller is the resulting income elasticity. A lower limit is the income elasticity estimated from the family budget data, which according to Ch. 16·5 is about 0.3. However, we can hardly expect such a low elasticity to be valid for the market statistics, one reason being that these data include consumption at restaurants and other premises, a sector of the consumption that has increased markedly during the period under analysis.

From what we have said it would seem that we strike a fair estimate if the income elasticity of cheese is taken to be about 0.5. In Table 1·6·3 this figure has been put between brackets, the estimate not being very reliable. If applied for prediction, the validity will largely depend upon whether the future development will be influenced by factors other than price and income in the same manner as was the case in the inter-war period.

c. *Eggs.* Reliable yearly data for egg consumption are lacking, and only the general trend can be roughly estimated. Hence it is not possible to perform a simultaneous estimation of price and income elasticities in the usual way. According to estimates for the two decades during the inter-war period there has been an increase from 6.21 kg to 8.08 kg per capita, which is about 30%, whereas real income has increased by 28% per capita. The real price of eggs was falling during the period 1920–33, and shows then an increase up to 1939, yet without reaching the level of prices at the end of the 'twenties. The real price of eggs was 20% lower during the first decade, on the average, than during the second. With these data, on the assumption that price and income elasticities are equal, the resulting elasticity is 0.6. On the basis of data from cooperative societies, Wold (1940) has estimated the price and income elasticities as 1.0 and 0.7, respectively.

5. Vegetable foods.[1] – Market statistics that can be used for demand analysis are lacking for many separate items of vegetable agricultural products, but data are available for a few of the most important items. This section will report the results obtained for (a) flour, (b) sugar and syrup, (c) potatoes.

a. *Flour.* The quantity data refer to the total consumption of wheat and rye flour. In Sweden these two varieties cover more than 90% of total flour consumption. As explanatory variables we have used (i) the average price of wheat and rye flour, (ii) the average price of the main food items of animal origin, and (iii) income. The resulting elasticities are shown in Table 1.

TABLE 17·5·1. *Demand elasticities for flour. Market statistics 1921–39.*

Elasticity with respect to			Ratio γ, %
price of flour	price of animal foods	income	
e_{11}	e_{12}	E_1	
−.28	—	—	99
—	−.74	—	90
—	—	−.61	56
.65	−1.06	—	87
−.35	—	−.62	54
—	−.48	−.57	48
.15	−.56	−.56	48
±.38	±.29	±.09	

We see that the variations in flour demand are somewhat better explained by income and price of animal foods than by income and price of flour, and that there is almost nothing to be gained if flour price is introduced as a third regressor. The results indicate that the price elasticity of flour is small, and the large standard error shows that the estimate has a wide margin of uncertainty.

The analysis suggests that flour consumption has been fairly inelastic w.r.t. flour prices during the inter-war period. On the other hand, the negative cross elasticity indicates that the effect of rising prices in the animal sector is to increase flour consumption, whereas a lowering of prices for animal foods has opened up possibilities of reducing flour consumption and thereby of improving the standard of nourishment. In other words, if prices fall for animal foods the response will be an increase in the proportion of animal foods to cereals, not only because the demand for animal foods will increase, but also because the demand for cereals will decrease. Owing to the considerable standard errors in the elasticity estimates these conclusions are somewhat tentative. (The standard errors given in Table 1 have been obtained by the classical formula.) We shall see, however, that the results are in agreement with the elasticities to be given in the next section for the aggregates of animal and vegetable foods.

Flour consumption has been rather strongly on the decrease during the period considered. Table 1 shows that the income variable explains much more of the development than the price variables. Further, we note that the income elasticity is not much affected if the prices are introduced as regressors. The income elasticity is strongly negative, the estimate obtained being about −0.55. This is the estimate given in Table 1·6·3. By way of an alternative approach we have made a rough attempt to apply a demand function with variable elasticity. The demand function and the income elasticity obtained are

$$Q(\mu) = 73.9 \frac{\mu}{\mu - 34.6} \qquad E_\mu Q = -\frac{34.6}{\mu - 34.6}.$$

The function employed is of Törnqvist's type, as in (16·6·1), and adapted so as to apply to inferior commodities. The parameters have been estimated from average income and consumption during the two decades, the income index being 77 and 100, and the flour quantity 134.2 and 113.0 kg, respectively.

b. *Sugar and syrup.* Our explanatory variables are (i) the price of lump sugar, (ii) the same series of animal food prices as in the analysis of flour demand, (iii) income. The data for 1939 have been excluded from the analysis, owing to the large purchase of sugar for storage during the months shortly after the opening of World War II. The elasticities obtained are shown in Table 2.

Before examining the results we recall from Ch. 16·5 that the income elasticity for sugar and syrup, according to the family budget data for 1933, is 0.01 for industrial workers and low grade employees, and 0.08 for middle-class families. For farmers and farm workers the figures are 0.2 and 0.4. The lower elasticity for workers and employees than for middle-class families may be accidental, but it may also be due to home baking being more frequent in families with low incomes. The demand for bakery products, which contain sugar and syrup, increases markedly with income, in workers' and employees' families. This tendency is present in all social strata, but not so much in the middle class. Further, with income increase there is a fairly strong increase in the demand for other food products containing sugar, such as sweets, fruit preserves, and soft drinks. There are thus several reasons for expecting that the income elasticities for sugar that are estimated from family budget data tend to underrate the actual increase of sugar consumption that occurs with increasing income.

We see from Table 2 that the market statistics give us considerably higher values for income elasticity than were obtained from the budget data. The estimation is disturbed by multicollinearity, however, since income and sugar price are strongly intercorrelated, the correlation coefficient being -0.87. We are accordingly led to apply conditional regression analysis. With price and income for explanatory variables, and with one elasticity fixed, we obtain

$$e_{11} = 0.46 - 0.38 E \qquad E = 1.07 - 1.98 e_{11}$$

where the fixed elasticity is written to the right in each relation. Alternatively, we have formed the conditional estimates on the basis of a fixed ratio $\lambda = E/e$. Some of the estimates thus obtained are shown in Table 2.

TABLE 17·5·2. *Demand elasticities for sugar and syrup. Market statistics 1921–38.*

Elasticity w.r.t.			Ratio γ, %		Conditional elasticity w.r.t.			Ratio γ, %
price of sugar	price of animal foods	income		λ	price of sugar	price of animal foods	income	
e_{11}	e_{12}	E			e_{11}	e_{12}	E	
.46	—	—	36	—	.39	—	.2	28
—	1.28	—	85	—	.31	—	.4	25
—	—	1.07	31	—	.24	—	.6	20
.49	−.22	—	35	*1.0*	.34	—	.34	27
A: .22	—	.64	22	*0.8*	D: .36	—	.29	28
—	.59	.98	21	—	E: .40	−.07	.2	29
B: .11	.40	.80	19	—	.30	.09	.4	24
.2	—	.68	22	—	.21	.24	.6	21
.3	—	.48	24	*1.0*	F: .34	−.01	.34	27
C: .4	—	.28	28	*0.8*	G: .37	−.04	.29	28

Standard errors:

A: ±.06	—	±.13		D: ±.05	—	±.04
A: ±.07	—	±.16		E: ±.07	±.29	—
B: ±.08	±.20	±.15		F: ±.04	±.25	±.04
C: —	—	±.13		G: ±.05	±.26	±.04

Table 2 also shows the standard errors for the main estimates. With income and sugar price as regressors, the classical formula gives the standard errors 0.06 and 0.13, respectively, for the price and income elasticities. The autocorrelative formula has given slightly higher standard errors (0.07 and 0.16). With animal food price for third regressor the standard error of the cross elasticity turns out to be large, or 0.20, but for the two other elasticities the standard errors remain about the same as before. For these and for the conditional estimates, the standard errors are based on the autocorrelative formula. We see that the elasticity estimates obtained by conditional regression have smaller standard errors than the ordinary estimates, as was to be expected. Comparing the two approaches of conditional regression, we find, as before, that fixing λ seems to be the preferable device, since the resulting estimates are more plausible and their standard errors smaller.

Turning to the results obtained when the price of animal foods is introduced as a third regressor, the difficulty of multicollinearity remains, or is even more pronounced. Making use of conditional regression, and, for example, fixing the income elasticity, we obtain the system

$$e_{11} = 0.49 - 0.49\,E \qquad e_{12} = -0.20 + 0.70\,E.$$

A number of alternative conditional estimates are recorded in Table 2. We see that the conditional elasticity w.r.t. sugar price turns out to be practically the same, whether the price of animal foods is used as explanatory variable or not. Further the conditional regression analysis suggests that the price of animal foods has little or no influence upon the sugar demand.

With regard to the above comments, and since the rule of thumb of Ch. 6·5 leads us to expect that income elasticity is not higher than price elasticity, we may regard an income elasticity of 0.30 and a price elasticity of 0.35 as plausible estimates. These estimates have been given in Table 1·6·3.

c. *Potatoes*. Since the total consumption of potatoes is known only with large margins of error, the yearly figures cannot be used for an estimation of price elasticities. According to available figures for the food consumption of potatoes, including the use of potatoes in the food industry, the yearly average was 171.1 kg per capita in the period 1920–29 and 157.8 in 1930–39. With income as single explanatory variable this gives − 0.3 for the income elasticity. It goes without saying that this estimate is uncertain, since the consumption of potatoes may in the long run have been influenced by the price of potatoes and other food items.

According to the figures given in Ch. 16·5 the income elasticity for potatoes as estimated from budget data is about − 0.1 for small farmers and 0.1 for farm workers. For workers and low grade employees the income elasticity is, on the average, about 0, whereas the different family types have given elasticities that in several cases lie well to the negative side. In the budget data, of course, the item "potatoes" does not include the products of the food industry.

The market statistics giving only a vague indication of the demand elasticities for potatoes, we have to strike our estimates with regard on the one hand to the income elasticity for potatoes as estimated from budget data, on the other hand to our previous results for other commodities. In Table 1·6·3 we have introduced − 0.20 as a tentative estimate for the elasticity w.r.t. income as well as price.

6. Aggregates of vegetable and animal foods.[1] – Thus far in our analysis of market statistics we have considered the demand for specified foods. We shall now investigate the demand for large aggregates of food items. Aggregate elasticities being relevant in applications that require a simultaneous treatment of several commodities, such results are of special importance in demand prediction, where it is desirable to work on several alternative assumptions regarding the trends in population figures, incomes and prices, and where a separate treatment of the food items would accordingly lead one into a maze of details, not to speak of the large amount of calculation involved. In the present section we shall consider the groups of animal and vegetable food items, and in the next we shall finally sum up the whole food sector.

In Ch. 16 we pointed out as a dominant feature in the development of food consumption in Sweden that there was a gradual shift from cheap vegetable foods to expensive and more health-protective animal foods, a development that was possible thanks to the rise in real income per capita. At the same time, the total food consumption in calories per capita has reached saturation level, and at least during the inter-war period it was rather stable. We shall now examine to what extent the changes in the balance between vegetable and animal foods were caused by changes in prices and incomes.

Tables 17·1·1–2 show the market statistics employed in the analysis of the aggregate demand for vegetable and animal foods. The estimates given for total calorie consumption cover all important foodstuffs, as seen from the following specification.

Vegetable foods.

a. Agricultural products: Flour and grain from wheat, rye, corn and oats; peas and beans; potatoes; sugar.

b. Other vegetable products: All kinds of imported fruits and berries; rice.

Animal foods.

a. Agricultural products: Meat; milk; butter; cheese; eggs.

b. Other animal foods: Margarine; fish.

The items "agricultural products" include the foods for which the consumption has hitherto in the main been covered by Swedish products. The other food aggregates include a few typical colonial products, and fish. Margarine, being a substitute for butter, has been included under the heading of animal foods.

According to calorie estimates for the entire food sector, the items included in our analysis cover about 96%. We have excluded certain foods, such as Swedish fruits, berries, green vegetables and other items contributing little to the calorie total, omissions which are due to shortcomings in the available data regarding quantities and prices of these items. There are thus wide margins of uncertainty in the estimated changes from year to year in the yield of Swedish berries, fruits and green vegetables. For such items as game, edible fats other than butter and margarine, whey-cheese, honey, etc., there is the further difficulty that the statistics of current prices are not reliable.

The results reported in the present section refer to demand functions with constant elasticities. A first set of elasticity estimates has been derived on the basis of the data for the whole period 1921–39. In view of the exceptional price and income conditions in the period immediately after World

TABLE 17·6·1. *Price and income elasticity for vegetable and animal foods evaluated in calories. Market statistics.*

(i) Item group (ii) Period	Vegetable foods			Animal foods		
	Price elasticity	Income elasticity	Ratio γ, %	Price elasticity	Income elasticity	Ratio γ, %
Agricultural products:						
1921–1939........	−.32	—	71	.34	—	86
»	—	−.21	74	—	.23	63
» .... A:	−.21	−.11	67	.35	.23	36
1923–1938........	−.36	—	71	.43	—	75
»	—	−.34	61	—	.24	73
»	−.26	−.23	48	.40	.23	39
1923–1930........	−.14	—	88	.57	—	72
»	—	−.20	74	—	.23	71
»	.07	−.26	55	.45	.18	47
1930–1938........	.26	—	94	.12	—	77
»	—	−.11	93	—	.05	93
»	.00	−.12	93	.46	.27	38
All foods:						
1921–1939........	−.36	—	78	.60	—	81
»	—	.16	81	—	.41	44
» .... B:	−.25	−.10	72	.44	.37	15
1923–1938........	−.43	—	75	−.55	—	79
»	—	.29	64	—	.37	55
»	−.27	−.22	51	.48	.35	15
1923–1930........	−.09	—	96	.95	—	52
»	—	.17	79	—	.51	33
»	.08	−.21	68	.36	.41	24
1930–1938........	.16	—	97	−.04	—	98
»	—	−.20	99	—	.06	86
»	.01	−.08	96	.38	29	40

Standard errors:

A: ±.11   ±.07   ±.06   ±.03
B: ±.13   ±.06   ±.04   ±.02

War I and the tendencies to hoarding (notably of sugar) during the last peace year 1939, calculations have also been made for the shorter period 1923–38. In addition, an attempt has been made to analyse the consumption pattern during a period of increasing economic activity (1923–30) and during the whole of a trade cycle (1930–38).

In the first phase of the analysis we have confined our calculations to price and income elasticities, disregarding cross elasticities. These results are shown in Table 1.

With price and income as regressors, the residual ratio γ is on the whole considerably lower for the animal foods than for the vegetables. The poor fit of the regression relation to the observed quantities in the case of vegetables may be due either to our having disregarded some relevant explanatory variable, or to observational errors and other deficiencies in the data under analysis. In practice both these features will always enter the picture, disturbing the analysis to a greater or lesser degree. In the present case we may stress, in particular, the shortcomings of the quantity data. In general, it was possible to take stock changes into account only in the production sector and in the wholesale market, but not in the retail market and in households. Most of the vegetable foods are better suited for storage than are animal foods, and an incompleteness in the storage correction may therefore be expected to be of more consequence in the analysis of the vegetable foods. Further we note that we have rather incomplete knowledge of the changes in the yearly consumption of potatoes, and in the same way the data for peas and beans are somewhat unreliable. For the period 1923–38, however, the ratio γ is 51% and 48% for all vegetable foods and agricultural vegetable foods, respectively, showing that price and income variations could explain about half of the variation in the consumption of vegetables.

The standard errors are moderate, but for the short periods 1923–30 and 1930–38 they are of course fairly large. Between the two periods mentioned the income elasticities decreased in absolute value for vegetables as well as for animal foods. The real income having increased rapidly between the two periods, these results are in agreement with what our analysis of family budget data revealed concerning the variation of income elasticities with the income level.

The results in Table 1 for agricultural vegetable foods and all vegetable foods for periods 1921–39 and 1923–38 may be summed up in the price elasticity − 0.2 or − 0.3 and the income elasticity − 0.1 or − 0.2. For animal foods, the results for all of the four periods may be summed up in the following elasticities:

	Price elasticity	Income elasticity
Agricultural animal foods......	0.4 or 0.5	0.2 or 0.3
All animal foods	0.35 or 0.45	0.3 or 0.4

The aggregate of all animal foods contains the same items as agricultural animal foods, except that fish and margarine have been included. Fish constitutes only about 2% of the total calorie intake, or 5% of animal food consump-

tion. Between 1920–29 and 1930–39 the increase in fish consumption was
11.5% per capita, and at the same time the real income increased by 30%,
which gives an estimate of 0.4 for the income elasticity. According to calculations of the type given in Table 16˙5˙3 the income elasticity for fish was 0.3
or 0.4 among workers and employees. Hence we may infer that if we exclude
fish from the aggregate of all animal foods, any change in the elasticity will
be a small one (since the market statistics for fish are rather unreliable, they
have not been subjected to separate elasticity calculations). It follows that the
difference between the elasticities for the two aggregates of animal foods is
in the main due to the development of margarine consumption. As already
pointed out, there was a sharp increase in margarine demand during the
beginning of the 1920's, and in the 1930's the increase was considerably
slower. This is sufficient to explain why the income elasticities for the two
aggregates of animal foods present different trends in the inter-war period.

The negative price elasticities obtained for vegetable foods indicate that
an increase in the prices of vegetable products would lead to an increase in
the consumption of vegetables, and, conversely, that a lowering of the prices
would lead to a decrease in consumption. In itself there is nothing absurd
in such a state of things. It may well be, however, that the price elasticity
would be modified if we made use of more explanatory variables, and regarding
the demand for vegetables we should in particular introduce the price of
animal foods. Similarly it is desirable to examine how the price elasticity
of animal foods is affected if the price of vegetable foods is introduced as an
additional explanatory variable. For such calculations of cross elasticities,
however, high requirements must be fulfilled by the statistical data as regards
both quality and number of observations. Since the short 1923–30 and 1930–38
series hardly proved sufficient for an analysis with two explanatory variables,
we cannot expect them to serve for an extension of the analysis. In the
case of the 1921–39 and 1923–38 series, on the other hand, the results
obtained with two regressors seem to be sufficiently stable to permit a tentative calculation of cross elasticities. The results of an analysis along this
line are shown in Table 2.

In Table 2 the quantity data for vegetable foods and animal foods are
subjected to a regression analysis with the same set of three explanatory
variables. Thus the total yearly consumption of vegetable foods has been
approximated by (i) the average price per 10000 calories of all vegetable foods,
(ii) the corresponding price for animal foods, and (iii) the income. The same
three series have been used for the analysis of the total consumption of animal
foods. For the agricultural products we have used the average prices of animal
and vegetable agricultural products and the income series.

Comparing the results in Tables 1 and 2 we find two features of great interest.

TABLE 17·6·2. *Price, cross and income elasticities for vegetable and animal foods evaluated in calories. Market statistics.*

(i) Item group (ii) Period	Vegetable foods				Animal foods			
	price elast.	cross elast.	income elast.	Ratio γ, %	price elast.	cross elast.	income elast.	Ratio γ, %
Agricultural prod.:								
1921–1939 A	.05	−.36	−.24	60	.37	−.01	.24	36
1923–1938 B	.02	−.40	−.36	37	.49	−.04	.27	23
All foods:								
1921–1939 C	−.11	−.18	−.12	69	.41	.04	.36	14
1923–1938 D	−.07	−.30	−.26	43	.47	.01	.35	15

Standard errors:

$$
\begin{array}{llllllll}
\text{A:} & \left\{\begin{array}{l} \pm.17 \\ \pm.18 \end{array}\right. & \begin{array}{l} \pm.19 \\ \pm.20 \end{array} & \begin{array}{l} \pm.10 \\ \pm.11 \end{array} & \begin{array}{l} \pm.11 \\ \pm.11 \end{array} & \begin{array}{l} \pm.10 \\ \pm.10 \end{array} & \begin{array}{l} \pm.05 \\ \pm.05 \end{array} \\
\text{B:} & \pm.12 & \pm.14 & \pm.07 & \pm.07 & \pm.06 & \pm.04 \\
\text{C:} & \left\{\begin{array}{l} \pm.18 \\ \pm.19 \end{array}\right. & \begin{array}{l} \pm.17 \\ \pm.18 \end{array} & \begin{array}{l} \pm.06 \\ \pm.08 \end{array} & \begin{array}{l} \pm.06 \\ \pm.05 \end{array} & \begin{array}{l} \pm.06 \\ \pm.06 \end{array} & \begin{array}{l} \pm.02 \\ \pm.05 \end{array} \\
\text{D:} & \pm.12 & \pm.13 & \pm.05 & \pm.06 & \pm.07 & \pm.03
\end{array}
$$

One is that the cross elasticities of the demand for animal foods are nearly zero. Or, otherwise expressed, the price and income elasticities of animal foods remain the same, on the whole, when the price of vegetables is included as explanatory variable. The second point is that the price elasticities for vegetable foods have changed radically, showing that the cross elasticity of the demand for vegetable foods cannot be neglected. Further, we note that the income elasticities of vegetable foods have become somewhat more negative. The results in Table 2 may be summed up in the following figures.

Swedish agricultural products	Price el.	Cross el.	Income el.
Vegetable foods	about 0.0	− 0.3 or − 0.4	− 0.2 or − 0.3
Animal foods	0.4 or 0.5	about 0.0	0.2 or 0.3
Total food demand			
Vegetable foods	about − 0.1	− 0.2 or − 0.3	− 0.1 or − 0.2
Animal foods	0.4 or 0.5	about 0.0	0.3 or 0.4

Our elasticity calculations for the inter-war period thus indicate that the demand for vegetable foods, notably cereals, has been considerably more sensitive to changes in the prices of animal foods than in the prices of vegetables. The demand for animal foods, on the other hand, has shown a clear dependence on the changes in the prices of animal foods, whereas it is scarcely influenced, if at all, by the price development of vegetable foods. The situation may be summed up in the conclusion that *the changes in demand between vegetable and animal foods are, at a constant income level, mainly determined by the changes in the prices of animal foods.*

Regarding the significance of the elasticity estimates in Table 2 we note as a favourable indication that the residual ratio γ is fairly low, especially for the animal foods, showing that a rather close fit to the observed consumption is obtained when using the two price series and the income as regressors. The standard errors being given in Table 2, we see that these are moderate for the elasticities referring to animal foods. The demand for vegetable foods has given considerably larger standard errors, though not so large that the elasticity estimates can be regarded as indeterminate. Further we note that the classical and the autocorrelative formulae have given nearly the same standard errors. This is due to the fact, in itself a favourable indication of the significance of the analysis, that the regression residuals present an irregular behaviour, so that their correlograms could in most cases be fitted by a correlogram of the simple type of a moving average of first order.

The price and cross elasticities are accompanied by considerable standard errors. Hence it is desirable to subject the estimates to other tests, and in particular it is of interest to check the cross elasticities with regard to a priori relationships. The Hotelling-Juréen relation (6·3·2) is not strictly applicable in the present case, since the expenditure for animal and vegetable foods forms a substantial proportion of the consumer income. We are instead led to apply the Slutsky relation (6·3·1), from which (6·3·2) has been derived by way of an approximation. Letting the subscripts 1, 2 refer to vegetable and animal foods, respectively, relations (6·3·1–2) may be written

(1) $$\frac{x_2}{x_1}\cdot\frac{e_{21}-x_1\cdot E_2}{e_{12}-x_2\cdot E_1}=1;\quad \frac{x_2}{x_1}\cdot\frac{e_{21}}{e_{12}}\sim 1 \text{ with } x_i=\frac{p_i q_i}{\mu}\quad (i=1,2).$$

For the application of Slutsky's relation (1a) we require an estimate of the expenditures in question relative to consumer income. Making use of family budget data to estimate the total food expenditure relative to the income (the food percentage), and basing the partition into vegetable and animal foods upon the market statistics under analysis, we have obtained the estimates given below in round figures.

Expenditure in per cent of income for	Agricultural products	Total food demand
Vegetable foods; or 100 x_1	10	12.5
Animal foods; or 100 x_2	25	27.5

We are now in a position to apply the tests (1). Calculating the two ratios, our four different sets of data give the following results.

Period	Test ratios (1) for: Agricultural products		Total food demand	
	(1a)	(1b)	(1a)	(1b)
1921–39..............	.30	.10	.06	− .50
1923-38..............	.53	.25	.31	− .09

Since the ratios obtained do not lie in the close neighbourhood of unity, the expected value, the test results seem rather negative, at least at first sight. We note as a favourable feature, however, that the results are definitely better when we form the Slutsky ratio (1a), which is exact, than when we form the Hotelling-Juréen ratio (1b), which is approximate. Further, we note that the ratios come nearer to unity for agricultural products than for total food demand, and also for the shorter of the two periods, the one which excludes the years at the beginning and the end of the inter-war period, when economic conditions were exceptional.

On closer inspection we find that the test ratio (1a) can attain the theoretical value, unity, if one of the cross elasticities involved is allowed to vary within its confidence interval. To prove this statement we shall use (1a) to determine one cross elasticity when the other is given. For example, considering the total food demand for 1921–39 and making use of the observed income elasticities, (1a) gives

$$(2) \qquad\qquad 2.2\, e_{21} - e_{12} = 0.132.$$

Letting one of these cross elasticities be given by Table 2, the other can be calculated so as to make the ratio (1a) exactly equal to unity. Fixing alternately e_{12} and e_{21}, we obtain in this way:

$$e_{12} = -0.18 \text{ gives } e_{21} = -0.02; \qquad e_{21} = 0.04 \text{ gives } e_{12} = -0.04.$$

As stated, the resulting cross elasticities deviate from the values given in Table 2 by amounts that are not large relative to the standard error. Similarly, taking the agricultural products 1923–38 for a second example, we obtain:

$$e_{12} = -0.40 \text{ gives } e_{21} = -0.10 \qquad e_{21} = -0.04 \text{ gives } e_{12} = -0.26.$$

Having now used (1a) to test the elasticities obtained by ordinary regression analysis, an alternative procedure is to make use of (1a) as a conditional relation in forming the normal equations of the regression. It turns out that there are different ways of arranging such a conditional regression analysis. Referring to Ex. IV, 32b–c for a similar situation, we shall finally give two sets of estimates of this type.

$e_{11} = 0.01$; $e_{12} = -0.39$; $E_1 = -0.36$; $e_{22} = 0.51$; $e_{21} = -0.07$; $E_2 = 0.28$

$e_{11} = 0.00$; $e_{12} = -0.38$; $E_1 = -0.35$; $e_{22} = 0.53$; $e_{21} = -0.09$; $E_2 = 0.29$.

Both series of estimates refer to agricultural products, 1923–38. We know that the test ratio (1), say H, is $H = 53\%$ for the ordinary regressions. The conditions imposed on the two sets of estimates are, respectively, $H_1 = 80\%$ and $H_2 = 100\%$, so that the theoretical relation (1) is exactly fulfilled for the estimates in the second row. We see that the conditions have only led to a quite small adjustment in the elasticity estimates. Further we note that the residual ratio γ is 36.6% for vegetable foods and 23.1% for animal foods, and that the ratios γ obtained for the conditional estimates lie very near these minimum values. For the conditional regressions, in fact, the two values obtained for vegetable foods are $\gamma_1 = 36.6\%$ and $\gamma_2 = 36.8\%$, and those for animal foods $\gamma_1 = 23.3\%$ and $\gamma_2 = 24.0\%$. In view of the results obtained, it may be said that this application gives clear evidence of the possibilities and advantages of conditional regression analysis.

In a prediction of future trends in consumption, the underlying estimates of the income elasticity are of fundamental importance. We see that in Table 2 it is the income elasticities that have the smallest standard errors. It must be emphasized, however, that the greater accuracy thus indicated for these estimates may well be illusory. Total consumption, population figures and incomes are involved in trends that over periods of moderate length are fairly linear, and it is clear that if there are accumulating errors in some of these series the errors will affect the estimates of income elasticities, without this being necessarily revealed in the standard errors.

7. Total food demand.[1] – In the course of our analysis we have mentioned several times that the total calorie intake has stabilized and that there were no systematic changes upwards or downwards during the inter-war period. This much is obvious from a glance at the figures in Table 17·1·1. The same conclusion may be brought out by elasticity calculations, the result

TABLE 17·7·1.[2] *Price and income elasticity of total calorie intake. Market statistics 1921–39.*

	Agricultural products			Total food demand		
	Price elasticity	Income elasticity	Ratio γ, %	Price elasticity	Income elasticity	Ratio γ, %
Estimate	−.01	−.04	94	.08	.07	83
Standard error	±.08 ±.10	±.03 ±.04	— —	±.09 ±.11	±.03 ±.04	— —

being that the total calorie intake per capita has been nearly independent of the changes in prices and income. Table 1 shows the estimates obtained in a simultaneous calculation of price and income elasticities. The figures confirm the conclusion that the improvement in the food standard in Sweden during the inter-war period has not taken the form of an increase in the calorie intake.

The aggregate elasticities for vegetable and animal foods deduced in Ch. 17·6 may serve as a criterion or measure of the improvement in the food standard. Alternatively, the food standard may be studied on the basis of a volume index that refers to quantities consumed instead of the calorie intake. In the investigations of Juréen (1952) price and volume indexes have been calculated for the food aggregates that are covered by his calorie series, with inclusion also of the coffee consumption. Table 2 shows the elasticities obtained from the index data.

The income elasticity being estimated as 0.2 or 0.3, the interpretation is that an increase in real income of, say, 10% would at constant prices give rise to an increase of the food volume by 2 or 3%, and accordingly to an increase of food expenditure by the same percentage. A general decrease of food prices by 10% at constant real income would on the other hand lead to an increase of the food volume by about 2% and to a decrease in food expenditure by about 8%. It must be kept in mind that the elasticities mentioned are collective for the whole population, and that they refer to the inter-war period. Theoretically, the individual income elasticity for an underelastic group of commodities should be somewhat smaller than its price elasticity [Theorem 6·5·1]. For the period 1921–39, however, we have obtained a collective estimate that is slightly higher. We note that the difference between the collective elasticities is not statistically significant. Even if it had been, however, the result would not imply a contradiction between theory and observation. The migration and the levelling of incomes in Sweden during the inter-war period have brought about an appreciable increase in consumption, and this trend affects the collective income elasticity.

TABLE 17·7·2.[3] *Price and income elasticity of total food demand, measured by a quantity index. Market statistics.*

	1921–39			1926–37		
	Price elasticity	Income elasticity	Ratio γ, %	Price elasticity	Income elasticity	Ratio γ, %
Estimate	.21	.28	22	.23	.23	35
Standard error	±.05	±.02	—	±.06	±.04	—

Chapter 18.

CONSUMPTION PREDICTION

1. Prediction estimates of demand elasticities.[1] – In the following consumption forecasts for Sweden we have used the results of the elasticity calculations in Chs. 16 and 17. Our basis is the demand elasticities obtained by analysis of the market statistics for the whole country during the inter-war period. In some cases, however, these figures have been slightly modified so as to take proper account of the results given by the family budget data. We have also made use of the local demand elasticities that were calculated in the 1940 investigation. We shall now summarize the elasticity figures to be used in our forecast experiments.

The consumption of *flour* has decreased strongly during the inter-war period. The analysis in Ch. 17 has shown that the variation in the price of flour has been an unimportant factor in this development. It is true that we have observed a positive price elasticity, but this is quite small and subject to considerable statistical error. On the other hand the demand for flour has been markedly influenced by the prices in animal foods, the tendency being for flour demand to increase with increasing animal food prices, and vice versa. However, it is the change in average income which has ultimately been the main determining factor in flour demand. In our forecasts we have assumed demand to be unelastic with regard to flour price. For the cross elasticity with regard to the price index for animal foods we have taken the value − 0.50 and for the income elasticity − 0.60.

The data for *potatoes* are too unreliable for the calculation of a price elasticity. There is evidence, however, that the influence of price changes is quite unimportant, even if as in the case of flour we cannot exclude the possibility of a small positive price elasticity. The income elasticity on the other hand is negative, again just as for flour, at least the long-term elasticity. Thus, the course of the private consumption of potatoes in the 'twenties and 'thirties indicates an income elasticity of about − 0.3. The industrial consumption of potatoes (for the production of starch and spirits) has hitherto shown a tendency to increase with rising national income. For the total demand for potatoes we have based our forecasts on an income elasticity of − 0.2. The available data do not allow us to determine whether the demand is influenced by prices other than that of potatoes.

The consumption of *sugar* (including syrup and the sugar used in the food industry) rose sharply in Sweden during the inter-war period, the increase per capita being almost 40%. Any further increase is considered to be undesirable from the nutritional point of view; in fact, a decrease would be all to the good. However, the continued growth of real income which is anticipated (increasing 'welfare') would, given a constant sugar price, stimulate demand and more than counterbalance the campaigns for reduced sugar consumption. In any case we can be fairly sure that industrial consumption of sugar will continue to rise. We have taken the value 0.4 for the forecast estimate of the income elasticity as compared with the value 0.3 arrived at in Ch. 17·5. For the price elasticity we have used the value obtained in Ch. 17·5 rounded off to 0.3. The estimates are somewhat tentative, being based on conditional regression analysis, but we note that they are to some degree supported by the family budget data, which indicate rather low income elasticities [cf Ch. 16·5].

The consumption of *milk* (including cream) has shown itself to be almost independent of income changes during the inter-war period. This is to some degree a result of the sharply falling birth rate in Sweden during these years, which has had a restraining effect on the per capita consumption. However, even if we assume that future demographic developments will be more normal, all the available evidence combines to show that the income elasticity for milk must be very low in Sweden. We have taken the forecast elasticity to be 0.1. For the price elasticity we have used 0.3. For milk alone (excluding cream) the corresponding estimates are 0.0 and 0.2, respectively.

For *butter and margarine* (direct summation) the market statistics for the inter-war period give an income elasticity of 0.5–0.6, whereas the 1940 investigation gave 0.2–0.3. The difference depends to a large extent on the continuous levelling of incomes and on the migration from country to town with the resulting increase in average consumption, tendencies which affect the first-mentioned figures. It is very likely that these tendencies will continue even in the future, and since the forecasts refer to national consumption our choice is between 0.5 and 0.6. For our final estimate we have taken 0.5. This implies, in other words, that the income levelling and country-town migration are assumed to continue at approximately the same rate as during the inter-war period. For the price elasticity the 1940 report yields an estimate of about 0.5, and our later investigations a somewhat higher estimate. The price and income elasticities are thus approximately equal, which agrees with the general argument of Ch. 6·5 (vegetable oils and other substitutes for butter *and* margarine are relatively unimportant in Sweden). Remembering what we have said about income levelling and migration it is possible, however, that the prediction estimate of the income and price elasticities should be somewhat higher.

As stressed in Ch. 17·3, the rapid rise in margarine consumption in the beginning of the 'twenties can only partly be explained by the changes in prices and income. Separate elasticity calculations for butter and margarine therefore give unsatisfactory results if we consider data for the entire inter-war period. The butter elasticities for the years 1926–39, on the other hand, would appear to be acceptable, viz. in round figures 0.90 for the price elasticity, – 0.35 for the cross elasticity w.r.t. margarine price and 0.55 for the income elasticity. It will be noted that the sum of price and cross elasticities, which according to Ch. 15·5 should give the butter demand elasticity on the assumption of proportional price changes for butter and margarine, is 0.55, the same figure as for the income elasticity. The coefficients for butter are thus plausible in that they are consistent both among themselves and in comparison with the coefficients for the total butter and margarine demand. It may however be added that the 1940 investigation gave considerably higher values for the price as well as for the cross elasticity for butter (1.45 and –0.75, respectively, according to the cooperative societies' data), while the sum of these elasticities is only slightly higher than ours. We shall return to this point in the following section.

For *cheese* we have taken price elasticity 0.2 and income elasticity 0.5. The second figure is considerably lower than that obtained from the market statistics of the inter-war period, while on the other hand it is higher than the family budget estimate. The figure 0.5 must be regarded as a tentative estimate with a wide margin of error. A faulty estimate of the cheese demand, however, has relatively little effect on the estimates of total consumption of milk and dairy products.

The forecasts for *meat* have been based entirely on the results summarized in Table 17·2·5.

For *egg* demand the national statistics supply a basis only for very rough calculations, the resulting price and income elasticities being about 0.6. In the 1940 investigation, which for egg demand used the cooperative societies' material, the price and income elasticities obtained were 1.0 and 0.7, respectively. These values have been used in our forecasts.

The market elasticities for the whole of Sweden have been briefly summarized in Table 1·6·3, which also gives income elasticities for workers according to the family budget data, together with price elasticities for the Stockholm market.

In the forecast spanning World War II we have used the constant elasticities indicated above. However, as shown in Ch. 16, the income elasticities fall with rising income. For moderate changes in the average income it is true that there will in general be no great difference if we use variable instead of constant elasticities. In a forecast stretching over 20 or 30 years, on the other hand, we may expect such substantial changes in the national income that the assumption of constant elasticities cannot be considered completely realistic. To take this into account we have applied Törnqvist's demand function (1·1·5a) as an alternative in the long-term forecasts. In doing so we have chosen 1930–39 as the base period, and as base elasticities for this period the constant elasticities indicated above. The parameters $\alpha = d(\infty)$ and β have been estimated in a very simple manner, by substituting the observed demand $d(\mu)$ and average income μ for the 1930–39 period in formula (1·1·5a), and by determining β from the relation $E = \beta/(\mu + \beta)$ [cf Ex. II, 12].

2. A forecast spanning World War II. – The estimates of demand elasticities presented in Ch. 16–17 were worked out partly during the war years 1942–45, and partly during the immediately preceding years (the 1940 report). The major part of the consumption forecasts arrived at on the basis of our elasticity estimates has been published in a report issued by a government committee [see Ref. 20]. Before we give a survey of these results, we shall in this section present a more limited forecast, which spans World War II and can thus be compared with the actual figures [see Juréen (1950)].

A forecast which is based on the results of a demand analysis can at best give an approximate picture of the future course of consumption on the assumption of specified changes in prices and income. This is a consequence of the obvious fact that there are a host of factors other than price and average income which influence demand. It often happens that this effect cannot be directly measured, for the good reason that quantitative observations on the factors are in many cases completely lacking. Thus, as a rule, it will not be possible to take into account such important circumstances as the levelling of the income distribution, the rural depopulation, the changes in the age distribution of the consumers, and so on. Another source of inexactness is that the price series used in the demand analysis are naturally subject to errors of observation, despite the fact that great care has been taken to eliminate such errors as far as possible.

In view of the uncertainties of a forecast it is important to see whether food consumption after the abolition of rationing has stabilized at a level which corresponds to the inter-war demand structure and the changes in prices and income that have taken place under the forecast period. This was the primary purpose of the investigation described in the present section. The investigation compares the *observed consumption* for 1949/50 with the *predicted consumption*, calculated on the assumption that price and income changes are the only factors that have influenced consumption habits since the 1930's. Those changes in consumption which cannot be explained in this way may, in the main, be regarded as the total effect of the imperfections discussed above.

TABLE 18·2·1. *Index figures for population and national income, 1930–50.*

Year	Population			National income		
1930–1939	100.0	—	—	100.0	—	—
1937–1939	101.2	100.0	—	118.7	100.0	—
1939	101.6	100.4	100.0	125.0	105.3	100.0
1950	113.5	112.2	111.7	316.8	266.9	253.5
Year	**Income per capita**			**Real income per capita**		
1930–1939	100	—	—	100	—	—
1937–1939	117	100	—	113	100	—
1939	123	105	100	115	102	100
1950	(279)	(238)	(227)	(169)	(149)	(146)

In this particular forecast we note the extra difficulty that the demand structure may have been modified by war-time rationing, which affected all principal foodstuffs except milk and potatoes. It is clear that such a comparison is valuable for the light it sheds on the scope and limitation of demand analysis in its practical applications. In particular, it will serve as a useful preparation for the long-term forecasts we shall carry out in the next sections.

The consumption data for the various agricultural products which will be used for the period 1930–39 are taken from our main source of market statistics [Juréen (1952)] and those for the years during and after the war from the consumption investigations made by the Agricultural Marketing Board.[1] The price data were compiled mainly from the Social Welfare Board's statistics. For the income series we have used the total private income figures based on the official tax statistics. These have been revised by the State Economic Research Institute, which has also formed an estimate of the 1949 national income and a forecast for 1950.[2] Incomes and prices are expressed in standardized money value, using the consumer price index of the Social Welfare Board. It should be emphasized that moderate errors in this index have little effect on the results of the demand analysis, since the price and income elasticities for the foodstuffs in question are in general roughly equal. The figures for population and income are presented in Table 1.

It should be noted that the average individual income gives an exaggerated impression of the real increase in income since before the war. This is partly due to the fact that the number of tax-payers has increased automatically as a result of the decay in money value (a number of people have exceeded the taxation limit of an income of 600 crowns without having necessarily received any real increase in income). Besides, the net income left after tax payment has risen at a slower rate than the gross income. The figures for 1950 in Table

1 may thus give a false impression of the importance of income increases for the changes in consumption since before the war. On the other hand it should be noted that income levelling proceeded considerably more rapidly during the 'forties than it had before, so that a demand analysis based on average incomes is liable to underestimate the consumption of certain foodstuffs, particularly those of animal origin.

According to the calculations of the State Economic Research Institute the increase in real wages since 1939 has an average value of approximately 30%. The calculations also show that in 1950 the real national income per capita was between 10 and 20% higher than for the last peace year.[3] Making use of these estimates we have in our forecasts allowed for two alternatives for the per capita increase in real income since 1939, viz. 30 and 15%. In the first case we have calculated real prices by dividing nominal prices by the Social Welfare Board's consumer price index. In the second case, however, such real prices are not comparable with the income increase since the consumer price index does not refer to the average rise in the cost of living for the whole country but to the rise for the so-called index family. Investigations of the quantity and value of the total national consumption indicate that these 'real' prices should be reduced by something like 10%, which gives a price increase for different commodities more in keeping with the increase in national income since inter-war years. The two alternatives give practically the same final result, so that we shall here consider only the first case.

It was not until the spring of 1949 that the last food items were released from rationing in Sweden. The production year 1.IX.1949–31.VIII.1950 here considered was, thus, the first year after the war entirely free from rationing. Prices and quantities for that year, as well as for 1930–39, are shown in Table 1·6·4, which also gives the predicted consumption for 1949/50. For comparison the table also includes consumption data for 1942, when rationing was severest. In Table 1·6·3 the price elasticity for potatoes and the income elasticity for cheese have been given as tentative estimates and have therefore been bracketed. The figure for "observed" egg consumption in 1949/50, which is based among other things on an estimate of the number of hens, is very uncertain. Judging from a comparison of hen counts in recent years and before the war, however, there is every reason to conclude that the estimated increase since 1930–39 in egg production — and thus also in egg consumption — is probably on the large side. As a result of such comparisons as well as of the analysis here reported the Swedish figures for egg consumption have recently been officially revised.[4]

Corresponding to Table 1·6·4 we give in Table 2 the absolute and relative changes in per capita consumption for 1949/50 as compared with 1930–39.

We see that, apart from eggs, the relative difference between predicted and observed demand is greatest for edible fats. The difference is, however,

TABLE 18·2·2.[1] *Per capita consumption 1949/50 against 1930–39.*

Food item	Change in consumption expressed in			
	kilograms		per cent	
	predicted	observed	predicted	observed
Milk and cream	+ 17	+ 6	+ 7	+ 2
consumer milk	+ 3	+ 13	+ 1	+ 6
Butter and margarine........	+ 2.2	+ 5.0	+ 11	+ 26
butter...................	+ 0.8	+ 3.0	+ 7	+ 28
margarine	+ 1.4	+ 2.0	+ 16	+ 23
Cheese	+ 0.9	+ 0.8	+ 13	+ 12
Eggs......................	+ 0.5	(+ 3.4)	+ 6	(+ 42)
Meat......................	+ 0.6	+ 1.2	+ 1	+ 3
meat, excluding pork	− 0.8	− 3.1	− 3	− 13
pork	+ 1.4	+ 4.3	+ 6	+ 20
Wheat and rye flour........	− 9.9	− 8.8	− 11	− 10
Sugar (refined).............	+ 5.1	+ 4.6	+ 12	+ 11
Potatoes	− 9	− 8	− 7	− 6

largely apparent. In Sweden the main items are butter and margarine, but other fats are also consumed, such as synthetic lard, coconut fat and vegetable oils. The consumption of these secondary fats fell, partly as a result of shortage, from 6 300 tons during the 'thirties to about 4 000 tons in 1949/50. On a per capita basis this consumption has decreased by approximately 40 % (besides which we note a probable decrease for fats such as pork lard). It is beyond doubt that an increase in the consumption of butter and margarine took place during the 'forties at the expense of these secondary fats, on the whole independently of prices and incomes.

This, however, does not provide a complete explanation of the increase in butter consumption beyond the predicted figure. It is fairly certain that average butter consumption was also influenced by the acceleration of income levelling during the 'forties relative to the inter-war period. We can, thus, draw the conclusion that the collective income elasticity for butter had a higher value than that estimated from the market statistics for 1926–39 and a considerably higher value than that estimated from the family budget data. It may be added that the agreement with the observed figures is not improved if we make use of the price and cross elasticities obtained in the 1940 investigation.

For the total consumption of meat there is a slight increase of 3% per capita, which stands in fairly close agreement with the predicted value of 1% when we consider the sharp drop in consumption during the war. However, the consumption of pork increased and that of other meats decreased more than indicated by the prediction. We note that this is not entirely a case of a voluntary shift in consumer habits. The discrepancy depends, at least to some extent, on the fact that the processed food industry is still confronted with a real shortage of meats other than pork. (The headings for meat include the raw materials for the processed food industry, which is thus not analysed separately.) The change in the price relation of pork to other meats has induced the industry to use more pork than before. However, the shortage of the other meats seems to have brought about greater changes in the consumption of raw materials than would be expected from the modified price relation alone. During the inter-war period there was no such shortage which could have influenced the elasticities calculated for this period.

The results for milk provide an example of how sensitive a demand prediction may be even to quite small modifications in the underlying assumptions. The price and income elasticities for the inter-war period are somewhat higher for milk and cream than for milk alone. The trend from 1930–39 up to 1949/50 indicates that an elasticity calculation for the whole period would have given a contrary result. The change in the estimate cannot however be a matter of more than about 0.1. It may further be added that, so far as cream is concerned, the change in the consumption pattern is explained by the fact that substitutes for cream (certain fat emulsions) came into widespread use during the war, and that these have to some extent remained on the post-war market.

Table 3 sums up the forecast deviations for the foodstuffs considered, with consumption volumes calculated on the basis of retail prices for 1949/50 (nominal prices). At the same time, the table gives a picture of the quantitative changes since before the war in the consumption of the more important foodstuffs.

As we see, the total consumption volume per capita for the commodities considered has increased since 1930–39 more than predicted. The main difference lies in the marked increase in the consumption of butter and eggs. The increase in egg consumption is however, as before indicated, probably not as large as shown by the available statistics. As regards butter the increase depends, as also indicated before, partly on the fact that the consumption of fats other than butter and margarine has declined since before the war.

For the remaining foodstuffs the agreement between prediction and observation is fairly close. The total consumption of edible fats has increased by about 20% per capita since 1930–39, as compared with the figure of 26% for butter and margarine. If we allow for this and furthermore exclude eggs from Table 3, we find a predicted volume increase for the remaining foodstuffs which

TABLE 18·2·3.[2] *Per capita consumption of the more important foodstuffs, expressed in retail prices for 1949/50, crowns per year.*

Food item	1930–39	1949/50 Predicted	Observed
Milk and cream..............	86.0	91.7	88.0
Butter......................	59.9	64.4	76.7
Margarine...................	22.6	26.3	27.8
Cheese......................	23.5	26.6	26.2
Eggs	27.3	29.0	(38.8)
Meat, excluding pork.........	86.8	83.9	75.7
Pork	70.4	74.9	84.2
Wheat and rye flour	58.8	52.3	53.0
Sugar (refined)	38.1	42.7	42.2
Potatoes....................	33.1	30.7	31.0

constitutes 70% of the observed increase. It should be added that the remaining 30% does not form a true estimate of the effect on consumption exerted by factors other than prices and incomes, since, as we emphasized at the outset, there are several sources of observational error which disturb the analysis.

It may be added that the present comparison serves as a test on the substantial reduction in the income elasticities for cheese that were obtained for the inter-war period, and similarly, if we consider the unconditional estimates recorded, for sugar. The reductions were originally introduced in the long-term predictions which we shall describe in the next section. Since the agreement between predicted and observed consumption for 1949/50 is very close, we see that these reductions have been justified.

We have now examined the main discrepancies and agreements for our forecast of consumption in 1949/50. The investigation shows that consumer habits, after release from the restraint of rationing, have *not* returned to the pre-war pattern, but have, on the whole, adjusted themselves to the prices and incomes prevailing since the war. The course of the demand reactions is in line with the demand structure as revealed by the analysis of the inter-war data. The changes in the demand structure that were produced by rationing have, with certain minor exceptions, proved to be of a temporary nature.

3. Long-term forecasts for the more important foods. – It is clear from the preceding that the long-term consumption development is primarily dependent on the rate at which the income level changes. As a consequence, we cannot form any prediction of future consumption without making definite assumptions concerning the rate of increase of the national in-

TABLE 18·3·1.[1] *Consumption of foodstuffs 1930–70. Assumed yearly increase in real income: 1.8% per capita.*

Yearly	Consumption in kg per capita			Yearly	Consumption in kg per capita		
	Alternative A	Alternative B			Alternative A	Alternative B	
		$E(\mu)$	kg			$E(\mu)$	kg
Bread grains, E = −.60				*Butter and margarine, E = .50*			
1930–1939	113.0	−.53	113.0	1930–1939	19.5	.50	19.5
1950	98.4	−.38	101.9	1950	21.9	.44	21.7
1960	87.9	−.29	95.7	1960	25.0	.40	23.5
1970	78.9	−.23	91.2	1970	26.3	.35	25.2
Sugar,[a] E = .40				*Cheese, E = .50*			
1930–1939	48.5	.40	48.5	1939[γ]	5.43	.	5.43
1950	53.2	.35	52.9	1950	7.10	.48	7.07
1960	57.3	.30	56.2	1960	7.79	.43	7.70
1970	61.6	.27	59.2	1970	8.53	.39	8.28
Potatoes, E = −.20				*Meat, excluding pork, E = .30*			
1930–1939	158	−.20	158	1930–1939	24.0	.30	24.0
1950	151	−.15	152	1950	25.7	.25	25.6
1960	145	−.12	148	1960	27.2	.22	26.7
1970	140	−.10	145	1970	28.7	.19	27.8
Milk,[β] E = .10				*Pork, E = .30*			
1930–1939	256	.	256	1930–1939	22.5	.30	22.5
1950	272	.10	272	1950	24.1	.25	24.0
1960	277	.09	276	1960	25.5	.22	25.1
1970	282	.07	281	1970	26.9	.19	26.0

[a] Including syrup.
[β] Including cream.
[γ] Owing to the exceptionally sharp increase in cheese consumption 1930–39, we have taken 1939 as base year for the forecast.

Eggs, E = .70

1930–1939	8.08	.70	8.08
1950	9.50	.65	9.44
1960	10.83	.61	10.62
1970	12.29	.56	11.80

come. In our forecasts we have allowed for the three alternatives of 10, 20 and 30% increase in the real income per capita over a 10 year period (i.e. 0.9, 1.8 and 2.7% per year). The second hypothesis corresponds to the actual long-term development in Sweden (since 1860), while the first alternative assumes only half this rate of increase. The third alternative implies a very sharp rate of increase, which was in fact, however, somewhat exceeded during the inter-war period 1921–39. During World War II the Swedish national

TABLE 18·3·2.[2] *Private and industrial consumption of the more important agricultural products, predicted for 1960 and 1970; in 1 000 tons.*

Food item	Consumption	Consumption for an income increase assumed to be					
		small		moderate		large	
	1930–39	1960	1970	1960	1970	1960	1970
Wheat and rye	704	692	671	663	632	641	606
Other cereals	147	138	127	138	127	138	127
Sugar and syrup^a	302	373	385	389	410	404	432
Potatoes	983	1 046	1 032	1 025	1 005	1 012	984
Milk and cream$^\beta$	1 597	1 892	1 912	1 912	1 947	1 933	1 968
Butter and margarine	121	155	160	163	175	171	187
Cheese	34	50	52	53	57	56	62
Meat	290	347	356	359	373	368	387
Eggs	50	68	72	74	82	79	91

^{a} As raw sugar. $^\beta$ 1 litre cream counted as 5 litres milk.

income increased but slightly. For the period 1939–50 we have accordingly, in all three cases, reckoned with an average rate of increase only half of that assumed for the long-term prediction.

The real price level and the price relations for the different foodstuffs have in this section been taken as constant and equal to those prevailing during the base period 1930–39. In addition we shall in the next section, by way of an example, calculate the effect of a change in price level upon the total demand for agricultural products.

As to income elasticities, the calculations have been carried out on two alternative assumptions, viz. (A) constant elasticities, corresponding to demand function (1·1·1b), and (B) variable elasticities, corresponding to function (5·5·1) or (5·5·4a).[3]

Results calculated on this basis for the immediate future are presented in Table 1, which, for considerations of space, includes only figures obtained for the second income alternative. A principal aim of the consumption forecast has been to compare the resulting trends with independent forecasts of agricultural production. For this reason we have in Table 1 expressed flour and bread consumption in bread grains (in Table 2 we have followed the same procedure for other cereals).

Table 2 gives the predicted total consumption in Sweden of the more important foodstuffs, as calculated on the basis of Table 1, alternative B. A population forecast is necessary for such a prediction, and we have used that calculated by Dr. H. Hyrenius (1944) at the request of the 1949 agricultural committee. According to Dr. Hyrenius, the population should increase from an average value of 6.2 million during 1930–39 to 6.9 million in 1960, and then remain approximately constant until 1970. However, the predicted population figure was exceeded already in 1950–51, for one thing on account of immigration during and after the war. Although the rate of increase has fallen considerably in recent years, it is clear that the population forecast is on the small side. For this reason the predicted values in Table 2 are somewhat low.

Table 2 includes the results for all three income hypotheses. In view of the Swedish real income trend since the war, it would seem that the highest alternative is the most plausible one. On the other hand we must allow for the possibility that the strong and stable economic prosperity which has marked recent years may have been exceptional.

According to Table 2 we can expect a fairly strong continued increase in the consumption of animal foods, while the consumption of the plainer vegetable foods will decrease despite the rise in population. For the vegetable foods the decrease per capita is so marked that we can hardly expect it to be neutralized if Hyrenius' forecast should be exceeded by the actual population figures.

4. The balance between vegetable and animal foods.[1] – The gradual shift in consumption from the plainer vegetable foods to animal foods is of fundamental importance for agriculture. This is due to the considerable energy losses which are inevitable when vegetable foods are refined to animal foods. For Sweden it is estimated that the production of a certain calorie quota in the form of animal foods requires an area 5 or 6 times larger than the area necessary for the production of the same calorie supply in the form of vegetable foodstuffs. If in the present treatment we disregard the possibility of import and export changes for foodstuffs, fertilizers, and other agricultural raw materials, we can expect that the shift in consumption habits consequent upon increased income will call for an increased agricultural yield. We thus conclude that, *in order to satisfy the rising demand for high quality foodstuffs following an increase in national income, it will be necessary to expand the volume of agricultural production, expressed in harvest units.* This conclusion holds good even if the individual calorie demand remains unchanged.

It seems probable, however, that the calorie demand will increase somewhat. We note that the calorie consumption per capita for the foodstuffs included in Table 18·3·2 is, on the assumption of a moderate income increase, expected to have risen about 5% by 1970. According to the Swedish nutrition experts, such a slight rise in calorie demand may be desirable since

TABLE 18·4·1. *Total calorie demand forecast for Sweden in 1970. Agricultural products and margarine.*

	10^9 calories		Change in per cent	Change resulting from	
	1930–39	1970		population increase	other factors
Vegetable foods..........	3 940	4 050	+ 3	+11	− 8
Animal foods............	3 110	4 150	+33	+12	+21
Total..................	7 050	8 200	+16	+11	+ 5

the continual increase in the size of the human body should be accompanied by some increase in nutritional needs. Since it is likely that calorie requirements were not completely satisfied before the war for the poorer sections of the community, we can expect some further increase in the average calorie consumption with rising national income.

According to the assumption of Ch. 18·3, the population will in 1970 exceed that of the base period by fully 10%. On the assumption of a moderate increase in income, the per capita demand will rise by 5%, the result being that the total consumption in calories should rise by 16% from 1930–39 to 1970. Table 1 shows the forecast thus obtained for the products included in Tables 18·3·1–2.

For 1970 the forecast gives the ratio 49.4 : 50.6 for the consumption of vegetable and animal foods. As seen from Table 1·6·5 the corresponding ratio for the years around 1880 has been estimated at 75 : 25. The proportion of vegetables in the total consumption of agricultural products has since fallen at an average rate of just over 3 units every ten years, and for our base period 1930–39 it was about 56%. Table 2 shows developments during the inter-war period and future developments as predicted on the assumption of a moderate income increase. The table further shows the total food content of vegetable and animal proteins.

In the forecasts here reviewed we have thus far considered calculations based on the price relations prevailing during 1930–39 between animal and vegetable foodstuffs as well as between agricultural products and other commodities. However, prices for agricultural products were during the 1930–39 period such that the farmers' income level was considerably lower than that for comparable urban groups. A general increase in producer and consumer prices of agricultural products above the 1930–39 level will have the effect of retarding the predicted transition from vegetable to animal foods. We shall now report an attempt to estimate the effect on consumption caused by such a general change in the relative price level.

Let us assume that, some time before 1970, consumer prices for agricul-

TABLE 18·4·2. *The relative content of calories and proteins in vegetable and animal agricultural products, 1920–1970.*

Years	Calories		Proteins	
	Vegetable	Animal	Vegetable	Animal
1920–1929	61	39	48	52
1930–1939	56	44	42	58
1950	53	47	37	63
1960	51	49	35	65
1970	49	51	33	67

tural products are increased by 10% over the 1930–39 level. The calculations then show the predicted consumption of animal foods to be roughly $160 \cdot 10^9$ calories lower than the figure given in Table 2. In the calculation we have assumed that the price elasticity for animal agricultural products falls from 0.45 around 1950 to 0.35 around 1970. In relative figures the fall in consumption for a specified price increase should thus be less marked at a future instant than at present. However, since the volume of consumption increases with rising income, the fall in consumption when expressed in absolute figures will, on our assumptions concerning the price elasticity, remain roughly constant. According to Ch. 17, on the other hand, the total calorie demand is almost insensitive to price and income changes. Hence it is probable that the consumption of vegetable agricultural products will at the same time show some slight increase, despite the fact that these products are also subject to the assumed price increase. This is due to the negative cross elasticity [see Ch. 17]. It is however impossible to predict this increase with any accuracy, for one thing because part of the calorie reduction may be covered by increased consumption of foodstuffs other than those considered here (fish, green vegetables, etc.). Since it is of interest to obtain at least some idea of how the potential market for agricultural products is influenced by a price increase, we have assumed by way of example that the increase of vegetable agricultural products will cover half the calorie reduction, that is, $80 \cdot 10^9$ calories. If we assume for the sake of simplicity that the entire increase will be taken up by flour and bread consumption, the increase amounts to 28 million kgs of bread grain, or approximately 30 million harvest units. The decrease in animal food demand, on the other hand, represents roughly 230 million harvest units.

Compared with the prediction based on constant prices, an increase in real prices of 10% would cut the production volume necessary to satisfy demand by 200 million harvest units. The estimate varies between 230 and 170 million if the increase in calorie consumption of vegetable agricultural products is assumed to lie somewhere between zero and $160 \cdot 10^9$ calories, i.e. the total reduction for animal foodstuffs. The figure arrived at, 200 million harvest units, is roughly 2% of a normal Swedish harvest, or about equal to the normal harvest increase for a three year period.

5. The long-term balance between consumption and agricultural production.[1] – In Sweden the degree of self-support (production as a percentage of consumption) for agricultural products including margarine has since the end of the 19th century up to about 1930 been 80% or somewhat more; it then rose and during the 'thirties attained an average of 96%. Of this 96%, however, 5% should be accounted to the import of fodder and 12% to the import of fertilizers.

On account of firstly the rather unfavourable topographic and climatic conditions and secondly the relatively high agricultural wages in comparison with most of the big producing countries, it is a well-recognized fact that Sweden under normal conditions will not be able to compete to any great extent in the world agricultural market without considerable economic loss. The chief aim of the long-term Swedish agricultural policy being to assure the farmers the same standard of living as other productive groups in the country, it is therefore expected that the internal Swedish agricultural prices will normally exceed the world market prices.

In this situation it is clear that long-term changes in self-support are of the greatest importance for the agricultural policy. Will the marginal agricultural yield fall off so sharply that self-support decreases? Will production keep pace with the increase in consumption due to rising population and improved standard of living? Or, as a third alternative, is it possible that production will continue to increase at the same high rate as during the inter-war period, with a consequent risk of overproduction?

Applied demand analysis can help to give concrete answers to such vital questions, but demand, of course, is only one side of the matter. The investigations described in Part V, which have been made on behalf of government committees for agricultural planning, form part of a larger programme where they have been coordinated with supply studies. It would fall outside the scope of this monograph to enter in detail upon the methods available for the study of the other side of the question, changes in production. Since, however, we have here a good example of how the results of a demand analysis can contribute to practical economic planning, we shall conclude this chapter with a short review of the production forecasts made in Sweden, and then compare the predicted trends in production and consumption. The material is drawn from the main official report on the subject [Ref. 20; cf also Juréen (1952)].

It is natural to assume that the increase in agricultural production known from the past in the form of increased yield per acre or per animal fodder unit will continue, the question being whether the tendency will be retarded or accelerated. On the other hand we note that changes in the total area cultivated were very small during the period considered, and it has therefore been natural to base the forecasts on the assumption of constant area.

Three different alternatives have been adopted as regards the continued yearly increase in total production until 1970. The first alternative, called *weak production increase*, is based on extrapolated values from a logistic curve fitted to the actual production increase from 1880 to 1940; this leads to a rate of increase which gradually falls off to a yearly value of 40 million harvest units in 1970. The second alternative, called *moderate production increase*, is essentially based on the extrapolation of a linear trend fitted to the same period; this gives a constant yearly increase up to 1970 of 65 million harvest units. The third alternative, called *strong production increase*, is derived from the production increase during the last 30 years, but is somewhat lower, account being taken of the disturbing effect of World War II on agricultural production; this gives a constant yearly increase of 79 million harvest units. These three figures are respectively 0.45%, 0.7% and 0.9% of the present normal Swedish production.

In the construction of agricultural production forecasts there are in particular two factors of importance besides the increase in yields per acre. One is the import of fodder; the other is the animal yield per fodder unit.[2] Regarding the import of fodder, three alternatives have been considered, viz. (a) a falling import vanishing some time before 1970, (b) the same import surplus as during the 'thirties, i.e. about 500 million fodder units, and (c) an import increasing by 20% every ten years, that is, a somewhat smaller relative increase than during the inter-war period.

Regarding the animal yield per fodder unit, an estimate of the trend in the average yield can be obtained by comparing the consumption of animal foodstuffs with the amount of vegetable fodder used. During the inter-war period the average yield increased from 510 to 535 calories per fodder unit in ten years. In estimating the changes in the size of the future animal production there is however another factor which must be taken into account. If we consider an amount of fodder which is exclusively used for food production, the average yield per fodder unit must obviously be larger than the total average. Both animal food production and the consumption of fodder have increased during the 'thirties relative to the 'twenties. The increase depends partly on changes in the animal stock, partly upon an intensified production (especially of milk). A study of each of these factors has revealed that the yearly amount actually used 1930–39 is well over 500 million fodder units of vegetable fodder *more* than that required ten years previously. The intensified feeding has resulted in an increased animal food production of almost $350 \cdot 10^9$ calories yearly, that is, an average of *between 650 and 700 calories* per unit of extra fodder. Investigations would seem to show that this figure has increased somewhat in the long run, and in the rough forecasts made since World War II it has been assumed that the animal food production per extra fodder unit will be 700 calories in round figures. Remembering that the average yield for all vegetable fodder was about 500 calories per fodder unit during the inter-war period, we see that the forecast assumptions lead to an increasing average yield per fodder unit as animal food production is intensified. Such a trend, we repeat, would be in agreement with earlier experience.

Should overproduction occur, it is of course impossible to say in advance which branches of agricultural production would first show a surplus. The difficulty is perhaps best avoided by assuming complete self-support as regards vegetable foodstuffs for direct consumption. This assumption implies that that part of the total production which is not required to cover the forecasted vegetable consumption will be used for animal food production. (This of course does not mean that in practice it is only animal foodstuffs that run the risk of overproduction.)

The different assumptions concerning the import of fodder have largely the same effect on the animal production forecasts as the assumptions for the internal fodder production. As a result, some combinations of different alternatives will lead to practically the same forecast. Thus for example we obtain roughly the same increase in animal food production if we assume weak production increase and constant fodder import or moderate production increase and falling fodder import, etc. The rates of increase obtained under alternative combinations are as follows:

Production increase	Import of fodder	Average yearly increase in animal food production, 1930/39–1970
weak	falling	0.6%
weak *or* moderate	constant } falling	0.9%
weak *or* moderate *or* strong	rising constant } falling	1.1%
moderate *or* strong	rising constant }	1.3%
strong	rising	1.4%

As a background to the forecasts we note that the total production of animal agricultural products rose by 2.1% per year during the period 1876–1939 and by 1.9% during 1921–39. All of our forecasts thus indicate a slower rise in animal food production than previously.

Turning to the consumption side of the question, the income elasticities obtained in Ch. 16˙5 lead to the following estimates of the average yearly increase in animal food demand for different trends in the national income.

Increase in national income	Average yearly increase in animal food consumption, 1930/39–1970
weak	0.6%
moderate	0.8%
strong	1.0%

If we compare the different forecasts for production and consumption of animal foodstuffs, we see that production will, under the assumption of constant cultivated area, for most of the alternatives increase faster than consumption, and this is particularly the case for the more plausible alternatives.

As mentioned before the degree of self-support for agricultural products, including margarine, is estimated as high as 96% for the 'thirties. In view of these results we may conclude that Sweden will soon find herself in the novel situation of agricultural overproduction.

Concerning the time when a production surplus can be expected, we recall that the forecasts are based upon the price relation between agricultural and other products which held during the 'thirties. To give an idea of the effect of a change in this relation on demand and thus on the possibility of over-production, we recall from the analysis in Ch. 17˙7 that the total consumption, calculated in production units, will be reduced by about 2% if the relative price level of agricultural products should rise by 10%. Since 2% of the total production roughly corresponds to the forecasted production increase over a 3 year period, this means that such a rise in price will bring the risk of over-production 3 years nearer.

One should of course not exaggerate the value of estimates and forecasts of the type here described. The assumptions upon which they are based are in several respects rather arbitrary. Further, we must remember that the actual development may be affected to a greater or lesser degree by factors of which we have not taken account (notably immigration). The calculations are there-fore nothing but an evaluation of the trend which may be expected under certain specified assumptions. On the other hand it would be a serious mistake to ignore the picture of the future supplied by the calculations. In particular it should be noted that even that alternative which we termed "strong produc-tion increase", and which should lead to a production surplus as early as before 1960, is considerably lower than the production increase which took place during the twenty years between the two wars.

Even if only six years have passed since the main results of our forecasts were published in Sweden, it can be of interest to examine briefly the actual production and consumption during this time. To judge from available figures the national income has increased somewhat faster than the highest of our three alternatives. On the other hand the relative price of agricultural products has been increased to a considerably higher level than that of 1930–39. The total consumption has followed the highest alternative, in agreement with prediction. As regards production we note that the total area cultivated is practically the same as for 1930–39. The agricultural yield per acre has since the war followed the highest of our alternatives, and the import of fodder is now only slightly lower than for 1930–39.

Taking these few but important facts into account we conclude that production should have risen faster than consumption, relative to our forecasts. Such has in fact been the case. The Swedish degree of self-support is now, in 1952, at the critical 100% and can be expected to somewhat exceed this value in the next production year.

Thus, the risk of overproduction, which had little more than theoretical interest during the lean years 1940–45, has now become of immediate importance. Swedish agriculture has reached, not unexpectedly, the situation when a delicate balancing will have to be made between, on the one hand, a permanent agricultural export with its great economic risks, and, on the other hand, a retardation of production, primarily by reduction of cultivated area, with its consequent social and political difficulties.

APPENDIX NOTES

It is not difficult to write research papers. The difficulty is to write papers to which sound research has to pay attention, because they build on a deep and slowly acquired insight into the field under analysis.

R. Granit.

Modern science with its enormous literature suffers from difficulties of communication, like a tower of Babel, and the present tendencies to nationalize science do not make for better understanding. A habit seems rather to be on the increase to regard foreign literature as *terra incognita*, the contributions of which it is a merit to 'rediscover'. In compiling the following notes the author has tried to avoid such onesidedness. Since a systematic tilling of the field would be a major task in itself, completeness has not been aimed at, however, and the author is aware of the fact that the selection suffers from other shortcomings as well.

Genuine innovations, such as Pareto's discovery that the theory of consumer demand can dispense with the concept of measurable utility, are not difficult to cover by proper references, and it is so much the easier as important innovations are scarce. After all, for good and evil, science like any sector of human activity is largely ruled by the *mimesis* that has been stressed so convincingly by Arnold Toynbee. It is however more difficult to give fair references when a new idea, often not brought out in its full significance when first presented, has given the impulse to intense discussion and further progress. Such is the case with index theory between 1930 and 1940, the development originating in Konyus' article, which at first was known only by a somewhat misleading review. There is further the difficulty of doing justice to eclectic works, the importance of which does not lie in novel arguments, but rather in propagating relevant ideas that already lie in the air.

The old advice still holds that it pays to study the classics in the original. The primary purpose of the following notes is to help the reader to trace how the problems have gradually emerged and how the methods for their treatment have been improved and more firmly established. In cases where the contributions are numerous, one or two pioneering works are referred to explicitly, the later development being covered by a reference to some expository survey.

Preface. [1]A list of striking forecast failures is discussed by Stuart Chase in his stimulating book "The proper study of mankind" (Phoenix, London, 1950). Attitudes towards forecasting differ greatly among economists; see e.g. the display of opinions in Ref. 14, Vol. 11 (1949), especially the comment pp. 352–367. — [2]Fig. 1 is borrowed from Bäcklin (1935). — [3]For the analysis illustrated in Fig. 2, see Schultz (1938, Table 11). Cf also Wold (1949a, p. 2 f).

Ch. 1`2. [1]Engel's main work (1895) is pioneering as well as classic in the analysis of family budget data. A principal conclusion has become known as Engel's law: As income increases, the expenditures on different items have changing proportions, and the proportions devoted to urgent needs decrease, luxuries and semi-luxuries increase.

Ch. 1˙3. [1]In regional data on quantities, prices, etc., we have another type of market statistics. Interesting attempts have been made to employ regional market statistics for the purpose of demand analysis [see Houthakker (1951), and, also for further references, Verhulst (1952)]. — [2]For a statistical material that lends itself to the interpretation that the grocers influence the wholesale price, see Roos (1934, chart XXIX).

Ch. 1˙4. [1]See Wold (1949a). — [2]For a statistical investigation of the price mechanism, see Roos (1942). Empirical studies in this direction are very scarce. To explore the mechanism, another type of approach is to study the merchants' price policy on an interview basis [see Hall and Hitch (1939); cf also Ref. 15, especially Ch. 11].

Ch. 1˙5. [1]The terminology of regression analysis is not perfectly established. A distinction of importance is between what we have called the *disturbance* of a causal relation like (1˙4˙3a) and the *residual* of a regression relation like (1). The disturbance is a subject-matter concept, referring to the influence of causal factors not explicitly introduced as explanatory, whereas the term residual refers to the deviations that arise when a statistical scatter is approximated by a least-squares regression. The distinction between disturbances and residuals thus applies to any statistical regression that serves to estimate a causal relationship [see e.g. Wold (1945)].

Ch. 1˙6. [1]For the literature up to 1938 the reader may consult the bibliography of Schultz (1938). A survey of demand studies based on family budget data has been given by Colin Clark (1950). The works of Schultz and Clark give numerous references, but they are not complete, which could hardly be expected in view of the abundance of material. — [2]See Stone (1945, 1948, 1951b), Prest (1949), Tobin (1950) and Houthakker (1952), to note only a few of the many important contributions in this series. — [3]See Ref. 19, p. 989. The analysis of the material is due to P. P. Sveistrup, the research director of this large investigation. — [4]See Ref. 20.

Ch. 2˙1. [1]For excellent surveys of least-squares approximation, see Whittaker-Robinson (1924, Ch. 9) and Aitken (1939, Ch. 6).

Ch. 2˙2. [1]For an exposition with numerous illustrations, see Ezekiel (1941). — [2]For the use of regression analysis in biological assay, see Finney (1952). His excellent monograph may also be referred to as typical for how in experimental analysis the choice of regression is passed over as a matter of course. — [3]See also Wold (1945, §6) and (1949a). The interpretation of regression in terms of one-way causal dependencies is of course no new feature in the treatment of nonexperimental data [see e.g. Tinbergen (1939) and Eisenhart (1939)]. We have found it proper however to introduce a special term for the purpose since there is a diverging line of approach, where a causal interpretation is rejected. We shall return to this controversial issue in Chs. 2˙4 (ii), 2˙7 (i) and 3˙2. — [4]Current terminology reflects the causal interpretation that is traditionally in the picture in regression analysis applications. Thus in biological assay we note the terms *dosage* and *effect* variable, in experimental psychology *stimulus* and *response* variable. We see that these terms refer to the treatment of experimental data. Ezekiel (1930) has *causal* and *resultant* variable, terms that apply as well to the treatment of nonexperimental data. The present monograph borrows from Reiersöl's terminology (1945), which includes *causal* and *effect* variable, and *regressator* and *regressand*. — [5]Cf Wold (1943–44, III, p. 110). — [6]The situation being the same as in an experiment, let us consider Fig. 2˙2˙1. Writing $y = a + bx$ for the empirical regression line shown in the graph, suppose this is based on n experiments. Now let x_0, y_0 be observations that refer to a particular experiment of the same type, but not one of the n given experiments. Suppose we know y_0, that is, the effect observed. Further suppose that for some reason or other the value x_0 of the cause variable is not known, and that we wish to estimate x_0. In this rather special problem we may distinguish two cases. (a)

Nothing is known of how the value x_0 has been chosen. In such a case x_0 should be estimated by solving for x in $y_0 = a + bx$, that is, by inverting the regression of y on x obtained from the n experiments. (b) Suppose we know that x_0 is taken at random from a distribution of the same type as the distribution of x in the n given experiments; say e.g. that this is an equally weighted distribution (i.e., the n values of x occur in equal frequencies at a number of equidistant points of the x-axis). Then a more accurate estimate of x_0 can be obtained by using the regression of x on y in the n given experiments. The recommendation under (a) is in line with current practice [see e.g. Finney (1952, p. 24)], and is also in agreement with the conclusions of other authors who have paid special attention to the problem [see Winsor (1946) and Lindley (1947, section 5˙5); cf also Wold (1949a, p. 11)]. It stands to reason that (a) is usually the appropriate assumption. Case (b) is in this context rather artificial, but has been taken up here because it gives an instructive application of the ceteris paribus clause referred to earlier in Ch. 2˙2 when dealing with situation A.

Ch. 2˙3. [1]See R. A. Fisher (1935; especially Chs. 2–3); see also Cochran-Cox (1950, Ch. 1˙13–19). A penetrating review of the validity of randomization has been given by Anscombe (1948). For a discussion of efficiency aspects, in particular the rationale of balanced (and at the same time randomized) designs, see Gossett (1936) and Yates (1939). It would seem that the rationale of randomization offers important problems for further consideration. In particular, the regression aspect has not as yet been fully explored [see Ex. IV, 15 for some results in this direction]. — [2]For an appraisal of the results of regression analysis in different types of application, see Ezekiel (1941, Ch. 23).

Ch. 2˙4. [1]For reviews, see Wold (1945), Lindley (1947) and Reiersöl (1950). — [2]This result is due to Gini (1921), who was the first to make explicit use of a model of type (1 a–c). — [3]Hence the familiar conclusion that, if present in the regressors, the observational errors will give rise to a bias in the regression, but if present only in the regressand they will be harmless. — [4]See Koopmans (1936), also for further references. — [5]For a second example we may consider n measurements (x_i, y_i) made in order to determine the position of a straight steel rod relative to a fixed coordinate system (x, y). Cf also Ex. IV, 19. — [6]Another feature that detracts from the power of the approach (1)–(3) is that, in addition to the parameters β_i, it works with twice as many unknowns $\varepsilon_\nu^{(t)}$, $x_\nu^{(t)}$ as observations. As a consequence, the approach does not lead to consistent estimates of the $x_\nu^{(t)}$ (their estimation error will be of the same order as the error variance, and does not tend to zero with increasing number of observations), an important point stressed by Koopmans (1936, p. 61). Hence the application to empirical data cannot be guided by the device familiar from least-squares regression, viz. to evaluate the $\varepsilon_\nu^{(t)}$ and compare them with factors not included in the analysis. The estimates of the error-free observations $x_\nu^{(t)}$ not being consistent, the approach (1)–(3) well deserves to be called a "night train analysis". — [7]The laws of mechanics and electricity are the classical examples of reversible laws (note, in the ideal case of zero friction and resistance). Irreversibility and its connexion with the increase of entropy are treated in any physics textbook; for an illuminating exposition, see Zemansky (1937, Chs. 8–10). — [8]For an explicit rejection of the idea of causal interpretation, see Koopmans (1945, p. 449). Cf also Samuelson (1947, p. 9). — [9]See Tintner (1952, especially p. 122), also for further references. — [10]A clarifying discussion is due to Eisenhart (1939). — [11]A thorough and systematic review of the sources of observational errors and related defects in economic statistics has recently been given by Morgenstern (1950). The reader may however become neurasthenic by all the imperfections recorded unless he remembers that in economics the difficulty is not so much to know what is relevant as to know what can be ignored. — [12]See e.g. the treatment of income data in Ch. 17˙1 and the real price data in Ch. 18˙2.

Ch. 2˙5. [1]See e.g. Cramér (1945, Chs. 29˙8, 29˙12 and 37˙2–3). — [2]The argument has been forcefully stressed by Persons (1924). Cf also Ezekiel (1941, p. 351 f). Durbin and Watson (1950–51) have established a small-sample test for the presence of autocorrelation in regression residuals. — [3]Wold (1950; 1951a). — [4]In recent years, spatial intercorrelation has been dealt with in several investigations, but the results thus far obtained refer to cases where the observations follow a regular sample pattern, as the survey lines in Matérn's pioneering study (1947) on sampling problems in forestry.

Ch. 2˙6. [1]This is of course a long known feature, but it is surprising that in the early literature on regression analysis it was given almost no attention. For a clear statement of the situation, see Ezekiel (1930, p. 261). — [2]Frisch (1934, especially p. 86). In the present context we need not specify whether the regression considered refers to a statistical scatter or a probability distribution. Frisch's original work was set in statistical terms; a corresponding analysis of probability distributions was carried out by Koopmans (1936). Here as in (2˙4˙1–3) a difficulty in dealing with observational errors is that their variances are in general unknown and cannot be uniquely estimated from the sample. If they are known a priori, a large sample test for multicollinearity is available; see Tintner (1952, p. 127f), also for further references. — [3]See Wold (1940, §10, and 1943–44, II, §65). Multicollinearity is dealt with from the same viewpoint by Tobin (1950) and Stone (1951b). Conditional regression is, of course, a straightforward adaptation of a device well known from the general method of least-squares approximation; see e.g. Whittaker and Robinson (1924, section 129).

Ch. 2˙7. [1]The following quotation is typical for the wholesale dismissal of least-squares regression: *"That is, it is impossible to derive statistically the demand functions from market data without specification of the supply functions involved."* See Girshick and Haavelmo (1947, p. 83; the italics are from the original). — [2]The field is full of pitfalls, and the author is far from believing that all of them have been located. The system (*) $x_t = a + \beta y_t + z_t'$; $y_t = \gamma + \delta x_{t-1} + z_t''$ has been considered by Koopmans (1942), who on elimination of y_t obtains (**) $x_t = \varepsilon + \zeta x_{t-1} + z_t$ and rightly argues that the least-squares regression would be biased if applied to relation (**). We see, however, that system (*) is recursive; hence each of relations (*) can be estimated by least-squares regression, provided z_t' is uncorrelated with y_t and z_t'' uncorrelated with x_{t-1}. In the resulting regressions we may eliminate y_t, which leads to an asymptotically unbiased estimate of relation (**). This application of the theorem behind (2˙5˙2) is instructive, and illustrates (a) that a least-squares regression may be handled as a theoretical relation, in accordance with our remark Ch. 2˙2 (i), and (b) that such operations must be performed *after* having carried out the least-squares estimation, not *before*, in accordance with our remark Ch. 2˙2 (ii). — [3]The first attempts in this direction are due to Haavelmo (1943; 1944) and Mann and Wald (1943). The main work is Koopmans, ed. (1950) [Ref. 7]. For a recent survey, see Tintner (1952, Ch. 7); see also T. W. Anderson (1951). The present exposition of structural systems (2) is partly based on a seminar lecture given by Dr. Koopmans at Uppsala in 1950. — [4]See Wold (1949a; 1951b–c). Cf also Bentzel and Wold (1946). — [5]Wold (1951c). — [6]See this section, App. note 3. For applied work, see Klein (1950) and Christ (1951); cf. also Clark (1949), where a structural system is estimated by the use of least-squares regression. — [7]Koopmans (1945, pp. 459–461) has an argument which is formally of the same general type as that of Bentzel and Wold (1946), but his conclusions differ, as can be seen from the following passage (p. 461): "It is worth stressing that in the demand equations the choice of dependent variable is made on grounds that have nothing to do with the demand side of the market. It is based on the form of *another* equation in a model designed to reflect the economic mechanism of the formation of price and quantity."

With reference to a principle enunciated by Koopmans and Reiersöl (1950, p. 169f), the author agrees that a theoretical model should be constructed without thought of whether it is identifiable or not. As regards recursive models, these form the natural basis for econometric analysis because they are the most general linear systems that allow a causal interpretation. From this viewpoint it is an accidental feature that they have the merit of being always identifiable. — [8]The author is here thinking of identification from the viewpoint of the simple rule of thumb used by Koopmans (1949, p. 134). Cf also Ex. IV, 29.

Ch. 2˙8. [1]For an excellent survey of Gauss' contributions, see Whittaker and Robinson (1924). As regards Markov's treatment, see Plackett (1949). — [2]In Cochrane and Orcutt's paper the situation is discussed on the basis of artificial sampling experiments. Cf also Wold (1950). — [3]See Whittaker and Robinson (1924, sections 113–115). — [4]See Cramér (1945, Ch. 33˙2–3). — [5]Cramér (1945, Chs. 29˙12 and 37˙3). — [6]For an instructive case in point, see Ex. IV, 12, which Mr. Durbin has kindly placed at my disposal.

Ch. 2˙9. [1]The essential feature in controlled experiment is the possibility of randomized replications, but otherwise there is no sharp distinction between experimental and non-experimental data. Specifically, the soil variation in plant experiments is on the borderline. The intense discussion of this case has shown that the randomized experiment is here of somewhat limited scope, not as regards validity, but as regards efficiency [see Anscombe (1948) and Yates (1939), also for further references].

Ch. 3˙1. [1]For a review with more detailed references, see Wold (1943–44). — [2]For further references to dynamic approaches in demand analysis, see Evans (1930), Davis (1941), Tintner (1952). Cf also Ch. 7˙7. — [3]Duesenberry (1949, Ch. 2˙3).

Ch. 3˙2. [1]The present section is mainly based on an earlier review by the author (1951b); cf also (1949a) and Bentzel–Wold (1946). An excellent introduction to dynamic economics has recently been given by Baumol (1951). For further references on the gradual transition from static to dynamic or quasi-dynamic approaches, see Schultz (1938). — [1a]The terminology originates from mechanics, where it was authorized by Lord Kelvin (1886). For the adaptation to economics, see Frisch (1929), who duly stressed the interpretation of theoretical relationships in terms of economic forces exerted by individuals and groups of individuals. A definition often used in economics is that a theoretical model is static or dynamic according as one or more time points are involved, but this definition is formal and tends to obscure the essential thing, viz. the subject-matter interpretation in terms of economic forces. — [2]Foreshadowed by the verbal discussion of Hanau (1927), the cobweb argument was brought out explicitly and formally by several independent authors in 1930, among them Ezekiel, whose excellent survey (1938) gives detailed references. — [3]Having stressed the formal agreement between model (1˙4˙1) and Samuelson's dynamization of equilibrium systems, it should perhaps be pointed out that there is a difference or at least a shift in emphasis, inasmuch as each relation in (1˙4˙1) expresses the hypothesis of a unilateral causal dependence, whereas the causal interpretation is pushed aside or ignored by Samuelson (1947, see especially p. 9). — [4]See Lundberg (1937) for these references and also for a more detailed review. — [5]For surveys, see Tinbergen (1940), Samuelson (1948) and Baumol (1951). For the distinction between *ex ante* and *ex post* considerations in sequence analysis, see also Lundberg (1937). — [6]Outstanding contributions on this line are due to Lundberg (1937), Harrod (1948) and Hicks (1950). — [7]In using this term, which is very much to the point, I am drawing freely from a discussion with Mr. R. Stone on the rationale of Tinbergen's approach. — [8]In stressing this ideal, the author does not wish to be dogmatic. In economic research there is room for purely empirical research as well as purely theoretical analysis. This is essentially a matter of division of labour, and the degree of coordination between theory and empiricism will largely depend upon the problems under consideration and the statistical data available. With reference to investigations like the business cycle studies by Burns and Mitchell (1946) [cf also the price studies by Mills (1936)], the empirical approach has been criticized by Koopmans (1947). Although in agreement with his views in the main, I think that his criticism is somewhat exaggerated, and that it should be counterbalanced by a warning against theorizing without any contact with realities, a ubiquitous phenomenon in our days. The extremes are dangerous on the theoretical as well as the empirical side, but the empirical extreme is inefficient rather than misleading. — [9]See Clark (1949) and, also for further references, R. Stone (1951a).

Ch. 3´5. [1]See Ayer (1936), an excellent introduction to logical empiricism. For references on the development of logical empiricism, see also von Wright (1943) and Jörgensen (1948). — [2]See e.g. M. H. Stone (1932, Ch. 1´5). — [3]In economic theory there are other interesting cases of isomorphism; for a survey, see Pikler (1951). — [4]There is the possibility of interviewing one or more consumers, asking them which of two prescribed budget changes they would prefer. At least one of the changes, however, will necessarily refer to an *imagined* situation. As a consequence, the interviews will not constitute a genuine stimulus-response experiment in the sense of experimental psychology. — [5]For illuminating discussion, see also Reder (1947), Samuelson (1947) and Duesenberry (1949). — [6]For example, favourite themes are to discuss whether effect always follows after cause or may be simultaneous in time, and whether predictability is a criterion of causality. Such discussion is futile unless it starts from an operational definition of causality. For a case in point, see Wilkie (1950). — [7]See e.g. Jeffreys (1937, pp. 54 and 211). For a discussion that has run into the dangers of treating causality as a metaphysical concept, see Weyl (1949, section 23).

Ch. 4´1. [1]The exposition of Paretoan theory in Part II follows, in the main, Wold (1943–44). For the fundamental notions in Ch. 4´1, see §2; for the axioms in Ch. 4´2, see §30; and for the regularity assumptions in Ch. 4´3, see §30 and §37.

Ch. 4´2. [1]Our first two axioms are essentially the same as the first group of axioms introduced by Frisch (1926) in his treatment of pre-Paretoan theory.

Ch. 4´3. [1]Theorems 1–3 are fundamental existence theorems; cf Wold (1943–44, §31 and §37). In earlier treatments, the representation (1) was introduced by way of an assumption. — [2]The notion of preference function is due to Pareto (1906). The fact that the same indifference map is obtained for different functions $\Psi(x)$ constitutes the mathematical content of Pareto's discovery that the theory of consumer demand can dispense with the notion of measurable utility.

Ch. 4´4. [1]Theorems 1–6 belong to the classic fundamentals in Paretoan and pre-Paretoan theory [cf Ch. 3´1, also for references]. The present exposition is improved mainly in two respects, viz. (a) the case of terminal contact, with one or more $q_i = 0$, is dealt with explicitly, and (b) it is stressed that (7) makes no sufficient condition of optimality if fulfilled merely at the point of contact q. — [2]See e.g. Allen (1938, Ch. 18´9).

Ch. 4´5. [1]It seems that Konyus (1924) was the first to introduce income as an explicit variable in the demand functions; see also Marschak (1931) and Allen and Bowley (1935). Following Walras (1874), the traditional device in the earlier theory of consumer demand has been to use one of the commodities as *numéraire*, taking its price to be the monetary unit. — [2]Working on the assumption (3´1´1) of additive utilities, relations of type (2)–(3) were deduced by Walras (1874, p. 122). It was only recently that relations (2)–(3) made their explicit appearance in Paretoan theory; cf Marschak (1931, p. 55), Samuelson (1942, p. 76), Wold (1940, p. 87; 1943–44, §12). — [3]In essence, (7) is due to Pareto (1909, p. 581) and (6) to Slutsky (1915, p. 10–11).

Ch. 4´6. [1]Wold (1943–44, §25). — [2]Pareto (1909, pp. 546–557). — [3]Hicks and Allen (1934), Allen (1938) and Hicks (1939). Cf also Evans (1930, p. 119f). — [4]Allen (1938, p. 441).

— [5]From Marshall (1890) and onwards a list of authors can be cited who have taken demand functions for the basic concept in their economic theory, without trying to interpret them in terms of preference fields. The list includes Cassel (1918), who vigorously rejected any kind of 'value theory'. Samuelson's theory (1947) of 'revealed preference' may, as pointed out by Wold (1951d), be regarded as a variation of the demand function approach. — [6]Wold (1943–44, §51, Theorem X, and §53, Remark 2b). For a corresponding theorem on Samuelson's theory of revealed preference, see Houthakker (1950). As brought out by obligations explicitly mentioned in Houthakker's paper, his main theorem is mathematically equivalent to our theorem on the demand function approach [cf also Wold (1951d)].

Ch. 4˙7. [1]This section follows Wold (1943–44, §30–32 and §44), but Theorems 2–3 have been added, and the construction of the preference function $U(q_1, \ldots, q_n)$ has been simplified at the expense of its continuity. — [2]An attempt to deal directly with the case of indivisible units has been made by R. Stone (1951a, pp. 15–18).

Ch. 4˙8. [1]For a more detailed treatment, see Wold (1943–44, §33–36). — [2]As regards this passage of the proof I am indebted to Dr. O. Reiersöl for pointing out a mistake in the original treatment, and for indicating the proof now given.

Ch. 5˙1. [1]The introduction of the logarithmic derivative under the name of elasticity is one of the convenient devices that economics owes to Marshall (1890). The system of notation is still rather fluent; the one adopted here follows Wold (1940) and is a combination of the notations used by Hicks and Allen (1934) and Frisch and Haavelmo (1938). — [2]This convention implies that income elasticities E and price elasticities e will as a rule be positive, while cross elasticities e have a tendency to be negative for necessities and positive for luxuries. [See Ch. 6˙5.] — [3]See Gallego-Diaz (1945); cf also Frisch (1932, p. 35). For the approximate formula (3), see Allen (1934); cf also Ex. 2. — [4]For a detailed exposition, see Allen (1938, Ch. 10).

Ch. 5˙2. [1]Price-consumption curves were considered by Pareto (1911, p. 595). Income-consumption curves were introduced in preference field theory during its revival in the 'thirties; see Hicks and Allen (1934); cf also Frisch (1936) and Hicks (1939). — [2]Cansado and Wold (1950, Theorem 1). — [3]Attributed to Giffen by Marshall (1890). — [4]See Wold (1948b), also for the illustration in Fig. 5˙2˙2.

Ch. 5˙3. [1]See Slutsky (1915); cf also Mosak (1942). — [2]For statements A and C, see Slutsky (1915); for B, see Hicks and Allen (1934).

Ch. 5˙4. [1]Wold (1943–44, §52). The problem was posed by Pareto (1911, pp. 617–619), but his solution is not correct.

Ch. 5˙5. [1]Törnqvist (1941).

Ch. 5˙6. [1]Questions referring to aggregate commodities have in recent years been discussed by several authors. For treatments of special interest from the present viewpoints, see Ruby Norris (1941), Samuelson (1947) and von Hofsten (1952). — [2]Wold (1943–44, §57; cf also 1940, p. 49f). — [3]Leontief (1936, section 3), Hicks (1939, especially p. 312f). We give here an analytical version of Leontief's proof. Hicks' argument, which makes use of infinitesimals, is not complete, since the integrability is not established.

Ch. 6˙1. [1]Slutsky (1915, p. 16) gives (2), which Schultz (1938, p. 621) converts into (1). — [2]Samuelson (1942, p. 79) and, independently, Wold (1940, p. 87 and 1943–44, §58). For a special case, see (5˙4˙3).

Ch. 6˙2. [1]Hicks and Allen (1934, p. 208).

Ch. 6˙3. [1]Hotelling (1932, p. 594) and Juréen (1949, p. 390). Cf also Wold (1943–44, §59).

Ch. 6˙4. [1]Wold (1943–44, §57; cf also 1940, p. 22).

Ch. 6˙5. [1]The theorem is due to Törnqvist (1941). On the basis of empirical analysis of the demand for necessities, the relation $E < e$ had been conjectured by Wold (1940, p. 88). — [2]Wold (1943–44, §58).

Ch. 7˙2. [1]The exposition in Ch. 7˙2–3 follows Wold (1943–44, §47–49 and §56; cf also 1940, §7). It will be noted that our treatment differs from the approach of Hicks (1939, see especially Appendix note 10), who sets out to establish a set of stability conditions for market demand. Not only is Hicks' argument superfluous; his conditions are also illusory, for they refer to the convexity of a market indifference surface, a surface which in general does not exist [see Exs. 27 and 55]. We see that this is a pitfall of the same type in which the marginal substitution approach is trapped unless it is supplemented by the integrability condition [Theorem 4˙6˙1].

Ch. 7˙3. [1]Cf Wold (1943–44, corollaries in §57–59).

Ch. 7˙4. [1]The stratification approach can be used with advantage in empirical analysis; for an instructive study, see Lubell (1947). — [2]For a survey of this and related works by Roy, see Schultz (1938, pp. 120–128). — [3]This assumption is not at all confirmed by family budget data, but Roy's approach is included here because it gives a nice illustration of the flexibility of the stratification method. — [4]For the economics of price discrimination, see Joan Robinson (1945, Book V); cf also Stigler (1947).

Ch. 7˙5. [1]The proof given here is new.

Ch. 7˙6. [1]The argument and the conclusion are, of course, of old standing. See e.g. Duesenberry (1949, p. 12). — [2]See Bernstein (1927). — [3]As regards the analytical treatment, on the other hand, the individual preferences are in Paretoan theory formally represented as mutually independent, but this is a formal device which is legitimate since the approach is static. In a dynamic approach the latent interdependencies will in general have to be allowed for explicitly [this remark qualifies a previous comment by the author; see Wold (1943–44, III, foot-note p. 74)]. — [4]There is by now an extensive literature on the subject; see Marschak (1950), also for further references. — [5]In their analysis of risk situations the authors make use of a utility curve of the same form as S in our Fig. 7˙6˙1 (p. 122).

Ch. 7˙7. [1]In reading Katona's work it must be remembered that in psychology the terms static and dynamic analysis have a slightly different emphasis as compared with the usage in economics. We take it that any economic analysis in terms of behaving units is dynamic in the psychological sense. A static economic approach roughly corresponds to the psychological analysis of routine patterns of behaviour, whereas a dynamic approach is concerned with the motives behind changes in the behaviour patterns [cf Ch. 3˙2, Appendix note 1a].

Ch. 8˙1. [1]For the incorporation in wage theory of the approach of Ch. 8˙1, see Hicks (1932) and Stigler (1947); cf also Robertson (1931). The analysis of labour supply on a utility basis was initiated by Jevons (1871, Ch. 4); cf also Frisch (1932). The approach in terms of Paretoan indifference curves of leisure-income was used by Knight (1933, p. 117) and followed up by Stigler (1947, p. 188f) and Hénon (1949). For an empirical study of labour supply, see Schoenberg and Douglas (1937).

Ch. 8˙2. [1]The theorem is essentially due to Jevons (1871) and Edgeworth (1881); cf also Stigler (1947, p. 79f). — [2]As a consequence, Bowley (1924, p. 8) finds that the barter equilibrium is uniquely determined. We note that von Neumann and Morgenstern (1944, sections 61˙2–3) arrive at the same conclusion, but their approach is different, being based on the assumption of utilities that are not only quantitative but also additive over different individuals, so that the barter makes their total joint utility a maximum.

Ch. 8˙3. [1]The field has been surveyed by Staehle (1935) and Frisch (1936); see also Ulmer (1949) and von Hofsten (1952). As regards the practical problems of index construction, see Ref. 18. — [2]See e.g. Hardy, Littlewood and Pólya (1934, Ch. 2˙5). We note that the inverse of the harmonic mean $\mathfrak{P}_H$ equals the arithmetic mean of the inverse price ratios p_i^0/p_i^1. — [3]The subsequent propositions A–D and G are embodied in Konyus' work (1924). See also the excellent review by Staehle (1935). — [4]The same type of graph was used by Schultz (1939, p. 4). — [5]The preference field application of Divisia's chain index is due to Roy (1942). — [6]For the first two statements, see Roy (1942); cf also Ville (1946). — [7]Frisch (1936, p. 16). For the notion of price compensation, see also Hicks (1942). — [8]See Hotelling (1932). — [9]Theorem H is due to Staehle (1935, p. 178). For comment, see Schultz (1939, p. 6). Cf also Frisch (1936), whose exposition of Staehle's contribution is however disturbed by a slip: in formulae 5'28 all the equalities should be replaced by inequalities. As pointed out by Dr. S. Malmquist (seminar communication), the theorem can be proved by a simple argument in the price space: With reference to Fig. 8'3'1b, we see that if a parallel to $a p^0 A_0$ is drawn through p^1, say L, then L will cut λ_1 in a point p^*, which owing to the convexity of the indifference curves will lie above $p^{(1)}$. Hence $\omega p^0/\omega b > \omega p^0/\omega p^{(1)} > \omega p^0/\omega p^*$. According to Ex. 44, these inequalities will give us (15) if we let p^1 denote the reference prices and p^0 the comparison prices, and if L is the budget line $\Sigma p \cdot q^0 = \mu^*$.

Exs. II. [1]Part of the material suitable for theorems will instead be presented as exercises. Known results will be covered by references to the original works, to the best of the author's knowledge. Otherwise, the exercises are either commune bonum, as Exs. 3–4 and 10–11, or novel contributions, in Part II notably Exs. 8–9, 23, 27 and 60. — Ex. 1. [1]Jevons (1871), from whom the first three columns are quoted, attributes King's law to Davenant. — Ex. 27. [1]This exercise illustrates an earlier remark by the author (1943–44, III, p. 89). — Ex. 41. [1]Wold (1943–44, III, p. 70). — Ex. 44. [1]Seminar communication. — Ex. 46. [1]Samuelson's claim (1947, p. 111) that the theory of consumer demand can be developed on the sole basis of the inequality (1) was later withdrawn as mistaken. [See Samuelson (1950); cf also Wold (1951d).] — Ex. 50. [1]Seminar communication. — Ex. 59. [1]Communicated by Dr. Malmquist when acting as the faculty opponent of Dr. von Hofsten's thesis (1952). Part of the theorem is embodied in a brief remark by Frisch (1936, p. 16), viz. the definition of the chain index and the comment that it satisfies the circular test. The interpretation in terms of continuous price compensation seems to be new. — Ex. 60. [1]The formal aspects of this isomorphism are well known ever since Pareto (1906) and have been utilized by several authors, among them Samuelson (1947) and Verhulst (1952). It will be noted that the novel feature of the theorem lies in the distinction between the isomorphisms relative to Paretoan and pre-Paretoan theory.

Ch. 9'1. [1]The exposition of the stationary process in Part III is strictly limited to aspects of immediate relevance for regression methods as applied in demand analysis. To obtain a wider perspective, the reader may consult the surveys by Cramér (1947) of the general theory of stochastic processes and by Moyal (1949) of the stationary processes. For a more detailed treatment of the material of Ch. 9'1–3 and Ch. 10, see Wold (1938). — [2]Kolmogorov (1933). — [3]For the general definition of conditional expectations, see Kolmogorov (1933, Ch. 5'4), where it is also shown that formulae (10) extend to probability distributions in a denumerable infinity of dimensions. — [4]Frisch (1928) was the first to make systematic use of vector and matrix methods in statistics. One of the fruits he reaped thereby is relation (13), which is isomorphic with Gram's criterion. [See (12'1'9); cf also Cramér (1945, Ch. 22'5).]

Ch. 9'2 [1]See Khintchine (1934); cf also Wold (1938, §16) and Doob (1944).

Ch. 9'3. [1]Since $W(\lambda)$ is a function of bounded variation, the series is always convergent, and at least in any point of continuity of $W(\lambda)$ its sum equals $W(\lambda)$. See e.g. Zygmund (1935). — [2]For the groundwork of stationary vector processes, see Cramér (1940).

Ch. 9˙4. [1]Birkhoff-Khintchine's theorem lies deeper, but otherwise the material of Ch. 9˙4 is an immediate result of the application of ergodic theory to stationary processes. Readers who wish to follow up the relations with ergodic theory are referred to the excellent treatise by Hopf (1937) and a recent work by Maruyama (1949); for comment and further references, see also Cramér (1947, §19). — [2]For an elementary proof, see Kolmogorov (1937). — [3]In what follows we shall sometimes omit the qualification "almost all realizations" or "with probability 1". — [4]Cf Hopf (1937, p. 28). Ergodic theorems often being phrased in terms of the related notion of *metric transitivity*, we note that if a stationary process is metrically transitive it is also ergodic, and conversely; see Hopf (1937, p. 30). — [5]Theorem 1 combines and extends arguments used by Aall Barricelli (1946), who considered systems $\{F_x\}$ which are constructed on the basis of a single time-series, and by Grenander (1950, p. 267), who considered the relation $F_x = F$ in the special case $z_t = z_t(x; u_1)$. — [6]Yule (1927).

Ch. 10˙1. [1]The exposition in Ch. 10 is in the main based on Wold (1938). For Ch. 10˙1, cf also Wold (1951a). — [2]For complete proofs of theorems (i)–(iv) the reader may consult Kolmogorov (1933) and Khintchine (1933). For surveys of recent developments, see Feller (1945) and Loève (1950).

Ch. 10˙2. [1]The terminology of stationary processes is not too well established. "Process of moving summation" is a term adopted from Kolmogorov (1941); otherwise, the terminology in Ch. 10˙1-3 follows Wold (1938). — [2]Time-series models of this type were first considered by Yule (1921; 1926) and Slutsky (1927). For the general definition, and for applications to empirical data, see Wold (1938, §§10, 23, 26 and 31). — [3]Figs. 1–2 are drawn from the applications given by Wold (1938), a reference that the reader may follow up for an analysis of the two correlograms. — [4]Wold (1938, pp. 152–154). — [5]This type of approach was initiated by Yule (1927). Cf also Wold (1938, §§10, 24–25, 29 and 32). — [6]Wold (1938, pp. 97–99).

Ch. 10˙3. [1]Wold (1938, §14 and §19). Cf also Kolmogorov (1939) and Moyal (1949, p. 166). — [2]For a survey of main results in periodogram analysis, see Kendall (1946, Ch. 30˙41–54).

Ch. 10˙4. [1]See Wold (1938; p. 120f), also for references to the related "sinusoidal limit theorems" by Slutsky (1927) and V. Romanovsky (1932). See also Maruyama (1949, Theorem 8). — [2]Yule's treatment overlooks the divergent case, which has given rise to some inconsistency, also in later works on autoregression. For comment, see Wold (1938, §29; cf also 1950, p. 285). — [3]See Maruyama (1949), also for further references.

Ch. 11˙1. [1]For detailed references, here and in the rest of Ch. 11˙1, see Wold (1938) and Whittle (1951; 1952). — [2]The criterion was first proposed by Abbe (1863), and a large-sample theory was developed by Helmert (1905). — [3]I am indebted to Dr. Whittle for placing at my disposal a summary of his thesis work and of later research results, including the illustrations in Ch. 11˙2-3.

Ch. 11˙2. [1]For Theorems 1–3, see Whittle (1951; 1952a). — [2]With reference to the distinction made by Neyman (1950, Ch. 5˙4˙6) between the exact λ^*-criterion and the heuristic λ-principle, we note that (3) is a λ^*-criterion for two composite normal hypotheses. The λ^*-criterion can in the present case be established both by Neyman-Pearson's argument (1933) of similar regions and, as shown by Lehmann and Stein (1948), by limiting the probability of an error of the second kind. Further, adopting the viewpoint of classical theory of statistical inference, we note an interesting feature in the present application of the maximum likelihood method: Considering the distinction between regular and singular cases of estimation made by Cramér (1945, p. 479) for ordinary variables and extended to stochastic processes by Grenander (1950, p. 211), the classical theory is concerned with the regular case, whereas Theorem 9˙4˙1 reveals that for nondeterministic stationary processes it will in general be the singular case that is of primary importance. — [3]The limiting case when the roots p or q fall on the periphery of the unit circle is not covered by Whittle's theory in its present state of development. — [4]See Cramér (1945, Ch. 17˙7).

Ch. 11˙3. [1]The test function (1) has been established by Whittle (1951) on the basis of assumptions of Bayes' type. It will be noted that Whittle's test coincides with Neyman's heuristic λ-principle. For a different approach which formally leads to the same test function (1), see Wald (1943, sections 13–14).

Ch. 11˙4. [1–2]Whittle (1952a–b).

Ex. III. [1]As in Part II, some of the exercises bring fresh material, among them Exs. 10–11, 28 and 32. — Ex. 9. [1]For other examples of the same type, see Wold (1938, p. 129f). — Ex. 12. [1]Cf Wold (1938, p. 130f), where the formula that corresponds to the first ζ_t is incorrect. — Ex. 15. [1]See Wold (1938), also for further references. For the extension to systems of difference equations, see e.g. Baumol (1951). — Ex. 18. [1]I am indebted to Prof. M. Bartlett for pointing out a slip regarding the range of η_t in the original publication. — Ex. 20. [1]Seminar communication. In Ex. 20a the case when the λ_i are multiples of $2\pi/n$ is elementary matter in periodogram analysis. — Ex. 23. [1]Seminar communication. — Ex. 25. [1]The simplified proof given here was presented by Dr. U. Grenander when acting as the faculty opponent of Dr. Whittle's thesis (1951). — Ex. 26. [1]Cf also Wold (1938, Theorem 9 and p. 170). — Ex. 28. [1]For related results, see Walsh (1947).

Ch. 12˙1. [1]The concepts suitable for the purpose are provided by the theory of (real) Hilbert space. For the general definitions in Ch. 12˙1, see M. H. Stone (1932, Ch. 1˙1–3). — [2]Reference is made to Kowalewski (1909, p. 435f), a detailed exposition which covers Theorems 1–2 and is also instructive with regard to the applications of least-squares approximation to be made in (12˙6˙2–3).

Ch. 12˙2. [1]Yule (1907). Cf also Wilks (1949, p. 277). — [2]See Ex. 6, making $f_{h+1} = (1, \ldots, 1)$. — [3]Cramér (1945, Ch. 23˙2).

Ch. 12.3. [1]Wold (1938, p. 78). — [2]Wold (1946). The simplified proof given here is due to Prof. G. Elfving (written communication). — [3]Wold (1945). The symmetry does not constitute a strong argument, but the theorem is included because it provides an argument against an otherwise unsettled conjecture by Frisch (1934, p. 80), viz. that if many regressors are introduced a regression coefficient has a tendency to return to the value obtained with a small number of regressors.

Ch. 12˙4. [1]Cramér (1945, pp. 274 and 304).

Ch. 12˙5. [1]The exposition in Ch. 12˙5, which is quite elementary, is based on Wold (1938, especially pp. 101–103, and 1948a). By the employment of methods of spectral analysis, the prediction theory of stationary processes has been carried further in important works by Kolmogorov (1939; 1941) and Wiener (1949). Kolmogorov considers the space aspect of prediction, whereas Wiener, in line with his earlier work (1930), is mainly concerned with the phase aspect.

Ch. 12˙6. [1]Wold (1938, Theorem 7). — [2]In my original theorem the two components are called singular and regular; more appropriate are the terms deterministic and nondeterministic later introduced by Doob (1944). The term singular is perhaps acceptable, being a direct extension of Frisch's notion of a singular distribution in a finite number of variables [cf (9˙1˙13)], but the term regular is not good, since it associates with smoothness, which is a property of the deterministic component with its functional regularity rather than of the nondeterministic component with its irregular randomness.

— [3]For the stationary process, Cramér (1939) has established a decomposition which corresponds to the classic decomposition of the spectral function $W(\lambda)$ into one discontinuous, one absolutely continuous, and one continuous, nondifferentiable component [see Cramér (1947, p. 190)]. As shown by Kolmogorov (1941) the nondeterministic component $\{\zeta_t\}$ in (1) will coincide with Cramér's absolutely continuous component, provided the integral in (4) is finite.

Ch. 12·7. [1]Wold (1948a; 1951b). — [2]Wold (1948a, Lemma).

Ch. 13·2. [1]The exposition in Ch. 13·2 is based on Wold (1950; 1951a). — [2]See Cramér (1945, Ch. 37·1–3), also for references to R. A. Fisher, Bartlett, and later authors. For references to the work of Laplace and Gauss, see Whittaker and Robinson (1924, sections 113–115). — [3]See Cramér (1945, Chs. 23·2–3, 27·7 and 28·4); see also K. Pearson (1901) and Yule (1907). — [4]In Ch. 2 we have stressed the possibility of using both specifications A–B for the purpose of causal analysis. It may be remarked, however, that specification B was not primarily devised for the purpose of causal analysis in the original works of Galton and Yule.

Ch. 13·3. [1]We follow here a device used by Plackett (1949). — [2]The proof is, in essence, the same as that given by Plackett (1949).

Ch. 13·4. [1]For Theorems 1–2 and remarks (ii)–(v), see Wold (1950). — [2]Theorems 1–2 thus remain valid if the observed variables contain trends or are otherwise evolutive. Cf Ex. 14 and the illustration in Ch. 13·5. — [3]This proof was suggested to me by Mr. J. Durbin, and it is also given by Watson (1951). — [4]This corollary is essentially implied in the Gauss-Fisher formula (13·2·6), for on the specification A of Ch. 13·2 the regressors are allowed to be non-random, and may present any pattern of auto- and intercorrelation.

Ch. 13·5. [1]For a rigorous proof, see Cramér (1945, Chs. 27·7 and 28·4). — [2]See Cramér (1937, p. 60).

Ch. 14·1. [1]The original calculations have been performed with more decimals than recorded here, so that the rounding-off may give rise to deviations of a unit or so in the last decimal. This remark applies to most of the calculations in Chs. 14–18.

Ch. 14·2. [1]The material of this section is taken from Wold (1940, p. 51f; cf also 1943–44, III, §62). — [2]The general method of diagonal regression is due to Frisch (1934). In the case of two variables the same device was used by Lehfeldt (1914), whose paper is of considerable historical interest in showing that, less than 40 years ago, demand analysis was a virgin field, where little or nothing was known by way of empirical results. See also Ex. 3.

Ch. 14·3. [1]See Wold (1940, §22). Argument (c) is due to Mr. L. Juréen.

Ch. 14·5. [1]This is the section where the temptation has been greatest to include a comparison with investigations in other countries, a temptation to which the author has not succumbed, however, since it would break the flow of the exposition. The treatment in Ch. 14·5, which follows Wold (1940, §24), has for its main purpose to prepare the way for the applications to be made in Part V. For a survey of empirical investigations of the age scale of consumption, reference is made to the condensed but very illuminating review by Woodbury (1944). — [2]Wold (1940, Fig. 14). — [3]Quoted from the Swedish source publication, Ref. 22, I, p. 18*. For the German-Austrian scale, see also Woodbury (1944, p. 462). The American scale is called so in Ref. 22, where it is presented from the viewpoint of a nutritional norm. — [4]Wold (1940, Tables 6–7).

Ch. 14·6. [1]Wold (1940, formulae 82 and 104). — [2]Wold (1940, Tables 10–11). For the 1933 survey, the comparison between the elasticities obtained by direct pooling and the average elasticities involves a slight approximation, the two calculations being based on different sets of published tables. The average elasticities are calculated from the whole samle of workers' and low grade employees' families (stratum 1), in all 1024 families. The direct pooling refers to a sample of 1108 families, which also includes a small number of middle-class families (stratum 2). In the pooling we have made use of the two lowest of the three income classes; these include 910 of the 1050 families in stratum 1, but only 13 of the 195 families in stratum 2. — [3]See R. A. Fisher (1950, section 49˙1); see also Wilks (1944, §9˙7). In the present application the classification into sub-strata is made w.r.t. family size. For a two-way classification for the same purpose, see Stuvel and James (1950).

Ch. 14˙7. [1]The argument has long been known; see Wold (1940, §25) and, also for further references, Marschak (1931, pp. 43 and 55). — [3]For references to Keynes' argument from the viewpoint of empirical analysis, see Katona (1951, especially p. 135). — [3]I am indebted to Mr. Juréen for the argument and the conslusion that follow.

Ch. 15˙2. [1]While $L^* C L^*$ is necessarily symmetric, it is only by accident that in the present case $L^* C$ turns out to be symmetric.

Ch. 15˙3. [1]See e.g. Yule (1926, p. 4). — [2]This argument has been strongly vindicated by Frisch and Waugh (1933, p. 387) and Roos (1934, pp. 14, 246 and, in particular, 250). — [2]Frisch and Waugh (1933, p. 387). Cf Wold (1940, §28), also for the discussion that follows. — [4]See Schultz (1938, Chs. 16–17; especially p. 556).

Ch. 15˙4. [1]This is one of the classic arguments in demand analysis. For a discussion, see Schultz (1938, p. 150).

Ch. 15˙5. [1]Wold (1940, §39).

Exs. IV. [1]Among the exercises that constitute new contributions we note Exs. 15, 27–28 and 31–32. — Ex. 4. [1]This type of graph is related to the *bunch map* introduced by Frisch (1934) as a tool in his confluence analysis approach [see Ch. 2˙4 (i)]. — Ex. 10. [1]The first part of the theorem is embodied, in essence, in a remark by Ezekiel (1930, p. 261). — Ex. 12. [1]Written communication. — Ex. 29. [1]This result qualifies a remark by the author in *Mathematical Reviews 12* (1951), p. 433. — Ex. 31. [1]Matrix regression is related to the interpretation that Christ (1951) gives of the reduced form (2˙7˙3) in the approach of structural systems (2˙7˙2).

Ch. 16.3. [1]Juréen (1952).

Ch. 16˙4. [1]Juréen (1952).

Ch. 16˙5. [1]Wold (1940, Table 10b). Cf Ch. 14˙6, App. note 2. — [2]Wold (1940, Table 12). — [3]Wold (1940, Table 13). — [4]Juréen (1952).

Ch. 16˙6. [1–2]Juréen (1952). Regarding the problem of fitting Törnqvist's functions to empirical data, see Exs. IV, 20–22. — [3]Juréen (1952). The consumer units have been evaluated, throughout, in the German-Austrian scale. The high level of the demand curve for 1923 may to a large extent be explained by changes in the proportion flour: baked bread during the post-war crisis.

Ch. 17˙1. [1]Juréen (1952). The quantities in Table 1a are specified as follows. Meat except pork: Beef, veal mutton, and horse flesh. Flour: Flour and grain from wheat and rye. Sugar: Sugar and syrup evaluated as raw sugar. (The data for 1939 have been excluded since sugar, being suitable for home storage, was hoarded in large quantities in 1939.) Regarding Table 1b, see Ch. 17˙6. — [2]Juréen (1952). The price data are based on the retail prices compiled by the Social Welfare Board, except for imported fruits and berries, where we have used the import price increased by 80 %. The prices given for aggregate commodities are weighted averages, with the consumed quantities as weights. We note the following items. Meat except pork: Average price of beef, veal, and mutton. (For horse flesh, which is consumed in small quantities only, retail prices are not available.) Flour: Average price of wheat flour and rye flour. Sugar: Price of lump sugar. (During the inter-war period, the price development of other forms of sugar and of syrup was parallel to that of lump sugar.)

Ch. 17˙2. [1]The material in this section is, in the main, drawn from Juréen (1952). Cf also Wold (1940, Ch. 10).

Ch. 17˙3. [1]Juréen (1949; 1952). Cf also Wold (1940, Ch. 8).

Ch. 17˙4. [1]Juréen (1949; 1952). Cf also Wold (1940, Chs. 7 and 9).

Ch. 17˙5. [1]Juréen (1952).

Ch. 17˙6. [1]Juréen (1949; 1952).

Ch. 17˙7. [1]Juréen (1952). — [2]The standard errors are calculated by the classical formula (first row) and by the autocorrelative formula (second row). — [3]The standard errors are based on the classical formula.

Ch. 18˙1. [1]Juréen (1950; 1952).

Ch. 18˙2. [1]Juréen (1950, Table 5). — [2]Juréen (1950, Table 6).

Ch. 18˙3. [1-2]Juréen (1952). — [3]The constant estimates are those obtained for the inter-war period, and these have also been used for the base period 1930–39. An exception has been made for bread grains, where the data indicate a marked decrease in the price and income elasticities during the inter-war period; the data for 1920–29 have therefore been included in the application of Törnqvist's demand function, which has led to a lower income elasticity for the base period (– 0.53) than for the whole inter-war period (– 0.60). For milk demand, the forecast based on constant elasticity assumes $E = .10$, whereas the variable forecast elasticity is $E = .10$ up to 1950 and then decreasing.

Ch. 18˙4. [1]Juréen (1952).

Ch. 18˙5. [1]Juréen (1952). — [2]The fodder unit is a measure of evaluation which is nearly the same as the harvest unit.

BIBLIOGRAPHY

A. Numbered references: Collective publications, including transactions of meetings, team work reports, official statistics, etc.

1. J. Neyman, ed.: *Proceedings of the Berkeley symposium on mathematical statistics and probability*. Vol. 1 (1949): 1945–46 symposium. Vol. 2 (1951): 1950 symposium. Univ. Press, Berkeley, Cal. 501 and 666 pp.
2. *Proceedings of the international statistical conferences, Washington 1947*. Vol. 5 (1949). Eka, Calcutta; also issued as Supplement to Econometrica, Vol. 17. 340 pp.
3. *Proceedings of the XIIth international dairy congress, Stockholm 1949*. Vol. 4 (1949). Hæggströms, Stockholm. 837 pp.
4. *Travaux présentés a la 26ᵉ Session de l'Institut international de statistique, Berne 1949*. Published separately by the Organization Committee (1950; Stämpfli, Berne; 468 pp.) and as Vol. 32, Part II of Bulletin Inst. Intern. Statist. The verbal proceedings of the Session are being published as Vol. 32, Part I (in press 1952) of the same Bulletin.
5. *Economic essays in honour of Gustav Cassel*. 1933; Allen & Unwin, London. 720 pp.
6. *Försäkringsmatematiska studier*. (Essays in honour of Filip Lundberg.) 1946; Almqvist & Wiksells, Uppsala. 292 pp.
7. T. C. Koopmans, ed. (1950): *Statistical inference in dynamic economic models*. Cowles Commission Monograph no. 10. Wiley, New York, N.Y. 438 pp.
8. O. Lange, F. McIntyre and Th. Yntema, eds. (1942): *Studies in mathematical economics and econometrics. In memory of Henry Schultz*. Univ. Press, Chicago, Ill. 292 pp.
9. H. L. Rietz, ed. (1924): *Handbook of mathematical statistics*. Houghton Mifflin, Boston, Mass. 221 pp.
10. *Readings in business cycle theory*. 1944; Blakiston, Philadelphia, Penn. 494 pp.
11. *Readings in the theory of income distribution*. 1946; Blakiston, Philadelphia, Penn. 718 pp.
12. H. S. Ellis, ed. (1948): *A survey of contemporary economics*. Blakiston, Philadelphia, Penn. 490 pp.
13. T. Wilson and P. W. S. Andrews, eds. (1951): *Oxford studies in the price mechanism*. Clarendon, Oxford. 274 pp.
14. National Bureau of Economic Research, New York, N. Y.: *Studies in income and wealth*.
15. ——, Committee on price determination (1943): *Cost behavior and price policy*. 356 pp.
16. —— (1951): *Conference on business cycles*. 427 pp.
17. Consumer finances, annual surveys since 1947. *Federal Reserve Bulletin*, and separately from the Federal Reserve Board, Washington, D. C.
18. International Labour Office (1947): *Cost-of-living statistics. Methods and techniques for the post-war period*. Geneva. 56 pp.
19. Statistical information about Greenland, VII. 1946. (Danish.) *Beretninger vedrørende Grønlands styrelse 2*, 914–992.

20. Agricultural Committee of 1942: Plans for agricultural politics, I–III. (Swedish.) *Swedish Official Reports (SOU)* 1946: 42, 46 and 61. 282, 606 and 149 pp.

21–25. Swedish Official Statistics (Swedish, with summaries and table explanations in French):

    21. Central Bureau of Statistics: *Statistical Yearbook, 1925* and *1951.* 330 and 436 pp.

    22. Social Welfare Board: *Costs of living in Sweden 1913–14.* Part I (1921; 493 pp.): Main results. Part II (1918; 8 volumes): Local monographs. Part III (1919; 196 pp.): Budget accounts of individual families.

    23. —— (1929): *Costs of living in towns and industrial communities, 1923.* 199 pp.

    24. —— (1935–36): Conditions of living and consumption habits among small farmers, farm workers and forestry workers, 1933. *Sociala Meddelanden 1935,* 361–371 and *1936,* 338–353, 627–648.

    25. —— (1938): *Conditions of living and consumption habits in towns and industrial communities, 1933.* 327 pp.

B. Dated references: Scientific papers, monographs and other individual works

ABBREVIATIONS

AMS   Annals of Mathematical Statistics.
EMG   Ergebnisse der Mathematik und ihrer Grenzgebiete.
GE   Giornale degli Economisti (Milan).
JASA   Journal of the American Statistical Association.
JRSS   Journal of the Royal Statistical Society.
SA   Skandinavisk Aktuarietidskrift (Stockholm).
SOU   Statens Offentliga Utredningar (Stockholm).
TE   Trabajos de Estadistica (Madrid).

N. Aall Barricelli (1946): *Sur le fondement théorique pour l'analyse des courbes climatiques.* Thesis (Oslo); unpublished.

A.C. Aitken (1935): On least squares and linear combination of observations. *Proc. Roy. Soc. Edinburgh, 55,* 42–48.

—— (1939): *Statistical mathematics.* 4th ed. 1945. Oliver and Boyd, Edinburgh. 153 pp.

R. G. D. Allen (1934): The concept of arc elasticity of demand. *Rev. Econ. Stud. 1,* 226–228.

—— (1938): *Mathematical analysis for economists.* Macmillan, London. 548 pp.

—— and A. L. Bowley (1935): *Family expenditure.* Staples, London. 145 pp.

——: See also Hicks.

T. W. Anderson (1951): Estimating linear restrictions on regression coefficients for multi-variate normal distributions. *AMS 22,* 327–351.

F. Anscombe (1948): The validity of comparative experiments. *JRSS (A) 111,* 181–200.

G. B. Antonelli (1886): *Sulla teoria matematica della economia pura.* Folchetto, Pisa. Reprinted 1951 in *GE* (New series) *10,* 233–263.

N. Arley and K. R. Buch (1950): *Introduction to the theory of probability and statistics.* Wiley, New York, N.Y. 236 pp. (Original in Danish, 3rd ed. 1946. Gad, Copenhagen.)

K. J. Arrow (1951): *Social choice and individual values.* Cowles Commission Monograph no. 12, Wiley, New York, N.Y. 99 pp.

A. J. Ayer (1936): *Language, truth and logic.* 2nd ed. 1949. Gollancz, London. 160 pp.

E. Bäcklin (1935): The X-ray crystal scale, the absolute scale and the electronic charge. *Nature 135*, 32–34.

M. Bartlett (1946): On the theoretical specification and sampling properties of autocorrelated time-series. *JRSS (B) 8*, 27–41.

W. J. Baumol, in association with R. Turvey (1951): *Economic dynamics. An introduction.* Macmillan, New York, N.Y. 262 pp.

R. Bentzel and H. Wold (1946): On statistical demand analysis from the viewpoint of simultaneous equations. *SA 29*, 95–114.

S. Bernstein (1927): Sur l'extension du théorème limite du calcul des probabilités aux sommes des quantités dépendantes. *Mathematische Annalen 97*, 1–59.

A. L. Bowley (1924): *The mathematical groundwork of economics.* Clarendon, Oxford. 98 pp.

——: See also Allen.

K. R. Buch, see Arley.

A. F. Burns and W. C. Mitchell (1946): *Measuring business cycles.* National Bureau of Economic Research, New York, N.Y. 560 pp.

E. Cansado (1950): Vector interpretation of Slutsky's relation. (Spanish with English summary.) *TE 1*, 29–36.

—— and H. Wold (1950): Some properties of price-consumption curves and income-consumption curves. *TE, 1*, 37–48.

G. Cassel (1918): *Theoretische Sozialökonomie.* 4th ed. 1927. Scholl, Leipzig. 649 pp.

C. Christ (1951): A test of an econometric model for the United States, 1921–1947. In *Ref. 16*, 35–107.

C. Clark (1949): A system of equations explaining the United States trade cycle, 1921 to 1941. *Econometrica 17*, 93–124.

—— (1950): Consumption of primary products as a function of real income, I–III. *Review of Economic Progress 2*, nos. 8–11.

W. G. Cochran and Gertrude M. Cox (1950): *Experimental designs.* Wiley, New York, N.Y. 454 pp.

D. Cochrane and G. H. Orcutt (1949): Application of least-squares regression to relationships containing autocorrelated error terms. *JASA 44*, 32–61.

A. Cournot (1838): *Recherches sur les principes mathématiques de la théorie des richesses.* Hachette, Paris. American ed. 1927; Macmillan, New York, N.Y. 213 pp.

Gertrude M. Cox, see Cochran.

H. Cramér (1937): Random variables and probability distributions. *Cambridge Tracts in Mathematics, no. 36.* Univ. Press, Cambridge. 121 pp.

—— (1940): On the theory of stationary random processes. *Annals of Math. 41*, 215–230.

—— (1945): *Mathematical methods of statistics.* Almqvist & Wiksells, Uppsala. Parallel ed. 1946; Univ. Press, Princeton, N.J. 575 pp.

—— (1947): Problems in probability theory. *AMS 18*, 165–193.

H. T. Davis (1941): *The theory of econometrics.* Principia, Bloomington, Ind. 482 pp.

F. Divisia (1925–26): L'indice monétaire et la théorie de la monnaie. *Revue d'Econ. Pol. 39*, 842–861, 980–1008, 1121–1151 and *40*, 49–87; also separately at Sirey, Paris.

J. L. Doob (1944): The elementary Gaussian processes. *AMS 15*, 229–282.

—— (1949): Time series and harmonic analysis. In *Ref. 1, Vol. 1*, 303–344.

P. H. Douglas, see Schoenberg.

J. S. Duesenberry (1949): *Income, saving and the theory of consumer demand.* Harvard Univ. Press, Cambridge, Mass. 128 pp.

J. Durbin and G. S. Watson (1950–51): Testing for serial correlation in least-squares regression; I–II. *Biometrika 37*, 409–428 and *38*, 159–178.

F. Y. Edgeworth (1881): *Mathematical psychics.* Kegan Paul, London. 2nd ed., London School of Economics Reprint of Scarce Works. 150 pp.

C. Eisenhart (1939): The interpretation of certain regression methods, and their use in biological and industrial research. *AMS 10*, 162–186.

G. Elfving (1952): Optimum allocation in linear regression systems. *AMS 23*, 255–262.

E. Engel (1895): Die Lebenshaltung belgischer Arbeiter-Familien früher und jetzt. *Bulletin Inst. Intern. Statist. 9*, 1–124; with an Appendix, pp. 1–54.

G. C. Evans (1930): *The mathematical introduction to economics.* McGraw-Hill, New York, N.Y. 177 pp.

M. Ezekiel (1930): *Methods of correlation analysis.* 2nd ed. 1941. Wiley, New York, N.Y. 531 pp.

—— (1938): The cobweb theorem. *Q. J. Econ. 52.* Also in *Ref. 10,* 422–442.

W. Feller (1945): The fundamental limit theorems in probability. *Bull. Amer. Math. Soc. 51,* 800–832.

D. Finney (1947): *Probit analysis.* 2nd ed. 1952. Univ. Press, Cambridge. 318 pp.

I. Fisher (1892): Mathematical investigations in the theory of value and prices. *Trans. Connecticut Acad. 9,* 1–124; also as Thesis (Yale, 1891).

—— (1922): *The making of index numbers.* 3rd ed. 1927. Houghton Mifflin, Boston, Mass. 526 pp.

R. A. Fisher (1925): *Statistical methods for research workers.* 11th ed. 1950. Oliver and Boyd, Edinburgh. 354 pp.

—— (1935): *The design of experiments.* 4th ed. 1947. Oliver and Boyd, Edinburgh. 260 pp.

M. Friedman and L. J. Savage (1948): The utility analysis of choices involving risk. *J. Pol. Econ. 56,* 279–304.

R. Frisch (1926): Sur une problème d'économie pure. *Norsk Matematisk Forenings Skrifter (1), no. 16.* 40 pp.

—— (1928): Correlation and scatter in statistical variables. *Nordisk Statistisk Tidskrift 8,* 36–102.

—— (1929): Static and dynamic approaches in economic theory. (Norwegian.) *Nationaløkonomisk Tidsskrift 41,* 321–379.

—— (1930): Necessary and sufficient conditions regarding the form of an index number which shall meet certain of Fisher's tests. *JASA 25,* 397–406.

—— (1932): *New methods of measuring marginal utility.* Mohr, Tübingen. 142 pp.

—— (1933): Propagation problems and impulse problems in dynamic economics. In *Ref. 5,* 171–205.

—— (1934): *Statistical confluence analysis by means of complete regression systems.* University Institute of Economics, Oslo, Publication no. 5. 192 pp.

—— (1936): Annual survey of economic theory: The problem of index numbers. *Econometrica 4,* 1–38.

—— and T. Haavelmo (1938): The demand for milk in Norway. (Norwegian.) *Statsøkonomisk Tidsskrift 52,* 1–62.

—— and F. V. Waugh (1933): Partial time regressions as compared with individual trends. *Econometrica 1,* 387–401.

J. Gallego-Diaz (1945): A note on the arc elasticity of demand. *Rev. Econ. Stud. 12,* 114–115.

C. Gini (1921): Sull' interpolazione di una retta quando i valori della variabile indipendente sono affetti da errori accidentali. *Metron 1, no. 3,* 63–82.

M. A. Girshick and T. Haavelmo (1947): Statistical analysis of the demand for food: Examples of simultaneous estimation of structural equations. *Econometrica 15*, 79–110.

H. Gossen (1854): *Entwicklung der Gesetze des menschlichen Verkehrs, und der daraus fliessenden Regeln für menschliches Handeln.* 2nd ed. 1889, Prager, Berlin. 277 pp.

W. S. Gossett (1936): Comparison between balanced and random arrangements of field plots. *Biometrika 29*, 363–379.

U. Grenander (1950): *Stochastic processes and statistical inference.* Thesis (Stockholm); also in *Arkiv för Matematik 1*, 195–277.

A. Guiraum, J. Tena and H. Wold (1950): Cartes d'indifférence à fonctions de demande données. *TE 1*, 49–68.

T. Haavelmo (1943): The statistical implications of a system of simultaneous equations. *Econometrica 11*, 1–12.

—— (1944): The probability approach in econometrics. *Econometrica 12, Suppl.*, 1–118.

——: See also Frisch and Girshick.

R. L. Hall and C. J. Hitch (1939): Price theory and business behaviour. *Oxford Economic Papers, no. 2.* Also reprinted in *Ref. 13*, 107–138.

A. Hanau (1927): Die Prognoze der Schweinepreise. *Vierteljahrshefte zur Konjunkturforschung. Sonderheft 2*; 41 pp. 2nd ed., 1928 (Sonderheft 3). 3 rd ed., 1930 (Sonderheft 7).

G. H. Hardy, J. E. Littlewood and G. Pólya (1934): *Inequalities.* Univ. Press, Cambridge. 314 pp.

R. F. Harrod (1948): *Towards a dynamic economics.* Macmillan, London. 169 pp.

F. R. Helmert (1905): Über die Genauigkeit der Kriterien des Zufalls bei Beobachtungsreihen. *Sitzungsberichte der Kgl. Preussischen Akad. der Wissenschaften 1905*, 594–612.

R. Hénon (1949): Offre et demande d'effort de l'ouvrier au travail. In *Ref. 2*, 287–294.

J. R. Hicks (1932): *The theory of wages.* Macmillan, London. 3rd ed. 1948; Peter Smith, New York, N.Y. 247 pp.

—— (1939): *Value and capital.* 2nd ed. 1946. Clarendon, Oxford. 340 pp.

—— (1942): Consumers' surplus and index-numbers. *Rev. Econ. Stud. 9*, 126–137.

—— (1950): *A contribution to the theory of the trade cycle.* Clarendon, Oxford. 201 pp.

—— and R. G. D. Allen (1934): A reconsideration of the theory of value. *Economica 1*, 52–75 and 196–219.

C. J. Hitch, see Hall.

E. Hopf (1937): Ergodentheorie. *EMG 5 no. 2;* also separately at Springer, Berlin. 2nd ed. 1948, Chelsea, New York, N.Y. 83 pp.

H. Hotelling (1932): Edgeworth's taxation paradox and the nature of demand and supply functions. *J. Pol. Econ. 40*, 577–616.

H. S. Houthakker (1950): Revealed preference and the utility function. *Economica 17*, 159–174.

—— (1951): Some calculations on electricity consumption in Great Britain. *JRSS (A) 114*, 359–371.

—— (in press 1952): The econometrics of family budgets. *JRSS (A).*

H. Hyrenius (1944): *The future labour supply in agriculture.* (Swedish.) SOU 1944: 65. 196 pp.

S. F. James, see Stuvel.

H. Jeffreys (1937): *Scientific inference.* Univ. Press, Cambridge. 272 pp.

S. Jevons (1871): *The theory of political economy.* 2nd ed. 1879. Macmillan, London. 315 pp.

J. Jörgensen (1948): *The development of logical empiricism.* (Danish.) Luno, Copenhagen. 97 pp.

L. Juréen (1949): The demand for milk and dairy products in Sweden. In *Ref. 3*, 383–403.

L. Juréen (1950): Food consumption forecasting and the abolishment of agricultural subventions. (Swedish.) *Ekonomisk Tidskrift 52*, 175–195.

—— (in press 1952): *The agricultural production and food consumption in Sweden.* (Swedish.) SOU.

G. Katona (1951): *Psychological analysis of economic behaviour.* McGraw-Hill, New York, N.Y. 347 pp.

M. Kendall (1943; 1946): *The advanced theory of statistics, I–II.* Griffin, London. 457 + 521 pp.

A. Khintchine (1933): Asymptotische Gesetze der Wahrscheinlichkeitsrechnung. *EMG 2 no. 4;* also separately at Springer, Berlin. 2nd ed. 1948; Chelsea, New York, N.Y. 82 pp.

—— (1934): Korrelationstheorie der stationären stochastischen Prozesse. *Mathematische Annalen 109,* 604–615.

L. R. Klein (1950): *Economic fluctuations in the United States, 1921–41.* Cowles Commission Monograph no. 11. Wiley, New York, N.Y. 174 pp.

F. H. Knight (1933): *Risk, uncertainty and profit.* Houghton Mifflin, Boston, Mass.; 2nd ed., London School of Economics Reprint Series. 381 pp.

A. Kolmogorov (1933): Grundbegriffe der Wahrscheinlichkeitsrechnung. *EMG 2 no. 3;* also separately at Springer, Berlin. Amer. ed. 1950, Chelsea, New York, N.Y. 74 pp.

—— (1937): Ein vereinfachter Beweis des Birkhoff-Khintchineschen Ergodensatzes. *Rec. Math. (Sbornik) N.S.* 2, 367–368.

—— (1939): Sur l'interpolation et extrapolation des suites stationnaires. *C. R. Acad. Sci. Paris, 208,* 2043–2045.

—— (1941): Stationary sequences in Hilbert space. (Russian.) *Bull. State Univ. Moscow, Mathematics, 2 no. 6.* 40 pp.

A. A. Konyus (1924): The problem of the true index of the cost of living. (Russian.) *Econ. Bull.* (Inst. Econ. Conjuncture, Moscow) *9–10.* English translation 1939 in *Econometrica 7,* 10–29.

T. C. Koopmans (1936): *Linear regression analysis of economic time series.* Thesis (Leiden); also separately at Bohn, Haarlem. 132 pp.

—— (1942): Serial correlation and quadratic forms in normal variables. *AMS 13,* 14–33.

—— (1945): Statistical estimation of simultaneous economic relationships. *JASA 40,* 448–466.

—— (1947): Measurement without theory. *Rev. Econ. Statist. 29,* 161–172.

—— (1949): Identification problems in economic model construction. *Econometrica 17,* 125–144.

—— and O. Reiersöl (1950): The identification of structural characteristics. *AMS 21,* 165–181.

G. Kowalewski (1909): *Einführung in die Determinantentheorie.* Veit, Leipzig. 3rd ed. 1942, Chelsea, New York, N.Y. 550 pp.

R. A. Lehfeldt (1914): The elasticity of demand for wheat. *Econ. J. 24,* 212–217.

E. L. Lehmann and C. Stein (1948): Most powerful tests of composite hypotheses. I. Normal distributions. *AMS 19,* 495–516.

W. Leontief (1936): Composite commodities and the problem of index numbers. *Econometrica 4,* 39–59.

D. V. Lindley (1947): Regression lines and the linear functional relationship. *JRSS (B) 9,* 218–244.

J. E. Littlewood, see Hardy.

M. Loève (1950): Fundamental limit theorems of probability theory. *AMS 21,* 321–338.

H. Lubell (1947): Effects of income redistributions on consumers' expenditures. *Amer. Econ. Review 37,* 157–170.

E. Lundberg (1937): *Studies in the theory of economic expansion*. Thesis (Stockholm); also separately at King, London. 265 pp.

—— (1945): Survey of the income and consumption situation. (Swedish.) *Meddelanden från Konjukturinstitutet, Ser. B: 3*. 35 pp.

S. Malmquist (1948): *A statistical analysis of the demand for liquor in Sweden*. Thesis (Uppsala); also separately at Almqvist & Wiksells, Uppsala. 135 pp.

H. B. Mann and A. Wald (1943): On the statistical treatment of linear stochastic difference equations. *Econometrica 11*, 173–220.

J. Marschak (1931): *Elastizität der Nachfrage*. Mohr, Tübingen. 144 pp.

—— (1950): Rational behaviour, uncertain prospects, and measurable utility. *Econometrica 18*, 111–141.

A. Marshall (1890): *Principles of economics*. 8th ed. 1946. Macmillan, London. 871 pp.

G. Maruyama (1949): The harmonic analysis of stationary stochastic processes. *Memoirs Fac. Sci. Kyūsyū Univ. (A) 4*, 45–106.

B. Matérn (1947): Methods of estimating the accuracy of line and sample plot surveys. (Swedish with English summary.) *Meddelanden från Statens Skogsforskningsinstitut, 36 no. 1*. 138 pp.

F. G. Mills (1936): *Prices in recession and recovery*. National Bureau of Economic Research, New York, N.Y. 581 pp.

W. C. Mitchell, see Burns.

F. Modigliani (1949): Fluctuations in the savings-income ratio: A problem in economic forecasting. In *Ref. 14; Vol. 11*, 371–441.

H. L. Moore (1919): Empirical laws of demand and supply and the flexibility of prices. *Pol. Sci. Quarterly 34*, 546–567.

—— (1925): A moving equilibrium of demand and supply. *Q. J. Econ. 39*, 357–371.

O. Morgenstern (1950): *On the accuracy of economic observations*. Univ. Press, Princeton, N.J. 101 pp.

——: See also von Neumann.

J. L. Mosak (1942): On the interpretation of the fundamental equation in value theory. In *Ref. 8*, 69–74.

J. Moyal (1949): Stochastic processes and statistical physics. *JRSS (B) 11*, 150–210.

J. Neyman (1950): *First course in probability and statistics*. Holt, New York, N.Y. 350 pp.

—— and E. S. Pearson (1933): On the problem of the most efficient tests of statistical hypotheses. *Phil. Trans. Roy. Soc. (A) 231*, 289–338.

Ruby T. Norris (1941): *The theory of consumer's demand*. Yale Univ. Press, New Haven, Conn. 206 pp.

G. H. Orcutt, see Cochrane.

V. Pareto (1895): La legge della domanda. *GE 10*, 59–68.

—— (1906): *Manuale di economia politica*. French eds. 1909 and 1927. Giard, Paris. 695 pp.

—— (1911): Economie mathématique. *Encyclopédie Sci. Mathém. 1, no. 4*, 591–640.

E. S. Pearson, see Neyman.

K. Pearson (1901): On lines and planes of closest fit to systems of points in space. *Philosophical Magazine (6) 2*, 559–572.

W. M. Persons (1924): Correlation of time series. In *Ref. 9*, 150–165.

A. Pikler (1951): Optimum allocation in econometrics and physics. *Weltwirtschaftliches Archiv, 66*, 97–132.

R. L. Plackett (1949): A historical note on the method of least squares. *Biometrika 36*, 458–460.

G. Pólya, see Hardy.

A. R. Prest (1949): Some experiments in demand analysis. *Rev. Econ. Statist. 31*, 33–49.

M. H. Quenouille (1947): A large-sample test for the goodness of fit of autoregressive schemes. *JRSS (A) 110*, 123–129.

—— (1949): Approximate tests of correlation in time-series. *JRSS (B) 11*, 68–84.

M. W. Reder (1947): *Studies in the theory of welfare economics*. Columbia Univ. Press, New York, N.Y. 208 pp.

O. Reiersöl (1945): *Confluence analysis by means of instrumental sets of variables*. Thesis (Stockholm); also in *Arkiv för Matematik, Astronomi och Fysik, 32 A, no. 4*. 119 pp.

—— (1950): Identifiability of linear relations between variables which are subject to error. *Econometrica 18*, 375–389.

——: See also Koopmans.

D. H. Robertson (1931): Wage-grumbles. In *Economic fragments*, King, London; also in *Ref. 13*, 221–236.

G. Robinson, see Whittaker.

Joan Robinson (1945): *The economics of imperfect competition*. Macmillan, London. 352 pp.

C. F. Roos (1934): *Dynamic economics*. Cowles Commission Monograph no. 1. Principia Press, Bloomington, Ind. 275 pp.

—— (1942): Dynamics of commodity prices. In *Ref. 8*, 268–292.

R. Roy (1930): La demande dans ses rapports avec la répartition des revenus. *Metron 8, no. 3*, 101–153.

—— (1935): *Etudes économétriques*. Sirey, Paris. 145 pp.

—— (1942): De l'utilité. *Actualités Scientifiques et Industrielles, no. 930*. 47 pp.

P. A. Samuelson (1941): The stability of equilibrium: Comparative statics and dynamics. *Econometrica 9*, 97–120.

—— (1942): Constancy of the marginal utility of income. In *Ref. 8*, 75–91.

—— (1947): *Foundations of economic analysis*. Harvard Univ. Press, Cambridge, Mass. 447 pp.

—— (1948): Dynamic process analysis. In *Ref. 12*, 352–387.

—— (1950): The problem of integrability in utility theory. *Economica 17*, 355–385.

L. J. Savage, see Friedman.

Erika H. Schoenberg and P. H. Douglas (1937): Studies in the supply curve of labor. *J. Pol. Econ. 45*, 45–79.

H. Schultz (1938): *The theory and measurement of demand*. Univ. Press, Chicago, Ill. 817 pp.

—— (1939): A misunderstanding in index-number theory, etc. *Econometrica 7*, 1–9.

W. A. Shewhart (1939): *Statistical method from the viewpoint of quality control*. Dept. of Agriculture, Washington, D.C. 155 pp.

E. Slutsky (1915): Sulla teoria del bilancio del consomatore. *GE 51*, 1–26.

—— (1927): The summation of random causes as the source of cyclic processes. (Russian with English summary.) *Problems of Economic Conditions* (Inst. Econ. Conjuncture, Moscow), *3*. Revised English ed. 1937 in *Econometrica 5*, 105–146.

H. Staehle (1935): A development of the economic theory of price index numbers. *Rev. Econ. Stud. 2*, 163–188.

C. Stein, see Lehmann.

G. J. Stigler (1947): *The theory of price*. Macmillan, New York, N.Y. 340 pp.

M. H. Stone (1932): Linear transformations in Hilbert space. *Amer. Math. Soc. Colloquium Publ. no. 15*. 622 pp.

R. Stone (1945): The analysis of market demand. *JRSS (A) 108*, 286–382.

—— (1948): The analysis of market demand: an outline of methods and results. *Revue Inst. Intern. Statist. 16*, 23–35.

R. Stone (1951a): *The role of measurement in economics*. Univ. Press, Cambridge. 87 pp.

—— (1951b): The demand for food in the United Kingdom before the war. *Metroeconomica* 3, 8–27.

G. Stuvel and S. F. James (1950): Household expenditure on food in Holland. *JRSS (A)* 113, 59–80.

J. Tena, see Guiraum.

J. Tinbergen (1939): *Statistical testing of business cycle theories, II. Business cycles in the United States of America 1919–32*. League of Nations, Geneva. 244 pp.

—— (1940): Econometric business cycle research. *Rev. Econ. Stud. 7;* also in *Ref. 10*, 61–86.

G. Tintner (1952): *Econometrics*. Wiley, New York, N.Y. 370 pp.

J. Tobin (1950): A statistical demand function for food in the U.S.A. *JRSS (A)* 113, 113–141.

L. Törnqvist (1941): Review of H. Wold (1940). (Swedish.) *Ekonomisk Tidskrift 43*, 216–225.

—— (1945): On the economic theory of lottery-gambles. *SA 28*, 228–246.

R. Turvey, see Baumol.

M. J. Ulmer (1949): *The economic theory of cost of living index numbers*. Columbia Univ. Press, New York, N.Y. 106 pp.

M. Verhulst (1952): *Les industries d'utilité publique*. Presses Univ. de France, Paris. 254 pp.

J. Ville (1946): Sur les conditions d'existence d'une ophélimité totale et d'un indice du niveau des prix. *Ann. Univ. Lyon (A, 3) 9*, 32–39. English translation 1951 in *Rev. Econ. Stud. 19*.

V. Volterra (1906): Review of V. Pareto (1906). *GE 32*, 296–301.

E. von Hofsten (1952): *Price indexes and quality changes*. Thesis (Uppsala); also separately at Bonnier, Stockholm. 136 pp.

J. von Neumann (1941): Distribution of the mean square succession difference to the variance. *AMS 12*, 367–395.

—— and O. Morgenstern (1944): *Theory of games and economic behaviour*. 2nd ed. 1947. Univ. Press, Princeton, N.J. 625 pp.

G. H. von Wright (1943): *Logical empiricism*. (Swedish.) Söderströms, Helsinki. 188 pp.

A. Wald (1943): Test of statistical hypotheses concerning several parameters when the number of observations is large. *Amer. Math. Soc. Trans. 54*, 426–482.

——: See also Mann.

L. Walras (1874): *Eléments d'économie pure*. 5th ed. 1926. Durand-Auzias, Paris. 495 pp.

J. E. Walsh (1947): Concerning the effect of intraclass correlation. *AMS 18*, 88–96.

G. S. Watson (1951): *Serial correlation in regression analysis*. Thesis (Statistics Inst., Univ. of North Carolina); unpublished.

——: See also Durbin.

F. V. Waugh, see Frisch.

H. Weyl (1949): *Philosophy of mathematics and natural science*. Univ. Press, Princeton, N.J. 311 pp.

E. T. Whittaker and G. Robinson (1924): *The calculus of observations*. 4th ed. 1944. Blackie, London. 397 pp.

P. Whittle (1951): *Hypothesis testing in time-series analysis*. Thesis (Uppsala); also separately at Almqvist & Wiksells, Uppsala. 121 pp.

—— (in press 1952, a): Some results in time series analysis. *SA 35*. 13 pp.

—— (in press 1952, b): Tests of fit in time series analysis. *Biometrika 39*.

N. Wiener (1930): Generalized harmonic analysis. *Acta Mathematica 55*, 117–258.

—— (1949): *Extrapolation, interpolation, and smoothing of stationary time series*. Wiley, New York, N.Y. 163 pp.

J. S. Wilkie (1950): The problem of the temporal relation of cause and effect. *Brit. J. Philos. Sci. 1*, 211–229.

S. S. Wilks (1944): *Mathematical statistics.* Univ. Press, Princeton, N.J. 284 pp.

—— (1949): *Elementary statistical analysis.* Univ. Press, Princeton, N.J. 284 pp.

C. P. Winsor (1946): Which regression? *Biometrics Bull. 2*, 101–109.

H. Wold (1938): *A study in the analysis of stationary time series.* Thesis (Stockholm); also separately at Almqvist & Wiksells, Uppsala. 214 pp.

—— (1940): *The demand for agricultural products and its sensitivity to price and income changes.* (Swedish.) SOU 1940: 16.

—— (1943–44): A synthesis of pure demand analysis, I–III. *SA 26*, 85–118, 220–263 and *27*, 69–120.

—— (1945): A theorem on regression coefficients obtained from successively extended sets of variables. *SA 28*, 181–200.

—— (1946): A comment on spurious correlation. In *Ref. 6*, 278–285.

—— (1948a): On prediction in stationary time series. *AMS 19*, 558–567.

—— (1948b): On Giffen's paradox. *Nordisk Tidsskrift for Teknisk Økonomi 12*, 283–290.

—— (1948c): Random normal deviates. *Tracts for Computers, no. 25.* Univ. Press, Cambridge. 51 pp.

—— (1949a): Statistical estimation of economic relationships. In *Ref. 2*, 1–22.

—— (1949b): A large-sample test for moving averages. *JRSS (B) 11*, 297–305.

—— (1950): On least square regression with autocorrelated variables and residuals. In *Ref. 4*, 277–289 (see also the verbal proceedings).

—— (1951a): Series cronologicas estacionarias. *Monografias de Ciencia Moderna 28;* also in *TE 2*, 3–74.

—— (1951b): Dynamic systems of the recursive type – economic and statistical aspects. *Sankhyā 11*, 205–216.

—— (1951c): Review of Ref. 7, T. C. Koopmans, ed. (1950). *Econometrica 19*, 475–477.

—— (1951d): Demand functions and the integrability condition. *SA 34*, 149–151.

—— (in press 1952): Ordinal preferences or cardinal utility? *Econometrica 20*.

——: See also Bentzel, Cansado, and Guiraum.

R. M. Woodbury (1944): Economic consumption scales and their uses. *JASA 39*, 455–468.

E. J. Working (1927): What do statistical demand curves show? *Q. J. Econ. 41*, 212–235.

F. Yates (1939): The comparative advantages of systematic and randomised arrangements in the design of agricultural and biological experiments. *Biometrika 30*, 440–466.

G. U. Yule (1907): On the theory of correlation for any number of variables treated by a new system of notation. *Proc. Roy. Soc. 79*, 182–193.

—— (1921): On the time-correlation problem, with especial reference to the variate-difference correlation method. *JRSS 84*, 497–526.

—— (1926): Why do we sometimes get nonsense-correlations between time-series? *JRSS 89*, 1–64.

—— (1927): On a method of investigating periodicities in disturbed series, with special reference to Wolfer's sunspot numbers. *Phil. Trans. Roy. Soc. 226*, 267–298.

V. Zasuhin (1941): On the theory of multidimensional stationary random processes. *C. R. (Doklady) Acad. Sci. URSS, N.S. 33*, 435–437.

M. V. Zemansky (1937): *Heat and thermodynamics.* 2nd ed. 1943. McGraw-Hill, New York, N.Y. 390 pp.

A. Zygmund (1935): *Trigonometric series.* Warszawa. 331 pp.

LIST OF AUTHOR REFERENCES

[1] The transliteration of Russian names follows the system adopted by Mathematical Reviews, except in one or two cases where other forms are in current use.

SUBJECT INDEX